General Topology and its Relations to Modern Analysis and Algebra

Proceedings of the Symposium held in Prague in September, 1961

Scientific Editor: J. Novák
Reviewers: Z. Frolík, M. Katětov, V. Pták

Symposium on General Topology and Its Relations to Modern Analysis and Algebra, Prague, 1961

General Topology and its Relations to Modern Analysis and Algebra

Proceedings of the Symposium held in Prague in September, 1961

Academic Press
NEW YORK
and LONDON

Publishing House
of the Czechoslovak
Academy of Sciences
PRAGUE

DISTRIBUTORS IN WESTERN EUROPE AND THE WESTERN HEMISPHERE

ACADEMIC PRESS INC.
111 FIFTH AVENUE, NEW YORK 3, NEW YORK

Printed in Czechoslovakia

Foreword

The Czechoslovak Academy of Sciences jointly with the International Mathematical Union organized from the 1st to the 8th of September 1961 in Prague a Symposium on General Topology and its relations to modern Analysis and Algebra. At this meeting a number of new results achieved in the field of Topology and its applications were presented. This book issued by the Publishing House of the Czechoslovak Academy of Sciences includes, among other materials, these papers in the form submitted by the authors, i. e. either as abstracts or in a more detailed version.

The Organizing Committee of the Symposium and the Editorial Committee of the Proceedings hope that the present publication will be profitable to all specialists in the field of Topology and its applications and also to all mathematicians interested in the present state of General Topology. At the same time, they wish to express their thanks to all authors having forwarded their papers and also to all those who helped in preparing these Proceedings of the Symposium.

Editorial Committee

FROM THE REPORT OF THE ORGANIZING COMMITTEE

One of the initiators to organize a Symposium on General Topology under the auspices of the International Mathematical Union was the late Eduard Čech. Programme, place and time of the Symposium were consulted about with some prominent mathematicians from different countries. It was decided that the Symposium would be held in September 1961 in Prague and that in would be called "Symposium on General Topology and its relations to modern Analysis and Algebra". On the basis of the resolution of its Executive Committee the International Mathematical Union became sponsor of the Symposium along with the Czechoslovak Academy of Sciences. In the fall 1960, an Organizing Committee consisting of J. Novák (Praha) — Chairman, K. Kuratowski (Warszawa) — first Vice-chairman, M. Katětov (Praha) — second Vice-chairman, P. S. Alexandrov (Moskva) and M. Morse (Princeton) — delegates of IMU, K. Koutský (Brno), V. Pták (Praha), Š. Schwarz (Bratislava) — members, Z. Frolík (Praha) — Secretary, was formed. A three-member group consisting of the Chairman, the second Vice-chairman and the Secretary was responsible for preparing the Symposium.

The Organizing Committee invited a number of prominent mathematicians from different countries and several promising young mathematicians to take part in the Symposium. In addition, the Presidium of the Czechoslovak Academy of Sciences sent an invitation to the scientific institutions in a few other countries. Moreover, the Organizing Committee considered and accepted the applications of foreign mathematicians who manifested interest in attending the Symposium and, finally, some participants traveled to Prague privately.

Altogether ninety four mathematicians from abroad attended the Symposium. The corresponding list as well as the list of the Czechoslovak participants (53 persons) will be found below. Several mathematicians from abroad were accompanied by the members of their family. The foreign participants were housed in the International Hotel (where the sessions also were held) and in some other hotels. Several participants were accommodated, at their request, in the University Residences.

The work of technical character connected with the Symposium was arranged by the Organizing Committee. The Mathematical Institute of the Academy and the Faculty of Mathematics and Physics provided for its staff. In addition, the Organizing

Committee had a number of voluntary collaborators among young Prague mathematicians and their wives.

●

The first session of the Symposium took place on September 1st 1961. It was opened by the Chairman of the Organizing Committee J. Novák, K. Kuratowski delivered an address on behalf of the International Mathematical Union and J. Kožešník, General Secretary of the Academy, welcomed the Symposium in the name of the Czechoslovak Academy of Sciences. This was followed by the commemoration of Eduard Čech who died on March 15th 1960. M. Katětov, M. H. Stone, P. Alexandrov and K. Kuratowski made speeches devoted to the activity of Čech. The session was closed by the III. Sonata for violin and piano by B. Martinů presented by the members of Czech Trio, Dr. A. Plocek and J. Páleníček.

●

The scientific programme of the Symposium included 11 sessions devoted to scientific communications which were as far as possible divided in groups according to subject. The communications had in average 15—20 minutes, in individual cases 30 minutes or more in length. On some days, two parallel sessions took place. In addition, a special session was devoted to the discussion of problems. The list of the sessions along with the names of lecturers and the list of communications presented (including papers which were forwarded in written form) will be found below.

The closing session of the Symposium was held on September 8th. It was presided over by K. Kuratowski, first Vice-chairman of the Organizing Committee. At the beginning of this session, a letter from the President of the Czechoslovak Academy of Sciences, Zdeněk Nejedlý, was read. This was followed by the speeches of P. Alexandrov, M. H. Stone and K. Kuratowski. Before the closure of the session, M. Katětov thanked on behalf of the Czechoslovak members of the Organizing Committee the International Mathematical Union and the Czechoslovak Academy of Sciences for their efficient support of the Symposium; he also thanked all participants, institutions and organizations as well as all those who cooperated in preparing the Symposium.

During the Symposium, the Presidium of the Czechoslovak Academy of Sciences and the Minister of Education and Culture F. Kahuda organized receptions. After the closure of the Symposium, the Organizing Committee arranged for a banquet for all participants and collaborators. In addition, a number of cultural and similar events took place: a sightseeing tour of Prague, a whole day trip to the West Bohemian spas, visits of theaters and concerts etc. A special programme including excursions to the environs of Prague, sightseeing tours etc. was set up for the accompanying persons.

According to the opinion expressed by the participants the Organizing Committee considers that the Symposium was successful and that it brought a number of very interesting communications. In this connection, the participation of young mathematicians from different countries who contributed in a substantial way to the scientific programme should be mentioned.

The Symposium was held in an atmosphere of friendship and contributed to the establishment and strengthening of personal contacts between the scientists from different countries.

The Organizing Committee has the pleasant duty to express its most sincere thanks to the International Mathematical Union, to the Czechoslovak Academy of Sciences, to all participants and to all those who contributed to the success of the Symposium.

ИЗ ОТЧЕТА ОРГАНИЗАЦИОННОГО КОМИТЕТА

Одним из инициаторов организации симпозиума по общей топологии под покровительством Международного математического союза был покойный Эдуард Чех. О программе симпозиума, его месте и времени были проведены консультации с некоторыми выдающимися математиками из разных стран. Было решено, что симпозиум состоится в сентябре 1961 г. в Праге и будет называться ,,Симпозиум по общей топологии и ее связям с современным анализом и алгеброй". Организаторами симпозиума стали Международный математический союз, согласно решению его исполнительного комитета, и Чехословацкая академия наук. Осенью 1960 г. был создан организационный комитет в следующем составе: Й. Новак (Прага) – председатель, К. Куратовский (Варшава) – первый заместитель председателя, М. Катетов (Прага) – второй заместитель председателя, П. С. Александров (Москва) и М. Морс (Принстон) – делегаты Международного математического союза, К. Коутский (Брно), В. Птак (Прага), Ш. Шварц (Братислава) – члены, З. Фролик (Прага) – секретарь. Оперативная подготовка симпозиума была возложена на группу, состоявшую из председателя, второго заместителя председателя и секретаря оргкомитета.

Организационный комитет пригласил участвовать в симпозиуме ряд известных математиков из различных стран, а также некоторых молодых многообещающих научных работников. Кроме того, президиум Чехословацкой академии наук послал приглашения научным учреждениям в некоторых дальнейших странах. Сверх того, оргкомитет рассматривал и принимал также заявки иностранных математиков, пожелавших принять участие в симпозиуме, и, наконец, некоторые участники приехали в Прагу в качестве туристов.

Всего в симпозиуме приняло участие 94 иностранных математика. Их список, а также список 53 чехословацких участников симпозиума помещается ниже. Некоторых из иностранных участников сопровождали члены их семей. Заграничные участники были размещены в гостинице Интернационал (где также происходили почти все заседания симпозиума) и некоторых других гостиницах, а также – в тех случаях, когда они этого пожелали – в студенческих общежитиях.

Техническую работу, связанную с симпозиумом провел секретариат, состоявший главным образом из административных сотрудников Математического института Академии и физико-математического факультета Карлова университета. Оргкомитету содействовал также ряд добровольных сотрудников, главным образом из числа молодых пражских математиков и их жен.

•

Открытие симпозиума состоялось 1 сентября 1961 г. После вступительной речи председателя оргкомитета Й. Новака, выступили К. Куратовский от имени Международного математического союза и Я. Кожешник, главный ученый секретарь Чехословацкой академии наук, от имени Академии. Затем состоялось чествование памяти Эдуарда Чеха, скончавшегося 15 марта 1960 г. С речами, посвященными деятельности покойного, выступили М. Катетов, М. Стоун, П. С. Александров, К. Куратовский. Заседание было закончено III. сонатой для скрипки и фортепиано композитора Б. Мартину в исполнении членов Чешского трио д-ра А. Плоцека и Й. Паленичека.

•

Научная программа симпозиума включала 11 заседаний, посвященных научным сообщениям, продолжительностью обычно 15 – 20 минут, а в отдельных случаях 30 минут и больше, сгрупированным, по возможности, в соответствии с их тематикой. В некоторые дни были проведены одновременно два параллельных заседания. Сверх того, состоялось научное заседание, посвященное дискуссии о проблемах. Список заседаний с именами докладчиков и список сделанных сообщений (а также сообщений, поступивших в письменном виде) приводится ниже.

•

Заключительное заседание состоялось 8 сентября под председательством К. Куратовского, первого заместителя председателя организационного комитета. В начале заседания было зачитано приветственное письмо Президента Чехословацкой академии наук Зденека Неедлы. С речами выступили П. С. Александров, М. Стоун и К. Куратовский. В заключение М. Катетов от имени чехословацких членов оргкомитета выступил с выражением благодарности Международному математическому союзу и Чехословацкой академии наук за их всестороннюю поддержку симпозиума, а также всем участникам симпозиума, всем учреждениям, организациям и отдельным лицам, содействовавшим проведению симпозиума.

В течение симпозиума состоялся прием, устроенный президиумом Чехословацкой академии наук, и прием у министра школ и культуры др-а Ф. Кагуды. После окончания симпозиума был устроен совместный ужин для участников и сотрудников симпозиума. Кроме того состоялся ряд культурных и подобных мероприятий, в том числе осмотр города Праги, поездка в курорты западной Чехии, посещение театров, концертов и т. д. Для членов семей участников симпозиума была организована специальная программа, включавшая поездки по окрестностям Прагу, осмотр достопримечательностей и т. д.

В согласии с мнением, выражавшимся участниками, организационный комитет считает, что симпозиум прошел успешно и принес целый ряд очень интересных сообщений. В частности, оргкомитет считает нужным отметить, что большой вклад в научную программу симпозиума внесли молодые математики из различных стран.

Вся работа симпозиума проходила в атмосфере дружбы и явилась вкладом в дело международного научного сотрудничества и укрепления связей между учеными различных стран.

Организационный комитет считает своей приятной обязанностью выразить сердечную благодарность Международному математическому союзу, Чехословацкой академии наук, всем участникам симпозиума и всем, кто содействовали его успешному осуществлению.

LIST OF FOREIGN PARTICIPANTS

E. J. AKUTOWICZ (Montpellier), J. ALBRYCHT (Poznań), P. S. ALEXANDROFF (Moskva), A. ALEXIEWICZ (Poznań), R. D. ANDERSON (Baton Rouge), C. ANDREIAN-CAZACU (București), M. J. ANTONOVSKI (Tashkent), G. AQUARO (Bari), R. ARENS (Los Angeles), A. V. ARCHANGELSKI (Moskva), M. ARTEAGA (La Paz), C. BARBANCE (Paris), S. BERGMAN (Stanford), C. BESSAGA (Warszawa), R. H. BING (Athens, USA), M. BOGNÁR (Budapest), V. G. BOLTJANSKI (Moskva), K. BORSUK (Warszawa), H. BOSECK (Berlin), D. W. BUSHAW (Pullman, USA), M. CAŁCZYŃSKA (Warszawa), G. S. CHOGOSHVILI (Tbilisi), P. COURRÈGE (Paris), A. CSÁSZÁR (Budapest), K. CSÁSZÁR (Budapest), A. DELEANU (București), R. H. MCDOWELL (St. Louis, USA), C. H. DOWKER (London), R. DUDA (Wrocław), S. EILENBERG (New York), R. ENGELKING (Warszawa), P. ERDÖS (Budapest), J. FLACHSMEYER (Berlin), T. GANEA (București), L. GILLMAN (Rochester), B. GLEICHGEWICHT (Wrocław), A. GOETZ (Wrocław), S. W. GOLOMB (Pasadena), H. GRELL (Berlin), G. GRIMEISEN (Stuttgart), J. DE GROOT (Amsterdam), L. GUGGENBUHL (New York), R. HAKIM (Paris), S. HARTMAN (Wrocław), G. HELMBERG (Innsbruck), E. HEWITT (Seattle), E. HILLE (New Haven), W. HOLSZTYŃSKI (Warszawa), J. R. ISBELL (Seattle), M. JAFÉ (Paris), M. JERISON (Lafayette), L. V. KELDYSH (Moskva), J. L. KELLEY (Berkeley), V. L. KLEE (Seattle), K. KURATOWSKI (Warszawa), J. R. LEJEUNE (Paris), A. LELEK (Warszawa), Z. MAMUZIĆ (Beograd), W. MATUSZEWSKA (Poznań), B. MAZUR (Cambridge, USA), E. A. MICHAEL (Seattle), J. MIODUSZEWSKI (Wrocław), E. E. MOISE (Cambridge, USA), A. MOSTOWSKI (Warszawa), J. MUSIELAK (Poznań), JUN-ITI NAGATA (Osaka), M. S. NARASIMHAN (Bombay), M. NICOLESCU (București), W. ORLICZ (Poznań), P. PAPIĆ (Zagreb), B. A. PASYNKOV (Moskva), A. PEŁCZYŃSKI (Warszawa), V. POENARU (București), V. J. PONOMAREV (Moskva), J. PRADINES (Paris), F. RECILLAS JUAREZ (Mexico), D. ROLEWICZ (Warszawa), T. SHIROTA (Osaka), K. SIEKLUCKI (Warszawa), R. SIKORSKI (Warszawa), I. SINGER (Bucuresti), V. I. SKLYARENKO (Moskva), YU. M. SMIRNOV (Moskva), A. SOLIAN (București), M. H. STONE (Chicago), A. E. TAYLOR (Los Angeles), C. TELEMAN (București), L. A. TUMARKIN (Moskva), K. VARADARAJAN (Bombay), I. N. VEKUA (Novosibirsk), H. DE VRIES (Amsterdam), A. D. WALLACE (New Orleans), W. ŻELAZKO (Warszawa), A. ZYGMUND (Chicago).

LIST OF CZECHOSLOVAK PARTICIPANTS

M. Bázlik, S. Belohorec, J. Bílek, O. Borůvka, J. Bosák, I. Černý, K. Drbohlav, M. Fiedler, Z. Frolík, J. Fuka, Z. Groschaftová-Čechová, J. Hájek, O. Hájek, J. Hořejš, J. Jakubík, V. Jarník, M. Jiřina, M. Katětov, J. Kaucký, I. Kluvánek, M. Kolibiar, J. Kolomý, V. Kořínek, A. Kotzig, V. Koutník, K. Koutský, F. Krňan, J. Kurzweil, P. Mandl, I. Marek, L. Mišík, J. Nečas, F. Neumann, J. Novák, M. Novotný, V. Petrův, V. Polák, N. Poláková, V. Pták, B. Riečan, L. Rieger, A. Rosa, M. Sekanina, Š. Schwarz, K. Skalková, Z. Šidák, F. Šik, A. Švec, M. Švec, S. Tomášek, V. Trnková, V. Vítek, P. Vopěnka.

LIST OF COMMUNICATIONS

AKUTOWICZ E. J.	Certaines classes de distributions quasi-analytiques au sens de S. Bernstein.
ALEXANDROFF P. S.	On some Results concerning Topological Spaces and their Continuous Mappings.
ALEXIEWICZ A.	The Two Norm Spaces (*No manuscript available*).
ANDERSON R. D.	Homeomorphisms of 2-Dimensional Continua.
ANDREIAN-CAZACU C.	Méthodes topologiques dans la théorie des surfaces de Riemann.
АНТОНОВСКИЙ М. Я.	Метрические пространства над полуполями.
AQUARO G.	Completions of Uniform Spaces.
ARCHANGELSKI A. V.	Concerning the Weight of Topological Spaces.
ARENS R. F.	A Problem concerning Locally-A Functions in a Commutative Banach Algebra A.
BERGMAN S.	Distinguished Boundary Sets in the Theory of Functions of Two Complex Variables.
BESSAGA C., PEŁCZYŃSKI A.	On the Topological Classification of Complete Linear Metric Spaces.
BING R. H.	Applications of the Side Approximation Theorem for Surfaces.
BOGNÁR M.	Bemerkungen zum Kongressvortrag „Stetigkeitsbegriff und abstrakte Mengenlehre“ von F. Riesz.
БОЛТЯНСКИЙ В. Г.	Топологические полуполя и их применения.
BOLTJANSKI V. G.	On Imbeddings of Polyhedra into Euclidean Spaces.
BORSUK K.	Concerning the Dimension of ANR-Sets.
BOSECK H.	Darstellungen von Matrizengruppen über topologischen Körpern.
BUDACH L., GRELL H.	Arithmetisch-topologische Untersuchungen an Ringen mit eingeschränkten Minimalbedingungen.
CHOGOSHVILI G. S.	On Homology Theory of Non-closed Sets.
CSÁSZÁR A.	Complétion et compactification d'espaces syntopogènes.
DELEANU A.	Fixed-Point Theory on Neighborhood Retracts of Convexoid Spaces.
DOWKER C. H.	Mappings of Proximity Structures.
DUDA R.	Connexion between Convexity of a Metric Continuum X and Convexity of its Hyperspaces $C(X)$ and 2^X.
DUDA R.	Two Results Concerning Biconnected Sets with Dispersion Points (*Presented in written only*).

EILENBERG S.	A Remark on Duality (*Published with K. Kuratowski in Fundamenta Mathematicae* 50 (1962, 515—517)).
ERDÖS P., HAJNAL A.	On the Topological Product of Discrete λ-Compact Spaces.
FLACHSMEYER J.	Nulldimensionale Räume.
FRÉCHET M.	L'espace des courbes n'est qu'un semi-espace de Banach.
FROLÍK Z.	A Contribution to the Descriptive Theory of Sets and Spaces.
GANEA T.	Algebraic Properties of Function Spaces.
GILLMAN L.	Remote Points in βR.
GOETZ A.	A Notion of Uniformity for L-spaces of Fréchet.
GOLOMB S. W.	Arithmetica Topologica.
GRELL H. (see BUDACH L.)	
GRIMEISEN G.	Eine natürliche Topologisierung der Potenzmenge eines topologischen Raumes.
DE GROOT J.	Linearization of Mappings.
HARTMAN S.	Some Relations between Topological and Algebraic Properties of Topological Groups.
HELMBERG G.	Topologische Untergruppenräume.
HENRIKSEN M., JERISON M.	The Space of Minimal Prime Ideals of a Commutative Ring.
HEWITT E.	Some Applications of Compactness in Harmonic Analysis.
HILLE E.	Remarks on Transfinite Diameters.
ISBELL J. R.	Mazur's Theorem.
JERISON M. (see HENRIKSEN M.)	
KATĚTOV M.	On a Category of Spaces.
Келдыш Л. В.	Некоторые теоремы о топологическом вложении.
KELLEY J. L.	Descriptions of Čech Cohomology.
KLEE V. L.	Exotic Topologies for Linear Spaces.
KLUVÁNEK I.	Sur la représentation des transformations linéaires.
KOLIBIAR M.	Bemerkungen über Intervalltopologie in halbgeordneten Mengen.
KOUTSKÝ K., SEKANINA M.	Modifications of Topologies.
KURATOWSKI K.	The Space of Mappings into the Sphere and its Topological Applications.
KUREPA D.	On an Inequality concerning Cartesian Multiplication (*Presented in written only*).
LELEK A.	On Fixations of Sets in Euclidean Spaces.
MAMUZIĆ Z.	Abstract Distance and Neighborhood Spaces.
MAREK I.	Iterations of Linear Bounded Operators and Kellogg's Iterations.
MAZUR B.	On the Topology of Imbedded Spheres (*No manuscript available*).
MICHAEL E. A.	Collared Sets.
MIODUSZEWSKI J.	On Two-to-One Functions.
MIODUSZEWSKI J., ROCHOWSKI M.	Remarks on Fixed Point Theorem for Inverse Limit Spaces (*Presented in written only*).
MOISE E. E.	Periodic Homeomorphisms of the 3-Sphere.
MUSIELAK J.	On some Spaces of Functions and Distributions.
NAGATA J.	On Dimension and Metrization.

NARASIMHAN M. S.	Existence of Universal Connections.
NICOLESCU M.	Problème de l'analycité par rapport à un opérateur linéaire dans une algèbre normée.
NOVÁK J.	On the Sequential Envelope.
ORLICZ W.	Über gewisse Klassen von Modularräumen.
PAPIĆ P.	Sur les images continues des continus ordonnés.
PASYNKOV B. A.	Projection Spectra and Dimension.
PEŁCZYŃSKI A. (see BESSAGA C.)	
POENARU V.	Products of Spaces by [0, 1].
PONOMAREV V.	On Paracompact Spaces and Related Questions.
ROCHOWSKI M. (see MIODUSZEWSKI J.)	
SCHWARZ Š.	Probability Measures on Non-commutative Semigroups.
ŠEDIVÁ-TRNKOVÁ V.	Non-F-Spaces.
SEKANINA M. (see KOUTSKÝ K.)	
SHIROTA T.	On Division Problems for Partial Differential Equations with Constant Coefficients.
SIKORSKI R.	Applications of Topology to Foundations of Mathematics.
SINGER I.	Basic Sequences and Reflexivity of Banach Spaces.
SKLYARENKO V. I.	On Perfect Compactifications of Topological Spaces.
SMIRNOV YU. M.	On Dimensional Properties of Infinite-Dimensional Spaces.
SOLIAN A.	Semi-Topology of Transformation Groups.
STONE A. H.	Non-separable Borel Sets. (*Presented in written only.*)
STONE M. H.	Topological Aspects of Conformal Mapping Theory.
TAYLOR A. E.	The Boundary of the Spectrum of a Linear Operator.
TELEMAN C.	Sur la structure de certains groupes topologiques.
TUMARKIN L.	Concerning Infinite-Dimensional Spaces.
VARADARAJAN K.	Dimension, Category and $K(\Pi, n)$ Spaces.
WALLACE A. D.	Relations on Topological Spaces.

The list includes all papers presented at the sessions of the Symposium as well as those papers accepted by the Organizing Committee which could not be, for various reasons, presented during the Symposium and were forwarded in written only. In some cases the language and the title of the paper differ from those originally announced; in one case, a communication presented by two authors has been divided into two articles.

Remark. Russian names are, as a rule, transliterated as given by the authors.

SCIENTIFIC SESSIONS

For each session, the name of chairman is given, followed by those of authors of communications made in this session. In case of communications of two authors, the name of that having presented the paper is marked with an asterisk.

Friday 1 September

Afternoon session

J. Novák

P. S. Alexandroff, A. D. Wallace, R. Sikorski

Saturday 2 September

Morning session A

E. Hewitt

V. L. Klee, W. Orlicz, A. Alexiewicz, R. Arens, J. R. Isbell, I. Kluvánek, *C. Bessaga and A. Pełczyński, J. Musielak, I. Singer

Morning session B

K. Borsuk

R. H. Bing, E. E. Moise, R. D. Anderson, A. Lelek, B. Mazur, J. Mioduszewski

Monday 4 September

Morning session

P. S. Alexandroff

S. Eilenberg, T. Ganea, Jun-iti Nagata, E. A. Michael, Z. Frolík, V. J. Ponomarev

Afternoon session A

E. Hille

T. Shirota, A. E. Taylor, I. Marek, E. J. Akutowicz, S. W. Golomb

Afternoon session B

H. Grell

J. L. Kelley, L. Gillman, *P. Erdös and A. Hajnal, A. V. Archangelski, P. Papić, G. Grimeisen, L. V. Sklyarenko, V. Poenaru

Tuesday 5 September
Morning session
Š. Schwarz
K. Kuratowski, L. V. Keldysh, M. Fréchet (presented by a Czechoslovak mathematician), E. Hille, M. H. Stone, S. Bergman, C. Andreian-Cazacu

Afternoon session
R. Sikorski
Discussion of problems

Thursday 7 September
Morning session A
L. V. Keldysh
J. Novák, M. Katětov, C. H. Dowker, K. Koutský and *M. Sekanina, G. Aquaro, M. Bognár, V. Šedivá-Trnková, A. Goetz, Z. Mamuzić, A. Deleanu

Morning session B
A. D. Wallace
L. Budach and *H. Grell, Š. Schwarz, S. Hartman, G. Helmberg, *M. J. Antonovski and V. G. Boltjanski, H. Boseck, M. Kolibiar, M. Henriksen and *M. Jerison, C. Teleman, A. Soļian

Afternoon session
K. Kuratowski
K. Borsuk, G. S. Chogoshvili, K. Varadarajan, V. G. Boltjanski, B. A. Pasynkov, M. S. Narasimhan, R. Duda

Friday 8 September
Morning session
M. H. Stone
Yu. M. Smirnov, L. A. Tumarkin, E. Hewitt, J. de Groot, A. Császár

Remark. Further to the programme of the Symposium some participants delivered lectures, organized during the Symposium or after its closure. Among these lecturers were in particular J. Albrycht, T. Ganea, Jun-iti Nagata, P. Vopěnka. On the request of the latter the Editorial Committee wishes to state that the basic theorem of the paper of P. Vopěnka could not be proved. Only a weaker result formulated in the terms of mathematical logic and axiomatic theory of sets was proved.

EDUARD ČECH

1893—1960

COMMEMORATION OF EDUARD ČECH

Speeches of M. Katětov, M. H. Stone, P. S. Alexandroff, K. Kuratowski

M. KATĚTOV

(Translated from Czech)

We recall to memory today — almost one and a half years after his death — EDUARD ČECH, the greatest Czechoslovak mathematician, who produced exceptionally profound and fruitful ideas and results in such differing branches of mathematics as topology — general and algebraic — and differential geometry. There is one other reason why we should pay tribute to E. Čech on this occasion. It is the fact that he was really the initiator of the Symposium which commences with today's ceremony, although he did not live to see even the first preparations for it.

I should like to take this opportunity to mention some of the most important events in Čech's life.

Eduard Čech was born on the 29th of June, 1893 in Eastern Bohemia. After matriculation he began his studies in 1912 at the Charles University in Prague. He was forced to interrupt his studies during the war and completed them in 1920 when he presented a thesis on projective space, thus gaining the title of Doctor of Philosophy. He spent the years 1921—22 in Turin, where he worked with the outstanding Italian mathematician G. FUBINI. As a result of this most fruitful cooperation, two well-known books on projective differential geometry were published (in 1926 and later) under the joint authorship of Fubini and Čech.

In 1923 E. Čech was appointed docent at Prague University and a year later Professor of Mathematics at the newly founded University of Brno. In addition to this intensive work in differential geometry, E. Čech began — about the year 1928 — to get deeply interested in topology and to acquaint himself thoroughly with the current state of this discipline. His interest in topology gradually began to predominate. During the years 1930 and 1931, his last geometrical works of that period were published and in 1931 his first paper on topology appeared. In 1932 and 1933, he published his two fundamental works on algebraic topology — on the theory of homology in an arbitrary space and on the general theory of variaties and duality. During the period 1932—38, he published a number of further outstanding works, among them the well-known paper on the maximal compactification. About this period he visited Moscow and spent a year at the *Institute for Advanced Study* in Princeton. His lively personal contacts with Soviet, Polish and American mathematicians clearly date from this period.

After his return from the United States, E. Čech devoted much of his time to the training of young scientific workers. In particular, he led a *topological seminar* in Brno dealing with problems of general topology. This seminar which in a short time gave rise to a number of valuable results was attented by such mathematicians as BEDŘICH POSPÍŠIL, JOSEF NOVÁK, KAREL KOUTSKÝ and others. This work was unfortunately of short duration. After the Nazi occupation of Bohemia and Moravia in March of 1939 and the closing of all Czech centres of higher education in November of the same year, the seminar gradually ceased to meet and one of Čech's most gifted students B. Pospíšil perished at the hands of the Gestapo. After the liberation of Czechoslovakia in 1945, E. Čech returned to work with new enthusiasm as a convinced supporter of the progressive changes which were taking place in the life of our country. He moved to Prague University and from there to the present Mathematical Institute of the Czechoslovak Academy of Sciences. In 1954 he returned to a new position at the University. For several years he devoted much time and energy, on the one hand, to questions of the teaching of mathematics in which he had always had a great interest and, on the other, to organisational work.The successful foundation of the Mathematical Institute of the Czechoslovak Academy of Sciences was largely due to his latter activity. From the year 1949, he took up again his own scientific work. His main interest was, however, no longer topology, the development of which he naturally followed closely, but differential geometry where he again achieved outstanding results. The significance of his previous and new scientific work was acknowledged by the Government of the Republic by the granting of two *State Prizes* in 1951 and 1954. He was also decorated for his services by the President of the Republic with one of the highest *Orders* of the country.

As a result of his intensive and tireless work, Čech's health gradually became undermined. Despite the fact that during the latter years of his life he was seriously ill, he worked right up to his death on the 15th of March, 1960 to the utmost of his strength.

You will forgive me if I do not, on this occasion, make an analysis and appraisal of Čech's scientific contribution to topology. I should like only to mention some of the characteristics of E. Čech as a scientist and as a man and emphasise his significance for the development of mathematics in Czechoslovakia.

As far as I can judge — perhaps subjectively — one of the essential features of Čech's mathematical work was his ability to combine keen abstraction, deep analysis of concepts and an equally profound and spontaneous geometrical intuition and sense for the concrete. We may add still one more, perhaps less well-known, characteristic. It was his capacity for performing — patiently and with a sense for their real content — complicated and time-consuming computations, such as are often necessary in differential geometry. In view of these qualities, it is easier for us to understand how he could attain such successful results in such widely differing mathematical disciplines.

Čech's capability of abstraction, of detailed analysis of concepts until he had grasped their very essence, is clearly apparent in all his work, in particular in his contributions on homology and on compactification. His sense for the concrete and for the geometrical content can be observed in his approach to those problems where he had to look for the real content behind a complicated formal apparatus and in the emphasis which he placed (and in which he also instructed his students) on the construction of "concrete" individual examples.

One further outstanding quality of Čech as a mathematician was his keen sense for the unity of mathematics, for the interdependence between different mathematical disciplines. Čech's mathematical erudition was unusually wide and he tried to cultivate in his students an understanding of the unity of mathematics, a width and depth of mathematical knowledge.

Čech's fine qualities as a mathematician were necessarily connected with his understanding of the social position and role of mathematics, of the social responsibility of the scientist. He was deeply convinced that science must serve social progress, of which it is one of the driving forces, that it is the moral responsibility of the scientist to be an active citizen of this country and to take up on the complex problems of world development an equally responsible and decisive standpoint as he does to his own work. For this very reason, Čech devoted so much energy to organisational and pedagogical questions and, although himself remote from applications, actively advocated the speedier development of applied mathematical disciplines in our country.

Eduard Čech was in fact the first Czechoslovak mathematician (followed, it is true, by several others of his generation) to make a fundamental contribution to world mathematics and, in his particular branch, influenced scientific work in other countries. It may be said that with E. Čech Czechoslovak mathematics assumed an active place in the general stream of world development of mathematical science. There can be no doubt that this fact in turn had a beneficial effect on the level of mathematical work in Czechoslovakia.

E. Čech influenced directly or indirectly the larger part of the middle and younger generation of our mathematicians. In some cases, this took the form of a direct scientific influence, in other, no less important cases, of a general approach to mathematics and its problems. I should like to mention once again Čech's Brno seminar, which remains for us till today a model of the systematic work of a scientific team. Undoubtedly, Čech's influence will be felt for many years to come on the mathematical life of our country.

In many respects E. Čech presents us with an example difficult to emulate. His devotion to science knew no bounds. We shall always admire his exemplary diligence, the undauntable spirit with which he firmly upheld his views — arrived at on the basis of careful consideration — both in discussion and in practice. We mathematicians can only aim at emulating his creative enthusiasm, his keen penetration to the essence of a problem, his fundamental conception of mathematics as a whole. As citizens of this country and as scientists we have his example as a worker in the cause of science and progress which he considered to be – as in fact they are – inseparable and indivisible.

M. H. STONE

Mr. President, ladies and gentlemen,

I feel greatly honoured to be asked to speak today on this occasion. The only reason why I should have been asked is that mathematical colleagues interested in work done independently by Prof. E. ČECH and myself have been good enough to join our names to designate a theorem to which we both made contributions.

The paper in which Professor Čech discussed this very important theorem was published in USA under the title "On bicompact spaces", in 1937. This work has a close relation, at least historically, to the fundamental memoir of Alexandrov and Urysohn under the title "Mémoire sur les espaces topologiques compacts" which was published in 1929. The link between this work and the work of Prof. Čech was an equally well known paper of the Russian mathematician Tichonov "Über die topologische Erweiterung von Räumen", published in 1930. In the memoir of Alexandrov and Urysohn the general properties of topological spaces, and in particular of compact topological spaces, were studied in a very deep and detailed fashion. Many new problems were proposed there for the first time. The paper of Tichonov gave a resolution to one of these important new problems: Under what circumstances does a topological space possess an embedding, homeomorphic embedding, into a compact space, and in particular onto a dense subset of a compact space? The solution given by Tichonov to this problem actually contained information which Tichonov either did not observe or did not choose to emphasize. It was just this point which was the foundation of Prof. Čech's memoir "On bicompact spaces". He saw that by using the technique of Tichonov one could construct a maximal compact envelope for those spaces which are called completely regular. In his paper Prof. Čech studied many properties of such a space, he characterized the compact envelope, and he established its uniqueness. Speaking for myself, I may say that I found particularly interesting his observations on the question of when a space is determined by its compact envelope. This question in certain situations has a very simple answer. Equally interesting was his use of the compact envelope to define for topological spaces in general a notion of completeness and to relate this definition to the standard concept of completeness for metric spaces.

Perhaps I may be forgiven if I use this opportunity to say a few words about the relation of this work of Prof. Čech to the work which I was doing at the same time.

We worked quite independently. It was, I believe, at the *World Topological Congress* held in Moscow in 1935 that I first met Prof. Čech. At the Congress we both presented ideas which had a bearing on the problem of the compact envelope. My own concern was of very different nature from Prof. Čech's. For various reasons I had glimpsed a possibility of studying some of the problems raised by Alexandrov and Urysohn in the fundamental memoir which I have cited, by considering them as special cases of the general problem of enlarging a topological space. The essential notion which lies at the root of such a study is one to which we now refer by the name of filter. Filters had been introduced in the early thirties by Henri Cartan, and the methods which I developed for the study of the problem of compactification implicitly involved the notion of filter. However, since my attention to this problem had grown out of an interest in some algebraic structures which occur in topology, I used algebraic language in order to provide the machinery which could equivalently have been set up by the use of filters. It seems to me correct to say that by this type of discussion it was possible to attain a general understanding of the problem of adjoining new points to topological spaces so as to extend or enlarge these spaces in topologically interesting ways. It was also possible to solve some of the problems formulated in the memoir of Alexandrov and Urysohn. When I spoke at the Congress in Moscow in 1935, I had not yet tried to specialize this kind of consideration to particular spaces. It was only following that Congress that I reviewed the general structure of my work and saw what it involved for certain special kinds of space. From this review there emerged a demonstration of the existence, uniqueness and general characteristic properties of the compact envelope which Prof. Čech discovered at approximately the same time. A little later — and this was before the publication of Prof. Čech's paper — I realized that this specialization could be accomplished by the method of Tichonov. In later years I published such a demonstration, which is essentially only a modification of that given by Prof. Čech.

I have been at some pains to discuss these matters here because I think it is only in the light of some such comment that one can pass to a consideration of the consequences which have followed from this important contribution of Prof. Čech.

The explicit study of the compact envelope for completely regular spaces has occupied a good many mathematicians since that time, and a good deal has been added to the already detailed comments that were made by Prof. Čech in his fundamental paper. The use of the compact envelope for various topological purposes has been exploited to some extent, but I believe that its potentialities have not yet been exhausted. There remain many problems which can still be attacked by means of it: some which have to do with the dimensionality, some which have to do with the different kinds of compactification which one meets in problems of analysis, and so on. As for the more general procedures introduced by my papers it may be noted that they have not yet been exploited very vigorously. However, only recently some of the more complex techniques which I developed have found applications at the hands of Prof. Oxtoby. One reason why attention has been to some extent turned away from these matters is that we have had to concentrate our efforts on an attempt to understand the algebraic structure of the family of continuous functions on a completely regular space. This aspect of the topology of completely regular spaces, which is implicit in the work of Prof. Čech and explicit in my own work, has inspired many interesting contributions to mathematics. In particular it had a great deal to do with the modern study of normed rings and algebras, especially those defined over the real and the complex fields. It is for this reason, perhaps, that mathematicians with applications to analysis in mind have tended to concentrate their own topological studies upon what happens in the case of normed rings, especially those which appear in various mathematical situations. It may be noted that the general topological features which are the object of this sort of investigation still offer a rather mysterious but important field of study. I am sure that if Prof. Čech had lived he would himself have added to our knowledge of this particular domain. However, it was quite sufficient for a man who had written so many other important papers on topology that he should have made a single such basic contribution to such an interesting and important field as this.

In conclusion, I may say how deeply grateful I am for the privilege of expressing in this meeting organized as a memorial to Prof. Čech the sincere homage of all American mathematicians. — Thank you, Mr. President.

P. ALEXANDROFF

(Translated from Russian)

This Symposium, which has called together so many mathematicians specialising in general topology and associated fields, was initiated by the famous Czechoslovak mathematician Eduard Čech, one of the most outstanding exponents of this branch of mathematics.

We all feel deeply these sad moments when, instead of meeting prof. Čech in our midst and expressing to him our esteem for his work, we gather today to honour his memory.

In this brief session it is impossible to enumerate prof. Čech's scientific achievements — and unnecessary, indeed, since they must be familiar to all of us. I will therefore confine my remarks to the deep impression which Prof. Čech's work has made in mathematics.

His attention was not concerned solely with topology; together with Prof. G. Fubini of Bologna, he laid the foundations of projective differential geometry. However, let me speak only of Prof. Čech's topological papers.

These treat both general and algebraic topology. In general topology, Prof. Čech — together with Prof. M. H. Stone — discovered and defined the maximal compactification βX of any completely regular space X, and studied many of its interesting properties. In this connection, Prof. Čech also described a class of topological spaces now termed "complete in Čech's sense". The compactification βX has assumed a central place in topology; and we meet it in almost every paper on general topology. But its importance has far surpassed the bounds of topology itself; it is becoming a fundamental concept of other branches of mathematics, e. g. in functional analysis. Next to investigations connected with compact extensions of topological spaces, Prof. Čech's important contributions to general topology concern dimension theory. He was the first to realise the significance of a dimension theory not confined merely to spaces with countable basis; and that the study of considerably more general spaces raises in dimension theory a series of problems — often quite specific — both extremely interesting and difficult. Prof. Čech gave the first formal definition of the so-called "large" inductive dimension, and initiated its systematic study.

Several other contributions to general topology are of interest; but the ones mentioned suffice to fix indelibly the name of Prof. Čech in this branch of mathematics.

Prof. Čech also made considerable contributions to algebraic topology. In 1937 he connected the Alexander-Kolmogorov product with the classical notion of intersection, and thus clarified the geometrical meaning of this first homological operation.

Other important papers concerned local homological invariants, local duality theorems and general homological invariants of topological spaces.

Prof. Čech perfected the general method of constructing homological invariants by nerves of refined sequences of finite coverings; he used, systematically, open coverings in place of the closed coverings employed thereto, and rid himself of all limiting assumptions on the spaces studied. He first defined in all their generality the groups now bearing his name.

It is necessary to mention another important contribution to algebraic topology; at the *International Mathematical Congress in Zürich* held in 1932, Prof. Čech presented a paper containing a definition of the groups now called homotopy or Hurewicz groups. Prof. H. Hopf recalled this at last year's *Colloquium on Algebraic Topology*, also in Zürich.

This definition did not meet with the attention it merited; in fact, the commutativity of these groups for dimensions exceeding one was criticised (this was unfounded, as we now know).

Thus, Prof. Čech's definition of the homotopy groups was, in 1932, simply not understood — a situation extremely rare in modern mathematics. We must express our admiration at the intuition and talent of Prof. Čech, who defined the homotopy groups several years before W. Hurewicz.

We meet in Prague, one of the main centers of general topology, in the country one of whose sons was Eduard Čech. The Czechoslovak topological school — whose outstanding members are known over the world — was founded by Prof. Čech. This school is a living tribute to Prof. Čech, the best his country could give him.

K. KURATOWSKI

Monsieur le Président, Mesdames et Messieurs,

En faisant l'éloge du grand géomètre Edouard Čech et en m'associant à mes éminents collègues dans la haute appréciation de son oeuvre scientifigue et de son attrayante personnalité, je voudrais, dans ma courte allocution, mettre en lumière quelques aspects qu'eut son activité dans la coopération scientifique internationale.

La première dizaine de son activité scientifique fut vouée à la géométrie différentielle projective; il collabora alors intimement avec les géomètres italiens, avec Fubini en particulier. Lorsque il s'intéressa plus tard à la Topologie, c'est avec les mathématiciens polonais, américains et soviétiques qu'il prit contact. Il passa un an aux Etats Unis, notamment à Princeton. Il participa en 1935 au *Colloque International de Topologie à Moscou* et prit part au *Congrès International de Zurich*. A part cela il s'est rendu, à maintes reprises, à l'étranger ayant en vue d'organiser la coopération scientifique des mathématiciens de son pays avec ceux d'autres pays.

Le symposium qui vient d'être ouvert est dû, en grande mesure, à l'initiative d'Edouard Čech. Il désirait que cette réunion tenue sous les auspices d'un organisme international, fût une vraie rencontre internationale; il m'est agréable d'ajouter qu'il a tenu, en particulier, à la participation aussi grande que possible des mathématiciens polonais.

Car c'est à une coopération scientifique, la plus étroite, entre la Tchécoslovaquie et la Pologne — deux pays fraternels, ressuscités après la guerre — que Ed. Čech a voué ses efforts et son inépuisable énergie. C'est avec enthousiasme que nous nous rendîmes à la rencontre de son initiative. Rien ne pouvait être plus souhaitable que d'unir nos efforts à ceux de nos collègues et amis tchécoslovaques pour faire renaître la science dans nos pays dévastés et pour l'organiser à nouveau, conformément aux nouveaux devoirs envers nos Etats régénérés.

Comme conséquence de cette activité les liens entre les mathématiciens de nos deux pays se resserèrent. Chaque année on élaborait un accord concernant l'échange des chercheurs et des publications, ainsi que la participation réciproque aux congrès mathématiques. Ed. Čech vint lui-même participer au *Congrès des mathématiciens polonais* en 1947 et en 1948. C'est sur son initiative que fut organisé, ici à Prague, en 1949 un *Congrès*, très réuissi, *polono-tchécoslovaque*.

La coopération de Ed. Čech avec les mathématiciens polonais ne se réduisit pas aux problèmes d'organisation. Très souvent nous avons poursuivi les mêmes idées, nous étions partisans des mêmes tendances en mathématiques.

Permettez-moi d'en citer un exemple. Il y a une quarantaine d'années, aux débuts de l'Ecole Polonaise de Topologie, l'un des points de notre programme fut de débarasser la Topologie du plan de la méthode d'approximation des continus par des lignes polygonales, méthode utilisé fréquemment au commencement du XX-ème siècle. Ainsi, par exemple, procédait Schönflies dans son fameux traité de 1908; fameux non seulement comme essai de synthèse de la Topologie du plan d'alors, mais bien connu aussi et souvent cité à cause de nombreux théorèmes faux dont quelques-uns donnèrent d'ailleurs lieu aux découvertes ultérieures de Brouwer. Les fautes commises par Schönflies dans ses démonstrations avaient comme source la méthode dont je viens de parler: pénible, fort compliquée et peu appropriée aux problèmes topologiques.

Or, Ed. Čech était un partisan ardent de l'idée de remplacer cette méthode par des procédés purement topologiques. Il l'a prouvé non seulement dans ses écrits, mais l'a manifesté aussi dans de nombreux entretiens que j'ai eu le plaisir d'avoir avec lui à diverses occasions. La réalisation de cette idée obtint – comme on le sait – un succès complet. Elle conduisit d'une part à une théorie de la topologie du plan débarrassée des approximations par lignes polygonales, dont l'expression culminante a été atteinte dans la thèse de M. Eilenberg, soutenue à l'Université de Varsovie. D'autre part, l'analyse des notions qui intervenaient dans les raisonnements topologiques d'alors a contribué considérablement au développement de la topologie des espaces abstraits qui, inspirée par les idées de Ed. Čech, a atteint en Tchécoslovaquie un développement éclatant.

Grâce à ses mérites scientifiques éminents, Ed. Čech devint l'un des plus célèbres mathématiciens contemporains. En Pologne ses qualités personnelles et les mérites qu'il eut dans établissement de la coopération scientifique polono-tchécoslovaque, l'ont promu au rang des savants les plus vénérés et les plus populaires. En témoignage de la haute appréciation de ses mérites, l'Académie Polonaise des Sciences l'élut comme membre étranger, l'Université de Varsovie lui accorda le titre de docteur honoraire et la Société des Sciences de Wrocław l'invita à devenir son premier membre étranger.

Sa mort prématurée a malheureusement interrompu son oeuvre. En tant qu'ami intime de Ed. Čech, je voudrais exprimer le désir, sûrement partagé par ses amis répandus dans le monde entier, que, par l'intermédiaire de ses nombreux élèves et sous les auspices de ses éminents collègues tchécoslovaques, son oeuvre continue à vivre et à se développer.

SCIENTIFIC COMMUNICATIONS

CERTAINES CLASSES DE DISTRIBUTIONS QUASI-ANALYTIQUES AU SENS DE S. BERNSTEIN

E. J. AKUTOWICZ
Montpellier

1. Introduction. Une découverte particulièrement heureuse de S. BERNSTEIN était qu'il n'existe pas une approximation polynomiale à une fonction continue non identiquement nulle d'une précision trop élevée si la fonction donnée prend la valeur zéro dans une partie assez étendue de son domaine de définition. Autrement dit, si la convergence d'une suite de polynomes est suffisamment rapide, alors la limite possède nécessairement une certaine raideur. Précisons cet énoncé. Etant donnée une courbe γ et une suite infinie n_k d'entiers positifs, les classes $C(n_k, \gamma)$ de Bernstein se composent des fonctions f définies et continues sur γ et y admettant une approximation

$$\sup |f(x) - P_k(x)| \leqq r^{n_k}, \quad (0 < r < 1),$$

P_k désignant un polynome de degré n_k.

Théorème (BERNSTEIN, H. SZMUSZKOWICZÓWNA [1]). *Si une fonction appartenant à une classe $C(n_k, \gamma)$ s'évanouit sur un sousensemble $\gamma_0 \subset \gamma$ de capacité logarithmique positive, alors elle est identiquement nulle.*

Notre but sera de résumer quelques résultats du même genre dans le cadre de distributions à support discret. A ce moment il est évident que la topologie d'espace fonctionnel jouera un rôle important; dans le cas dont nous nous occuperons elle est définie par un ensemble de normes de Banach. Les démonstrations détaillées paraîtront prochainement dans les Annales de l'Ecole Normale Supérieure.

2. L'espace fondamental. On connait la notion de distribution ou fonction généralisée; c'est une forme linéaire continue définie sur un espace fondamental de „bonnes" fonctions. Nous allons discuter l'espace suivant, composé de certaines fonctions holomorphes [2].

Soient a, b, C trois paramètres positifs et $B(b)$ la bande $|y| < b$ dans le plan de la variable $z = x + iy$. Désignons par $\mathscr{A}_{a,b}$ l'espace vectoriel de toutes les fonctions $f(z)$ holomorphes dans la bande $B(b)$ et elles que

$$(1) \qquad |f(z)| \leqq C \exp(-a|x|), \quad z \in B(b),$$

pour une constante $C = C(f)$. Posons

$$\|f\|_{a,b} = \sup_{z \in B(b)} |f(z)| \exp a|x| \quad (a, b \text{ fixés}).$$

Muni de cette norme, $\mathscr{A}_{a,b}$ est un espace de Banach. On considère l'espace vectoriel

$$\mathscr{A} = \bigcup_{a,b} \mathscr{A}_{a,b}$$

comme une limite inductive des espaces $\mathscr{A}_{a,b}$. Le dual fort $\mathscr{A}'$ est formé de certaines distributions. La transformation de Fourier est un automorphisme dans les deux espaces $\mathscr{A}$, $\mathscr{A}'$; grâce à cette circonstance on peut établir l'analogie entre nos résultats et celui de Bernstein que nous venons de citer.

On note $\langle S, f \rangle$ la valeur de $S \in \mathscr{A}'$ en $f \in \mathscr{A}$.

Un ensemble borné $\mathscr{B} = \mathscr{B}(a, b, C)$ est constitué par des fonctions $f(z)$ qui satisfont à l'inégalité (1) avec a, b, C fixes. La convergence de S vers T dans la topologie de $\mathscr{A}'$ veut alors dire que

$$\sup_{f \in \mathscr{B}} |\langle S - T, f \rangle|$$

tend vers 0 pour un ensemble borné arbitraire $\mathscr{B}$ dans $\mathscr{A}$.

On peut caractériser les fonctions appartenant à $\mathscr{A}$ de la manière suivante.

Proposition. *Une fonction $f(x)$ définie sur la droite réelle et indéfiniment dérivable appartient à l'espace $\mathscr{A}$ si et seulement s'il existe des constants c, h, k pouvant dépendre de f telles que les inégalités suivantes aient lieu:*

$$|x^n f(x)| \leqq ch^n n!\,, \quad |f^{(n)}(x)| \leqq ck^n n!\,, \quad n = 0, 1, \ldots$$

On sait qu'il correspond à chaque élément $\varphi \in \mathscr{A}'$ une fonction $\varphi(z)$ holomorphe dans $y \neq 0$ et soumise aux conditions naturelles de croissance sur les horizontales telle que

$$\varphi = \lim_{\substack{y \to 0 \\ y > 0}} \varphi(x + iy) - \lim_{\substack{y \to 0 \\ y < 0}} \varphi(x + iy)\,,$$

les limites étant prises dans $\mathscr{A}'$ [3].

3. Un problème de quasi-analyticité dans $\mathscr{A}'$. Prenons une fonction $\varphi(z)$ holomorphe dans le demi-plan supérieur telle que la limite

$$\lim_{y \to 0} \varphi(x + iy)$$

existe dans $\mathscr{A}'$. Elle définit alors un élément $\varphi \in \mathscr{A}'$. Il s'ensuit que φ est la transformée de Fourier d'un élément Φ appartenant, lui aussi, à $\mathscr{A}'$. Notre hypothèse est que le support de Φ se trouve dans la partie non négative de l'axe réel.

Désignons par $a_1 < a_2 < \ldots$ une suite de nombres positifs et par $\mathscr{D}_N$ l'ensemble de distributions d'ordre inférieur ou égal à N dont les supports soient contenus dans l'ensemble

$$A_N = \{\pm a_1, \ldots, \pm a_N\}\,.$$

Ainsi un élément de $\mathscr{D}_N$ est une combinaison linéaire des dérivées d'ordre inférieur ou égal à N des mesures de Dirac portées par les points de A_N.

On étudie alors l'approximation d'un élément φ satisfaisant lesdites conditions par des éléments de $\mathscr{D}_N$ lorsque $N \to \infty$. La meilleure approximation de φ sera par définition

$$E_N = E_N(\mathscr{B}, \varphi) = \inf_{D_N \in \mathscr{D}_N} \sup_{f \in \mathscr{B}} |\langle \varphi - D_N, f \rangle| \tag{2}$$

où $\mathscr{B} = \mathscr{B}(a, b, C)$ désigne un ensemble borné de l'espace $\mathscr{A}$. Notons $\mathscr{B}_N = \mathscr{B}_N(a, b, C)$ la trace sur $\mathscr{B}$ de l'hyperplan défini par

$$f^{(n)}(a_k) = 0\,, \quad a_k \in A_N\,; \quad 0 \leqq n \leqq N\,.$$

Posons

$$F_N = \mathscr{B}_N(a, b + 2, C)\,,$$

$$\Delta_N = \sup_{f \in F_N} |f(z_0)|\,, \quad (1 + b < \operatorname{Im} z_0 < 2 + b)\,.$$

Théorème 1. *L'inégalité*

$$\underline{\lim}\, \sqrt[N]{E_N} < \overline{\lim}\, \sqrt[N]{\Delta_N}$$

entraîne $\varphi = 0$.

On remarque que la quantité Δ_N est un espèce de capacité.

Les étapes suivants montrent l'idée de la démonstration.

1° On laisse tomber la condition extrémisante

$$\inf_{D_N \in \mathscr{D}_N}$$

dans (2) après avoir montré l'existence d'un élément extrémal D_N^0.

2° On remarque que $g(t) \in \mathscr{B}_N(a, b, C)$ entraîne

$$\frac{g(t)}{t - t_o} \in \mathscr{B}_N(a, b, C)$$

en raison de $\operatorname{Im} z_0 > 1 + b$. On a donc la minoration

$$E_N \geqq \sup_{g \in \mathscr{B}_N(a,b,C)} \left| \left\langle \varphi, \frac{g}{t - z_0} \right\rangle \right|. \tag{3}$$

3° En développant le noyau de Cauchy dans une série de puissances convenables on arrive à la seconde minoration

$$E_N \geqq C^{te} \,.\, \sup_{f \in F_N} \left| \int \frac{\varphi(t) f(t)}{t - z_0} \, dt \right|, \tag{4}$$

l'intégrale étant étendue sur l'horizontale $\operatorname{Im} t = p_0$, $(\operatorname{Im} z_0 < p_0 < 2 + b)$. La constante ne dépend pas de N.

4° En combinant les inégalités (3) et (4) et en utilisant la formule de Cauchy on achève la démonstration.

Dans le cas où la suite a_k coïncide avec les entiers naturels on a un énoncé plus direct:

Théorème 2. *Il existe une constante absolue* $r_0 > 0$ *de telle sorte que si l'on a*

$$\lim \sqrt[N^2]{E_N(\mathscr{B}, \varphi)} < r_0\,,$$

alors $\varphi = 0$.

Remarquons que la racine N^2-ième est l'analogue naturelle de la racine N-ième qui intervient dans le théorème de Bernstein sur l'approximation polynomiale uniforme.

La démonstration résulte du Théorème 1 par un choix convenable d'une fonction intervenant dans la concurrence définissant la quantité Δ_N. On trouve que $r_0 \geqq \geqq 3/e^2$. Je ne connais pas la valeur exacte de r_0.

4. Quasi-analyticité de distributions à support ponctuel. Soit φ un élément de $\mathscr{A}'$ ayant l'origine comme support. Un tel élément peut être exprimé par une série infinie de dérivées de la mesure de Dirac,

$$\varphi = \sum c_n \delta^{(n)} , \tag{5}$$

la série convergeant pour la topologie de $\mathscr{A}'$. Nous allons étudier l'approximation à φ par des combinaisons linéaires de $\delta^{(n)}$. (Ici la question se pose d'éclaircir la relation entre les sommes partielles de (5) et les éléments D_N^0 de meilleure approximation.) Vu l'invariance des espaces $\mathscr{A}$, $\mathscr{A}'$ vis-à-vis de la transformation de Fourier, notre problème revient à l'étude de l'approximation polynomiale de la fonction entière de type exponentiel nul qui est la transformée de Fourier de φ. Notons Φ cette fonction entière.

Tandis que pour le Théorème 1on avait supposé la transformée de Fourier Φ nulle sur une demi-droite, maintenant la prémisse homologue de celle-là sera l'existence de lacunes dans la série (5). Le problème d'approximation est encore lié à un second problème extrémal. Désignons par Σ l'ensemble des indices n pour lesquelles c_n diffère de 0 dans (5). Soit $\mathscr{B}$ un ensemble borné de $\mathscr{A}$ et posons

$$r_N = r_N(\mathscr{B}) = \sup |G^{(N)}(0)| , \quad N \in \Sigma ,$$

le supremum étant relatif à l'ensemble des fonctions $G \in \mathscr{B}$ telles que $G^{(n)}(0) = 0$ pour $n \in \Sigma - \{N\}$.

Théorème 3. *Soit Σ une suite d'entiers non negatifs de densité $d < \frac{1}{2}$ dans l'ensemble des entiers non negatifs. Soit φ une distribution de la forme (5) telle que sa transformée de Fourier Φ soit d'ordre $\varrho > 0$ (au sens de la théorie des fonctions entières). Si la meilleure approximation E_N de φ vérifie l'inégalité*

$$\lim \frac{N \log N}{\log^+ (r_N/E_N)} < \varrho \tag{6}$$

alors $\varphi = 0$.

Dans les hypothèses où nous nous sommes placés, l'évaluation (6) n'est pas loin d'être la meilleure possible. Or, pour tout $\varphi \neq 0$ on a

$$E_N(\mathscr{B}, \varphi) \geqq r_N(\mathscr{B}) \, |c_N| , \quad N \in \Sigma . \tag{7}$$

Prenons pour Σ une suite d'entiers impairs et étudions l'approximation d'un φ de telle sorte que $\varrho = 1$ et $|c_n| \, n!$ ne croit pas. Etant donné $\mathscr{B}(a, b, C)$ il existe alors une fonction intervenant dans la définition de r_N ayant des poles *en* $\pm\, ib_1$ $(b_1 > b)$. De (7) il vient

$$\underline{\lim}\ \sqrt[N]{(E_N/|c_N|\, N!)} \geqq \frac{1}{b}\,.$$

D'autre part, les conditions imposées à φ entraînent

$$\overline{\lim}\ \sqrt[N]{(E_N/|c_N|\, N!)} \leqq \frac{1}{b}\,.$$

5. Caracterisation du dual $\mathscr{A}'$. Pour l'espace fondamental $\mathfrak{A}$ qui se compose des fonctions holomorphes sur une courbe fermée Γ sur la sphère de Riemann, M. G. Köthe a caractérisé le dual $\mathfrak{A}'$ comme l'espace $\mathfrak{A}_0$ de toutes les fonctions localement holomorphes dans le complémentaire de Γ qui s'annulent à l'infini. Rappelons que l'espace $\mathfrak{A}$ est une limite inductive définie à partir de la famille des normes de la convergence uniforme sur les voisinages compactes de Γ, et que $\mathfrak{A}_0$ est une limite projective donnée par les normes de la convergence uniforme sur les compacts du complémentaire de Γ. Un résultat de cette simplicité ne subsiste pas pour la droite.

D'après C. Roumieu [3] à chaque élément $\varphi \in \mathscr{A}'$ correspond une fonction holomorphe $\varphi(x + iy)$ dans $y \neq 0$ telle que l'égalité à la fin du numéro 2 tient et de telle sorte que quels que soient H_1, H_2, K positifs, il existe une constante A telle que

$$|\varphi(x + iy)| \leqq A \exp \frac{|x|}{K} \quad \text{dans} \quad \frac{1}{H_1} \leqq |y| \leqq \frac{1}{H_2}\,, \tag{8}$$

et réciproquement à chaque fonction $\varphi(x + iy)$ de cette sorte correspond un élément $\varphi \in \mathscr{A}'$. On appelle la fonction $\varphi(x + iy)$ une indicatrice de φ. Cette fonction est déterminée seulement à une fonction entière près, de la même croissance. Notons par J_0 l'ensemble de ces fonctions entières. Par la famille de normes

$$\|\varphi(x + iy)\|_{H_1, H_2, K} = \sup_{\frac{1}{H_1} \leqq |y| \leqq \frac{1}{H_2}} |\varphi(x + iy)| \exp\left(-\frac{|x|}{K}\right)$$

on munit l'espace $\mathscr{A}_0$ de fonctions holomorphes dans $y \neq 0$ satisfaisant à (8) de la topologie d'une limite projective. Désignons par $\tilde{\mathscr{A}_0}$ l'espace quotient

$$\tilde{\mathscr{A}_0} = \mathscr{A}_0 / J_0$$

(J_0 est fermé dans $\mathscr{A}_0$). C'est un espace de Fréchet défini par la famille de normes habituelles.

Théorème 4. *L'espace vectoriel topologique $\tilde{\mathscr{A}_0}$ est isomorphe au dual $\mathscr{A}'$.*

Bibliographie

[1] *H. Szmuszkowiczówna*: Un théorème sur les polynômes et application à la théorie des fonctions quasi analytiques. Comptes Rendus Acad. Sci. Paris, t. *198* (1934), 1119–1120.
[2] *G. Doetsch*: Handbuch der Laplacetransformation I. Basel 1953.
[3] *C. Roumieu*: Sur quelques extensions de la notion de distribution. Ann. Sci. Ec. Norm. Sup. t. *77* (1960), 41–120.
[4] *G. Köthe*: Die Randverteilungen analytischer Funktionen. Math. Zeits. *57* (1952), 13–33.
[5] *G. Köthe*: Dualität in der Funktionentheorie. J. reine angew. Math. *191* (1953), 153—172.

ON SOME RESULTS CONCERNING TOPOLOGICAL SPACES AND THEIR CONTINUOUS MAPPINGS

P. ALEXANDROFF

Moscow

The purpose of this paper is to give a review of some – more or less new – results and problems on the subject. Special attention is paid to the theory of metrization and related questions: in spite of the now classical and definitive metrization theorems of Nagata-Smirnov and Bing the subject is not exhausted and has shown unexpected progress in the very last years.

Theorems concerning the invariance of topological properties under continuous mappings and the representation of topological spaces as images of zero-dimensional spaces are also treated. The last chapter is devoted to some aspects of dimension theory of general spaces.

1

There are two general questions which can be roughly formulated as follows:

A. *Which spaces can be represented as images of "nice" (e. g. metric or zero-dimensional, etc.) spaces under "nice" continuous mappings?*

B. *Which spaces can be mapped onto "nice" spaces by "nice" mappings?*

Only continuous mappings will be considered in that what follows: among them there are very different kinds of mappings which are „nice" from different view-points: first of all, there are closed and open mappings; next mappings $f\colon X \leftarrow Y$ may be classified by properties of the counter-images of single points, $f^{-1}\, y\ y \in Y$.

Thus we call a mapping *metrizable* if all the $f^{-1}\, y$ are metrizable spaces. Among them there are *compact metrizable* mappings ($f^{-1}y$ are compacta). Mappings are *bicompact*, if all $f^{-1}\, y$ are bicompacta. Closed bicompact mappings are called *perfect*. A mapping with bicompact boundaries of the counter-images $f^{-1}y$ is called *peripherally bicompact*, or simply *π-bicompact*. Very interesting are the *S-mappings* (of YU. SMIRNOV and A. H. STONE): these are the mappings whose counter-images $f^{-1}y$ are spaces with countable bases; and so forth.

On the other hand, given an open covering ω of X, one calls a mapping $f\colon X \to Y$ an *ω-mapping* if each point $y \in Y$ has a neighbourhood Oy with $f^{-1}Oy$ contained in some element of ω; the notion of a ω-mapping is fundamental in the whole newer development of dimension theory.

It may happen that a mapping of certain type assumes further properties when considered for a restricted class of spaces: a classical example is that every continuous $f: X \to Y$ becomes closed for bicompact X and Hausdorff Y.

Another remarkable case of this kind is discovered by I. A. VAINŠTEIN: a closed $f: X \to Y$ is always π-bicompact if X and Y are metric. This result has been strengthened by A. H. Stone: Given a metric X and a closed $f: X \to Y$; then Y is metrizable if and only if f is π-bicompact.

Next we give some examples of problems of type B.

It has been proved by myself as long ago as in 1924 that every metrizable locally separable space is a sum of mutually disjoint open and closed separable subspaces. Obviously this property is not only necessary but also sufficient for a regular locally separable space to be metrizable. Thus we can say: A locally separable regular space is metrizable if and only if it may be mapped on a metric discrete space by an S-mapping.[1]) YU. SMIRNOV raised the following question: Which metric spaces are S-mappable on a zerodimensional space? Smirnov obtained only a partial answer to this question: namely, he proved that every metric strongly paracompact[2]) space belongs to this category; but there exist non-strongly paracompact spaces which can be mapped by an S-mapping on zero-dimensional metric spaces. On the other hand, if a space allows a closed S-mapping on a zero-dimensional space, it is strongly paracompact; but not all strongly paracompact metric spaces allow such a map.

The following important theorem was essentially proved (although not explicitly stated) by C. H. DOWKER [7], 1948 (and reproved by M. Katětov and V. Ponomarev):

In order that a regular space X be paracompact it is necessary and sufficient that to each open covering ω of X there exists an ω-mapping $f: X \to Y$ of X onto a metric space. The final compact (= Lindelöf) spaces are characterized by assuming Y separable metric in this theorem.

The following theorems of Z. FROLÍK are fundamental in this field:

I. The (completely regular) space X is paracompact and complete (in Čech's sense) if and only if there exists a perfect mapping of X onto a complete metric space.

The second theorem of Z. Frolík belongs to the type A.

II. Let $f: X \to Y$ be closed, X complete metric. The space Y is metric if and only if it is complete (in Čech's sense).

As concerns results of type A, there is the following theorem by V. PONOMAREV [19]:

All spaces with the first Hausdorff axiom of countability and only these spaces are open images of metric spaces.

But, as just proved by A. ARCHANGELSKI [5], a collective normal space which is an image of a metric space under an open bicompact mapping is metrizable.

[1]) A discrete metric space (and in fact a discrete T_1-space) is a space all of whose points are isolated.

[2]) Strongly paracompact means that every open covering has a star-finite refinement.

There is an example of A. H. Stone of an open compact $f: X \to Y$, where X is metric but Y is not metrizable. V. Ponomarev proved that under these conditions a paracompact Y is always metrizable. V. Ponomarev proved even more: he calls a mapping $f: X \to Y$ of a metric X a *uniform mapping* if for each $y \in Y$ and each neighbourhood Oy, the distance $\varrho(f^{-1}y, X \setminus f^{-1}Oy)$ is positive. Now if X is metric, Y paracompact and $f: X \to Y$ open and uniform, then Y is metrizable.

A. Archangelski proved furthermore [5]:

If X is metrizable, Y is a T_1-space, $f: X \to Y$ is closed and uniform, then Y is metrizable.

A. Archangelski [5] calls a mapping $f: X \to Y$ of a metric X *completely uniform* if to each $y \in Y$ and its neighbourhood Oy, a smaller neighbourhood $O_1 y$ can be found in such a way that

$$\varrho(f^{-1}O_1 y, X \setminus f^{-1}Oy) > 0 .$$

He settles completely the problem by proving the following theorem:

If X is metric, $f: X \to Y$ open and completely uniform, then the T_1-space Y is metrizable.

The natural question as to which spaces are images of metric spaces under open S-mappings is answered by V. Ponomarev [19], who proved that these spaces and none other have a pointcountable basis.

I considered the condition of existence of a point-countable basis while working on metrization of locally separable (and indeed of locally compact) spaces. I have shown that if this condition is satisfied in a regular locally separable space, then this space is a union of disjoint open and closed separable subspaces and thus is metrizable.

As Yu. Smirnov showed that a locally metrizable space is metrizable if and only if it is paracompact while a separable metric space is even strongly paracompact, it is easily seen that for the metrizability of a regular locally separable space each of the following conditions is necessary and sufficient:

1. paracompactness, 2. strong paracompactness, 3. existence of a point countable basis, 4. existence of a locally countable basis, 5. existence of a star-countable basis, 6. decomposition into disjoint open separable subspaces.

But let us return to spaces with a point countable basis and to their characterization as open S-images of metric spaces.

V. Ponomarev [19] showed that the existence of a point-countable basis is preserved under open S-mappings (while it is obviously not preserved under arbitrary open mappings). The question whether this property is preserved under closed metrizable (or even compact metrizable) mappings remains open.

A. Archangelski and Z. Frolík have proved that a bicompact space which is a closed image of a metric space is metrizable, while A. Miščenko [16] proved recently that every bicompact space with a point-countable basis is metrizable; on the other hand he has constructed a non-metrizable paracompact (normal) space with a point-countable basis. It remains unknown if in this example the assumption of paracompactness can be replaced by final compactness.

Before going further in strengthening the first Hausdorff axiom of countability, let us recall the general metrization theorem by P. URYSOHN and myself [1], proved in 1923 as the first theorem of its kind; today this theorem seems much more natural and satisfactory than it seemed 38 years ago. We called a family $\Sigma = \{\omega_\alpha\}$ of open coverings of given space X *complete* if it has the following property: for each point $x \in X$ and each element $V_\alpha \in \omega_\alpha$ containing this point, the set $\{V_\alpha\}$ so obtained is a basis of the point x in the space X. An alternate formulation of this condition is obviously the following one:

To each $x \in X$ and its neighbourhood Ox there exists in Σ a ω_α such that the star of α in ω_α is contained in Ox.

Our second definition is the following: a covering ω' is a regular refinement of the covering ω, if for each two elements U'_1, U'_2 of ω' with $U'_1 \cap U'_2 \neq 0$ there exists an $U \in \omega$ containing $U'_1 \cap U'_2$. Obviously the condition of a regular refinement is less restrictive than that of a star-refinement.

The metrization theorem of Urysohn and myself is as follows: A space X is metrizable if and only if there exists in this space a countable complete family of open coverings

$$\omega_1, \omega_2, \ldots, \omega_n, \ldots$$

such that each ω_{n+1} is a regular refinement of ω_n.

One proves easily that in a paracompact regular space the condition concerning regular refinements may be omitted (because of the existence in such a space of star-refinements for any covering). Thus *a necessary and sufficient condition for metrizability of a regular space consists simply in paracompactness and in the existence of a countable complete family of coverings.* (V. Ponomarev).

Remark 1. As first noted by A. Miščenko [16], there exists a regular non-paracompact space in which every covering has a regular refinement.

Remark 2. We say that the space X is symmetrizable if a symmetric function $\varrho(x, x') = \varrho(x', x) \geqq 0$ of two points of X can be defined in such a way that $\varrho(x, x') = 0$ is equivalent with $x = x'$ and $x_0 \in X$ belongs to the closure of a set $M \subseteq X$ if and only if $\inf \varrho(x_0, x) = 0$. We say further that a symmetrziable space is a Cauchy space if it allows a symmetric metric in which each convergent sequence of points $x_n \to x_0$ is a Cauchy sequence (in the sense that $\varrho(x_m, x_n) \to 0$ when $m, n \to \infty$).

A. LUNC [14] has shown that the space of all countable ordinals (with the obvious order topology) is a symmetrizable(!) space but not a symmetrizable Cauchy space. In a joint paper V. NIEMYTZKI and myself [2] have proved that a space X is a symmetrizable Cauchy space if and only if it has a countable complete family of open coverings.

Thus a paracompact symmetrizable Cauchy space is metrizable.

After all these remarks we shall define a property of a topological space which is stronger than the existence of a pointcountable basis. Namely, define a *point-regular basis* as an open basis $\mathfrak{B}$ with the following property:

Any infinite set of elements of $\mathfrak{B}$ containing a given point x is a basis of this point.

It is immediate that every point-regular basis is pointcountable. Moreover, a point-regular basis can also be defined as a basis having the following property:

For each point x and its neighbourhood Ox there is only a finite number of elements of the basis which contain the point x and have points in common with $X \setminus Ox$.

As each element of a point-regular basis is contained in a maximal element of this basis, while any covering by such maximal elements is necessarily point-finite, one can easily conclude weak paracompactness[3]) of spaces having a point-regular basis. Furthermore, if ω_0 is the set of all maximal elements of the given point-regular basis $\mathfrak{B}$, then $\mathfrak{B} \setminus \omega_0$ is again a (point-regular) basis[4]) $\mathfrak{B}_1$, while ω_0 is a point-finite covering of X.

Similarly, the set of all maximal elements of $\mathfrak{B}_1$ is a point-finite covering ω_1 of X and $\mathfrak{B}_1 \setminus \omega$ is a point-regular basis.

In this manner we obtain a sequence

$$\omega_0, \omega_1, \ldots, \omega_n, \ldots$$

of point-finite coverings which is easily seen to be complete. Thus if the space X is paracompact and has a point-regular basis, then X is metrizable, by the Ponomarev version of the theorem of Urysohn and myself [4].

Thus we obtain the following metrization theorem (proved by myself in [1]):

A necessary and sufficient condition for the metrizability of a Hausdorff space is paracompactness combined with the existence of a point-regular basis.

As X is weakly paracompact, paracompactness in this theorem may be replaced by collective normality.

A. Archangelski [6] made a further step in this direction of investigating the metrization problem, and this step is definitive. He calls a basis $\mathfrak{B}$ *regular* if to each point x and to each neighbourhood Ox, a smaller neighbourhood O_1x can be found such that only a finite number of elements of the basis $\mathfrak{B}$ has common with both O_1x and $X \setminus O_1x$.

In the same way as weak paracompactness of a space X follows from the existence of a point-regular basis in X, the ordinary paracompactness of X is a consequence of the existence of a regular basis. As every T_1-space with a regular basis is regular, we have:

---

[3]) Weakly paracompact means that every open covering has a point-finite refinement.

[4]) One must be careful — in an obvious manner — with the single point elements virtually present in the basis.

Archangelski's [6] metrization theorem: *In order that a T_1-space be metrizable it is necessary and sufficient that this space have a regular basis.*

2

Until now we have only considered those aspects of the general problems A and B which are more or less connected with metrization and countability. Now let us mention some results and problems concerning the representation of topological spaces as continuous images of zero-dimensional spaces.

I think the first results in this field were some theorems of Hurewicz and myself (proved around 1925); I proved [3] that compacta (i. e. compact metric spaces) are identical with those Hausdorff spaces which are continuous images of the Cantor discontinuum; W. HUREWICZ proved (almost at the same time) his famous characterization of compacta of dimension $\leqq n$ as $(n + 1)$-to-1 images of zero-dimensional compacta (or of closed subsets of the Cantor set). Both theorems were the objects of important generalizations until the last years (in particular I have in mind the tremendous generalizations of the results of W. Hurewicz now given by J. NAGATA and E. SKLYARENKO, concerning infinite dimensional compacta).

I proved that every bicompact space of weight τ is a continuous image of a zero-dimensional bicompact space of the same weight, and in fact of a closed subset of the generalized Cantor discontinuum $\mathscr{D}^\tau$ of the same weight τ; the question then arose whether every bicompact space of weight τ is a continuous image of the discontinuum $\mathscr{D}^\tau$ itself. The negative solution of this question is given by E. SZPILRAJN-MARCZEWSKI who also proved some properties of the bicompact spaces now called dyadic, which are such images. E. Marczewski proved that every family of disjoint open subsets of a dyadic bicompact space is at most countable. Further important results are due to N. A. SHANIN [24] and A. ESENIN-VOLPIN. N. A. Shanin proved that no dyadic bicompact space is the sum of a well-ordered increasing family of nowhere dense subsets.[5]) A second theorem by Shanin states that if an ordered bicompact space (with the natural order-topology) is dyadic, then it is necessarily homeomorphic to a compactum lying on the real line.

A. Esenin-Volpin proved that a dyadic bicompact space with first Hausdorff axiom of countability is metrizable.

Thus the dyadicity of a bicompact space is a very strong restriction. On the other hand, L. IVANOVSKI and V. KUSMINOV succeeded in proving the very remarkable theorem that every bicompact topological group (considered as topological space) is a dyadic bicompact space.

In a joint paper appeared in vol. 50 of the Fundamenta Mathematicae, V. Ponomarev and myself have given a characterization of dyadic bicompact spaces and also

[5]) This theorem of Shanin represents a generalization of Baire's theorem on category; for non-dyadic bicompacts it does not hold in general.

of irreducible[6]) dyadic bicompact spaces in terms of coverings. But a characterization of these important spaces by means of more simple and direct set-theoretical properties is still an open problem. Actually we do not know whether a dyadic bicompact space which is of character τ at each point (and thus, according to A. Esenin-Volpin, has weight τ) is the image of $\mathscr{D}^\tau$ under an irreducible mapping.

Now let us pass to general non-compact spaces. To my knowledge the only result in this area is a theorem of Ponomarev [20] asserting that every normal (and in fact every completely regular) space X of weight τ is the image of a certain set $X_0 \subseteq \mathscr{D}^\tau$ under an irreducible perfect mapping.

Of course X_0 is a completely regular space and zero-dimensional in the sense that ind $X_0 = 0$.

The question arises as to when can we suppose dim $X_0 = 0$ in Ponomarev's theorem?

The answer given by Ponomarev is as follows:

Let us call a T_1space X_0 *perfectly zero-dimensional* if each open covering of X_0 has a refinement whose elements are disjoint open (and indeed open-closed) sets; obviously, this property is equivalent to paracompactness combined with dim $X_0 = 0$. Then the following theorem holds:

Among all regular spaces the paracompact ones are characterized by the property that they are perfect images of perfectly zero-dimensional spaces.

The following is an open question:

Is every normal X a perfect image of a normal X_0 with ind $X_0 = 0$?

In concluding this part of my report, it should be emphasized that the problems of types A and B are special cases of the general problem:

Which properties of a space are invariant under multivalued continuous mappings?

In this formulation I understand the continuity of a multivalued mapping in the classical sense of W. Hurewicz which is as a matter of fact, the sense of Cauchy: a multivalued $f: X \to Y$ (where all fx are closed in x) is continuous, if for each neighbourhood Ofx of the closed set fx there exists a neighbourhood Ox of x such that[7]) $fOx \subseteq Ofx$. The inverse mapping f^{-1} sends each point

$$y \in Y \quad \text{into} \quad f^{-1}y = \mathscr{E}(x \in X,\ fx \ni y).$$

A rather detailed theory of multivalued continuous mappings is elaborated by V. Ponomarev in three consecutive papers [21–23].

I will mention here only the following results of these papers.

[6]) An irreducible dyadic bicompact space is the image of $\mathscr{D}^\tau$ under an irreducible continuous mapping. A mapping $f: X \to Y$, $Y = fX$, is called irreducible if there is no closed $A \subset X$, $A \neq X$ with $fA = Y$.

[7]) The image fM of a set $M \subseteq X$ (the "large image") means the set $fM = \bigcup_{x \in M} fx$. If fA is closed for all closed sets A, then f is called closed; if fH is open for all open sets H, f is called open.

A multivalued continued mapping $f : X \to Y$ is said to be *perfect* if it is closed and if for every $x \in X$ and $y \in Y$, the sets fx and $f^{-1}y$ are bicompact.[8])

One of the advantages of the use of multivalued mappings is that the notion of a perfect mapping (like some other important notions) than becomes symmetric: if f is perfect, so is its inverse f^{-1}.

V. Ponomarev proved that all the following properties of a completely regular space are invariant under a perfect multivalued mapping (and thus invariant in both directions, from X to Y and from Y to X):

bicompactness, local bicompactness, paracompactness,
countable paracompactness, completeness in the sense of E. Čech.

This last invariance is a consequence of one of the extension theorems proved by V. Ponomarev [2] for multivalued continued mappings.

From his four theorems of this kind I shall mention here three.

1st extension theorem.[9]) Every closed Y-bicompact mapping $f : X \to Y$ of the T_1-space X onto the T_1-space Y has an extension to a closed mapping ωf of ωX onto ωY: if $\xi = \{A\} \in \omega X$ then

$$\omega f(\xi) = \bigcap_{A \in \xi} [fA]_{\omega Y} .$$

Here ωX, ωY mean, as always, the Wallman extension of X and Y.

V. Ponomarev [21] calls an extension $\varphi : \omega X \to \omega Y$ of a mapping $f : X \to Y$ *bilateral*, if $\varphi^{-1} : \omega Y \to \omega Y$ is an extension of $f^{-1} : Y \to X$.

2nd extension theorem. In order that a mapping of the T_1-space X onto the T_1-space Y have a closed bilateral extension $\varphi : \omega X \to \omega Y$, it is necessary and sufficient that f be perfect. Then ωf is the desired extension and it is the only one which is minimal in the sense that for any closed extension $\varphi : \omega X \to \omega Y$ the inclusion $\omega f(\xi) \subseteq \subseteq \varphi(\xi)$ holds for all $\xi \in \omega X$. For a bilateral extension $\varphi : \omega X \to \omega Y$ we have

$$\varphi(\omega X \setminus X) = \omega Y \setminus Y \quad \text{and} \quad \varphi^{-1}(\omega Y \setminus Y) = \omega X \setminus X .$$

For normal X, Y we have $\omega X = \beta X$, $\omega Y = \beta Y$, and the invariance of the Čech completeness is a consequence of this situation.

The continuity of a multivalued mapping is equivalent to the closedness of its inverse mapping f^{-1}; if f^{-1} is both closed and open, f is called *strongly continuous*.

The **third extension theorem** of Ponomarev is concerned with Y-bicompact strongly continuous mappings of a normal space X onto a normal Y, and asserts that such a mapping f allows precisely one strongly continuous extension $\beta f : \beta X \to \beta Y$;

---

[8]) The bicompactness of all $fx \subseteq Y$ is called Y-bicompactness, the bicompactness of all $f^{-1}y \subseteq X$ X-bicompactness of f.

[9]) All mappings are supposed multivalued continuous; brackets mean closure.

this extension is moreover minimal (in the above sense) in the class of all closed extension. If f is open, then βf is also open.[10])

3

1. This last part of my report is devoted to some questions of general dimension theory. Corresponding to the general aim of this paper I shall deal mainly with problems concerning general spaces. But it is impossible not to mention the tremendous progress in the last years of dimension theory of infinite-dimensional spaces which is mainly due to J. NAGATA, YU. SMIRNOV and his pupils B. LEVSHENKO and E. SKLYARENKO.

P. Urysohn was the first to suppose that there are two quite different types of infinite dimensional spaces and particularly of infinite-dimensional compacta (= compact metric spaces): the weakly infinite-dimensional (now universally called the countable dimensional) spaces which can be decomposed into a sum of a countable number of zero-dimensional subspaces, on the other hand those which do not allow such a decomposition. Urysohn formulated the conjecture that the Hilbert cube is strongly infinite-dimensional. Hurewicz proved this conjecture by showing that the Hilbert cube X has the following property:

(A) In X there is a countable number of pairs of closed disjoint sets (A_i, B_i), $i = 1, 2, \ldots$ (i.e. $A_i \cap B_i = \varnothing$) such that whenever closed C_i separate A_i from B_i, the intersection $\bigcap C_i$ is non-void. As no countable-dimension space can have this property (A) I called spaces with this property *essentially infinite-dimensional*; at the same time I formulated the following definition:

We say that a compactum X has the property (A′) if there exists a sequence of n-dimensional cubes Q^n, $n = 1, 2, 3, \ldots$, Q^n a face of Q^{n+1}, and of essential mappings $f_n : X \to Q^n$, such that if π_n^{n+1} denotes the natural projection of the cube Q^{n+1} onto its face Q^n, we have

$$f_n = \pi_n^{n+1} f_{n+1} .$$

The definitions bring forward, in a natural manner, these two problems:

1° are the properties (A) and (A′) equivalent for every bicompactum?

2° is anyone of these properties equivalent to the property of a compactum of not having a countable dimension?

B. Levshenko [13] has given a positive answer to the first of these questions; the second remains open.

As concerns the countable-dimensional compacta I will mention only the following result of Nagata-Sklyarenko:

In order that a compactum X not have a countable dimension it is necessary and sufficient that for every mapping f of the Cantor discontinuum C onto X there is at

[10]) This last result was first proved by Ponomarev under a suplementary hypothesis that f is X-bicompact, and thus perfect; A. TAIMANOV [27] showed that this hypothesis may be omitted.

least one point $x \in X$ with an uncountable counter-image $f^{-1}x \subset C$ (which thus has the power of the continuum).

On the other hand, if X has a countable dimension, then there exists a mapping $f: C \to X$ with all counter-images $f^{-1}x$ finite.

It is in my opinion an interesting question to investigate for an X with non-countable dimension, the set X_0 of all points $x \in X$ with an uncountable counter-image $f^{-1}x$. What is the structure of this set? can it be of finite or countable dimension?

I will not dwell any more on infinite-dimensional spaces as there is a rather complete report by Yu. Smirnov on the subject.

2. It is well known that any n-dimensional compactum is the limit space of an n-dimensional projection spectrum (i. e. an inverse spectrum whose elements are simplicial finite complexes). Freudenthal proved that any n-dimensional compactum is the limit space of an n-dimensional polyhedral spectrum (i. e. an inverse spectrum whose elements are polyhedra and whose projections are continuous mappings).

B. Pasynkov [17], [18] and independently S. Mardešić [15] have proved that there are n-dimensional bicompacta which are not limit spaces of n-dimensional polyhedral spectra (although every bicompactum is the limit space of a polyhedral spectrum; but it may be impossible to have in this spectrum projections „onto"). Moreover, B. Pasynkov proved that if an n-dimensional (in the sense $\dim X = n$) bicompactum X is the limit of an n-dimensional polyhedral spectrum with simplicial projections, then necessarily $\operatorname{ind} X = \operatorname{Ind} X = \dim X = n$. Thus the problem of spectral representation of bicompacta is intimately connected with one of the most important problems of dimension theory of general spaces, the problem of interrelations between the different dimensional characteristics of these spaces ($\operatorname{ind} X$, $\operatorname{Ind} X$, $\dim X$). In connection with this problem, B. Pasynkov studied different kinds of spectral approximations; among a number of interesting results (cf. his report to this Symposium) this led to a proof of *the identity*

$$\dim X = \operatorname{ind} X = \operatorname{Ind} X$$

not only for all locally bicompact groups but also for all factor-spaces $X = G/H$ of such a group over a closed subgroup.

I believe this is a very important result indeed. Further progress in the theory of approximation of bicompacta is due to S. Mardešić, who proved that every n-dimensional bicompactum is the limit space of an inverse spectrum whose elements are n-dimensional compact metric space — an unexpected and remarkable result. Mardéšič has applied this theorem to obtain another proof of E. Sklyarenko's [22] theorem stating that for every normal space X there exists a bicompact extension bX of the same dimension and weight wbX as X,

$$\dim X = \dim bX\,, \quad wX = wbX\,.$$

The question then arises whether there exists, for all n-dimensional bicompacta (and thus, in virtue of Sklyarenko's theorem, for all n-dimensional normal spaces X)

of weight τ, a universal n-dimensional bicompactum B_τ^n of the same weight τ (universal in the sense that B_τ^n should topologically contain all the n-dimensional X of weight τ).

Let us return to the problem of interrelations between dim X, ind X, Ind X for different spaces X. Obviously ind $X \leqq$ Ind X for all T_1-spaces.

M. Katětov and K. Morita proved the most important theorem that

$$\dim X = \operatorname{Ind} X$$

for all metric X, while it remains still unknown whether ind X = Ind X for metric spaces. The same identity ind X = Ind X also remains unproved for bicompact spaces: the only known result is dim $X \leqq$ ind X (which I have proved for bicompacta; this has been generalized by Yu. Smirnov and K. Morita to all final compact and even for all strongly paracompact spaces).

It was proved by A. Lunc and O. Lokuciewski that there exist bicompacta X with dim $X \neq$ ind X, a result which has been strengthened by P. Vopěnka in a way which appears exhaustive.

N. Vedenissov proved that dim $X \leqq$ Ind X for normal X; it remains unknown whether dim $X \leqq$ ind X holds for paracompact normal spaces.

In a joint paper by V. Ponomarev and myself, questions of this kind were considered from the view-point of families of coverings.

As mentioned previously, a family $\Sigma = \{\alpha\}$ of coverings α of a given space X is called *complete* if to each point $a \in X$ and to each neighbourhood Oa of this point there exists an $\alpha \in \Sigma$ such that the star $S_\alpha a$ of the point a in the covering α is contained in Oa. If we replace in this definition the point a and its neighbourhood Oa by an arbitrary closed set A and its neighbourhood OA, we obtain the definition of a *well-complete* family of coverings.

Finally, the family $\Sigma = \{\alpha\}$ is called *confinally complete* if each open covering ω of X has a refinement $\alpha \in \Sigma$.

Another important definition is the following:

We shall say that the closed covering α' is a strong refinement of α, if α' is a refinement of α and if each element of α is the union of all elements of α' contained in it,

$$A = \bigcup_{\substack{A' \in \alpha' \\ A' \subseteq A}} A' .$$

We can consider the relation of strong refinement as an ordering relation in the system $\Sigma = \{\alpha\}$ of closed coverings. In particular, $\Sigma = \{\alpha\}$ is directed if any two coverings $\alpha_i \in \Sigma$, $\alpha_2 \in \Sigma$ have a common strong refinement $\alpha \in \Sigma$.

Now V. Ponomarev and myself [3] proved the following theorems:

Theorem I. *If in the space X there exists a directed complete (resp. well-complete) family Σ of closed covering α, each of order $\leqq n + 1$, then for the space X (which in this case is obviously normal) there hold the relations* ind $X \leqq n$ (*or* Ind $X \leqq n$ *respectively*), *and (obviously)* dim $X \leqq n$.

In this case for any subspace $B \subseteq X$ which is the intersection of some $p + 1$ elements of a fixed $\alpha \in \Sigma$ there exists a directed complete (or well-complete respectively) family of closed coverings β, each of order $\leqq n - p + 1$, such that ind $B \leqq n - p$ (Ind $B \leqq n - p$ respectively).

In this theorem the coverings $\alpha \in \Sigma$ can be supposed finite as well as locally finite.

Next we confine ourselves to bicompact normal spaces. In this case "complete" means confinally complete.

We call a bicompactum X with dim $X = n$ perfectly n-dimensional, if in X there exists a directed complete family of finite closed coverings. In this case we have by theorem I

$$\dim X = \operatorname{ind} X = \operatorname{Ind} X .$$

Now any n-dimensional bicompactum X (in the sense dim $X = n$) has complete systems Σ of closed (even of closed canonical[11]) coverings of order $n + 1$. Now it follows from theorem I that in the case of dim $X \neq$ ind X none of these families of coverings can be directed. This means that if we direct the given family Σ (say, of canonical coverings α of order $n + 1$) by adding new canonical coverings, then these new coverings necessarily fail to be of order $\leqq n + 1$. This negative result seems to be the most interesting consequence of theorem I.

Theorem II. *Every perfectly n-dimensional bicompactum is the image of a zero-dimensional bicompactum under an* $(n + 1)$*-to-*1 *continuous mapping.*

On the other hand, every bicompactum X which is the image of a zero-dimensional one under an $(n + 1)$-to-1 mapping has a complete family of (even canonical) coverings of order $n + 1$ and therefore has dim $X \leqq n$; thus

Theorem III. *Among all n-dimensional bicompacta, the perfectly n-dimensional and only these are* $(n + 1)$*-to-*1 *images of zero-dimensional bicompacta.*

It follows that a perfect n-dimensional bicompactum is not an image of a zero-dimensional bicompactum under a $(1, k)$-mapping with $k < n + 1$.

It is of course possible to give a suitable generalization of these results to the paracompact case (for theorem I this generalization is immediate).

References

[1] *П. Александров:* О метризации топологических пространств. Bull. Acad. polon. sci. Sér. sci. math., astron. et phys. *8* (1960), 135—140.

[2] *П. Александров* и *В. Немыцкий:* Условие метризуемости топологических пространств и аксиома симметрии. Матем. сб. *3*(45) (1938), 663—672.

[3] *П. Александров* и *В. Пономарев:* О некоторых классах n-мерных пространств. Сибирск. матем. ж. *1* (1960), 1—13.

[11]) A covering is called canonical if its elements are the closures of disjoint open sets. A mapping $f: X \to Y$ is called $(n + 1)$-to-1 if for each $y \in Y$ the inverse image $f^{-1}y$ contains at most $n + 1$ points.

[4] *P. Alexandroff* et *P. Urysohn:* Une condition nécessaire et suffisante pour qu'une classe (L) soit une classe (D). C. r. Acad. sci. Paris *177* (1923), 1274—1276.

[5] *А. Архангельский:* Об отображениях метрических пространств. Докл. АН СССР, 1962 (в печати).

[6] *А. Архангельский:* О метризации топологических пространств. Bull. Acad. polon. sci. Sér. sci. math,. astron. et phys. *8* (1960), 589—595.

[7] *C. H. Dowker:* An Extension of Alexandroff's Mapping Theorem. Bull. Amer. Math. Soc. *54* (1948), 386—391.

[8] *А. Есенин-Вольпин:* О зависимости между локальным и интегральным весом в диадических бикомпактах. Докл. АН СССР, *68* (1949), 441—444.

[9] *H. Freudenthal:* Entwicklungen von Räumen und ihren Gruppen. Compositio math. *4* (1937), 145—234.

[10] *Z. Frolík:* On the topological product of paracompact spaces. Bull. Acad. polon. sci. Sér. sci. math., astron. et phys. *8* (1960), 747—750.

[11] *Л. Ивановский:* Об одной гипотезе П. С. Александрова. Докл. АН СССР, *123* (1958), 785—786.

[12] *В. Кузьминов:* О гипотезе П. С. Александрова в теории топологических групп. Докл. АН СССР, *125* (1959), 727—729.

[13] *Б. Левшенко:* О сильно бесконечномерных пространствах. Вестн. Моск. ун-та. Матем., механ. № *5*, 1959, 219—228.

[14] *А. Лунц:* Симметрическая метрика в пространстве трансфинитных чисел. Успехи матем. наук, 1962 (в печати).

[15] *S. Mardešić:* On covering dimension and inverse limits of compact spaces. Illinois J. Math. 1960, no. *4*, 278—291.

[16] *А. Мищенко:* О пространствах с точечно счетной базой. Докл. АН СССР, 1962 (в печати).

[17] *Б. Пасынков:* О полиэдральных спектрах и размерности бикомпактов, в частности бикомпактных групп. Докл. АН СССР, *121* (1958), 45—48.

[18] a) *Б. Пасынков:* Об обратных спектрах и размерности. Докл. АН СССР, *138* (1961), 1013—1015.

б) *Б. Пасынков:* Об отсутствии полиэдральных спектров для бикомпактов. Докл. АН СССР, *142* (1962), 546—549.

[19] *В. Пономарев:* Аксиомы счетности и непрерывные отображения. Bull. Acad. polon. sci. Sér. sci. math., astron. et phys., *8* (1960), 127—133.

[20] *В. Пономарев:* Нормальные пространства как образы нульмерных. Докл. АН СССР, *132* (1960), 1269—1272.

[21] *В. Пономарев:* Новое пространство замкнутых множеств и многозначные непрерывные отображения бикомпактов. Матем. сб. *48* (1959), 191—212.

[22] *В. Пономарев:* О свойствах топологических пространств, сохраняющихся при многозначных непрерывных отображениях. Матем. сб. *51* (1960), 515—536.

[23] *В. Пономарев:* О продолжении многозначных отображений пространств на их бикомпактные расширения. Матем. сб. *52* (1960), 847—862.

[24] *Е. Скляренко:* О вложении нормальных пространств в бикомпакты того же веса и той же размерности. Докл. АН СССР, *123* (1958), 36—39.

[25] *Ю. Смирнов:* О сильно паракомпактных пространствах. Изв. АН СССР, Сер. матем. *20* (1956), 253—274.

[26] *Н. Шанин:* О произведении топологических пространств. Тр. Матем. ин-та АН СССР, *24* (1948).

[27] *А. Тайманов:* Продолжение монотонных отображений в монотонные отображения бикомпактов. Докл. АН СССР, *135* (1960), 23—25.

[28] *И. Вайнштейн:* О замкнутых отображениях метрических пространств. Докл. АН СССР, *57* (1947), 319—321.

[29] *И. Вайнштейн:* О замкнутых отображениях. Ученые зап. Моск. ун-та *155* (1952), 3—53.

[30] *Н. Веденисов:* Замечания о размерности топологических пространств. Ученые зап. Моск. ун-та *30* (1939), 131—139.

HOMEOMORPHISMS OF 2-DIMENSIONAL CONTINUA

R. D. ANDERSON[1])

Baton Rouge

The purposes of these investigations are

(1) to establish apparatus for exhibiting homeomorphisms between spaces and of a space onto itself where isotopy-type mappings are not possible because the spaces are not locally homologically trivial,

(2) to establish apparatus for characterizing compact metric spaces in terms of sequences of coverings particularly where the local structure of the space has not previously been identified, and

(3) to characterize various classes of homogeneous locally connected metric continua.

Specific results are obtained for some 2-dimensional continua. Further results concerning other 2-dimensional and some higher-dimensional continua can be anticipated.

The particular method of description to be used is suggested by a refinement sequence of finite closed non-overlapping connected partitionings of the space, one in which the elements are homeomorphic to each other and admit general sequential type descriptions.

A triple of sequences $(\{F_i\}, \{\varphi_i\}, \{\alpha_i\})$ is an inverse incidence system provided that, for each i,

(1) F_i is a finite set,

(2) φ_i is a map of F_{i+1} onto F_i,

(3) α_i is a reflexive and symmetric binary (incidence) relation on F_i, and

(4) if $(a, b), (b, c) \in \alpha_{i+1}$ then $(\varphi_i(a), \varphi_i(c)) \in \alpha_i$.

The pair $(\{F_i\}, \{\varphi_i\})$ is an inverse system whose inverse limit L is a zero-dimensional compact metric space. In the uses we make, the sets $\varphi_i^{-1}(f)$ will be non-degenerate and thus L will be a Cantor set.

Let R be a binary relation on L defined by $(\{f_i\}, \{f_i^0\}) \in R$ provided that, for each i, $(f_i, f_i^0) \in \alpha_i$. Using condition (4) of the definition above, it follows that R is an equivalence relation and that the set L of equivalence classes defined by R is an upper semi-continuous decomposition $\tilde{L}$ of L. The collection $\tilde{L}$ (topologized) is called the inverse

[1]) ALFRED P. SLOAN Research Fellow: Much of this research is joint work of the author and J. E. Keisler.

incidence limit of $(\{F_i\}, \{\varphi_i\}, \{\alpha_i\})$. It is interesting to note that only binary incidence relations are needed for this structure.

The basic problem is to determine conditions on two sequences under which their inverse incidence limits are homeomorphic.

It is easy to see that the inverse incidence limit of an induced inverse incidence system obtained by taking subsequences of the original sequences is canonically homeomorphic to the original inverse limit.

It is routine but lengthy to define what might be called an amalgamation-refinement of an inverse incidence system which will itself be an inverse incidence system whose inverse incidence limit is canonically homeomorphic to that of the original. The basic argument is to start with two inverse incidence systems (subject to many extra conditions) and to construct inductively amalgamation-refinements of these which admit identifications with each other so that the two new (and hence the two original) inverse incidence limits are homeomorphic to each other.

This apparatus does not directly lead to homogeneity results because singular points (those in non-degenerate equivalence classes of the definition of inverse incidence limit) cannot be made by amalgamation-refinement procedures to correspond to non-singular points.

To handle homogeneity (and more general questions) we note that the mapping from L to $\tilde{L}$ can be factored through various upper semi-continuous decompositions of L. A necessary and sufficient condition that such a factoring W induce an (equivalent) inverse incidence system is that W be zero-dimensional.

The 2-dimensional cases. A finite collection G of simple closed curves is called a *κ-collection* if

(1) the intersection of any two is an arc or is null,
(2) the intersection of any three is a point or is null,
(3) G^* (the union of the elements of G) is connected, and
(4) except for a finite point set, each point of G^* is in exactly two elements of G.

A subcollection G^1 of a κ-collection G is called a *λ-collection* if $G \setminus G^1$ is a non-null collection of disjoint elements of G. In such case the union of the elements of $G \setminus G^1$ is denoted $B(G^1)$ and is called the boundary of G^1.

If G^1 is a λ-collection then $G^{1*} = G^*$ and hence G^{1*} is connected. If G^1 is a λ-collection then there is a unique κ-collection containing it.

A λ-collection whose boundary is a single simple closed curve is called a *μ-collection.*

Let G^1 be a μ-collection. If for any two arcs t_1 and t_2 such that (1) $t_1 \cup t_2 = B(G')$ and (2) $t_1 \cap t_2$ is a set of two points each in two elements of G^1, there exist two disjoint μ-collections X_1 and X_2 such that $X_1 \cup X_2 = G^1$, $X_1^* \supset t_1$, and $X_2^* \supset t_2$, then G^1 is said to be a *ν-collection.*

We are interested in two propositions which may or may not hold in the κ-extension G of a given μ-collection.

I. There exists an arc $\alpha \subset G^*$ such that (a) α is not in any element of G, (b) for some $g \in G$, $\alpha \cap g$ is the set of endpoints of α, and (c) α does not separate G^*.

II. The elements of G may be assigned orientations so that each arc which is the intersection of two elements of G inherits opposite orientations from these two simple closed curves.

A μ-collection whose κ-extension satisfies I and II is called a T-collection (toroidal collection).

A μ-collection whose κ-extension satisfies I but does not satisfy II is called a P-collection (projective collection).

Let $(\{F_i\}, \{\varphi_i\}, \{\alpha_i\})$ be an inverse incidence system where, for each i,

1. F_i is a k-collection,
2. for any $f \in F_i$, $\varphi_i^{-1}(f)$ is a ν-collection whose boundary is canonically identified with f, and
3. if $a, b \in F_i$, then $(a, b) \in \alpha_i$ if and only if $a \cap b \neq 0$.

The inverse incidence limit (I. I. L.) of such a sequence can be identified as follows:

1. If for each i and $f \in F_i$, $\varphi_i^{-1}(f)$ is a T-collection then the I. I. L. is called an orientable T-sphere or a non-orientable T-sphere according as F_1 satisfies or does not satisfy proposition II.
2. If for each i, and $f \in F_i$, $\varphi_i^{-1}(f)$ is a P-collection, then the I. I. L. is called a P-sphere.

The basic theorems are

Theorem 1. *Every two P-spheres are homeomorphic to each other. A P-sphere is homogeneous and 2-dimensional.*

Theorem 2. *Every two orientable T-spheres are homeomorphic to each other. An orientable T-sphere is homogeneous and 2-dimensional.*

Theorem 3. *Every two non-orientable T-spheres are homeomorphic to each other. A non-orientable T-sphere is homogeneous and 2-dimensional.*

These results together with known results for 2-manifolds almost classify continua with the properties that they are homogeneous and have bases for which every element has a simple closed curve boundary which separates (and separates locally) into two connected pieces. The one-dimensional universal curve also has these properties. The assumption of the sequential structure is, therefore, needed.

The k, λ, μ, and ν-collection definitions can be abstracted. In particular they can be changed so that the elements of F_i are universal curves with the resulting set being homogeneous and characterized.

It seems likely that similar results can be obtained for boundaries which are universal plane curves if the collections are orientable.

The basic pattern of argument is the same for Theorems 1, 2 and 3 as well as for the further propositions just suggested. Abstractions (now being sought) of the conditions and of the argument may produce a somewhat general theorem leading to a "machine" for establishing characterizations and homogeneity theorems for rather broad classes of applicable spaces.

We assume two inverse incidence systems $(\{F_i\}, \{\varphi_i\}, \{\alpha_i\})$ and $(\{G_i\}, \{\nu_i\}, \{\beta_i\})$ with similar structures defining them (such as tho seof Theorems 1, 2 or 3). We consider the creation of compatible amalgamation-refinement sequence systems. We may assert that the elements of F_1 may be so ordered $f_1, \ldots, f_k$ that for any $j < k$, the set $f_j, \ldots, f_k$ is a λ-collection. Then we proceed to match the elements $(f_1, \ldots, f_k)$ of F_1 with amalgams of elements of some G_n (or more properly the boundaries of such amalgams) so that incidence properties are preserved under the matching process. To do the matching we proceed inductively.

The pairs f_1 and $\{f_2, \ldots, f_k\}$ are such that $\{f_2, \ldots, f_k\}$ is a λ-collection. We choose any element g'_1 of G_1. The set of other elements of G_1 is a λ-collection. Further, g'_1 intersects the boundary of this collection in the same way that f_1 intersects $B(\{f_2, \ldots, f_k\})$. Proceeding by induction we then consider f_j and $\{f_{j+1}, \ldots, f_k\}$ and we are able to construct g'_j in some G_m such that g'_i intersects the elements of $\{g'_1, \ldots, g'_{j-1}\}$ in the same way as f_j intersects the elements of $\{f_1, \ldots, f_{j-1}\}$ respectively whereas the "complement" of $g'_1, \ldots, g'_j$ is a λ-collection whose boundary intersects $g'_1, \ldots, g'_j$ in the same way as $B(\{f_{j+1}, \ldots, f_k\})$ intersects $f_1, \ldots, f_j$.

Having established $(g'_1, \ldots, g'_k)$ as amalgams of some G_n, we may then proceed to consider the sets of G_{n+1} which project onto the simple closed curves of the set of which g'_1 is the boundary. We then order these and repeat the previous process in reverse remembering the intersections with $g'_2, \ldots, g'_k$ as we go along. Having finished the procedure for g'_1 we then consider g'_2. It is clear that the process admits iteration (modulo lemmas asserting that the individual steps can be taken). In this way, playing back and forth, we can proceed to set up our two compatible amalgamation-refinement sequence systems. It is worth noting that the kinds of conditions we use (and hope for) here must involve reduction processes on each of the two sequence systems. In this way our argument differs from some of those concerning Euclidean-type spaces where special properties of Euclidean space might enable us to use only a one-sided argument.

MÉTHODES TOPOLOGIQUES DANS LA THÉORIE DES SURFACES DE RIEMANN

C. ANDREIAN-CAZACU

Bucarest

La théorie des fonctions analytiques a été à la fois une des plus puissantes sources et un des plus beaux champs d'application de la topologie. L'oeuvre mathématique de mon maître, le Prof. S. STOÏLOW y apporta une contribution décisive: Outre la solution des problèmes fondamentaux: la caractérisation topologique des fonctions analytiques et du recouvrement riemannien, [1], S. Stoïlow a ouvert une nouvelle voie de recherche en définissant exclusivement à l'aide de leurs propriétés topologiques deux importantes classes de surfaces de Riemann de recouvrement: les surfaces avec la propriété d'Iversen [2] et les surfaces normalement exhaustibles [3].

Soit Σ une surface bi-dimensionnelle (variété à base dénombrable) orientable. Une transformation intérieure f d'une variété bi-dimensionnelle V dans Σ engendre un recouvrement riemannien, que nous allons désigner par Σ_f^V. Ce recouvrement est total au sens de S. Stoïlow, [1], si à toute suite de points $P_n \in V$ convergeant vers la frontière idéale de V (c'est-à-dire sans point d'accumulation dans V) correspond une suite de points $f(P_n) = p_n \in \Sigma$, qui converge vers la frontière idéale de Σ. Les surfaces normalement exhaustibles Σ_f^V sont caractérisées par l'existence d'une suite de domaines d'exhaustion $V_k \subset V$, satisfaisant aux conditions habituelles et de plus, tels que chaque V_k recouvre totalement sa projection $f(V_k) \subset \Sigma$. Cette classe de surfaces de Riemann constitue une généralisation directe des surfaces closes, chaque V_k ayant le même nombre fini de points sur tout point de $f(V_k)$ et la ramification donnée par la formule de Hurwitz. Quelque soit k, la frontière Γ_k de V_k, qui est formée par un nombre fini de courbes de Jordan, se projette sur la frontière γ_k de $f(V_k)$, qui consiste aussi d'un nombre fini de courbes de Jordan.

Dans le but d'étendre la formule de Hurwitz, ce qui lui a permis de mettre en évidence le contenu topologique de quelques théorèmes de la théorie des fonctions, [1], S. Stoïlow a défini le recouvrement partiellement régulier de Σ par V selon f par les conditions suivantes:

(β_1) Toute suite de points $P_n \in V$, qui tend vers la frontière de V se projette dans une suite de points $p_n \in \Sigma$, qui tend vers la frontière de Σ ou vers un nombre fini de courbes de Jordan γ, deux à deux disjointes, chacune séparant deux domaines disjoints de $\Sigma - \gamma$.

(β_2) La pré-image $f^{-1}(\gamma)$ est l'ensemble nul ou un ensemble compact dans V.

Dans quelques travaux antérieurs [4]–[7] j'ai établi différentes propriétés des surfaces normalement exhaustibles et j'ai défini et étudié les surfaces partiellement régulièrement exhaustibles Σ_f^V, qui admettent une exhaustion par domaines V_k, recouvrant partiellement régulièrement Σ par rapport à un nombre fini de courbes de Jordan γ_k deux à deux disjointes. Parmi ces surfaces se trouvent les surfaces de L. I. Volkovyski [8] et de T. Kuroda [9].

Dans cette comunication nous allons introduire de nouvelles classes de surfaces de Riemann, définies seulement par des propriétés topologiques de l'exhaustion. Nous allons inclure ainsi dans cette classification les surfaces données par les propriétés de leurs points de ramification de Kobayashi, Ahlfors et L. J. Volkovyski [8] ou par l'arbre topologique de R. Nevanlinna, E. Ullrich, H. Wittich et A. A. Goldberg [10]—[12].

Une généralisation tout à fait naturelle des surfaces partiellement régulièrement exhaustibles s'obtient si l'on renonce à l'hypothèse (β_2) ci-dessus et si l'on suppose à chaque étape de l'exhaustion que γ_k consiste d'un nombre fini de courbes de Jordan deux à deux disjointes et d'un nombre fini d'arcs de Jordan. Je désignerai par la lettre P (du mot polyédrique) les surfaces exhaustibles par une suite de domaines polyédriques V_k dont la frontière Γ_k se projette sur γ_k.

Puisque toute surface de Riemann admet une exhaustion par des domaines V_k limités par un nombre fini de courbes de Jordan analytiques et qu'une telle exhaustion remplit les conditions énumerées plus haut, toute surface pourrait être conçue comme une surface P. Pourtant, l'intêret de ce point de vue ressort dès que l'on ajoute des hypothèses supplémentaires sur les ensembles γ_k. De cette manière on peut approfondir les surfaces à ramification régulière au sens de Kobayashi, Nevanlinna et d'autres.

Les classes de surfaces A, W, Λ que nous définirons dans ce qui suit, ont leur origine dans les travaux de L. I. Volkovyski [8]. Nous rénoncerons désormais à l'hypothèse que l'exhaustion considérée de la surface V soit réalisée par des domaines polyédriques et nous considérons des exhaustions par des surfaces bordées V_k, caractérisées par certaines propriétés simples du recouvrement $\Sigma_f^{V_k}$.

Les surfaces A admettent une exhaustion par une suite de surfaces $V_k \subset V$, à connexion finie, dont la frontière relative Γ_k se compose d'un nombre fini de courbes ou d'arcs de Jordan qui se projettent sur un nombre fini de courbes de Jordan, deux à deux disjointes γ_k; chaque arc de Γ_k recouvre comme une spirale à une infinité de feuilles une des courbes de γ_k; de plus, chaque surface V_k contient un nombre fini de points de ramification, tous algébriques, projetés dans $\Sigma - \gamma_k$.

Les surfaces W diffèrent des surfaces A, en ce qui concerne l'hypothèse relative à la ramification: toute surface V_k contient un nombre fini de points de ramifications algébriques ou logarithmiques. Les surfaces Λ sont les surfaces W ayant un nombre fini de ramifications algébriques.

Evidemment, $A \subset W$, mais en même temps on peut etablir l'inclusion contraire $A \supset W$. En effet, si Σ_f^V est une surface de classe W et V_k une surface d'exhaustion ayant

L_k ramifications logarithmiques projetées dans les points $p_{1k}, \ldots, p_{lk}$, nous entourons ces points par voisinages v_{jk} suffisament petits et extrairons de V_k les pré-images non-compactes de ces voisinages, qui forment des voisinages des ramifications logarithmiques de V_k. La surface V_k' obtenu a les propriétés des surfaces d'exhaustion A, donc $\Sigma_f^{V_k'} \in A$. Par conséquent $\Sigma_f^V \in A$, puisqu'on peut former une suite d'exhaustion de V du type A.

De même nous considérons les surfaces à exhaustion formée par des V_k qui recouvrent sans frontière chacun des domaines de $\Sigma - \gamma_k$, ou bien des V_k tels que $\Sigma_f^{V_k}$ ait la propriété d'Iversen [2] ou de Blaschke [13] sur les domaines de $\Sigma - \gamma_k$ ou toute autre propriété de recouvrement. On pourra aussi supposer que γ_k soit un ensemble fini de courbes et d'arcs de Jordan.

A chaque surface de Riemann exhaustible d'une manière quelconque nous attacherons (comme nous l'avons fait dans le cas partiellement régulièrement exhaustible [6]) plusieurs ensemble fermés: $\mathscr{E}$ – l'ensemble des points $p \in \Sigma$, pour lesquels il existe des suites n_k de nombres naturels et des suites p_{n_k} de points de γ_{n_k}, tel que $p = \lim_{k\to\infty} p_{n_k}$; $\mathscr{M}$ – l'ensemble des points $p \in \Sigma$, qui sont limite de points p_k de γ_k: $p = \lim_{k\to\infty} p_k$; $\mathscr{A}$ – l'adhérence de l'ensemble des valeurs asymptotiques de la transformation f; $\mathscr{R}$, respectivement $\mathscr{L}$ – l'ensemble des limites des suites des projections des ramifications algébriques, respectivement logarithmiques de Σ_f^V.

Évidemment, $\Sigma \supset \mathscr{E} \supset \mathscr{M} \supset \mathscr{A} \supset 0$ pour les surfaces P ou A, chaque inclusion pouvant être stricte ou non.

En supposant $\mathscr{E} \neq \Sigma$, nous pouvons établir facilement des propriétés de recouvrement parmi lesquelles nous citons:

Si $\Sigma_f^V \in P$, les domaines maxima [1] d'un domaine compact $\Delta \subset \Sigma - \mathscr{E}$ recouvrent Δ totalement. Et si Δ est une région de $\Sigma - \mathscr{E}$ chaque composante connexe de sa pré-image en V engendre un recouvrement normalement exhaustible de Δ.

Si $\Sigma_f^V \in A$ et $p \in \Sigma - (\mathscr{A} \cup (\mathscr{M} \cap \mathscr{R}))$, il existe un voisinage fermé dont tous les domaines maxima sont normaux.

Il résulte de ces propositions des relations avec les propriétés LBl, LBl_1, LI. Si $\mathscr{A}$ est un ensemble de capacité logarithmique nulle, Σ_f^V est de classe Bl; si $\mathscr{E}$, $\mathscr{M}$ ou $\mathscr{A}$ est un ensemble totalement discontinu, Σ_f^V est de classe I, [6].

La formule de Hurwitz-Stoïlow, que nous avons étendue aux recouvrements engendrés par des domaines polyédriques quelconques à frontière formée par des courbes analytiques, constitue un instrument utile dans l'étude de la ramification des surfaces envisagées ci-dessus [14]. En effet, cette formule s'applique directement dans le cas de V_k compact, et autrement, en effectuant une exhaustion convenable de V_k. On obtient ainsi des théorèmes des disques. A titre d'exemple je me bornerai d'indiquer que les surfaces $A_{0\infty}$ simplement connexes de L. I. Volkovyski [8] peuvent avoir au plus 3 disques complètement ramifiés.

Les résultats concernant la ramification des surfaces permettent de préciser les critères du type. En effet, pour certaines surfaces P, A ou W on peut étendre les méthodes d'Ahlfors, Kobayashi et Volkovyski [8], en établissant des conditions d'appartenance à la classe de surfaces O_g.

Les méthodes métrico-topologiques qui ont permis à Ahlfors de construire sa célèbre théorie des surfaces régulièrement exhaustibles [15] peuvent être utilisées pour approfondir les propriétés des surfaces de recouvrement considérées ici. D'un côté on peut établir des critères pour que ces surfaces soient régulièrement exhaustibles, de l'autre on peut introduire des conditions métriques sur les courbes γ_k et en déduire des résultats relatifs aux surfaces Σ_f^V. En supposant, par exemple, que Σ soit la sphère et γ_k des cercles dont le rayon tend vers zéro avec $1/k$, on obtient les surfaces à points de ramification qui se rapprochent de L. I. Volkovyski [8].

Un autre cas important se présente quand les courbes γ_k forment une exhaustion de $\Sigma - \mathscr{E}$. Lorsque $\Sigma - \mathscr{E}$ se réduit à un seul domaine, ce cas généralise celui considéré par T. KURODA [9].

Dans l'exposé sommaire que j'ai fait, je me suis bornée à définir et indiquer des propriétés des classes P, A, W etc. dont l'intérêt réside dans le grand nombre de surfaces de Riemann qui y sont contenues et qui sont traitées ainsi d'un point de vue unitaire.

À côté de fructueuses recherches de G. T. WHYBURN [16], M. MORSE et M. HEINS [17], et de celles plus récentes de F. D. GAHOV, IU. M. KRIKUNOV, T. M. KOLOMITZEVA, I. M. MEL'NIK et A. I. POVOLOTZKII (voir la bibliographie dans [18], [19]), les résultats et les problèmes soulevés par l'introduction de ces classes de surfaces, qui ont leur origine dans l'oeuvre de S. Stoïlow, montrent une fois de plus la puissance et l'importance des méthodes topologiques dans la théorie des fonctions analytiques.

Bibliographie

[1] *S. Stoïlow*: Principes topologiques de la théorie des fonctions analytiques. Gauthier-Villars, Paris 1938, ou 1956.

[2] *S. Stoïlow*: Note sur les fonctions analytiques multiformes. Annales de la Soc. Polonaise de Math., 1952, *25*, 69–74.

[3] *S. Stoïlow*: Sur les surfaces de Riemann normalement exhaustibles et sur le théorème des disques pour ces surfaces. Compositio math., 1940, *7*, 428–435.

[4] *C. Andreian Cazacu*: Über die normal ausschöpfbaren Riemannschen Flächent. Math. Nachrichten, 1956, *15*, 2, 77–86.

[5] *C. Andreian Cazacu*: Suprafete riemanniene partial regular exhaustibile. Consfătuirea de Geometrie și Topologie, Iași 1958, 219—226.

[6] *C. Andreian Cazacu*: Suprafete riemanniene partial regulat exhaustibile. Studii și Cerc. Mat., 1959, *10*, 2, 307–323.

[7] *C. Andreian Cazacu*: Überlagerungseigenschaften der Riemannschen Flächen. Revue Math. pures et appl., *1961*, *6*, 4, 685—701.

[8] *Л. И. Волковыский:* Исследование по проблеме типа односвязной римановой поверхности. Труды мат. инст. Стеклова. Москва-Ленинград, 1950, *34*.

[9] *T. Kuroda*: Remarks on some covering surfaces. Revue Math. pures et appl., 1957, *2*, 263–268.

[10] *R. Nevanlinna*: Eindeutige analytische Funktionen, Springer. Berlin Göttingen Heidelberg 1936, 1953.

[11] *H. Wittich*: Neuere Untersuchungen über eindeutige analytische Funktionen. Ergebn. Math. u. ihrer Grenzgebiete, Heft 8, Springer, Berlin-Göttingen-Heidelberg 1955.

[12] *А. А. Гольдберг:* Об одном классе римановых поверхностей. Мат. сб., 1959, *49* (*91*), 4, 447 до 458.

[13] *M. Heins*: On the Lindelöf principle. Ann. of. Math. 1955, *61*, 440–473.

[14] *C. Andreian Cazacu*: Über eine Formel von S. Stoïlow. Revue Math. pures et appl., 1960, *5*, 1, 59–74.

[15] *L. Ahlfors*: Zur Theorie der Überlagerungsflächen. Acta Math., 1935, *65*, 157–194.

[16] *G. T. Whyburn*: Topological Analysis. Princeton University Press 1958.

[17] *M. Morse*: Topological Methods in the Theory of Functions of a Complex Variable. Princeton University Press, 1947, Ann. Math. Studies *15*.

[18] *И. М. Мельник:* К топологическим методам теории функций комплексного переменного. Докл. А Н СССР, 1960, *131*, 5, 1015—1018.

[19] *А. И. Поволоцкий:* Индексы особых точек псевдоаналитических функций. Докл. А Н СССР, 1959, *129*, 2, 265—267.

МЕТРИЧЕСКИЕ ПРОСТРАНСТВА НАД ПОЛУПОЛЯМИ

М. АНТОНОВСКИЙ,

Ташкент

В работе [1] нами были введены понятие топологического полуполя и понятие метрического пространства над полуполем. Я не привожу определений этих понятий, так как они сформулированы в статье В. Г. Болтянского „Топологические полуполя и их применения" (см. настоящий сборник, стр. 106). Здесь будет рассматриваться сходимость, полнота, компактность и др. вопросы. Использование метрики над произвольными полуполями позволило доказать обобщения таких теорем, как теорема Хаусдорфа (необходимое и достаточное условие компактности), теорема Кантора (необходимое и достаточное условие полноты) и др. Автору кажется особенно привлекательным, что, несмотря на весьма общий характер доказываемых теорем (их естественной областью применения являются вполне регулярные топологические пространства), формулировки этих теорем ничем не отличаются от классических. В конце доклада вводится понятие усиленной полноты, связанное с недавними работами Вл. Птака и И. Л. Келли [2], [3]. Это понятие позволяет перенести теорему Банаха об открытых отображениях на случай нормированных (и даже метрических) пространств над полуполями. Излагаемые здесь результаты были получены совместно В. Г. Болтянским, Т. А. Сарымсаковым и автором доклада.

Прежде всего мы дадим другое, эквивалентное определение естественной топологии метрического пространства над полуполем, основывающееся на понятии сходящейся последовательности. Пусть X — метрическое пространство над полуполем E и Ξ — некоторое направленное множество. Всякое отображение $x : \Xi \to X$ мы будем называть *последовательностью* типа Ξ в пространстве X. Образ $x(\xi)$ элемента $\xi \in \Xi$ при отображении $x : \Xi \to X$ мы будем также обозначать через x_ξ, что позволит нам записывать последовательность в привычном виде $x = \{x_\xi\}$, $\xi \in \Xi$. Пусть Ξ и H — два направленных множества. Отображение $\varphi : H \to \Xi$ будем называть *конфинальным*, если для любого элемента $\xi_0 \in \Xi$ найдется такой элемент $\eta_0 \in H$, что $\varphi(\eta) > \xi_0$ при $\eta > \eta_0$. Пусть теперь $x = \{x_\xi\}$ — произвольная последовательность типа Ξ в X и $\varphi : H \to \Xi$ — конфинальное отображение. Определим последовательность x^φ типа H в X, положив для любого элемента $\eta \in H$:

$$(x^\varphi)_\eta = x_{\varphi(\eta)}\,.$$

Последовательность x^φ мы будем называть *подпоследовательностью* последовательности x (соответствующей конфинальному отображению $\varphi : H \to \to \Xi$).

Последовательность x типа Ξ в X будем называть *сходящейся* к точке $a \in X$, если выполнено следующее условие: для любой окрестности нуля U в метризующем полуполе E существует такой элемент $\xi_U \in \Xi$, что $\varrho(x_\xi, a) \in U$ при $\xi > \xi_U$. Сходимость мы будем обозначать записью $\lim\limits_{\xi \in \Xi} x_\xi = a$, или $x \to a$. Иначе говоря, если $\lim\limits_{\xi \in \Xi} x_\xi = a$ в X, то $\lim\limits_{\xi \in \Xi} \varrho(x_\xi, a) = 0$ (в E) и обратно.

Пусть $x = \{x_\xi\}$ — некоторая последовательность типа Ξ в метрическом пространстве X над полуполем E. Точку $a \in X$ мы будем называть *предельной* для последовательности x, если, каковы бы ни были окрестность нуля U в полуполе E и индекс $\xi \in \Xi$, существует такой индекс $\xi' > \xi$, что $\varrho(a, x_{\xi'}) \in U$.

Пусть X — метрическое пространство над полуполем E. Последовательность $\{x_\xi\}$ типа Ξ в пространстве мы будем называть *фундаментальной*, если для любой окрестности нуля U в полуполе E существует такой элемент $\xi_U \in \Xi$, что $\varrho(x_{\xi'}, x_{\xi''}) \in U$ при $\xi', \xi'' > \xi_U$. Метрическое пространство X будем называть *полным*, если любая его фундаментальная последовательность является сходящейся. Пусть Ξ — произвольное направленное множество и для каждого $\xi \in \Xi$ выбрано некоторое подмножество M_ξ метрического пространства X. Если при $\xi' > \xi''$ выполнено включение $M_{\xi'} \subset M_{\xi''}$, то систему множеств $\{M_\xi\}$ мы будем называть *Ξ-системой множеств* в X. Далее, Ξ-систему множеств $\{M_\xi\}$ в X будем называть *стягивающейся*, если для любой окрестности нуля U в полуполе E существует такой элемент $\xi_U \in E$, что $\varrho(x, y) \in U$ для любых двух точек $x, y \in M_{\xi_U}$.

При таком выборе определений сохраняются классические взаимоотношения между указанными понятиями. Так, например, справедливы следующие утверждения. Никакая последовательность не может сходиться одновременно к двум различным точкам. Всякая подпоследовательность сходящейся последовательности сходится к той же самой точке. Точка a тогда и только тогда принадлежит замыканию множества $A \subset X$ (в естественной топологии метрического пространства X над полуполем E), когда существует сходящаяся к точке a последовательность, составленная из точек множества A. Пусть X и Y — метрические пространства над полуполем E и $f : X \to Y$ — произвольное отображение; отображение f непрерывно тогда и только тогда (относительно естественной топологии пространств X и Y), когда для любой сходящейся последовательности $\{x_\xi\}$ в X последовательность $\{f(x_\xi)\}$ сходится в Y и $\lim\limits_{\xi \in \Xi} f(x_\xi) = f(\lim\limits_{\xi \in \Xi} x_\xi)$.

Далее, всякая сходящаяся последовательность фундаментальна. Если некоторая подпоследовательность фундаментальной последовательности сходится, то и сама последовательность сходится к той же точке. Если X — полное метрическое пространство над полуполем E, то всякое замкнутое подмножество пространства X (рассматриваемое как метрическое пространство над E) полно. Для любой стягивающейся Ξ-системы множеств $\{M_\xi\}$ пересечение $\bigcap_\xi M_\xi$ состоит не более чем из одной точки. Метрическое пространство X над полуполем E тогда и только тогда полно, когда всякая стягивающая Ξ-система непустых замкнутых в X множеств имеет непустое пересечение (теорема Кантора). Полуполе E, рассматриваемое как метрическое пространство над E, тогда и только тогда полно, когда оно изоморфно некоторому полуполю R_Δ. Всякое метрическое пространство X над полуполем R_Δ изометрично вкладывается в некоторое полное метрическое пространство X^* над R_Δ; при этом X всюду плотно в X^* и пространство X^* этими условиями определяется однозначно, с точностью до изометрии (теорема Хаусдорфа). Более полно, пусть $\varphi : X \to X_1^*$ и $\psi : X \to X_2^*$ — такие изометричные вложения пространства X в полные пространства X_1^* и X_2^* соответственно, что $\overline{\varphi(X)} = X_1^*$, $\overline{\psi(X)} = X_2^*$. Тогда существует (и притом только одно) такое изометрическое отображение $g : X_1^* \to X_2^*$ пространства X_1^* на пространство X_2^*, что $g \circ \varphi = \psi$. Пусть X — метрическое пространство над произвольным полуполем E. Тогда E изоморфно вкладывается в полуполе R_Δ (см. [1], 10.2), благодаря чему X может рассматриваться и как метрическое пространство над полным полуполем R_Δ, после чего оно может быть изометрично вложено в полное метрическое пространство X^* над R_Δ. Таким образом, в случае метрического пространства над неполным полуполем E изометричное вложение в полное пространство происходит при помощи двух процессов: пополнения метризующего полуполя E и последующего пополнения пространства X над пополненным полуполем.

Наконец, отметим еще обобщение теоремы Хаусдорфа о компактных метрических пространствах. Пусть X — метрическое пространство над полуполем E. Пусть, далее M и S — произвольные подмножества пространства X и U — некоторая окрестность нуля в полуполе E. Множество S мы будем называть U-сетью в множестве M, если для любой точки $x \in M$ можно найти такую точку $s \in S$, что $\varrho(x, s) \in U$. Будем, далее, называть пространство X *вполне ограниченным*, если для любой окрестности нуля U в метризующем полуполе E существует в X конечная U-сеть. Оказывается, что метрическое пространство X над полуполем E тогда и только тогда компактно (в естественной топологии), когда оно вполне ограниченно и полно. (Отметим, во избежание недоразумений, что топологическое пространство мы называем компактным, если из любого его открытого покрытия можно выделить конечное подпокрытие.) Доказательство сформулированной теоремы непросто; оно существенно опирается на теорию абстрактных спектров, развитую П. С. Александровым. Отметим также, что метрическое пространство X над полуполем E тогда и только тогда компактно (в естественной топологии), когда любая последовательность в X имеет по крайней мере одну предельную точку. Точно так же, метрическое пространство X над полуполем E компактно тогда и только тогда, когда из всякой последовательности его точек можно выделить сходящуюся подпоследовательность.

В заключение изложим понятие усиленной полноты и сформулируем теорему Банаха об открытых отображениях. Пусть X — метрическое пространство над полуполем E, множество Δ неразложимых корней которого бесконечно. Последовательность $\{x_\xi\}$ типа Ξ в X назовем *слабо фундаментальной*, если для любой окрестности нуля U в полуполе E существует такой элемент $\xi_U \in \Xi$, что для любых элементов $\xi_1, \xi_2 > \xi_U$ найдется элемент $\xi_2' > \xi_2$, удовлетворяющий условию

$$\varrho(x_{\xi_1}, x_{\xi_2'}) \in U .$$

Ясно, что всякая фундаментальная последовательность является также слабо фундаментальной.

Важную роль в дальнейшем будет играть некоторое направленное множество Ω, связанное с метризующим полуполем. Именно, элементами множества Ω являются всевозможные конечные подмножества множества Δ, где Δ — совокупность всех неразложимых корней метризующего полуполя E. Направленность в множестве Ω определяется по включению, т. е. $\mu_1 < \mu_2$ (где $\mu_1, \mu_2 \in \Omega$), если $\mu_1 \subset \mu_2$.

Метрическое пространство X над полуполем E будем называть *усиленно полным*, если всякая его слабо фундаментальная последовательность типа Ω имеет сходящуюся подпоследовательность. Очевидно, что всякое усиленно полное пространство полно.

Теорема (обобщение теоремы Банаха об открытых отображениях). *Пусть X и Y — метрические пространства над полуполем R_Δ, причем пространство X усиленно полно. Пусть, далее, $f: X \to Y$ — непрерывное отображение, обладающее следующим свойством: для произвольной заполненной*[1]) *окрестности нуля U в полуполе R_Δ существует такая окрестность нуля U^f в полуполе R_Δ, что*

$$\overline{f(\Omega(x, U))} \supset \Omega(f(x), U^f)$$

для любой точки $x \in X$. Тогда для любой окрестности нуля V в полуполе E имеет место соотношение

$$f(\Omega(x, U + V)) \supset \Omega(f(x), U^f) .$$

Из этого, в частности, вытекает, что отображение f открыто.

[1]) См. [1], стр. 30.

Литература

[1] *М. Я. Антоновский, В. Г. Болтянский, Т. А. Сарымсаков:* Топологические полуполя. Ташкент, 1960 г.

[2] *V. Pták*: Completeness and the open mapping theorem. Bull. Soc. math. France, *86* (1958), 41–74.

[3] *J. L. Kelley*: Hypercomplete linear topological spaces. The Michigan Math. J., *5* (1958), 235–246.

COMPLETIONS OF UNIFORM SPACES

G. AQUARO

Bari

First some definitions and notations, introduced elsewhere (cf. [1]), will be recalled:

(i) X is a completely regular topological space,

(ii) $\mathfrak{a}$ is an infinite cardinal number,

(iii) $\mathscr{B}_{\mathfrak{a}}(X)$ is the class of all locally finite open coverings of X of the form $(U_\iota)_{\iota\in I}$, each of which fulfils the following conditions:

$$\operatorname{card}(I) \leqq \mathfrak{a}$$

(i.e., the cardinal number of the index set I does not exceed $\mathfrak{a}$); there exists a closed covering $(F_\iota)_{\iota\in I}$ of X such that, for each $\iota \in I$, the two closed subsets F_ι and $X - U_\iota$ are completely separated (according to [5]),

(iv) $\mathscr{A}_{\mathfrak{a}}(X)$ is the uniform structure on X having as a fundamental system of "entourages" (i. e., a base of the filter of "entourages") in the BOURBAKI sense, the set of all subsets B of $X \times X$ of the form

$$B = \bigcup_{\iota\in I} (U_\iota \times U_\iota).$$

Because of lemma 2, § 8 and def. 4, § 3 of [1], the above uniform structure $\mathscr{A}_{\mathfrak{a}}(X)$ coincides with the "$\mathfrak{a}$-struttura uniforme" of [1] def. 4, § 3. Therefore, in view of prop. 3, § 3 of [1], the uniform structure $\mathscr{A}_{\mathfrak{a}}(X)$ agrees with the underlying topology of the completely regular space X.

Now, consider the completion $\upsilon_{\mathfrak{a}}(X)$ of X under the uniform structure $\mathscr{A}_{\mathfrak{a}}(X)$. It is well-known that

The completely regular space $\upsilon_{\mathfrak{a}}(X)$ together with a certain standard uniform structure $\mathscr{U}$ is complete, and the couple $(\upsilon_{\mathfrak{a}}(X), \mathscr{U})$ is related to the couple $(X, \mathscr{A}_{\mathfrak{a}}(X))$ in the following way: there exists an injection j of X in $\upsilon_{\mathfrak{a}}(X)$ such that

1. *$j(X)$ is dense in $\upsilon_{\mathfrak{a}}(X)$,*
2. *j is a uniform isomorphism of X equipped with $\mathscr{A}_{\mathfrak{a}}(X)$ onto $j(X)$ equipped with the uniform structure $\mathscr{U}_{j(X)}$ induced by $\mathscr{U}$ on $j(X)$.*

Next we construct the class $\mathscr{B}_{\mathfrak{a}}(\upsilon_{\mathfrak{a}}(X))$ of coverings of $\upsilon_{\mathfrak{a}}(X)$ (as previously defined), and then construct the uniform structure $\mathscr{A}_{\mathfrak{a}}(\upsilon_{\mathfrak{a}}(X))$ in the same manner as $\mathscr{A}_{\mathfrak{a}}(X)$.

Theorem 1. *The following equality holds:*

$$\mathscr{U} = \mathscr{A}_{\mathfrak{a}}(\upsilon(X_{\mathfrak{a}})).$$

This result stated, the following definition is consistent:

Definition. A completely regular space X is said to be *$\mathfrak{a}$-complete* if and only if X, equipped with $\mathscr{A}_{\mathfrak{a}}(X)$, is a complete uniform space.

Theorem 1 provides many $\mathfrak{a}$-complete spaces; e. g. all $\upsilon_{\mathfrak{a}}(X)$. We shall return later to this point. For the moment we observe a few facts concerning $\mathfrak{a}$-completeness.

Note that, in [2], $\mathfrak{a}$-complete spaces were called "spazii $\mathscr{A}_{\mathfrak{a}}$-completi".

Lemma 1. *If M is a metrizable space having a base for its topology whose cardinal number does not exceed $\mathfrak{a}$ then M is $\mathfrak{a}$-complete (in the sense stated).*

Indeed any paracompact space having a base whose cardinal number does not exceed $\mathfrak{a}$ is $\mathfrak{a}$-complete in the sense stated.

Proposition 1. *If F is a closed subset of an $\mathfrak{a}$-complete space X, then the subspace F is also $\mathfrak{a}$-complete.*

Proposition 2. *If $(X_\lambda)_{\lambda \in L}$ is an unrestricted family of $\mathfrak{a}$-complete spaces then its product $\prod_{\lambda \in L} X_\lambda$ is also $\mathfrak{a}$-complete.*

Proposition 3. *If $(A_\lambda)_{\lambda \in L}$ is a family of subsets of a completely regular space X and, for each $\lambda \in L$, the subspace A_λ is $\mathfrak{a}$-complete then the intersection $\bigcap_{\lambda \in L} A_\lambda$ is also $\mathfrak{a}$-complete.*

Next we shall state a proposition which, as will be seen later, relates $\mathfrak{a}$-completeness to a known property of topological spaces.

Proposition 4. *A necessary and sufficient condition for a space X to be an $\mathfrak{a}$-complete space is that X be a closed subset of a product of metric spaces each having a base for its topology whose cardinal number does not exceed $\mathfrak{a}$.*

Of course, if we take

$$\omega = \text{card}\,(\mathbf{N}),$$

where $\mathbf{N}$ is the set of non negative integers, then it turns out that $\mathfrak{a}$-complete spaces are those and only those which are Q-spaces in the sense of HEWITT (realcompact spaces, according to [5]). Therefore $\mathfrak{a}$-completeness may be regarded as a generalization of realcompactness provided that, and this is to be explicitely remarked, there exists a measurable cardinal number (see [5] chap. 12).

Now we return to a completely regular space X, without any $\mathfrak{a}$-completeness assumption, and we consider the space $\upsilon_{\mathfrak{a}}(X)$ and the injection j as before.

Then:

3. *If f is a continuous map of X into an $\mathfrak{a}$-complete space Y then there exists a continuous map $\bar{f}$ of $\upsilon_{\mathfrak{a}}(X)$ into Y such that its restriction to $j(X)$ is exactly $f \circ g$ where g is the inverse map of the injection j.*

This property 3 together with properties 1 and 2 of $\upsilon_{\mathfrak{a}}(X)$ and j, determines $\upsilon_{\mathfrak{a}}(X)$ uniquely up to a homeomorphism. Therefore, taking $\mathfrak{a} = \text{card}\,(\mathbf{N})$ and recalling what we stated before, we obtain the well-known Hewitt extension of X as a dense subset of a Q-space (realcompactification of X, according to [5]) commonly denoted by $\upsilon(X)$.

Further, one must notice that X is an α-complete space if and only if it is (topologically) identical to $\upsilon_{\alpha}(X)$.

Other results may be obtained, which may be considered to be generalizations of analogous results already known for Q-spaces and Hewitt extensions, under the proviso on measurable cardinals mentioned above (see [2] and [3]).

Before closing this paper it must be remarked that the present writer, while attending the Topological Symposium in Prague, has been informed by J. R. ISBELL that some results of the same kind have been obtained by that author jointly with S. GINSBURG in [6].

Also as stated in the abstract, the writer does not know whether relations exist between α-complete spaces and E-compact spaces in the sense of R. ENGELKING and S. MRÓWKA (cf. [4]), although similarities exist.

All the results of this paper will be found in full detail, with some more information about α-completeness, in [2] and in a forthcoming paper [3].

References

[1] *G. Aquaro*: Ricovrimenti aperti a strutture uniformi sopra uno spazio topologico. Ann. mat. pura ed appl., (4), *47* (1959), 319–390.

[2] *G. Aquaro*: Completamenti di spazii uniformi. Ann. mat. pura ed appl., (4), *56* (1961), 87–98.

[3] *G. Aquaro*: Ancora intorno a completamenti di spazii uniformi. Ann. mat. pura ed appl. (forthcoming).

[4] *R. Engelking* and *S. Mrówka*: On *E*-compact spaces. Bull. Acad. polon. sci., Cl. 3, 6, *7* (1958), 429–436.

[5] *L. Gillman* and *M. Jerison*: Rings of Continuous Functions. Van Nostrand, Princeton (N. J.) (1960).

[6] *S. Ginsburg* and *J. R. Isbell*: Some Operators on Uniform Spaces. Trans. Amer. Math. Soc., *93* (1959), 145–168.

CONCERNING THE WEIGHT OF TOPOLOGICAL SPACES

A. ARCHANGELSKI

Moscow

1. The general addition formula. Let the space be represented as a sum of its subspaces X_α:

$$X = \bigcup_\alpha X_\alpha .$$

Let wX, wX_α be the weights of the corresponding spaces. Under what conditions the formula

$$wX = \sum_\alpha wX_\alpha \tag{1}$$

does hold?

In their "Mémoire sur les espaces topologiques compacts" [1], P. ALEXANDROFF and P. URYSOHN raised this question for the special case when X is a bicompactum, $X = X_1 \cup X_2$, X_1 closed, X_2 open, $wX_1 = wX_2 = \aleph_0$. Even this special question remained unanswered until 1956, when YU. SMIRNOV [2] proved formula (1) for a local bicompact X and a countable system of arbitrary subspaces X_α, $wW_\alpha = \aleph_0$.

Remark 1. For an arbitrary regular X formula (1) is easily proved in the following two cases:

a) the number of the X_α is finite; they are closed,[1]).

b) the number of the X_α is arbitrary; each X_α is dense in X.

Definition. A space X is said to be a *Borel space*, if X is a Borel set (of the classical Hausdorff type $G_{\delta\sigma\delta}\dots$, of an arbitrary countable ordinal class-number) in some bicompactum $B \supseteq X$.

Theorem 1. *Formula* (1) *holds in full generality* (*that means for an arbitrary number of arbitrary subspaces X_α of X*) *in each of the following two cases*:

(a) *X is a Borel space,*

(b) *X is an arbitrary subset of a perfectly normal bicompactum.*

The theorem of YU. SMIRNOV is obviously contained in our theorem 1.

2. Theorem 2. *Let f be a continuous mapping of a topological space X onto a topological space Y. If the space Y satisfies one of the conditions* (a), (b) *of Theorem* 1, *then*

$$wY \leq wX .$$

[1]) For a countable system of closed subspaces X_α of a regular X formula (1) does not necessarily hold.

In the special case of bicompact X and Y this theorem has been proved by P. ALEXANDROFF [3].

Corollary. *If under the hypotheses of Theorem 2 the space X is separable metric, then Y is metrizable.*

In this Corollary the assumption that X is separable, is essential. We have, however, the

Theorem 3. *Let Y be metric, while Y satisfies one of the conditions* (a) *or* (b) *of Theorem* 1. *Let $f: X \to Y = fX$ be closed continuous. Then Y is metrizable.*

3. One of the basic tools used for proving the above results, is the notion of a net of a topological space X. I call the system Σ of arbitrary subsets $M \subset X$ a *net* of X if for an arbitrary point $x \in X$ and an arbitrary neighborhood Ox of this point there exists a set $M \in \Sigma$ such that $x \in M \subseteq Ox$.

The following obvious properties of nets are of importance:

1. Let $X = \bigcup_\alpha X_\alpha$ and Σ_α be a net of X_α; then $\bigcup_a \Sigma_\alpha$ is a net of X.

2. Let f be a continuous mapping of X onto Y. This mapping transforms any net of X in a net of Y.

The following Lemma is fundamental for our purposes:

Lemma. *Let $X \subseteq B$, where B is a bicompactum. Let one of the following conditions be satisfied*:

1. *X is a Borel set (of any type $G_{\delta\sigma\delta\ldots}$).*
2. *B is perfectly normal.*

Suppose moreover that X contains a net of a cardinality τ. Then there exists an exterior open basis $\mathfrak{B}$ of X with respect to B (that is a system $\mathfrak{B}$ of open sets $\Gamma \subseteq B$ such that for any $x \in X$ and its neighbourhood Ox in B there exists a $\Gamma \in \mathfrak{B}$ with $x \in \Gamma \subseteq Ox$) the cardinality of which does not exceed τ.

4. The following theorems generalize the known results by P. ALEXANDROFF:

(a) *If the point x of the bicompactum B forms a generalized Borel set $G_{\delta\sigma\delta\ldots}$ of an arbitrary (not necessarily countable) class-number α, then the character of x in the space B is not greater than the cardinality τ of α.*

(b) *Let X be a Borel space. Then the character and the pseudocharacter of any. point of X are equal.*

The detailed proofs of the results communicated in this report can be found in my Notes [4, 5].

References

[1] *P. Alexandroff* et *P. Urysohn*: Mémoire sur les espaces topologiques compacts. Verhandelingen Kon. Akademie van Wetenschappen, Amsterdam, 1 sectie, XIV, № *1* (1929), 1–96. (Revised Russian translation: О компактных топологических пространствах, Труды математического института АН СССР им. В. А. Стеклова, *31* (1950); reedited in the collected papers: *П. С. Урысон:* Труды по топологии и другим областям математики. г. II, Москва, 1951.)

[2] *Ю. М. Смирнов:* О метризуемости бикомпактов, разлагающихся в сумму множеств со счетной базой. Fundam. math. *43*, (1956), 387–393.

[3] *P. Alexandroff*: On bicompact extensions of topological spaces, Supplementary Note. Matem. sbornik *5* (1939), 403–424.

[4] *А. Архангельский:* Аддиционная теорема для веса множеств, лежащих в бикомпактах. Докл. АН СССР, *126*, (1959), 239—241.

[5] *А. Архангельский:* О внешних базах множеств, лежащих в бикомпактах. Докл. АН СССР *132*, (1960), 495—496.

A PROBLEM CONCERNING LOCALLY-A FUNCTIONS IN A COMMUTATIVE BANACH ALGEBRA A

R. ARENS

Los Angeles

1. The object of this note is to point out the equivalence of a strengthened form (Problem (Δ, A)-*hol*) of the problem "*loc-A*" with a cohomological problem "Z^1", and also to present a condition sufficient to ensure that problem loc-A has a positive solution. Here A is any commutative Banach algebra A with unit.

We proceed to explain our terminology. Let $\Delta = \Delta(A)$ be the space $Hom\ (A, \mathbf{C})$ of non-zero homomorphisms of A on the complex numbers $\mathbf{C}$, with the topology induced by its embedding in A', the dual space weakly topologized. (When referring to the Stone-Jacobson topology, we will say *regularly* open, etc.)

2. The notion of holomorphic function is essential to our discussion. To introduce it, we use only the fact that A is a set of complex-valued functions on space of A'. *A simple* holomorphic function f in A' is one of the form $\varphi \circ \alpha$ where α is the mapping of A' into $\mathbf{C}^n$ induced by some n elements $a_1, \ldots, a_n$ of A_1 and φ is holomorphic in $\mathbf{C}^n$ (and thus has an open domain): $f(\xi) = \varphi(\xi(a_1), \ldots, \xi(a_n))$. We write $f \in$ hol (K) if f is holomorphic and defined at least on a set $K \subset A'$. For such f and K we let $[f]_K$ be the (equivalence) class of all g holomorphic in A' which agree with f in a neighborhood of K. If $K = \{\xi\}$ we write $[f]_\xi$. The class (an algebra) of all $[f]_K$ we denote by $Hol\ [K]$. If $f \in hol\ (K)$ then $[f]_\xi \in Hol\ [\xi]$ for every $\xi \in K$, but the converse is not always true except when K is compact (see [2]).

When precision requires it, we say '(A', A)-holomorphic' rather than merely 'holomorphic'. Similarly, '$Hol\ [K]$' may be amplified to '(A', A)-$Hol\ [K]$'.

3. We now take note of the algebra-structure of A_1 and let $K = \Delta$. *There is an algebra-homomorphism of* $Hol\ [\Delta]$ *into* A (indeed, onto A). This is one way of formulating the operational calculus of analytic functions for A, studied by G. E. Shilov, Calderón, Waelbrock, and the writer (see [1], [3]).

We may confine our discussion to semi-simple algebras. In that case the operational calculus just says that for each $f \in hol\ (\Delta)$ there is an element $a \in A$ such that $f \mid A = \hat{a}$.

4. Now, an analogous definition of functions holomorphic on Δ can be made by replacing the A' in section 2 above at once by Δ, leading to the concept of (Δ, A)-holomorphy. An operational calculus on such a basis would be stronger than that described in section 3. It would provide a homomorphism of a certain algebra of continuous functions F on Δ, into A. The functions F allowed would be those which, in the neighborhood of each point $\xi \in \Delta$, allow a representation of the form

$$F(\eta) = \varphi(\eta(a_1), \ldots, \eta(a_n))$$

for $\eta \in U_\xi$ where U_ξ is a neighborhood of ξ in Δ. If $f \in hol(\Delta)$ in the sense of (A', A') holomorphy then surely $f \mid \Delta \in hol(\Delta)$ in the sense of (Δ, A)-holomorphy. Converesly, if each $F \in (\Delta, A)$-*hol* (Δ) were to allow an extension f into a neighborhood of Δ in A', where $f \in (A', A)$-*hol* (Δ), then the stronger form of operational calculus would be possible.

G. E. Shilov (see I) considered this type of operational calculus, but he did not show how such an extension of F could be made. Anyway, we shall call this the *problem* (Δ, A)-hol.

There is an older problem, here to be called "*loc-A*" which is contained in (Δ, A)-*hol*. However, it is best to formulate it directly. Let a function F on Δ be called *locally A* if for each $\xi \in \Delta$ there is an $a_\xi \in A$ such that $F - a_\xi = 0$ in a neighborhood of ξ in Δ. Then the *problem loc-A* is this: Is every locally -A function representable by one $\hat{a}$ on all of Δ? An algebra for which this holds is called *sectionally complete.*

5. It is easy to see that if (Δ, A)-*hol* can be solved, then every $F \in hol(\Delta)$ in the second sense has an extension to an $f \in hol(\Delta)$ in the first sense (and conversely). We now show that this problem is equivalent to a certain cohomology problem.

We continue the discussion begun in section 2.

The union of all $Hol[\xi]$, $\xi \in A'$ can be topologized so as to be a *sheaf* S (an analytic sheaf, in a natural sense). We need to bring in the subsheaf $Z(\Delta)$ of those germs $[f]_\xi$ for which $f = 0$ on $\Delta \cap V$, V some neighborhood of ξ. Let S_Δ be the sheaf induced by S on Δ, and let Z_Δ be the subsheaf induced on Δ by $Z(\Delta)$. Then the sequence

$$0 \to Z_\Delta \to S_\Delta \to S_\Delta/Z_\Delta \to 0$$

is exact (for details, see [2]). Hence we obtain an exact cohomology sequence

$$0 \to H^0(Z_\Delta) \xrightarrow{i} H^0(S_\Delta) \xrightarrow{q} H^0(S_\Delta/Z_\Delta) \to$$
$$\xrightarrow{r} H^1(Z_\Delta) \to H^1(S_\Delta) \to \ldots,$$

for the space Δ.

We have shown in [2] *that* $H^1(S_\Delta) = 0$. We now assert that problem (Δ, A)-*hol* is equivalent to the problem of showing that q is *onto*. To see this, we must interpret $H^0(S_\Delta)$ and $H^0(S_\Delta/Z_\Delta)$. We recall that $H^0(T)$ is isomorphic to the group of sections of T over Δ. In particular, if $\sigma \in H^0(S_\Delta)$ then each $\sigma(\xi)$ determines an $[f_\xi]_\xi \in S_\Delta(\xi \in \Delta)$ such that when η is near to ξ then $[f_\eta]_\eta = [f_\xi]_\eta$. Thus we arrive at an $f \in hol(\Delta)$ such that $\sigma(\xi) = [f]_\xi$. On the other hand, for $\sigma \in H^0(S_\Delta/Z_\Delta)$, and we choose $[f_\xi]_\xi$ to represent $\sigma(\xi)$, then we cannot guarantee more than $[f_\eta]_\eta - [f_\xi]_\eta \in Z_\Delta$. This means that we have an F as in section 4. Conversely, such an F determines an element of $H^0(S_\Delta/Z_\Delta)$.

Thus $H^0(S_\Delta)$ and $H^0(S_\Delta/Z_\Delta)$ represent just the classes of data appropriate to the two kinds of operational calculi. This justifies our remark about q. Now if q is *onto*, then r must be the zero map. However, the range of r is $H^1 Z_\Delta)$ because $H^1(S_\Delta) = = 0$. Thus $H^1(Z_\Delta) = 0$ if q is onto, and conversely, obviously.

This shows that problem (Δ, A)-*hol* is equivalent to *problem* Z^1: to show $H^1(Z_\Delta) = 0$.

The theorem $H^1(S_\Delta) = 0$ can be used to show that the group G of invertible elements in A, modulo its component of 1, is isomorphic to the first cohomology group $H^1(\Delta, Z)$ of Δ with integer coefficients, and is thus the same for all algebras having a space of maximal ideals homeomorphic to a given compact Hausdorff space D.

6. To our knowledge, no algebra A has been shown to be *not* sectionally complete Concerning some algebras it is not known whether they are sectionally complete (E. Bishop has found that an algebra generated by rational functions of one element with the *sup*-norm, is sectionally complete.) We should like to present a condition sufficient (but not necessary) to ensure that each locally-A function f is given by an element $a \in A$; i. e., $f = \hat{a}$. This condition we call *combinatorial semiregularity*. It asks that whenever the *interiors* of the sets $\{f = \hat{a}_1\}, \ldots, \{f = \hat{a}_n\}$ cover Δ, then there exist regularly closed sets F_i, regularly open sets W_i, such that

$$F_i \subset W_i \subset \{f = \hat{a}_i\}$$

and $\Delta = F_1 \cup \ldots \cup F_n$. *Regular* algebras are evidently combinatorially semiregular. So are those in which $\{\hat{a} = 0\}$ has interior points only if $a = 0$ ("quasi-analytic"). Quasi-analytic algebras are in a sense the opposite of regular.

Theorem. *A combinatorially semiregular algebra is sectionally complete.*

Proof. Let f be a locally-A function defined on $\Delta(A)$. By the compactnes of Δ there exist $a_1, \ldots, a_n \in A$ such that

$$\Delta = \{f = \hat{a}_1\} \cup \ldots \cup \{f = \hat{a}_n\}\,.$$

This insures the existence of $F_1, \ldots, F_n, W_1, \ldots, W_n$ as in the preceeding definition. Let E_k be the complement of W_k. Then $K = E_k \cup F_k$ is regularly closed. Let J be the closed ideal of those $x \in A$ for which $\hat{x}$ vanishes on K. Then K is the space of maximal ideals of $Q = A/J$. Since E_k, F_k are closed and open relative to K, we have (Shilov, [3]) an element in Q which is 0 on one, and 1 on the other. Let this element be the canonical image in A/J of $u_k \in A$. Then $\hat{u}_k = 1$ on F_k and $\hat{u}_k = 0$ outside W_k. Consider the element $a = u_1 a_1 + v_1 u_2 a_2 + \ldots + v_1 v_2 \ldots v_{n-1} u_n a_n$ where $v_k = 1 - u_2$. It is not hard to verify that $f = \hat{a}$.

7. The preparation of this paper was supported in part by the Office of Naval Research (contract Nonr-233 (60)) and the National Science Foundation (Grant G-18999).

Bibliography

[1] *R. Arens*: The analytic-functional calculus in commutative topological algebras. Pacific Journal of Mathematics *11* (1961), 405—429.

[2] *R. Arens*: The problem of locally-*A* functions in a commutative Banach algebra *A*, Transactions of the American Mathematical Society, to appear in 1962.

[3] *G. E. Shilov*: On the decomposition of a commutative normed ring into a direct sum of ideals, Матем. сб., *32* (1953, in Russian), 353—364.

[4] *G. E. Shilov*: Analytic functions in a normed ring. Успехи мат. наук, *15* (1960), no. 3 (93) (in Russian), 181—183.

DISTINGUISHED BOUNDARY SETS IN THE THEORY OF FUNCTIONS OF TWO COMPLEX VARIABLES

S. BERGMAN
Stanford

1. Introduction. Every simply connected bounded domain of the z-plane can be conformally mapped onto the unit circle.

In analogy to mappings by functions of 1 c. v. (complex variable) in the theory of 2 (and more) c. v. we consider pseudo-conformal transformations, i. e. one-to-one mappings of the domains[1]) $\mathfrak{B}^4$ onto domain $\mathfrak{B}^{*4}$ by a pair

$$z_k = z_k^*(z), \quad k = 1, 2, \quad z = (z_1, z_2) \in \mathfrak{B}^4 \tag{1}$$

of functions of 2 c. v. z_1, z_2; $z_k^*(z)$ are holomorphic in $\mathfrak{B}^4$. (The functional determinant $D(z_1, z_2) = [\partial(z_1^*, z_2^*)/\partial(z_1, z_2)]$ is finite and does not vanish in $\mathfrak{B}^4$.)

The problem to decide whether two given domains can be pseudo-conformally mapped onto each other, i. e., the classification of pseudo-conformally equivalent[2]) domains, is an important question of the theory of functions of 2 c. v.

Domains admitting the group of linear transformation $z_k^* = z_k \exp(i\varphi m_k)$, $0 \leqq \varphi \leqq 2\pi$, onto itself are called (m_1, m_2)-domains. Here m_k are integers, without a common factor.

A domain admitting the group $z_k^* = z_k \exp(i\varphi_k)$, $0 \leqq \varphi_k \leqq 2\pi$, $k = 1, 2$ onto itself is called a Reinhardt domain. These domains represent the simplest class of (m_1, m_2)-domains. Using the method of the kernel function we can decide whether the given bounded domain $\mathfrak{B}^4$ can be mapped pseudo-conformally on a Reinhardt circular domain $\mathfrak{R}^4$ and determine the mapping function of $\mathfrak{B}^4$ onto $\mathfrak{R}^4$.

The domains with a distinguished boundary represent another interesting subclass of domains.[3])

In the following we shall study some properties of the boundaries of domains with distinguished boundary sets. These investigations yield various invariants in the case of p.—c. transformations $\boldsymbol{T}$, regular in the closed domain (i.e., in the case of mappings (1) which satisfy the previously described requirements in $\overline{\mathfrak{B}^4}$).

Dinstinguished boundary sets are defined using either $\mathbf{C}(\mathfrak{B}^4)$ or $\mathbf{L}^2(\mathfrak{B}^4)$.

$\mathbf{C}(\mathfrak{B}^4)$ is the class of functions holomorphic in $\mathfrak{B}^4$ and continuous in $\overline{\mathfrak{B}^4}$.

[1]) As a rule the upper index is the dimension of the set.

[2]) I. e. domains which by (1) can be mapped onto each other.

[3]) These two classes do not exclude each other. A bicylinder is a Reinhardt domain with a two-dimensional distinguished boundary.

$\mathbf{L}^2(\mathfrak{B}^4)$ is the class of functions $g(z)$ holomorphic in $\mathfrak{B}^4$ for which

$$\int_{\mathfrak{B}^4} |g(z)|^2 \, d\omega_z < \infty ,$$

$d\omega_z$ is the volume element, $\int$ is the Lebesgue integral.

In the first case we consider on the boundary $\boldsymbol{b}^3$ of $\mathfrak{B}^4$ *the smallest maximum set* $\mathfrak{D}$, i.e. the set of boundary points t, so that to every t, $t \in \mathfrak{D}$, a function $f(z) \in \mathbf{C}(\mathfrak{B}^4)$ exists with the property that[4])

$$|f(t)| > |f(z)| , \quad z \in \overline{\mathfrak{B}}^4 - t . \tag{2}$$

In the second case we determine the maximum of $|h(z)|^2$ of functions, which satisfy the conditions $\int_{\mathfrak{B}^4} |h(\zeta)|^2 \, d\omega_\zeta = 1$.

$$g(\zeta) = K(\zeta, \bar{z})/[K(z, \bar{z})]^{\frac{1}{2}} \tag{3}$$

is the function yielding this maximum and $|g(z)|^2 = K(z, \bar{z})$,[5]) $K \equiv K_{\mathfrak{B}^4}$, [5], p. 31 ff. For $z \to t$, where t is a boundary point of $\mathfrak{B}^4$, $K(z, \bar{z})$ goes (with some exceptions) to ∞. In a number of cases it has been shown that[6]) $\lim_{z \to t} (\widehat{zt})^n K(z, \bar{z})$ (for an appropriate n) does not vanish and is bounded. If $\boldsymbol{b}^3$ satisfies certain conditions, the order n equals 2, 3 or 4. See [6], chapt. I, p. 6 ff. Accordingly we introduce boundary points of n-th order, $n = 2, 3, 4$.

Remark. The geometrical structure of the boundary and certain invariants (derived from the kernel-function) exhibit different behaviour at boundary points of different order.

Let $\Phi(z)$ be holomorphic in $\overline{\mathfrak{B}}^4$ and $\Phi(z) = 0$ have only one point common with $\overline{\mathfrak{B}}^4$ ($\mathfrak{B}^4$ a bounded domain). If a function $\Psi(z)$ exists so that the p.-c. mapping

$$Z_1 = \Phi(z) , \quad Z_2 = \Psi(z) \tag{4}$$

is schlicht (one-to-one) in $\mathfrak{B}^4$, and the boundary $\boldsymbol{b}^3$ of $\mathfrak{B}^4$ at the point t is sufficiently regular, then t is of the third order. See [3]. If $\boldsymbol{b}^3 \cap [\Phi(z) = 0] = \mathfrak{S}^2$ is a (two-dimensional) segment of $[\Phi(z) = 0]$ and t is an interior point of $\mathfrak{S}^2$, then t is of the second order. If two analytic surfaces $\Phi(z) = 0$ and $\Psi(z) = 0$ pass through t and (4) is a schlicht mapping of $\mathfrak{B}^4$, then t is of the fourth order.

2. A generalization of the Schwarz lemma in domains with the smallest maximum boundary. To demonstrate the advantage of introducing the notion of the smallest maximum boundary in the present section, a generalization of the Schwarz lemma will be derived. Suppose that $\mathfrak{B}^4$ has a maximum boundary $\mathfrak{D}$ which is a proper part of $\boldsymbol{b}^3$. Further let us assume that $f(z)$, $p(z)$ and $f(z)/p(z)$ are functions of 2 c. v. which are holomorphic in $\overline{\mathfrak{B}}^4$. Finally let $p(z)$ vanish at least at one point of $\mathfrak{B}^4$, but $|p(\zeta)| > 0$ for $\zeta \in \mathfrak{D}$.[7]) Then

[4]) It should be noted that the smallest maximum sets occur in the theory of rings. See [9].

[5]) In the following $\mathfrak{B}^4$ will be replaced by $\mathfrak{B}$, when it appears as a subscript.

[6]) If N is the interior normal at the point t, $(\widehat{zt})$ is the length of the projection on N of the segment comnecting z and t. In the case of the points of the fourth order, $(\widehat{zt})$ is the distance between z and t.

[7]) If $p(z)$ vanishes at a point of $\mathfrak{B}^4$, $\min |p(Z)| = 0$ for $Z \in b^3$.

(1) $$|f(z)| \leqq |p(z)| \max_{\zeta \in \mathfrak{D}} |f(\zeta)| / \min_{\zeta \in \mathfrak{D}} |p(\zeta)| , \quad z \in \mathfrak{B}^4 .$$

See [4].

The inequality (1) can be improved as follows. Let $Q(Z)$, $Z = (x_1, y_1, x_2, y_2)$, $z_k = x_k + iy_k$, be a family $\mathbf{Q}$ of B-harmonic functions which are regular in $\mathfrak{B}^4$. Further let $\mathbf{Q}_n$, $n = 1, 2, 3, \ldots$ be subclasses of[8]) $\mathbf{Q}$, $\mathbf{Q}_n \subset \mathbf{Q}_{n+1}$, $\lim_{n \to \infty} \mathbf{Q}_n = \mathbf{Q}$.

If we approximate $\log |p(Z)|$ in the Tchebysheff sense by the $Q_n(Z)$, i. e. so that

(2) $$\max_{z \in \mathfrak{D}} |\log |p(z)| - Q_n(Z)| = \min = m(n) , \quad Q_n(Z) \in \mathbf{Q}_n ,$$

$$z = (x_1 + iy_1, x_2 + iy_2) , \quad Z = (x_1, y_1, x_2, y_2) ,$$

then $m(n)$ is a non increasing function of n. Therefore

(3) $$\lim_{n \to \infty} m(n) = m(\infty)$$

exists. Since

(4) $$|Q_n(Z)| \leqq m(1) + \max_{z \in \mathfrak{D}} |\log |p(z)||$$

the $Q_n(Z)$ form a normal family in $\mathfrak{B}^4$. A subset $Q_{n_\nu}(Z)$ exists, so that $\lim_{\nu \to \infty} Q_{n_\nu}(Z) = \mathbf{Q}^{(0)}(Z)$, $Z \in \mathfrak{B}^4$. Thus

(5) $$|f(z)| \leqq |p(z)| \exp[-\mathbf{Q}^{(0)}(Z)] \max_{Z \in \mathfrak{D}} |f(Z)| / e^{+m(\infty)} .$$

3. An analytic polyhedron. In order to gain a better insight in the theory of domains with distinguished boundary sets it is useful at first to restrict our considerations to the simplest type of these domains, namely to consider analytic polyhedra.

A domain bounded by finitely many segments of analytic hypersurfaces (see below) is called an *analytic polyhedron.*

We proceed to a precise description of domains to be considered in the following.

Let

(1) $$\mathfrak{H}^2(\lambda) = [\Phi(z, \lambda) = 0] , \quad \lambda = \text{const} , \quad \Phi \text{ complex} ,$$

where $\lambda \in \mathfrak{s}^1 = [0 \leqq \lambda \leqq 1]$, $z = (z_1, z_2)$, be a family of surfaces. Here

(2) $$[\Phi(z, \lambda_1) = 0] \cap [\Phi(z, \lambda_2) = 0] = 0 \quad \text{for} \quad 0 \leqq \lambda_1 < \lambda_2 < 1$$

and

(3a) $$[\Phi(z, 0) = 0] \cap [\Phi(z, 1) = 0] = 0 \quad \text{(case I)}$$

or

(3b) $$[\Phi(z, 0) = 0] = [\Phi(z, 1) = 0] \quad \text{(case II)}$$

(Hyp. 1a). Here $\Phi(z, \lambda)$, $\lambda \in \mathfrak{s}^1$, $z \in \mathfrak{B}^4$, is a continuously differentiable function of the real variable λ and of the complex variables z_1, z_2. $\mathfrak{B}^4$ is a sufficiently large domain, see below (Hyp. 1b).

---

[8]) E. g. $\mathbf{Q}$ is the class of B-harmonic polynomials, while $\mathbf{Q}_n$ are real parts of polynomials $\Sigma a_{\nu\mu} z_1^\nu z_2^\mu$, $\nu + \mu \leqq n$ (B-harmonic = the real part of a holomorphic function of 2 c. v.).

Let

(4) $$\mathfrak{h}^3 = \bigcup_{\lambda=0}^{1} \mathfrak{H}^2(\lambda) .$$

$\mathfrak{M}^4$ is a domain bounded by segments $\mathfrak{j}^3_\kappa$ of hypersurfaces $\mathfrak{h}^3_\kappa$ introduced by (4). If $\mathfrak{m}^3$ is the boundary of $\mathfrak{M}^4$,

(5) $$\mathfrak{m}^3 = \bigcup_{\kappa=1}^{n} \mathfrak{j}^3_\kappa , \quad \mathfrak{j}^3_\kappa = \mathfrak{h}^3_\kappa \cap \overline{\mathfrak{M}}^4$$

(Hyp. 1c). The $\Phi_\kappa(z, \lambda_\kappa)$ are holomorphic functions of 2 c. v. in $\overline{\mathfrak{M}}^4$ (Hyp. 1d). Every $\mathfrak{I}^2_\kappa(\lambda_\kappa) = \mathfrak{H}^2_\kappa(\lambda_\kappa) \cap \mathfrak{m}^3$ can be uniformized (Hyp. 1e). This means that a pair of continuously differentiable functions $h^k_\kappa(Z_\kappa, \lambda_\kappa)$, $k = 1, 2$, $Z_\kappa \in \mathfrak{R}^2_\kappa(\lambda_\kappa)$, of the complex variable Z_κ, and of the real variable λ_κ, $\kappa = 1, 2, \ldots, n$, exist with the following property:

(6) $$\mathbf{R}_{\lambda_\kappa} : \qquad z_k = h^k_\kappa(Z_\kappa, \lambda_\kappa) , \quad k = 1, 2 ,$$

is a one-to-one mapping of the cylinder $\bigcup_{\lambda_\kappa \in \mathfrak{s}^1} \mathfrak{R}^2_\kappa(\lambda_\kappa)$ onto $\mathfrak{j}^3_\kappa$. (Hyp. 1f). ($\bigcup_{\lambda_\kappa \in \mathfrak{s}^1} \mathfrak{R}^2_\kappa(\lambda_\kappa)$ lies in the space λ_κ, Re Z_κ, Im Z_κ.) For every fixed λ_κ, the $h^k_\kappa(Z_\kappa, \lambda_\kappa)$ are functions of 1 c. v. Z_κ, holomorphic in $\mathfrak{R}^2_\kappa(\lambda_\kappa)$ (Hyp. 1g).

(7) $$\mathfrak{R}^2_\kappa(\lambda_\kappa) = [0 < \varrho_0 \leqq r_\kappa(\lambda_\kappa) < |Z_\kappa| < 1]$$

(Hyp. 1h).

Let $\Psi^{(k)}(z)$, $k = 1, 2$, be two holomorphic functions of 2 c. v. *in* a bounded domain $\overline{\mathfrak{K}}^4$. By the Weierstrass preparation theorem, $\mathfrak{K}^4$ can be covered by finitely many neighbourhoods $\mathfrak{N}^4_p$ so that in every $\mathfrak{N}^4_p$

(8) $$\Psi^{(k)}(z) = z_1^{\nu_{kp}} \prod_{\nu=1}^{n_{pk}} (z_1 - \varphi^{(k)}_{p\nu}(z_2))^{\mu_{pk}} \, \Omega_{pk}(z) , \quad k = 1, 2 .$$

Here Ω_{kp} is a function which does not vanish in $\mathfrak{N}^4_p$, n_{pk} and μ_{pk} are integers.

If in every $\mathfrak{N}^4_p$

(9a) $$\nu_{1p} \cdot \nu_{2p} = 0 ,$$

(9b) $$\varphi^{(1)}_{p\nu_1}(z_2) \not\equiv \varphi^{(2)}_{p\nu_2}(z_2) ,$$

$$\nu_1 = 1, 2, \ldots, n_{p1} , \quad \nu_2 = 1, 2, \ldots, n_{p2} ,$$

then the $\Psi^{(k)}(z)$ will be called prime with each other in $\overline{\mathfrak{K}}^4$.

Lemma 3.1. *Let $\overline{\mathfrak{j}}^3$ be a given segment of an analytic hypersurface, which admits two representations*

(10) $$\overline{\mathfrak{j}}^3 = \bigcup_{\lambda \in \mathfrak{s}^1} \overline{\mathfrak{I}}^2(\lambda) = \bigcup_{\mu \in \mathfrak{s}^1} \overline{\mathfrak{H}}^2(\mu)$$

where $\overline{\mathfrak{I}}^2(\lambda) = [\Phi^{(1)}(z, \lambda)] = 0, \lambda \in \mathfrak{s}^1$ *and* $\overline{\mathfrak{H}}^2(\mu)$ $[\Phi^{(2)}(z, \mu) = 0]$, $\mu \in \mathfrak{s}^1$. *Further, for every* λ *and* μ *either* $\Phi^{(1)}(z, \lambda)$ *and* $\Phi^{(2)}(z, \mu)$ *are prime with each other in every sufficiently small domain* $\mathfrak{K}^4 \supset \overline{\mathfrak{j}}^3$ *or* $\overline{\mathfrak{I}}^2(\lambda)$ *is identical with* $\overline{\mathfrak{H}}^2(\mu)$. *Then*

(11) $$\overline{\mathfrak{I}}^2(\lambda) = \overline{\mathfrak{H}}^2(\mu^*(\lambda))$$

where $\mu^*(\lambda)$ *is a continuous and monotone function of* λ. *Compare* [7] *and* [8].

Therefore the decomposition of a segment $\mathfrak{j}^3$ into a sum of segments $\mathfrak{F}^2(\lambda)$ of analytic surfaces is essentially unique.

Let $\mathfrak{i}_\kappa^1(\lambda_\kappa)$ be the boundary curves of $\mathfrak{F}_\kappa^2(\lambda_\kappa)$,

$$\mathfrak{i}_\kappa^1(\lambda_\kappa) = \mathbf{R}_{\lambda_\kappa}\{[|Z_\kappa| = r_\kappa(\lambda_\kappa)] \cup [|Z_\kappa| = 1]\} \tag{12}$$

and $\mathfrak{i}_{\kappa\mathfrak{s}}^1(\lambda_\kappa) = \mathfrak{i}_\kappa^1(\lambda_\kappa) \cap \mathfrak{F}_\mathfrak{s}^3$, $\mathfrak{s} \neq \kappa$,

$$\mathfrak{i}_\kappa^1 = \bigcup_{\substack{\mathfrak{s}=1 \\ \mathfrak{s}\neq\kappa}}^{n} \mathfrak{i}_{\kappa\mathfrak{s}}^1 , \tag{13}$$

$$\mathfrak{G}_{\kappa\mathfrak{s}}^2 = \bigcup_{\lambda_\kappa \in \mathfrak{s}^1} \mathfrak{i}_\kappa^1(\lambda_\kappa) \cap \bigcup_{\lambda_\mathfrak{s} \in \mathfrak{s}^1} \mathfrak{i}_\mathfrak{s}^1(\lambda_\mathfrak{s}) , \tag{14}$$

$$\mathfrak{G}_\kappa^2 = \bigcup_{\substack{\mathfrak{s}=1 \\ \mathfrak{s}\neq\kappa}}^{n} \mathfrak{G}_{\kappa\mathfrak{s}}^2 . \tag{15}$$

Then

$$\mathfrak{D}^2 = \bigcup_{\kappa=1,\mathfrak{s}=1,\kappa\neq\mathfrak{s}}^{n} \mathfrak{G}_{\kappa\mathfrak{s}}^2 \tag{16}$$

is the distinguished boundary set of $\mathfrak{M}^4$. $\mathfrak{D}^2$ is a maximum boundary. Under some additional hypotheses, $\mathfrak{D}^2$ is the smallest maximum boundary.

4. Invariants in pseudo-conformal transformations of an analytic polyhedron. In accordance with the lemma 3.1 in a pseudo-conformal transformation $\mathbf{T}$ satisfying the condition (1.1) in $\overline{\mathfrak{M}}^4$, the lamina $\mathfrak{F}_\kappa^2(\lambda_\kappa)$ is mapped onto a lamina $\mathfrak{F}_\kappa^{*2}(\lambda_\kappa)$ of the domain $\mathfrak{M}^{*4} = \mathbf{T}(\mathfrak{M}^4)$. Indeed, $\mathbf{T}^{-1}$ is an one-to-one transformation of $\overline{\mathfrak{F}_\kappa^{*2}}(\lambda_\kappa)$ onto $\mathfrak{F}_\kappa^2(\lambda_\kappa)$, $\mathfrak{F}_\kappa^2(\lambda_\kappa)$ is a one-to-one image of $\overline{\mathfrak{R}_\kappa^2}(\lambda_\kappa)$, therefore

$$\mathbf{P}_{\lambda_\kappa} : z_k^* = z_k^*[h_\kappa^1[Z_\kappa, \lambda_\kappa), h_\kappa^2(Z_\kappa, \lambda_\kappa)] , \quad k = 1, 2 , \tag{1}$$

is a one-to-one analytic mapping of $\overline{\mathfrak{R}_\kappa^2}(\lambda_\kappa)$ onto $\overline{\mathfrak{F}_\kappa^{*2}}(\lambda_\kappa)$. In every $\overline{\mathfrak{R}_\kappa^2}(\lambda_\kappa)$ we consider the function

$$J_\kappa(Z_\kappa, \overline{Z}_\kappa, \lambda_\kappa) = \frac{\partial^2 \log K(Z_\kappa, \overline{Z}_\kappa)}{K\, \partial Z_\kappa\, \partial \overline{Z}_\kappa} , \quad K = K_{\mathfrak{R}_\kappa{}^2(\lambda_\kappa)} .$$

This function is invariant with respect to conformal transformations of $\mathfrak{R}_\kappa^2(\lambda_\kappa)$ onto itself. According to [12], [13], it assumes the value 2π on the boundary of $\mathfrak{R}_\kappa^2(\lambda_\kappa)$; at every interior point of $\overline{\mathfrak{R}_\kappa^2}(\lambda_\kappa)$, $J_\kappa > 2\pi$. The function

$$B(z) = J_\kappa(Z_\kappa, \overline{Z}_\kappa, \lambda_\kappa) , \quad z = \mathbf{P}_{\lambda_\kappa}(Z_\kappa) , \tag{2}$$

is defined on the boundary $\mathfrak{m}^3$ of $\mathfrak{M}^4$. $B(z)$ is invariant with respect to pseudo-conformal transformations $\mathbf{T}$. At every point of the distinguished boundary $\mathfrak{D}^2$,

$$B(z) = 2\pi , \tag{3}$$

at every point $\mathfrak{m}^3 - \mathfrak{D}^2$,

$$B(z) > 2\pi . \tag{4}$$

In the case where $\mathfrak{R}_\kappa^2(\lambda_\kappa)$ are simply instead of doubly connected, the function $B(z)$ is constant on the whole boundary $\mathfrak{m}^3$, and therefore our procedure leads to a triviality. If $\mathfrak{R}_\kappa^2(\lambda_\kappa)$ is an n-ply connected domain, $n > 2$, we can construct the function $B(z)$ which has similar properties as in the case $n = 2$.

5. A second type of invariants. In § 4 we obtained in the case of analytic polyhedra invariants with respect to pseudo-conformal mappings $\boldsymbol{T}$. In the present section we shall consider invariants of a different type.

Now the hypothesis (1h) can be replaced by a weaker one, namely we assume here that $\mathfrak{R}_\kappa^2(\lambda_\kappa)$ is an n-ply connected domain $1 \leq n \leq N < \infty$.

The analytic polyhedron $\mathfrak{M}^4$ is obviously a complex. The $\mathfrak{S}_{\kappa\mathfrak{s}}^2$, see (3.16), are its edges. In a pseudo-conformal mapping $\boldsymbol{T}$, the boundary $\mathfrak{m}^3$ goes again into the boundary $\mathfrak{m}^{*3}$ of $\mathfrak{M}^{*4} = \boldsymbol{T}(\mathfrak{M}^4)$. The $\mathfrak{S}_{\kappa\mathfrak{s}}^{*2} = \boldsymbol{T}(\mathfrak{S}_{\kappa\mathfrak{s}}^2)$. Since the mapping $\boldsymbol{T}$ is one-to-one and continuous the Betti group of the complex $\mathfrak{m}^3$ is preserved.

Similarly we form intersections of three (four) segments $\mathfrak{j}_{\kappa\mathfrak{s}}^3$ of analytic hypersurfaces, and we obtain a line (finite point set, respectively). Again the Betti groups of complexes obtained in this way are invariants with respect to pseudo-conformal transformations. This procedure can be extended to the case of general domains $\mathfrak{B}^4$ which possess the property that the kernel function $K_{\mathfrak{B}}$ is infinite of a certain order in the sense explained in § 1. Since the functional determinant of the mapping $\boldsymbol{T}$ does not vanish nor is infinite in $\mathfrak{B}^4$ the order of the infinity is preserved in this transformation, and thus the Betti group is an invariant with respect to the transformation $\boldsymbol{T}$.

6. Interior distinguished points. In § 5 we characterize the topological structure of the distinguished boundary. In analogy to this approach it is useful to apply topological methods in the study of the indicatrix of invariants at interior points of the domain.

$$(1) \qquad J(z) = \frac{K_{\mathfrak{B}}(z, \bar{z})}{T_{1\bar{1}}T_{2\bar{2}} - |T_{1\bar{2}}|^2}, \quad T_{m\bar{n}} = \frac{\partial^2 \log K(z, \bar{z})}{\partial z_m \partial \bar{z}_n}$$

is an invariant with respect to pseudo-conformal transformations. See [5] and [6]. The indicatrix[9]) $\mathfrak{n}^3(z_0)$ of an interior point z_0 of $\mathfrak{B}^4$ is divided by the hypersurface $J(z) = J(z_0)$ into parts. In a pseudo-conformal transformation the topological structure of the surface

$$(2) \qquad \mathfrak{T}^2(z_0) = \mathfrak{n}^3(z_0) \cap [J(z) = J(z_0)]$$

is preserved. Indeed, if the development of the functions (1.1) at $z_0 = (z_1^0, z_2^0)$ is

$$(3) \qquad (z_k^* - z_k^{*0}) = a_{10}^{(k)}(z_1 - z_1^0) + a_{01}^{(k)}(z_2 - z_2^0) + \ldots,$$

the indicatrix will be transformed by

$$(4) \qquad Z_k = a_{10}^{(k)} Z_1 + a_{01}^{(k)} Z_2 .$$

[9]) $\mathfrak{n}^3(z_0) = \sum T_{m\bar{n}}(z_0)\xi_m \bar{\xi}_n = \varepsilon^2$, where $z_0 = (x_1^0 + iy_1^0, x_2^0 + iy_2^0)$ and $\varepsilon > 0$ is sufficiently small.

Since (1.1) is a one-to-one mapping, $0 < |a_{10}^{(1)}a_{01}^{(2)} - a_{10}^{(2)}a_{01}^{(1)}| < \infty$, and (4) is also a one-to-one and continuous mapping. Consequently it preserves the topological structure of $\mathfrak{T}^2(z_0)$. As a rule $\mathfrak{T}^2(z_0)$ is a sphere. ($J(z) = J(z_0)$ intersects $\mathfrak{n}^3(z_0)$ into two parts). Points z_0 where $\mathfrak{T}^2(z_0)$ is different from a sphere are called *interior distinguished points of the invariant* $J(z)$.

In the case of a Reinhard circular domain, the center is either an isolated maximum or minimum of $J_{\mathfrak{B}}(z)$ or a minimax and $\mathfrak{T}^2(z_0)$ is one or several tori. The center is the only point of this type.

A condition necessary for a domain $\mathfrak{B}^{*4}$ to be a pseudo-conformal image of a Reinhardt circular domain, is the existence of an interior distinguished point $z_0^* \in \mathfrak{B}^{*4}$. The point z_0^* is either an isolated maximum or minimum of $J(z)$, or the indicatrix $\mathfrak{T}^2(z_0^*)$ is one or the sum of several tori.

If one (and only one) interior distinguished point z_0^* (as described before) exists in $\mathfrak{B}^{*4}$, we determine the so-called representative domain $\mathfrak{R}^4(\mathfrak{B}^{*4}, z_0^*)$ with respect to z_0^*. See [2], [11]. If the domain $\mathfrak{B}^{*4}$ is pseudo-conformally equivalent to a Reinhardt circular domain, the obtained domain $\mathfrak{R}^4(\mathfrak{B}^{*4}, z_0^*)$ becomes a Reinhardt circular domain. Thus a method has been given to decide whether a given domain $\mathfrak{B}^{*4}$ can be mapped onto a Reinhardt circular domain or not. For details see [3], p. 48 and [10].

A similar method can be used to decide whether two domains, say[10]) $\mathfrak{B}^{*4}$ and $\mathfrak{B}^4$, can be pseudo-conformally mapped onto each other. We determine the interior distinguished points of $\mathfrak{B}^4$ ($\mathfrak{B}^{*4}$ respectivelly) which lie in the domain

$$(5) \qquad J_1 \leqq J(z) \leqq J_2 \, .$$

(Here J_1 and J_2 are conveniently chosen constants.) The necessary conditions for $\mathfrak{B}^4$ to be pseudo-conformally equivalent to $\mathfrak{B}^{*4}$, is that

(a) the number n of the interior distinguished points $z^{(\nu)}$, and those of $z^{*(\mu)}$ in the domain (5) is the same;

(b) a correspondence between $z^{(\nu)}$ and $z^{*(\mu)}$ can be established so that in the corresponding points $z^{(\nu)}$ and $z^{*(\mu)}$, $J_{\mathfrak{B}}(z^{(\nu)})$ and $J_{\mathfrak{B}^*}(z^{*(\mu)})$ have the same value;

(c) the Betti group of $\mathfrak{T}^2(z^{(\nu)})$ and that of $\mathfrak{T}^2(z^{*(\mu)})$ in corresponding points are the same.

Under some additional assumptions, it is possible to show that n, $0 < n < \infty$, interior distinguished points exist in (5).

We construct the representative domains $\mathfrak{R}^4(\mathfrak{B}^4, z^{(\nu)})$ and $\mathfrak{R}^4(\mathfrak{B}^{*4}, z^{*(\mu)})$, $\nu = 1, 2, \ldots, n$, $\mu = 1, 2, \ldots, n$. The necessary and sufficient condition for $\mathfrak{B}^4$ to be pseudo-conformally equivalent to $\mathfrak{B}^{*4}$ is that domain $\mathfrak{R}^4(\mathfrak{B}^{*4}, z^{*(\mu)})$ can be obtained from $\mathfrak{R}^4(\mathfrak{B}^4, z(\nu))$ by a linear transformation [1], p 677 and [2].

10) We assume that $J_{\mathfrak{B}}(z)$ and $J_{\mathfrak{B}^*}(z)$ are not constant, and that there are isolated interior distinguished points of $J(z) \equiv J_{\mathfrak{B}}(z)$.

Bibliography

[1] *Bergman S.*: Über Hermitesche unendliche Formen, die zu einem Bereich gehören, nebst Anwendungen auf Fragen der Abbildung durch Funktionen zweier komplexen Veränderlichen. Berichte Berliner math. Gesellschaft, *26* (1927), 178–184; et Math. Zeit., *29*, 640–677.

[2] *Bergman S.*: Über die Existenz von Repräsentantenbereichen. Math. Ann., *102* (1929), 430–446.

[3] *Bergman S.*: Über die Kernfunktion eines Bereiches und ihr Verhalten am Rande. Journ. reine angew. Math., *169* (1933), 1–42, et *172* (1934), 89–128.

[4] *Bergman S.*: Über eine Integraldarstellung von Funktionen zweier Veränderlichen. Мат. сб. *1* (*43*), (1936), 851–862.

[5] *Bergman S.*: Sur les fonctions orthogonales de plusieurs variables complexes. Mém. d. Sc. math. *106* (1947), 1—61.

[6] *Bergman S.*: Sur la fonction-noyau d'un domaine et ses applications dans la théorie des transformations pseudo-conformes. Mém. d. Sc. math. *108* (1948), 1—80.

[7] *Bergman S.*: Some properties of meromorphic functions of two complex variables. To appear in the Bulletin de la Société des Sciences et des Lettres de Lodz.

[8] *Bergman S.* and *Schiffer M.*: Potential-theoretic methods in the theory of functions of two complex variables. Compositio Mathematica *10* (1952), 213–240.

[9] *Шилов Г. Е.*: О разложении коммутативного нормированного кольца в прямую сумму идеалов. Мат. сб. *32* (14), 1953), 353—364.

[10] *Springer G.*: Pseudo-conformal transformations onto circular domains. Duke Math. Journal *18* (1951), 411–424.

[11] *Welke H.*: Über die analytischen Abbildungen von Kreiskörpern und Hartogsschen Bereichen. Math. Ann. *103* (1930), 437–449. (Thèse, Münster, 1930.)

[12] *Zarankiewicz K.*: Sur la représentation conforme d'un domaine doublement connexe sur un anneau circulaire. C. R. Acad. Sc. *198* (1934), 1347–1349.

[13] *Zarankiewicz K.*: Über ein numerisches Verfahren zur konformen Abbildung zweifachzusammenhängender Gebiete. Zeitsch. f. ang. Math. und Mech. *14* (1934), 97–104.

ON THE TOPOLOGICAL CLASSIFICATION OF COMPLETE LINEAR METRIC SPACES

C. BESSAGA and A. PEŁCZYŃSKI
Warszawa

The topological classification of finite-dimensional linear spaces is quite easy. It is well-known that two finite dimensional linear spaces are homeomorphic if and only if thay have the same dimension. Moreover in this case there exists an isomorphism (linear homeomorphism) between those spaces. In the case of infinite dimensional spaces the situation is different. The topological and isomorphical (= linearly topological) clasifications are not the same. For example if $1 \leqq p' \neq p'' < +\infty$, then the spaces $l_{p'}$ and $l_{p''}$ are not isomorphic but, by a result of S. MAZUR (1930), they are homeomorphic.

One known topological invariant which distinguishes infinite-dimensional complete linear metric spaces is the density character of the space. Among the spaces of density character $\aleph$ there are $2^{\aleph}$ different isomorphical types. It is clear that the topological classification is coarser than the isomorphical one. However the hypothesis that all the spaces of the same density character are homeomorphic; is very problematic.

Now we shall consider some particular cases.

1. *Banach spaces. We know the following results*:

(1) $$l_p \sim l_2\,;\quad L_p \sim L_2 = l_2 \quad (1 \leqq p < \infty) \quad \text{(S. MAZUR [6])}\,.$$

(*The symbol* $X \sim Y$ *denotes that the space* X *and* Y *are homeomorphic*)

(2) $$c_0 \sim l_2 \quad \text{(M. J. KADEC [2])}\,.$$

(3) *Every separable infinite dimensional conjugate B-space* (*in particular every reflexive space*) *is homeomorphic to* l_2 (M. J. KADEC [3] and V. KLEE [4]).

(4) *Every B-space with density character* $\aleph$ *which contains a closed linear manifold homeomorphic to* $l_2(\aleph)$ *is homeomorphic to* $l_2(\aleph)$ (C. BESSAGA and A. PEŁCZYŃSKI [1]).

The proofs of (2) and (3) consist in the assigning to each element of the space a sequence of "coordinates" which are defined in metric terms under a convenient admissible norm. The proof of (4) makes use of some algebraic identities and properties of cartesian product of spaces. The crucial lemma is the following result of Bartle-Graves:

(5) *If* Y *is a closed linear subspace of a B-space* (*F-space*) X *then* $X \sim Y \times X/Y$ (BARTLE-GRAVES 1952). (See E. MICHAEL [7].) *In particular from* (4) *we obtain*

(4a) *Every separable B-space which contains an infinite-dimensional subspace with an unconditional basis is homeomorphic to l_2.*

We recall that the sequence (x_n) is an unconditional basis of the space X if every element x in X may be uniquely written as a sum $x = \sum_n t_n x_n$ and for every permutation (p_n), the series $\sum_n t_{p_n} x_{p_n}$ is convergent.

We deduce (4a) from (4). Let Y be a subspace of X with an unconditional basis. Then, by a result of R. C. JAMES, either Y contains a subspace isomorphic to the space c_0 or Y is isomorphic to a conjugate space. In both cases, by (3) and (2), X contains a subspace homeomorphic to l_2.

All known infinite-dimensional separable B-spaces fulfil the assumption of (4a), whence they are homeomorphic to l_2. In general case the solution of the classification problem for separable B-spaces is reduced to the positive answer to the following problem:

P. 1. Does every infinite-dimensional B-space contain an infinite-dimensional subspace with an unconditional basis?

We want to call your attention to the fact that this problem has purely linear character.

For nonseparable B-spaces the consequences of (4) are not so deep. However we can show that

(4b) $$m(\aleph) \sim l_2(2^{\aleph}) \sim l(2^{\aleph}).$$

2. Now we consider the case of locally convex metrisable complete spaces (F-spaces). It is natural to ask: Does there exist an F-space which is isomorphic to no B-space but is homeomorphic to l_2?

Let us consider the space A of all entire functions $f(z) = \sum_{n=0}^{\infty} t_n z^n$, with the topology of almost uniform convergence. Put

$$hf = (\sqrt[n]{|t_n|} \cdot t_n/|t_n|).$$

This formula defines a homeomorphic mapping from A onto the complex space c_0 (by the classical Cauchy-Hadamard formula). Hence $A \sim l_2$. In an analogical way we can prove that every nuclear Köthe space is homeomorphic to l_2. Combining this result with the theorem of Bartle-Graves and the following result of S. ROLEWICZ: [9]:

Let X be an infinite dimensional F-space. If X is isomorphic to no cartesian product $E \times s$, where E is a B-space, then X contains isomorphically a nuclear Köthe space,

we can show that all know separable infinite dimensional F-spaces except the space s are homeomorphic to l_2. Namely we obtain

(6) *Let X be an infinite-dimensional separable F-space. If either 1° X is isomorphic to no carthesian product $E \times s$, where E is a B-space or 2° $X = E \times s$ and $E \sim l_2$, then $X \sim l_2$.*

Hence we see that the classification problem for separable F-spaces is reduced to that of B-space and to the following questions:

P. 2. Is the space s homeomorphic to l_2?

About the nonseparable F-spaces we know nothing. In particular it seems to be interesting to answer the following question:

P. 3. Is the space $[l_2(\aleph)]^{\aleph_0}$ homeomorphic to $l_2(\aleph)$?[1])

For $\aleph = \aleph_0$ the answer is "yes". Morover from (6) it follows that for infinite dimensional B-space X we have $X^{\aleph_0} \sim l_2$.

3. In the case of *non-locally convex linear metric complete space* we know only a little. Mazur's result (1) can be automatically extended to the case $0 < p < 1$. However we do not know

P. 4. Is the space S of all measurable real functions on $[0, 1]$, homeomorphic to l_2?

The following problem seems to be very interesting

P. 5. Generalize the theorem of Bartle-Graves to the case of all linear metric complex spaces.

4. It seems to be interesting to introduce *other classifications* of an intermediate character between the isometrical classification and the topological one. From the analytical point of view it is natural to ask how "nice" a homeomorphism between two linear topological spaces may be. We notice that

(7) *Let X be an F-space. If there exist a B-space Y and a homeomorphism h, which uniformly maps Y onto X, then X is a B-space.*

(8) *Under the assumption that every infinite dimensional B-space is homeomorphic with its subspace of defect one, we obtain that if two spaces are homeomorphic, then they are radially homeomorphic, i. e. there is a homeomorphism h such that $\|hx\| = \|x\|$, $h(tx) = thx$.*

The Mazur homeomorphism between l_{p_1} and l_{p_2} satisfies the Hölder condition. We want to call your attention to the following unsolved questions:

P. 6. Let h be a homeomorphic mapping from a B-space X onto a B-space Y. Let us suppose that h and h^{-1} are Lipschitzian. Are then the spaces X and Y isomorphic?

P. 7. Are every two homeomorphic B-spaces uniformly homeomorphic (i. e. whether there exists such an homeomorphism h between these spaces that both h and h^{-1} are uniformly continuous).

5. Now we want to tell something about the topological equivalences of some *spaces of continuous functions*. The theorem (4a) implies

(9) *If Q is an infinite compact metric space then the space $C(Q) = R^Q$ of all real continuous functions defined on Q is homeomorphic to l_2.*

Since the space I^Q may be treated as the unit ball of $C(Q)$, then by a recent result of Klee I^Q is homeomorphic to l_2. The same is true for the spaces R_+^Q, X^Q and W^Q,

---

[1]) Added in proof: The answer to this problem is "yes". From this fact we can deduce that the result (4) holds true if we replace the word "B-space", by "F-space" — see [8].

where R_+ denotes the half-line, X — an arbitrary separable F-space, and W — the Hilbert cube. It seems to be very probable that

P. 8. If W is closed convex subset of an arbitrary separable B-space then W^Q is homeomorphic to l_2, for any infinite compact metric space Q.

On the other hand, if T is a separable metric space which is not an absolute retract then the space T^Q is not homeomorphic to l_2. One may ask

P. 9. Let T be a compact metric absolute retract. Is the space T^Q homeomorphic to l_2, Q being an infinite metric compact space?

We cannot answer this question even in the particular case where T is a continuum homeomorphic to the capital letter T.

References

[1] *C. Bessaga* and *A. Pełczyński*: Some remarks on homeomorphism of Banach spaces. Bull. Acad. Polon. Sci., Ser. sci. math. astr. phys. *8* (1960), 757—761.

[2] *M. J. Kadec*: On homeomorphism of certain Banach spaces (in Russian). Докл. АН СССР *92* (1953), 465—468.

[3] *M. J. Kadec*: A connection between weak and strong convergence (in Ukrainian). Zapowidi Akad. Nauk URSR, *9* (1959), 949—952.

[4] *V. Klee*: Mappings into normed linear spaces. Fund. Math. *49* (1960), 25—34.

[5] *V. Klee*: Topological equivalence of a Banach space with its unit cells. Bull. Amer. Math. Soc. *3* (1961), 286—289.

[6] *S. Mazur*: Une remarque sur l'homeomorphie des champs fonctionnels. Studia Math. *1* (1929), 83—86.

[7] *Ernest Michael*: Continuous selections I. Ann. of Mat., vol. *63* (1956), 361—382.

[8] *C. Bessaga* and *A. Pełczyński:* Some remarks on homeomorphisms of *F*-spaces. Bull. Acad. Polon. Sci., ser. sci. math. astr. phys. *10* (1962), 265—270.

[9] *C. Bessaga, A. Pełczyński* and *S. Rolewicz:* On diametral approximative dimension and linear homogenity of *F*-spaces. Ibidem *9* (1961) 677—683.

APPLICATIONS OF THE SIDE APPROXIMATION THEOREM FOR SURFACES

R. H. BING
Madison

By a surface we mean a closed set in a 3-manifold which is locally like the plane — each point of the surface lies in an open subset of the surface which is topologically equivalent to the interior of a circle.

Two surfaces may intersect in a peculiar set in Euclidean 3-space. Even two smooth surfaces may intersect in a set locally like the closure of the graph of $y = \sin(1/x)$. In fact, if K is any closed subset of a round 2-sphere S, there is a second two sphere S' (not necessarily round) such that S' contains K and lies except for K on the interior of S. On the other hand, the intersection of two polyhedral surfaces is always a polyhedron. (A surface is polyhedral if it is a geometric complex — the sum of a locally finite collection of triangular planar disks.) To bring about a reasonable intersection of surfaces, the Approximation Theorem for surfaces was proved. It is proved in [2] and may be stated as follows.

Theorem 1. Approximation Theorem for Surfaces. *Suppose S is a surface in a triangulated 3-manifold M and f is a non negative continuous function defined on S. Then there is a surface S' and a homeomorphism h of S onto S' such that*

a) $p(x, h(x)) \leqq f(x)$, $x \in S$ *and*
b) *S' is locally polyhedral at $h(x)$ if $f(x) > 0$.*

This Approximation Theorem for Surfaces has had several applications. O. G. HARROLD used it [10] to show that if P is polygon in E^3 which bounds a disk, then P bounds a polyhedral disk. He also used it to show that in various theorems where the hypothesis has previously required that certain 2-spheres be locally polyhedral on certain parts, these extra conditions could be dropped.

E. E. MOISE has shown [11] that if h is a homeomorphism of an open subset U of E^3 into E^3 and f is a non negative continuous function defined on U, then there is a homeomorphism h' of U onto $h(U)$ such that

a) h' is locally polyhedral at $x \in U$ if $f(x) > 0$ and
b) $p(h(x), h'(x)) \leqq f(x)$.

This is a very useful theorem and was used in [12] by Moise to prove that any 3-manifold can be triangulated.

The Approximation Theorem for Surfaces was extended to an Approximation

Theorem for 2-complexes in [6] to give alternative proofs of these two results of Moise.

In hearing papers given about mappings on 3-manifolds, I frequently hear the restrictions, "We restrict ourselves to piecewise linear homeomorphisms". While this restriction is sometimes necessary (as in the case of certain periodic homeomorphisms) it frequently is not and shows that the author is not proving as strong a theorem as he might have proved if he were acquainted with the results mentioned in the preceding two paragraphs.

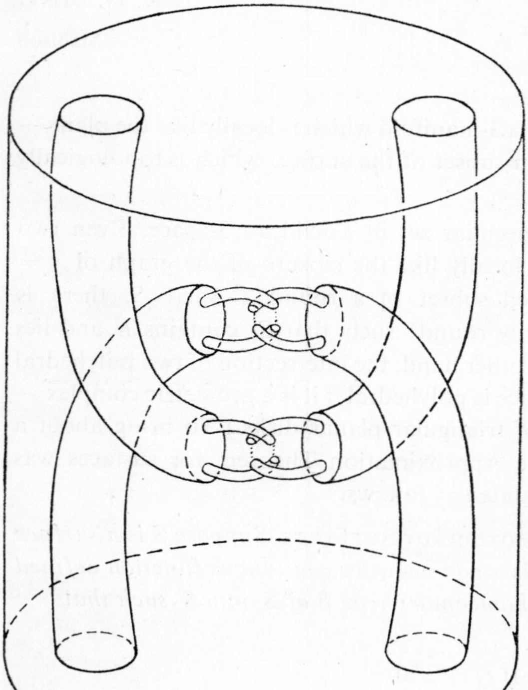

Fig. 1.

If S is a 2-sphere and T is a tetrahedron in E^3, there is a homeomorphism of S onto BdT (the boundary of T). If this homeomorphism can be extended to take E^3 onto itself, we say that S is tame. If the homeomorphism cannot be extended, we say it is wild. The 2-sphere shown in Figure 1 was obtained by starting with the boundary of a cylindrical can, replacing disks in the ends of the can by tubes that almost link, replacing disk in the ends of tubes with tubes, etc.

It is a wild 2-sphere since its interior (bounded complementary domain) is not simply connected (1-connected). Note that the 2-sphere can be approximated by a polyhedral 2-sphere which lies on the exterior of the wild 2-sphere. However, it cannot be approximated from the interior of the wild 2-sphere since an approximating polyhedral 2-sphere which was on the interior would cut off some of the small tubes. Hence, at best some parts of the approximating 2-sphere would fail to lie on the interior of the wild 2-sphere.

In a seminar Bob Williams asked if it might be possible to get a polyhedral approximation to any 2-sphere which would lie except for small disks on a prescribed side of the 2-sphere. It turns out that the answer is in the affirmative as given by the following result.

Theorem 2. Side Approximation Theorem for 2-Spheres. *Suppose S is a 2-sphere in E^3, $\varepsilon > 0$, and U is a component of $E^3 - S$. Then there is a polyhedral 2-sphere S' and a homeomorphism h of S onto S' such that*

a) *h moves no point more than ε and*

b) *S' contains a finite family of mutually exclusive disks, each of diameter less than ε, such that S' minus these disks lies in U.*

The proof of this theorem has been distributed in ditto form and will appear in the Annals of Mathematics [3]. The proof is modeled (with certain simplifications) after the proof the Approximation Theorem for Surfaces given in [2]. The construction is as might be expected in that S is used as a model and a polyhedral surface S' is constructed beside S with S' not being permitted to intersect S except in some feelers.

Without using the full strength of the Side Approximation Theorem but using merely the Approximation Theorem for Surfaces the following result had been proved [4]:

Theorem 3. *A 2-sphere S in E^3 is tame if for each $\varepsilon > 0$ and each component U of $E^3 - S$ there is a 2-sphere S in U, and a homeomorphism of S onto S' that moves no point more than ε.*

By using this result and the Side Approximation Theorem the following result may be established:

Theorem 4. *A 2-sphere S in E^3 is tame if $E^3 - S$ is 1-ulc.*

We say that a set is 1-*ulc* if for each $\varepsilon > 0$ there is a $\delta > 0$ such that if D is a disk and f is a map of $Bd\,D$ into a δ-subset of X, then f can be extended to map D into an ε-subset of X.

Outline of proof of Theorem 4. Theorem 4 is proved in [5] but the outline of the proof is as follows. We shall apply Theorem 3 so we only need to show that for each component U of $E^3 - S$, there is a 2-sphere in U that is a close homeomorphic approximation to S. It follows from the Side Approximation Theorem that there is a polyhedral 2-sphere S' which lies except for small polyhedral disks $D_1, D_2, \ldots, D_n$ in U. Since U is 1-*ulc*, D_i can be shrunk to a point on a small polyhedral singular disk E_i in U. Then $(S' - \sum D_i) + \sum E_i$ is a singular 2-sphere in U. By using results of C. D. Papakyriakopoulos regarding Dehn's lemma [3] the singular 2-sphere may be changed to a 2-sphere in U which is a close approximation to S.

Theorem 4 may be extended to apply to surfaces as well as 2-spheres. How this may be done and the details of the proof of Theorem 4 are to be found in [5].

A Sierpinski curve is a 1-dimensional subset of a disk D obtained by deleting from D a null sequence of interiors of disks such that each of these small disks lies on the interior of D and no two of them intersect each other. We say that a Sierpinski curve is tame if it lies on a tame 2-sphere. The following is another application of the Side Approximation Theorem which gives a strong affirmative answer to the question as to whether or not each 2-sphere in E^3 contains a tame arc.

Theorem 5. *For each 2-sphere S in E^3 and each $\varepsilon > 0$ there is a tame Sierpinski curve X on S such that each component of $S - X$ is of diameter less than ε.*

Outline of proof. It follows from an extension of Theorem 2 as shown in Figure 2 that there is a polyhedral 2-sphere S' such that S' lies except for small feelers (like F_1) on Int S. Cut off feelers like F_1 and replace them with a smooth disk so that the resulting 2-sphere S_1 lies on Int S'. An approximation to S_1 almost from the other side enables us to replace F_2 by a smooth disk so that the resulting 2-sphere S_2 can be approximated closely from both sides. In a similar fashion we replace S_2 by S_3 so as to remove small feelers like F_3 and replace S_3 by S_4 to remove feelers like F_4. If great care is exercised as done in [8], S_1, $S_2, \ldots$ converges to a 2-sphere S_∞ which shares a Sierpinski curve X with S so that each component of $S - X$ is of diameter less than ε. Furthermore S_∞ was chosen so that it could be homeomorphically approximated arbitrarily closely from both sides. It follows from Theorem 3 that S_∞ is tame.

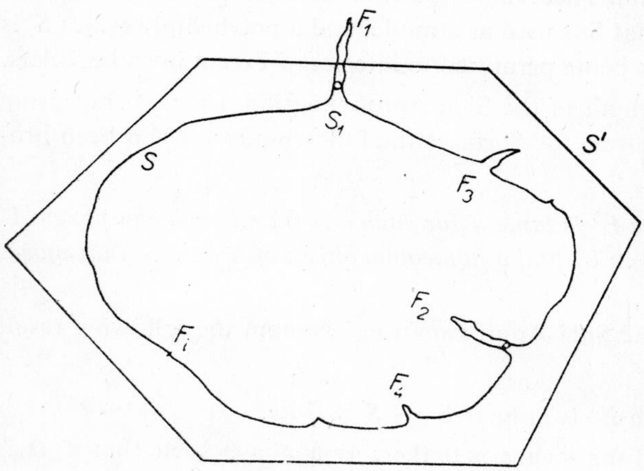

Fig. 2.

Some peculiar wild 2-spheres have been described. Some have the property that although their complements are simply connected, no disk in them is tame but each arc in them is tame. Some of them are even such that each Sierpinski curve in them is tame. DAVID GILLMAN and W. R. ALFORD have obtained such examples as modification of the ones given in [7]. However, Theorem 5 reveals that any 2-sphere whatsoever in E^3 can be obtained from a tame 2-sphere by removing small disks and putting on feelers. Also, the reversal of this operation changes every 2-sphere into a tame 2-sphere. This adds to our understanding of wild 2-spheres. Alford has shown [1] that there are uncountably many different kinds of wild 2-spheres.

Theorem 5 is used to prove the following result:

Theorem 6. *Each 2-sphere in each 3-manifold can be pierced by a tame arc.*

Details of the proof of the above result are found in [9] where it is shown that the 2-sphere is pierced at each point of the tame Sierpinski curve. D. Gillman has extended Theorem 6 to show that the places at which the 2-sphere can be pierced by a tame arc are actually the points of the 2-sphere which lie on tame arcs in the 2-sphere.

The following questions suggest themselves:

Question 1. What is the category of the points of a 2-sphere in E^3 at which it cannot be pierced by a tame arc? Conjecture – a 0-dimensional F_σ set.

Question 2. Can Dehn's lemma be extended to imply that if f is a map of a disk D into E^3 such that f^{-1} is $1-1$ on $f(\mathrm{Bd}D)$, then $f(\mathrm{Bd}D)$ bounds a disk in E^3.

Question 3. Can a homotopy 3-cell in E^3 be approximated by a real cell in the following sense.

Suppose U is a bounded, contractible open subset of E^3 and V is a neighborhood of $\mathrm{Bd}U$. Is there a 3 cell C in E^3 such that $U - V \subset C \subset U + V$.

Question 4. (Raised by Borsuk). If X is a contractible continuous curve in E^3 and $\varepsilon > 0$, is there a map f of X onto a contractible polyhedron such that f moves no point more than ε?

References

[1] *W. R. Alford*: Some „nice" wild two spheres in three space. Notices Amer. Math. Soc., vol. *8* (1961), 348.

[2] *R. H. Bing*: Approximating surfaces with polyhedral ones. Ann. Math., vol. *65* (1957), 456–483.

[3] *R. H. Bing*: Approximating surfaces from the side. Ann. Math. to appear.

[4] *R. H. Bing*: Conditions under which a surface in E^3 is tame. Fund. Math., vol. *47* (1959), 105–139.

[5] *R. H. Bing*: A surface is tame if its complement is 1-*ulc*. Trans. Amer. Math. Soc., vol. *101* (1961), 294—305.

[6] *R. H. Bing*: An alternative proof that 3-manifolds can be triangulated. Ann. Math., vol. *69* (1959), 37–65.

[7] *R. H. Bing*: A wild surface each of whose arcs is tame. Duke Journal, *28* (1961), 1–15.

[8] *R. H. Bing*: Each disk in E^3 contains a tame arc, Am. J. Math., to appear.

[9] *R. H. Bing*: Each disk in E^3 is pierced by a tame arc, Am. J. Math., to appear.

[10] *O. G. Harrold Jr.*: Some consequences of the approximation theorem of Bing. Proc. Amer. Math. Soc., vol. *8* (1961), 204–206.

[11] *Edwin E. Moise*: Affine structures in 3-manifolds, IV, Piecewise linear approximations of homeomorphisms. Ann. Math., vol. *66* (1959), 215–222.

[12] *Edwin E. Moise*: Affine structures in 3-manifolds, V, The triangulation theorem and Hauptvermutung. Ann. Math., vol. *56* (1952), 96–114.

[13] *C. D. Papakyriakopoulos*: On Dehn's lemma and the asphericity of knots. Ann. Math., vol. *66* (1951), 1–26.

BEMERKUNGEN ZUM KONGRESSVORTRAG „STETIGKEITSBEGRIFF UND ABSTRAKTE MENGENLEHRE“ VON F. RIESZ

M. BOGNÁR
Budapest

Es ist wohl bekannt, dass F. RIESZ in seinem an dem IV. internationalen mathematischen Kongress (1908) gehaltenen Vortrage [3] durch die axiomatische Aufnahme einiger Grundeigenschaften der Verdichtungsstelle den Weg zur Ausbildung der Idee des topologischen Raumes gezeigt hatte. Es ist aber weniger bekannt, dass er in demselben Referat auch darauf hingewiesen hat, dass durch die Art der Verdichtung eines Raumes noch nicht sämtliche wesentliche Stetigkeitseigenschaften desselben festgelegt werden. Infolgedessen führt er einen neuen Begriff, jenen der Verkettung ein, und nimmt einige Fundamentalpostulate als Axiomen auf. Einen ganz ähnlichen Gedanken können wir in der Definition des Nachbarschaftsraumes bei W. A. JEFREMOWITSCH (1934) [2] und Ju. M. SMIRNOW (1952) [4] finden.

Durch jede Verkettung eines Raumes ist zugleich eine zugehörige Verdichtung desselben bestimmt. Dagegen sind aber mit demselben Verdichtungstypus im allgemeinen mehrere Verkettungstypen verträglich. Riesz stellt das folgende Problem auf: unter welchen Bedingungen lässt sich ein Verkettungstypus als Teiltypus eines sogenannten „losesten“ Verkettungstypus auffassen? Diese Fragestellung ist zu dem von Ju. M. Smirnow formulierten und zuerst von ihm nachher in verschiedenen Weisen von Á. CSÁSZÁR und S. MRÓWKA [1] gelösten Problem der bikompakten Ausdehnung der Nachbarschaftsräume ganz analog.

Riesz hat auch eine Methode gezeigt, wie sich dieser „Obertypus“ eines Verkettungstypus im allgemeinen konstruieren lässt. Man betrachte als ideale Verdichtungsstelle jedes System von Teilmengen das den folgenden Bedingungen genügt:

1. Jede Obermenge einer Menge des Systems gehört auch dem Systeme an.

2. Wird eine Menge des Systems in zwei Teilmengen zerlegt, so gehört wenigstens eine von diesen Teilmengen dem Systeme an.

3. Jedes Paar von Mengen des Systems ist miteinander verkettet.

4. Das System ist vollständig, d. h. es ist in keinem reicheren Systeme, das die Bedingungen 1—3 befriedigt, enthalten.

5. Es gibt kein Element, welches Element oder Verdichtungsstelle sämtlicher Mengen des Systems wäre.

In unserem Referat möchten wir zeigen, wie man das Problem der bikompakten Ausdehnung der Nachbarschaftsräume mit Hilfe der Rieszschen idealen Punkte lösen kann. Es werden das Axiomensystem und die Terminologie von Smirnow benutzt (s. [4]).

Bemerken wir zuerst, dass wenn die Punkte des ursprünglichen Raumes auch zu den idealen Punkten gerechnet werden, so muss man die Bedingung 5 auslassen. Ausserdem ist die Bedingung 1 überflüssig; sie ist nämlich eine unmittelbare Folge der Bedingungen 2—4.

Die Schwierigkeit stellt die Bedingung 2 auf. Zur Vervollständigung eines aus zwei benachbarten Mengen bestehenden Systems ist nämlich die Bedingung 2 sehr unbequem. Diese Schwierigkeit wird folgendermassen gelöst: Zuerst definieren wir die abgeschlossenen Mengen der bikompakten Ausdehnung, und deren Punkte werden als spezielle abgeschlossene Mengen aufgefasst. Der folgende Gedanke ermöglicht dieses Verfahren.

1. Sei R ein regulärer Raum und P ein dichter Unterraum von R. Betrachten wir ein beliebiges System $\{M_\alpha; (\alpha \in A)\}$ von Teilmengen des Raumes P. Der Durchschnitt der in R genommenen abgeschlossenen Hüllen — $\bigcap_{\alpha \in A} \overline{M}_\alpha^R$ — ist offenbar eine in R abgeschlossene Menge. Durch die Regularität von R wird nun die Darstellbarkeit jeder abgeschlossenen Menge von R in dieser Form gesichert.

Wenn wir hier ein beliebiges System von abgeschlossenen Mengen $[Q_\beta; (\beta \in B)]$ betrachten, wo alle Q_β in der obigen Form darstellbar sind, d. h. $Q_\beta = \bigcap_{\alpha_\beta \in A_\beta} \overline{M}^R_{\alpha_\beta, \beta}$ $(M_{\alpha_\beta, \beta} \subset P)$, so ist ihr Durchschnitt $Q = \bigcap_{\beta \in B} Q_\beta$ in der Form $Q = \bigcap_{\alpha_\beta \in A_\beta, \beta \in B} \overline{M}^R_{\alpha_\beta, \beta}$ darstellbar, d. h. das den Durchschnitt Q darstellende System erhalten wir durch die Vereinigung der die einzelnen Q_β darstellenden Systeme.

Dieser Gedanke gibt uns die Möglichkeit zur Aufstellung der folgenden Definitionen:

2. Definition. Es sei P ein Nachbarschaftsraum. Ein beliebiges System von Teilmengen des Raumes P, $\mathfrak{M} = \{M_\alpha; (\alpha \in A)\}$ $(M_\alpha \subset P)$ wird *eine abgeschlossene Pseudomenge* — kurz APM — genannt.

3. Definition. Es sei $[\mathfrak{M}_\beta; (\beta \in B)]$ ein System von APM. *Der Durchschnitt* $\mathfrak{M} = \bigcap_{\beta \in B} \mathfrak{M}_\beta$ wird als die Vereinigung der Mengensysteme $\mathfrak{M}_\beta$ erklärt. D. h. M gehört zu $\mathfrak{M}$ dann und nur dann, wenn es eine die Bedingung $M \in \mathfrak{M}_\beta$ erfüllende APM $\mathfrak{M}_\beta$ gibt.

Es ist klar, dass diese Durchschnittbildung kommutativ und assoziativ ist. Ausserdem folgt aus $\mathfrak{M}_\beta = \mathfrak{M}$; $(\beta \in B)$ offenbar $\bigcap_{\beta \in B} \mathfrak{M}_\beta = \mathfrak{M}$.

4. Sei R ein bikompakter normaler Raum. Er bestimmt eindeutig einen Nachbarschaftsraum in R. Sei $\{M_\alpha; (\alpha \in A)\}$ ein beliebiges System von Teilmengen des Raumes R. Wir möchten mit Hilfe der Eigenschaften des Nachbarschaftsraumes R, ohne den Bereich der Teilmengen M_α zu verlassen, entscheiden, ob der Durchschnitt der abgeschlossenen Hüllen der Mengen M_α : $\bigcap_{\alpha \in A} \overline{M}_\alpha^R$ leer oder nichtleer ist.

Wenn der Durchschnitt nichtleer ist, so liegen die Mengen M_α paarweise nahe zueinander. Es ist sogar offenbar auch die folgende Bedingung erfüllt: *Bei einer beliebigen endlichen Zerteilung einer beliebigen Teilmenge $M_{\alpha'}$ des Systems: $M_{\alpha'} = M^1_{\alpha'} \cup \ldots \cup M^k_{\alpha'}$* (die einzelnen Teilmengen $M^i_{\alpha'}$ brauchen nicht disjunkt zu sein, *gibt es eine $M^i_{\alpha'}$, die zu allen M_α; $(\alpha \in A)$ nahe liegt.*

Diese Bedingung ist aber zum nichtleeren Wesen des Durchschnitts $\bigcap\limits_{\alpha \in A} \overline{M}^R_\alpha$ nicht nur notwendig, sondern auch hinreichend. Setzen wir nämlich voraus, dass der Durchschnitt leer ist. Dann kann man wegen der Bikompaktheit von R ein endliches Teilsystem $\{M_{\alpha_1}, \ldots, M_{\alpha_n}\}$ finden, so dass der Durchschnitt $\bigcap\limits_{j=1}^{n} \overline{M}^R_{\alpha_j}$ auch leer sei. Da R auch normal ist, gibt es offene Umgebungen G_j der $\overline{M}^R_{\alpha_j}$, deren Durchschnitt auch leer ist. Die abgeschlossenen Mengen $R - G_j$; $(j = 1, \ldots, n)$ überdecken daher den Raum R, folglich ist

$$M_{\alpha_n} \subset \bigcup_{j=1}^{n-1} (R - G_j)\,.$$

Sei

$$M^j_{\alpha_n} = M_{\alpha_n} \cap (R - G_j) \quad (j = 1, \ldots, n-1)\,.$$

Diese Mengen bilden eine endliche Zerteilung $M_{\alpha_n} = M^1_{\alpha_n} \cup \ldots \cup M^{n-1}_{\alpha_n}$ der Menge M_{α_n}. Hier ist wegen

$$\overline{M}^R_{\alpha_j}\, \delta (R - G_j)\,; \quad (j = 1, \ldots, n-1)$$

in der Tat

$$M^j_{\alpha_n}\, \bar{\delta} M_{\alpha_j}\,; \quad (j = 1, \ldots, n-1)\,,$$

d. h. bei dieser endlichen Zerteilung der Menge M_{α_n} ist die oben formulierte Bedingung nicht erfüllt.

Diese Bemerkung erlaubt uns, die folgende Definition aufzustellen:

5. Definition. Es sei P ein Nachbarschaftsraum. Eine APM $\mathfrak{M} = \{M_\alpha; (\alpha \in A)\}$ von P wird *leer* genannt — $\mathfrak{M} \sim \lambda$ — wenn es eine Menge $M_{\alpha'}$ des Systems $\mathfrak{M}$ und eine endliche Zerteilung $M_{\alpha'} = M^1_{\alpha'} \cup \ldots \cup M^k_{\alpha'}$ der Menge $M_{\alpha'}$ gibt, so dass jede $M^i_{\alpha'}$ von wenigstens einer Menge $M_{\alpha(i)}$ des Systems $\mathfrak{M}$ weit liegt:

$$M^i_{\alpha'}\, \bar{\delta} M_{\alpha(i)}\,; \quad (i = 1, \ldots, k)\,.$$

Nach diesen Vorbereitungen beweisen wir die Unizität der bikompakten Ausdehnung eines Nachbarschaftsraumes. Der Unizitätssatz wird folgendermassen formuliert:

Satz 1. *Sei der Nachbarschaftsraum P ein dichter Unterraum der bikompakten Haussdorfschen Nachbarschaftsräume R und R'. Dann kann man eine, den Raum R auf den Raum R' abbildende, und dabei die Punkte des Unterraumes P unverändert lassende Homeomorphie f finden.*

Beweis. Sei a ein beliebiger Punkt des Raumes R. Offenbar ist a Berührungspunkt gewisser Teilmengen von P. Betrachten wir das System $\mathfrak{A}$ sämtlicher a als Berührungspunkt erhaltender Teilmengen von P. $\mathfrak{A} = \{M_\alpha; (\alpha \in A)\}$ ist nach (4) eine im Sinne von (5) nichtleere APM. Sie ist dabei eine vollständige nichtleere APM, d. h. sie ist in keinem grösseren nichtleeren Systeme enthalten. Es ist nämlich nach (1) $\bigcap_{M_\alpha \in \mathfrak{A}} \overline{M}_\alpha^R$ gleich der einpunktigen Menge (a): $(a) = \bigcap_{M_\alpha \in \mathfrak{A}} \overline{M}_\alpha^R$, daher folgt aus $\{M, M_\alpha; (\alpha \in A)\} \sim \lambda$ nach (4) die Tatsache $\overline{M}^R \cap \bigcap_{M_\alpha \in \mathfrak{A}} \overline{M}_\alpha^R \neq \varnothing$, $a \in \overline{M}^R$, daraus aber $M \in \mathfrak{A}$.

Betrachten wir jetzt die abgeschlossene Teilmenge $\bigcap_{\alpha \in A} \overline{M}_\alpha^{R'}$ des Raumes R'. Sie ist nach (4) nichtleer. Sei $a' \in \bigcap_{\alpha \in A} \overline{M}_\alpha^{R'}$. Aus dem vollständigen nichtleeren Wesen der APM $\mathfrak{A}$ folgt nach (4), dass sämtliche, den Punkt a' in R' als Berührungspunkt erhaltende Teilmengen von P im Systeme $\mathfrak{A}$ vorkommen, und so ist nach (1) $(a') = \bigcap_{\alpha \in A} \overline{M}_\alpha^{R'}$, d. h. $\bigcap_{\alpha \in A} \overline{M}_\alpha^{R'}$ enthält nur den Punkt a'.

Definieren wir eine Abbildung f der Menge R in R' in folgender Weise: Sie soll einem beliebigen Punkt $a \in R$ den durch das obige Verfahren eindeutig bestimmten Punkt $a' \in R'$ zuordnen, d. h. $f(a) = a'$, wenn das System der Teilmengen von P die a in R als Berührungspunkt erhalten, mit dem Systeme jener die a' in R' als Berührungspunkt erhalten, zusammenfällt.

Die so erklärte f ist offensichtlich eine eineindeutige, die Punkte des Unterraumes P unverändert lassende Abbildung der Menge R auf die Menge R'.

Beweisen wir noch, dass f eine Homeomorphie ist. Wegen der Symmetrizität der Konstruktion genügt dazu schon der Beweis der Stetigkeit der Abbildung f^{-1}.

Sei F eine beliebige abgeschlossene Teilmenge des Raumes R. Wir müssen zeigen, dass $f(F)$ eine abgeschlossene Teilmenge des Raumes R' ist. Betrachten wir das System $\mathfrak{N} = \{N_\beta; (\beta \in B)\}$ sämtlicher Teilmengen von P, deren abgeschlossene Hüllen in R die Menge F enthalten. Dann ist nach (1) $F = \bigcap_{\beta \in B} \overline{N}_\beta^R$.

Sei $F' = \bigcap_{\beta \in B} \overline{N}_\beta^{R'}$. Wir zeigen, dass

$$F' = f(F).$$

Sei nämlich a ein Punkt des Raumes R, und betrachten wir das System $\mathfrak{A} = \{M_\alpha; (\alpha \in A)\}$ sämtlicher Teilmengen von P, die a als Berührungspunkt erhalten. Dann folgt aus $a \in F$ in der Tat $(a) \cap F \neq \varnothing$, und daher $(\bigcap_{\alpha \in A} \overline{M}_\alpha^R \cap \bigcap_{\beta \in B} \overline{N}_\beta^R) \neq \varnothing$. Hieraus folgt nach (4) $\mathfrak{A} \cap \mathfrak{N} \sim \lambda$, $(\bigcap_{\alpha \in A} \overline{M}_\alpha^{R'} \cap \bigcap_{\beta \in B} \overline{N}_\beta^{R'}) \neq \varnothing$, $(f(a) \cap F') \neq \varnothing$, und daher $f(a) \in F'$. Ähnlicherweise folgt aus $f(a) \in F'$ die Tatsache $a \in F$.

Nachdem wir die Unizität der bikompakten Ausdehnung eines beliebigen Nachbarschaftsraumes P bewiesen haben, machen wir einige Vorbereitungen zum Beweis der Existenz der bikompakten Ausdehnung.

6. Sei P ein Nachbarschaftsraum. Dann ist $\{M, N\}$ offenbar eine leere bzw. nichtleere APM (im Sinne von (5)), je nachdem $M \bar{\delta} N$ bzw. $M \delta N$ ist. Die APM $\{M\}$ ist leer oder nichtleer, je nachdem M eine leere oder nichtleere Teilmenge von P ist.

7. Wir ziehen einige einfache Folgerungen aus dem leeren oder nichtleeren Wesen einer APM $\mathfrak{M} = \{M_\alpha; (\alpha \in A)\}$.

a) Wenn $\mathfrak{M} \sim \lambda$, so ist bei beliebiger APM $\mathfrak{N} : (\mathfrak{M} \cap \mathfrak{N}) \sim \lambda$.

b) Wenn $\mathfrak{M} \nsim \lambda$, so können wir zum Systeme $\mathfrak{M}$ beliebige Obermengen der Mengen M_α hinzunehmen, und dabei bleibt das erweiterte System $\mathfrak{M}'$ noch immer nichtleer. Wir können sogar zum Systeme $\mathfrak{M}$ solche Teilmengen M von P hinzunehmen, deren abgeschlossene Hüllen Obermengen von wenigstens einer M_α; $(\alpha \in A)$ sind, und das erweiterte System $\mathfrak{M}''$ bleibt noch immer nichtleer.

8. *Sei $\mathfrak{M} = \{M_\alpha; (\alpha \in A)\}$ eine leere APM. Betrachten wir eine beliebige Menge $M_{\alpha''}$ aus dem Systeme $\mathfrak{M}$. Dann gibt es eine endliche Zerteilung $M_{\alpha''} = M^1_{\alpha''} \cup \ldots \cup M^n_{\alpha''}$ der Menge $M_{\alpha''}$, so dass jede $M^i_{\alpha''}$ von wenigstens einer Menge des Systems $\mathfrak{M}$ weit liegt.*

Beweis. Nach (5) gibt es eine $M_{\alpha'}$, eine endliche Zerteilung $M_{\alpha'} = M^1_{\alpha'} \cup \ldots \cup M^k_{\alpha'}$ und dazugehörige Mengen aus dem Systeme $\mathfrak{M} : M_{\alpha(1)}, \ldots, M_{\alpha(k)}$, so dass

$$M^i_{\alpha'} \,\delta M_{\alpha(i)} \quad (i = 1, \ldots, k)\,.$$

Betrachten wir bei jedem i $(i = 1, \ldots, k)$ eine Umgebung V_i der Menge $M^i_{\alpha'}$, die von $M_{\alpha(i)}$ noch immer weit liegt, d. h.:

$$V_i \,\delta\, M_{\alpha(i)}\,,$$

und dabei $(P - V_i)\,\delta\, M^i_{\alpha'}$.

Sei $V = \bigcup_{i=1}^{k} V_i$. Hier ist offensichtlich $(P - V)\,\delta\, M_{\alpha'}$.

Sei $n = k + 1$ und $M_{\alpha(n)} = M_{\alpha'}$. Sei für $i = 1, \ldots, n - 1$: $M^i_{\alpha''} = M_{\alpha''} \cap V_i$ und ausserdem $M^n_{\alpha''} = M_{\alpha''} \cap (P - V)$. Dann ist offenbar

$$M_{\alpha''} = M^1_{\alpha''} \cup \ldots \cup M^n_{\alpha''}\,,$$

und

$$M^i_{\alpha''} \,\delta\, M_{\alpha(i)} \quad (i = 1, \ldots, n)\,.$$

Damit haben wir die gewünschte Zerteilung erhalten.

9. Sei $\mathfrak{M} = \{M_\alpha; (\alpha \in A)\}$ eine nichtleere APM. Betrachten wir eine beliebige $M_{\alpha'}$ aus dem Systeme $\mathfrak{M}$ und eine beliebige endliche Zerteilung $M_{\alpha'} = M^1_{\alpha'} \cup \ldots \cup M^k_{\alpha'}$. Dann gibt es eine Teilmenge $M^i_{\alpha'}$, für die der Durchschnitt $\mathfrak{M} \cap \{M^i_{\alpha'}\}$ nichtleer ist.

Im entgegengesetzten Falle hätte nämlich nach (8) jede $M^i_{\alpha'}$; $(i = 1, \ldots, k)$ eine endliche Zerteilung $M^i_{\alpha'} = M^{i,1}_{\alpha'} \cup \ldots \cup M^{i,l(i)}_{\alpha'}$, so dass jede $M^{i,j}_{\alpha'}$ von wenigstens einer Menge des Systems $\mathfrak{M}$ weit wäre.

$$M_{\alpha'} = M^{1,1}_{\alpha'} \cup \ldots \cup M^{1,l(1)}_{\alpha'} \cup M^{2,1}_{\alpha'} \cup \ldots \cup M^{2,l(2)} \cup \ldots \cup M^{k,1}_{\alpha'} \cup \ldots \cup M^{k,l(k)}_{\alpha'}$$

wäre deshalb eine endliche Zerteilung der Menge $M_{\alpha'}$, bei der jede $M^{i,j}_{\alpha'}$ von wenigstens einer Menge des System $\mathfrak{M}$ weit wäre. $\mathfrak{M}$ wäre daher leer.

10. Sei $\{\mathfrak{M}_\beta; (\beta \in B)\}$ ein zentriertes System von abgeschlossenen Pseudomengen, d. h. der Durchschnitt jedes endlichen Teilsystems sei nichtleer. Dann ist $\mathfrak{M} = \bigcap_{\beta \in B} \mathfrak{M}_\beta$ auch eine nichtleere APM. (Bikompaktheitseingenschaft.)

Im entgegengesetzten Falle würden nämlich eine $M \in \mathfrak{M}$ und eine endliche Zerteilung $M = M^1 \cup \ldots \cup M^k$ existieren, so dass jede M^i von einer $M_i \in \mathfrak{M}$ weit sei. Die Mengen $M, M_1, \ldots, M_k$ müssten dann in dem Systeme $\mathfrak{M}_{\beta(0)}, \mathfrak{M}_{\beta(1)}, \ldots, \mathfrak{M}_{\beta(k)}$ vorkommen. So führt das leere Wesen des Durchschnitts $\mathfrak{M}_{\beta(0)} \cap \mathfrak{M}_{\beta(1)} \cap \ldots \cap \mathfrak{M}_{\beta(k)}$ zu einem Widerspruch.

Wie wir sahen, durch die abgeschlossenen Pseudomengen werden die abgeschlossenen Teilmengen der bikompakten Ausdehnung von P bestimmt. Dagegen können verschiedene APM dieselbe Menge bestimmen. Um eine eineindeutige Zuordnung zu erreichen, führen wir den Begriff der Äquivalenz von APM ein.

11. Definition. Zwei APM $\mathfrak{M}_1$ und $\mathfrak{M}_2$ werden *äquivalent* genannt: $\mathfrak{M}_1 \sim \mathfrak{M}_2$, wenn bei jeder APM $\mathfrak{N}$ die Bedingungen $(\mathfrak{M}_1 \cap \mathfrak{N}) \sim \lambda$ und $(\mathfrak{M}_2 \cap \mathfrak{N}) \sim \lambda$ gleichzeitig erfüllt oder gleichzeitig nicht erfüllt sind.

Diese Relation ist offenbar eine *Äquivalenzrelation*. Daher werden die abgeschlossenen Pseudomengen in *Äquivalenzklassen* zerfallen.

Die Klasse einer APM $\mathfrak{M}$ wird mit $\langle\mathfrak{M}\rangle$ bezeichnet.

12. *Aus* $\mathfrak{M}_1 \sim \mathfrak{M}_2$ *folgt* $(\mathfrak{M}_1 \cap \mathfrak{M}_2) \sim \mathfrak{M}_1$.

Beweis. Sei $\mathfrak{N}$ eine beliebige APM. Aus $\mathfrak{M}_1 \cap \mathfrak{N} \sim \lambda$ folgt nach (7a) $(\mathfrak{M}_1 \cap \cap \mathfrak{M}_2) \cap \mathfrak{N} \sim \lambda$. Setzen wir jetzt voraus, dass $\mathfrak{M}_1 \cap \mathfrak{N}$ nichtleer ist. Sei $N = N^1 \cup \cup \ldots \cup N^k$ eine beliebige endliche Zerteilung einer Menge N des Systems $\mathfrak{N}$. Dann kann man wegen (9) eine N^i finden, für die $\mathfrak{M}_1 \cap \mathfrak{N} \cap \{N^i\}$ nichtleer ist. Daraus folgt wegen $\mathfrak{M}_1 \sim \mathfrak{M}_2$, dass $\mathfrak{M}_2 \cap (\mathfrak{N} \cap \{N^i\})$ auch nichtleer ist. N^i liegt daher zu jeder Menge der Systeme $\mathfrak{M}_1, \mathfrak{M}_2$ und $\mathfrak{N}$ nahe. Deshalb ist nach (5) und (8) $(\mathfrak{M}_1 \cap \mathfrak{M}_2 \cap \cap \mathfrak{N}) \nsim \lambda$.

13. *Es seien* $\mathfrak{M}_\beta$; $(\beta \in B)$ *abgeschlossene Pseudomengen aus einer beliebigen Äquivalenzklasse. Die APM* $\mathfrak{M} = \bigcap_{\beta \in B} \mathfrak{M}_\beta$ *gehört dann zu derselben Äquivalenzklasse.*

Beweis. Zuerst bemerken wir, dass wenn die Indexmenge B endlich ist, so ist (13) eine unmittelbare Folge des Satzes (12).

Es sei B eine beliebige Indexmenge. Sei $\mathfrak{N}$ eine beliebige APM. Aus $(\mathfrak{M} \cap \mathfrak{N}) \nsim \lambda$ folgt nach (7a) $(\mathfrak{M}_\beta \cap \mathfrak{N}) \nsim \lambda$ für jedes $\beta \in B$.

Setzen wir jetzt voraus, dass $(\mathfrak{M}_\beta \cap \mathfrak{N}) \nsim \lambda$ für ein und daher für jedes $\beta \in B$. So ist nach der obigen Bemerkung für jedes endliche Teilsystem $\mathfrak{M}_{\beta_1}, \mathfrak{M}_{\beta_2}, \ldots, \mathfrak{M}_{\beta_k}$ in der Tat $(\mathfrak{M}_{\beta_1} \cap \ldots \cap \mathfrak{M}_{\beta_k}) \cap \mathfrak{N} \nsim \lambda$, und daher auch $(\mathfrak{M}_{\beta_1} \cap \mathfrak{M}_{\beta 2} \cap \ldots \cap \mathfrak{M}_{\beta_k}) \nsim \lambda$. Das System $[\mathfrak{N}, \mathfrak{M}_\beta; (\beta \in B)]$ ist also zentriert, und so ist nach (10)

$$\bigcap_{\beta \in B} \mathfrak{M}_\beta \cap \mathfrak{N} = \mathfrak{M} \cap \mathfrak{N} \nsim \lambda .$$

14. Definition. Das System $\{\mathfrak{M}_\beta; (\beta \in B)\}$ sei eine Äquivalenzklasse $\langle\mathfrak{M}_1'\rangle$. Nach (13) gehört die APM $\mathfrak{M} = \bigcap_{\beta \in B} \mathfrak{M}_\beta$ zu derselben Klasse, und daher kann man diese Klasse durch die Menge $\mathfrak{M}$ charakterisieren. Diese Menge wird *charakteristische Menge* der Klasse $\langle\mathfrak{M}_1'\rangle$ genannt, und mit $\langle\mathfrak{M}_1'\rangle^*$ bezeichnet.

Sei $\mathfrak{M}$ eine beliebige APM. So schreiben wir im folgenden statt $\langle\mathfrak{M}\rangle^*$ kurz $\mathfrak{M}^*$.

15. Die charakteristischen Mengen kann man offenbar auch durch die folgende Vollständigkeitseigenschaft bestimmen:

Die APM $\mathfrak{M}$ ist dann und nur dann eine charakteristische Menge, wenn sie mit keiner grösseren APM äquivalent ist, oder anders ausgedrückt, wenn aus $(\{M\} \cap \cap \mathfrak{M}) \sim \mathfrak{M}$ die Tatsache $M \in \mathfrak{M}$ folgt.

Ein einfaches Beispiel zur Bildung der charakteristischen Menge ist das folgende:

16. Sei M eine beliebige Teilmenge von P. Die Menge N gehört dann und nur dann zu $\{M\}^*$, wenn $M \subset \bar{N}^P$ ist.

Diese Tatsache ist eine unmittelbare Folge von (15) und (7b).

Für die charakteristischen Mengen wird auch die Vereinigung erklärt:

17. Definition. Es sei $\{\mathfrak{M}_\beta^*; (\beta \in B)\}$ ein System von charakteristischen Mengen. Dann wird *die Vereinigung* $\mathfrak{M}$ der Mengen $\mathfrak{M}_\beta^*$ — $\mathfrak{M} = \bigcup_{\beta \in B} \mathfrak{M}_\beta^*$ — als der Durchschnitt der Mengensysteme $\{\mathfrak{M}_\beta^*\}$ erklärt. Das heisst, es ist $M \in \mathfrak{M}$ dann und nur dann, wenn für jedes β: $M \in \mathfrak{M}_\beta$ ist.

18. Ohne den Beweis zu geben, erwähnen wir, dass die Vereinigung von charakteristischen Mengen wiederum eine charakteristische Menge ist. Diese Tatsache wird im folgenden nicht gebraucht.

19. Es sei $M \subset P$, und sei $M = \bigcup_{\beta \in B} M_\beta$ eine beliebige Zerteilung der Menge M. So ist nach (16) offenbar

$$\{M\}^* = \bigcup_{\beta \in B} \{M_\beta\}^* .$$

Nach diesen Vorbereitungen bilden wir den Begriff des idealen Punktes.

20. Definition. Eine APM $\mathfrak{A}$ wird *ein idealer Punkt* genannt, wenn $\mathfrak{A} \nsim \lambda$ und wenn bei einer beliebigen $\mathfrak{N}$ die Beziehung $\mathfrak{A} \cap \mathfrak{N} = \mathfrak{A}$ eine Folge der Relation $(\mathfrak{A} \cap \mathfrak{N}) \nsim \lambda$ ist.

Die Menge der idealen Punkte wird mit $\mathscr{R}$ bezeichnet.

21. Die idealen Punkte sind offenbar die vollständigen nichtleeren abgeschlossenen Pseudomengen, d. h. sie sind in keinem grösseren nichtleeren Systeme enthalten. Daher ist ein idealer Punkt immer eine charakteristische Menge.

Nach (9) folgt daraus, dass die idealen Punkte den die Bedingungen 1—4 erfüllenden *Riesz*schen Punkten gleich sind.

22. Sei (a) eine beliebige einpunktige Teilmenge von P. Dann ist $\{(a)\}^*$ offenbar ein idealer Punkt; wir werden ihn weiterhin mit a identifizieren. Bei dieser Auffassung ist offensichtlich $P \subset \mathscr{R}$.

23. Definition. Betrachten wir eine beliebige APM $\mathfrak{N}$. Die Menge der die Bedingung $(\mathfrak{A} \cap \mathfrak{N}) \nsim \lambda$ erfüllenden idealen Punkte wird *der Körper* der APM $\mathfrak{N}$ genannt und mit $\widetilde{\mathfrak{N}}$ bezeichnet.

24. Der Körper eines idealen Punktes $\mathfrak{A}$ ist die einpunktige Menge $(\mathfrak{A})$. Es ist nämlich $\mathfrak{A} \cap \mathfrak{A} = \mathfrak{A} \nsim \lambda$, und daher $\mathfrak{A} \in \widetilde{\mathfrak{A}}$; ferner ist bei einem die Bedingung

$(\mathfrak{A} \cap \mathfrak{B}) \nsim \lambda$ erfüllenden idealen Punkte in der Tat $\mathfrak{B} = \mathfrak{A} \cap \mathfrak{B} = \mathfrak{A}$, d. h. aus $\mathfrak{B} \in \widetilde{\mathfrak{A}}$ folgt $\mathfrak{B} = \mathfrak{A}$.

25. *Der Körper einer leeren APM ist offenbar die leere Menge* $\varnothing$.

26. *Da bei jedem idealen Punkt* $\mathfrak{A} = \{M_\alpha; (\alpha \in A)\}$ *die Menge P zwischen den Mengen* M_α *vorkommt, ist* $\widetilde{\{P\}} = \mathscr{R}$.

27. *Aus* $\mathfrak{M}_1 \sim \mathfrak{M}_2$ *folgt nach* (11), (20) *und* (25) $\widetilde{\mathfrak{M}}_1 = \widetilde{\mathfrak{M}}_2$.

28. *Ist der ideale Punkt* $\mathfrak{A} = \{M_\alpha; (\alpha \in A)\}$ *kein Element der Menge* $\widetilde{\mathfrak{N}}$, *wo* $\mathfrak{N} = \{N_\beta; (\beta \in B)\}$, *so kann man eine* $M_{\alpha'} \in \mathfrak{A}$ *und eine* $N_{\beta'} \in \mathfrak{N}$ *finden, so dass* $M_{\alpha'}\, \bar{\delta}\, \mathfrak{N}_{\beta'}$ *sei.*

Aus $(\mathfrak{A} \cap \mathfrak{N}) \sim \lambda$ folgt nämlich, dass bei einer beliebigen $M_{\alpha''}$ eine solche endliche Zerteilung $M_{\alpha''} = M^1_{\alpha''} \cup \ldots \cup M^k_{\alpha''}$ gebe, bei welcher jede $M^i_{\alpha''}$ $(i = 1, \ldots, k)$ von wenigstens einer der Mengen des System $\mathfrak{A} \cup \mathfrak{N}$ weit ist. Nach der Bedingung 2. von Riesz gibt es eine solche $M^j_{\alpha''}$, die im Systeme $\mathfrak{A}$ vorkommt, Es ist also $M^j_{\alpha''} = M_{\alpha'} \in \mathfrak{A}$ nahe zu sämtlichen M_α, sie muss daher von einer $N_{\beta'} \in \mathfrak{N}$ weit sein.

29. *Aus* $\mathfrak{M} = \bigcap_{\beta \in B} \mathfrak{M}_\beta$ *folgt* $\widetilde{\mathfrak{M}} = \bigcap_{\beta \in B} \widetilde{\mathfrak{M}}_\beta$.

Beweis. a) Ist $\mathfrak{A} \in \widetilde{\mathfrak{M}}$, so ist $\mathfrak{A} \cap \mathfrak{M} \nsim \lambda$, $\mathfrak{A} \cap \mathfrak{M}_\beta \nsim \lambda\ (\beta \in B)$, $\mathfrak{A} \in \widetilde{\mathfrak{M}}_\beta\ (\beta \in B)$, folglich $\mathfrak{A} \in \bigcap_{\beta \in B} \widetilde{\mathfrak{M}}_\beta$.

b) Ist $\mathfrak{A} \in \bigcap_{\beta \in B} \widetilde{\mathfrak{M}}_\beta$, d. h. $\mathfrak{A} \cap \mathfrak{M}_\beta = \mathfrak{A}\ (\beta \in B)$, so ist $\mathfrak{A} \cap \mathfrak{M} = \mathfrak{A} \cap (\bigcap_{\beta \in B} \mathfrak{M}_\beta) = \bigcap_{\beta \in B} (\mathfrak{A} \cap \mathfrak{M}_\beta) = \bigcap_{\beta \in B} \mathfrak{A} = \mathfrak{A}$, und daher ist $\mathfrak{A} \in \widetilde{\mathfrak{M}}$.

30. *Es seien* $\mathfrak{N}_1$ *und* $\mathfrak{N}_2$ *abgeschlossene Pseudomengen. Dann ist* $\widetilde{\mathfrak{N}}_1 \cup \widetilde{\mathfrak{N}}_2$ *der Körper einer APM; und zwar ist*

$$\widetilde{\mathfrak{N}}_1 \cup \widetilde{\mathfrak{N}}_2 = \widetilde{\mathfrak{N}^*_1 \cup \mathfrak{N}^*_2}\,.$$

Beweis. Nach (27) und (17) ist offenbar

$$\widetilde{\mathfrak{N}}_1 \cup \widetilde{\mathfrak{N}}_2 = \widetilde{\mathfrak{N}}^*_1 \cup \widetilde{\mathfrak{N}}^*_2 \subset \widetilde{\mathfrak{N}^*_1 \cup \mathfrak{N}^*_2}\,.$$

Wir haben daher nur noch die Gültigkeit von

$$\widetilde{\mathfrak{N}^*_1 \cup \mathfrak{N}^*_2} \subset \widetilde{\mathfrak{N}}^1_* \cup \widetilde{\mathfrak{N}}^*_2$$

zu beweisen.

Sei $\mathfrak{A} = \{M_\alpha; (\alpha \in A)\}$ ein die Bedingungen $\mathfrak{A} \notin \widetilde{\mathfrak{N}}^*_1$ und $\mathfrak{A} \notin \widetilde{\mathfrak{N}}^*_2$ erfüllender idealer Punkt. Wählen wir die Bedingungen $M_{\alpha_1}\, \bar{\delta}\, N_1$ und $M_{\alpha_2}\, \bar{\delta}\, N_2$ erfüllenden Mengen $M_{\alpha_1} \in \mathfrak{A}$, $M_{\alpha_2} \in \mathfrak{A}$, $N_1 \in \mathfrak{N}^*_1$, $N_2 \in \mathfrak{N}^*_2$; wegen (28) ist das möglich. Nehmen wir eine solche Umgebung U von M_{α_1}, die noch immer weit von N_1 ist; d. h. $U\, \bar{\delta}\, N_1$ und $(P - U)\, \bar{\delta}\, M_{\alpha_1}$.

Betrachten wir die Zerteilung $(M_{\alpha_2} \cap U) \cup (M_{\alpha_2} \cap (P - U))$ der Menge M_{α_2}. Da einer der zwei Teilen zur $\mathfrak{A}$ gehört, und $(M_{\alpha_2} \cap (P - U))\, \bar{\delta}\, M_{\alpha_1}$ gilt, so ist $M_{\alpha_2} \cap$

$\cap U = M_{\alpha_3} \in \mathfrak{A}$. Aus $M_{\alpha_3} \bar{\delta} N_1$ und $M_{\alpha_3} \bar{\delta} N_2$ folgt aber $M_{\alpha_3} \bar{\delta} (N_1 \cup N_2)$, und da $N_1 \cup N_2$ zur APM $\mathfrak{N}_1^* \cup \mathfrak{N}_2^*$ gehört, ist $\mathfrak{A} \cap (\mathfrak{N}_1^* \cup \mathfrak{N}_2^*) \sim \lambda$,

$$\text{und daher } \mathfrak{A} \notin \widetilde{\mathfrak{N}_1^* \cup \mathfrak{N}_2^*}.$$

31. Aus $\mathfrak{M} \nsim \lambda$ folgt $\widetilde{\mathfrak{M}} \neq \varnothing$, d. h. zur jeden nichtleeren APM gehört ein idealer Punkt — oder, anders ausgedrückt —, jede nichtleere APM kann man durch Hinzunahme einiger Teilmengen von P zu einer vollständigen nichtleeren APM ergänzen.

Dies folgt auf Grund des Zornschen Lemmas aus (10).

Nach diesen Vorbereitungen kommen wir zum Beweis der Existenz der bikompakten Ausdehnung der Nachbarschaftsräume. Der Existenzsatz wird folgendermassen formuliert:

Satz 2. *Es sei P ein beliebiger Nachbarschaftsraum. Dann gibt es einen den Raum P als dichten Unterraum enthaltenden bikompakten Hausdorffschen Nachbarschaftsraum $\mathscr{R}$.*

Beweis. Es sei P ein Nachbarschaftsraum. Sei $\mathscr{R}$ die Menge der idealen Punkte von P. Die abgeschlossenen Teilmengen von $\mathscr{R}$ seien die Körper der APM. Infolge (25), (6), (26), (29), (30), (10), (31) und (24) wird dadurch ein ebenfalls mit $\mathscr{R}$ bezeichneter bikompakter T_1-Raum definiert. $\mathscr{R}$ ist sogar ein T_2-Raum.

Betrachten wir nämlich zwei verschiedene Punkte $\mathfrak{A} = \{M_\alpha; (\alpha \in A)\}$ und $\mathfrak{B} = \{\mathfrak{N}_\beta; (\beta \in B)\}$ des $\mathscr{R}$. Aus $\mathfrak{A} \cap \mathfrak{B} \sim \lambda$ folgt dann nach (28) die Existenz der die Bedingung $M_{\alpha'} \bar{\delta} N_{\beta'}$ erfüllenden Mengen $M_{\alpha'} \in \mathfrak{A}$ und $N_{\beta'} \in \mathfrak{B}$. Betrachten wir eine von $N_{\beta'}$ weite Umgebung U der Menge $M_{\alpha'}$ in P, d. h. $U \bar{\delta} N_{\beta'}$ und $(P-U) \bar{\delta} M_{\alpha'}$. Daraus folgt, dass $\mathfrak{B} \notin \widetilde{\{U\}}$ und $\mathfrak{A} \notin \widetilde{\{P-U\}}$. Wegen (26), (27), (19) und (30) ist dann

$$\mathscr{R} = \widetilde{\{P\}} = \widetilde{\{P\}^*} = \widetilde{\{U\}^* \cup \{P-U\}^*} = \widetilde{\{U\}^*} \cup \widetilde{\{P-U\}^*} = \widetilde{\{U\}} \cup \widetilde{\{P-U\}}.$$

Wir haben damit die die Punkte $\mathfrak{A}$ bzw. $\mathfrak{B}$ erhaltenden disjunkten im $\mathscr{R}$ offenen Mengen $\mathscr{R} - \widetilde{\{P-U\}}$ und $\mathscr{R} - \widetilde{\{U\}}$ gefunden. $\mathscr{R}$ ist also tatsächlich ein Bikompakt.

Im folgenden werden wir den durch den Bikompakt $\mathscr{R}$ eindeutig bestimmten Nachbarschaftsraum auch mit $\mathscr{R}$ bezeichnen.

Für das Weitere ist es notwendig, die abgeschlossene Hülle einer beliebigen Teilmenge $\mathscr{N}$ des Raumes $\mathscr{R}$ einfach auszudrücken. Es ist in der Tat:

$$\overline{\mathscr{N}}^{\mathscr{R}} = \widetilde{\bigcup_{\mathfrak{A} \in \mathscr{N}} \mathfrak{A}}.$$

Nach (29) ist nämlich $\overline{\mathscr{N}}^{\mathscr{R}} = \bigcap_{\mathscr{N} \subset \widetilde{\mathfrak{M}}} \widetilde{\mathfrak{M}} = \widetilde{\bigcap_{\mathscr{N} \subset \widetilde{\mathfrak{M}}} \mathfrak{M}}$. $\mathscr{N} \subset \widetilde{\mathfrak{M}}$ bedeutet aber, dass $\mathfrak{A} \cap \mathfrak{M} = \mathfrak{A}$ für jeden $\mathfrak{A} \in \mathscr{N}$. Die Konsequenzen dieser letzten Bemerkung sind aber einerseits $\mathscr{N} \subset \widetilde{\bigcup_{\mathfrak{A} \in \mathscr{N}} \mathfrak{A}}$ und anderseits, dass aus $\mathscr{N} \subset \widetilde{\mathfrak{M}}$ — $(\bigcup_{\mathfrak{A} \in \mathscr{N}} \mathfrak{A}) \cap \mathfrak{M} = \bigcup_{\mathfrak{A} \in \mathscr{N}} \mathfrak{A}$ folgt. (S. auch (17).) Infolgedessen ist tatsächlich

$$\overline{\mathscr{N}}^{\mathscr{R}} = \widetilde{\bigcap_{\mathscr{N} \subset \widetilde{\mathfrak{M}}} \mathfrak{M}} = \widetilde{\bigcup_{\mathfrak{A} \in \mathscr{N}} \mathfrak{A}}.$$

In dem speziellen Falle, dass $\mathscr{N}$ einer Teilmenge M von P gleich ist (S. (22)), ist nach (22), (19) und (27)

$$\overline{\mathscr{N}}^{\mathscr{R}} = \overline{M}^{\mathscr{R}} = \bigcup_{a \in M} \widetilde{\{(a)\}^*} = \widetilde{\{\bigcup_{a \in M} (a)\}^*} = \widetilde{\{M\}^*} = \widetilde{\{M\}} .$$

Aus dieser Tatsache folgt sogleich nach (26), dass $\overline{P}^{\mathscr{R}} = \widetilde{\{P\}} = \mathscr{R}$ ist, d. h. P ist eine überall dichte Teilmenge des Raumes $\mathscr{R}$.

Wir müssen noch beweisen, dass der Nachbarschaftsraum P ein Unterraum des Nachbarschaftsraumes $\mathscr{R}$ ist. Betrachten wir dazu zwei beliebige Teilmengen M und N des Nachbarschaftsraumes P. Es ist nach (29) und (2)

$$\overline{M}^{\mathscr{R}} \cap \overline{N}^{\mathscr{R}} = \widetilde{\{M\}} \cap \widetilde{\{N\}} = \widetilde{\{M\} \cap \{N\}} = \widetilde{\{M, N\}} .$$

Wenn also $M \bar{\delta} N$, so ist nach (6) $\{M, N\} \sim \lambda$; wegen (25) ist daher $\overline{M}^{\mathscr{R}} \cap \overline{N}^{\mathscr{R}} = \widetilde{\{M, N\}} = \varnothing$.

Wenn aber $M \delta N$, so ist $\{M, N\} \nsim \lambda$, und wegen (31) folgt

$$\overline{M}^{\mathscr{R}} \cap \overline{N}^{\mathscr{R}} = \widetilde{\{M, N\}} \neq \varnothing .$$

Damit haben wir Satz II vollkommen bewiesen.

Literaturverzeichnis

[1] *Á. Császár-S. Mrówka;* Sur la compactification des espaces de proximité. Fund. Math., *46* (1958), 195—207.

[2] *В. А. Ефремович:* Геометрия влизости I. Мат. сб. (31), *73* (1952), 189—200.

[3] *F. Riesz*: Stetigkeitsbegriff und abstrakte Mengenlehre. Atti del IV Congresso Intern. dei Matem., Bologna, *2* (1908), 18–24.

[4] *Ю. М. Смирнов:* О пространствах близости. Мат. сб. (31), *73* (1952), 543—574.

ТОПОЛОГИЧЕСКИЕ ПОЛУПОЛЯ И ИХ ПРИМЕНЕНИЯ

В. БОЛТЯНСКИЙ

Москва

В работе [1] нами было введено понятие топологического полуполя. В докладе приводится определение топологического полуполя, теорема классификации для полуполей и некоторые применения к вполне регулярным топологическим пространствам, пространствам близости и равномерным структурам. Излагаемые здесь результаты были получены совместно М. Я. Антоновским, Т. А. Сарымсаковым и автором доклада.

Коммутативное ассоциативное топологическое кольцо E называется топологическим полуполем, если в E выделено некоторое множество K, удовлетворяющее следующим аксиомам:

1. $K + \overline{K} \subset K$, $K . K \subset K$;
2. $K - K = E$;
3. Если $M \subset \overline{K}$ — такое множество, что пересечение $\bigcap\limits_{x \in M} (\overline{K} + x)$ непусто, то существует такой элемент $y \in \overline{K}$, что

$$\bigcap_{x \in M} (\overline{K} + x) = \overline{K} + y ;$$

4. При $\alpha, \beta \in K$ уравнение $\alpha x = \beta$ имеет в K хотя бы одно решение;
5. Пересечение $\overline{K} \cap (-\overline{K})$ содержит только нуль (нулевой элемент кольца E);
6. Обозначим через F_α $(\alpha \in E)$ совокупность всех элементов $x \in E$, удовлетворяющих условию $\alpha x \in \overline{K}$. Тогда совокупность всех множеств вида $\beta + F_\alpha$ $(\alpha, \beta \in E)$ образует базисную систему замкнутых множеств топологического пространства E; иначе говоря, всякое замкнутое множество пространства E может быть получено из множеств вида $\beta + F_\alpha$ с помощью операций пересечения и конечного об'единения.

Элементы полуполя E, содержащиеся в K, называются *положительными*. Соотношения $x > 0$, $x \geqq 0$, $x > y$, $x \geqq y$ означают соответственно, что $x \in K$, $x \in \overline{K}$, $x - y \in K$, $x - y \in \overline{K}$.

Простейший пример полуполя строится следующим образом. Пусть Δ — произвольное множество. Обозначим через E совокупность всех действительных функций на множестве Δ, а через K $(= K_\Delta)$ — совокупность всех положительных действительных функций на Δ. Тогда, рассматривая в E обычные операции сложения и умножения функций и вводя в E тихоновскую топологию, мы получим полуполе, которое будем в дальнейшем обозначать через R_Δ. В этом полуполе множество $\overline{K}_\Delta$ состоит из всех неотрицательных действительных функций на Δ.

Оказывается, что с помощью полуполей вида R'_Δ можно дать описание всех вообще полуполей. Для формулировки соответствующей теоремы мы введем понятие *остова*. Пусть Δ — произвольное множество, R_Δ — соответствующее полуполе и K_Δ — множество всех его положительных элементов. Множество $\Sigma \subset \overline{K}_\Delta$ мы будем называть *остовом* на множестве Δ, если выполняются следующие два условия:

а) в множестве Σ существует такой элемент σ, что $\sigma \geqq 1$;

б) каковы бы ни были элементы $x, y \in \Sigma$, существуют такие элементы $\sigma_1, \sigma_2 \in \Sigma$, что $x + y \leqq \sigma_1$, $xy \leqq \sigma_2$.

Теорема. *Пусть Δ — произвольное множество и Σ — некоторый остов на нем. Обозначим через E_Σ множество всех элементов x полуполя R_Δ, для каждого из которых существует такой элемент $\sigma_x \in \Sigma$, что $|x| \leqq \sigma_x$. Тогда E_Σ есть подполуполе полуполя R_Δ; множество K_Σ его положительных элементов состоит из всех тех элементов $x \in K_\Sigma$, для которых выполнены включения $x \in E_\Sigma$, $x^{-1} \in E_\Sigma$. Обратно, любое полуполе представимо в таком виде. Более точно, если E — произвольное полуполе и Δ — множество всех его неразложимых корней* (см. [1]), *то на множестве Δ существует такой остов Σ, что полуполя E и E_Σ изоморфны* (причем изоморфизм устанавливается отображением φ, построенным в п. 10.2 работы [1]).

Приведем примеры к сформулированной теореме:

Пример 1. Примем за Σ множество всех положительных постоянных функций на Δ. Очевидно, что условия а) и б) в определении остова выполнены. Ясно, далее, что E_Σ состоит из всех ограниченных действительных функций на Δ. Согласно доказанной теореме, множество E_Σ (в индуцированной топологии) является полуполем. Множество K_Σ его положительных элементов состоит из всех положительных функций x на Δ, для которых $x \in E_\Sigma$, $x^{-1} \in E_\Sigma$. Иначе говоря, функция x тогда и только тогда принадлежит K_Σ, когда верхняя и нижняя грани ее значений на Δ существуют и положительны.

Пример 2. Пусть Δ — множество всех натуральных чисел, так что R_Δ состоит из всех последовательностей $(x_1, x_2, \ldots, x_r, \ldots)$ действительных чисел. Обозначим через Σ множество всех последовательностей вида

$$x_n = ae^{bn}, \quad n = 1, 2, \ldots,$$

где a и b — положительные числа. Легко видеть, что условия а) и б) выполняются, т. е. Σ есть остов на множестве Δ. Соответствующее полуполе E_Σ состоит из всех последовательностей, имеющих не более чем экспоненциальный рост, т. е. $\{x_n\} \in E_\Sigma$ тогда и только тогда, когда существуют такие положительные числа a и b, что

$$|x_n| < ae^{bn}, \quad n = 1, 2, \ldots$$

Согласно сформулированной теореме, множество K_Σ состоит из всех последовательностей $\{x_n\}$ положительных чисел, для которых обе последовательности $\{x_n\}$, $\{x_n^{-1}\}$ имеют не более чем экспоненциальный рост. Иначе говоря, последовательность $\{x_n\}$ тогда и только тогда принадлежит K_Σ, когда существуют такие действительные числа $a > 0$, $b > 0$, μ и ν, что

$$ae^{\mu n} < x_n < be^{\nu n}, \quad n = 1, 2, \ldots$$

Напомним теперь введенное в [1] понятие метрического пространства над полуполем. Пусть E — некоторое полуполе и K — множество всех его положительных элементов. Множество X будем называть *метрическим пространством* над полуполем E, если задано отображение (называемое *метрикой*)

$$\varrho : X \times X \to \overline{K},$$

удовлетворяющее следующим условиям $(x, y, z \in X)$:

1. $\varrho(x, y) = 0$ тогда и только тогда, когда $x = y$;
2. $\varrho(x, y) = \varrho(y, x)$;
3. $\varrho(x, y) + \varrho(y, z) \geqq \varrho(x, z)$.

Если U — произвольная окрестность нуля в метризующем полуполе E и $x \in X$, то через $\Omega(x, U)$ мы будем обозначать множество всех тех элементов $y \in X$, для которых $\varrho(x, y) \in U$. Совокупность всех множеств вида $\Omega(x, U)$ может быть принята за базу окрестностей в X (см. [1], п. 11,1). Получаемая таким образом топология называется *естественной топологией* метрического пространства X. Как показано в [1] (см. п. п. 11.4, 11.5), *естественная топология всегда является вполне регулярной и обратно, любое вполне регулярное топологическое пространство может быть метризовано над некоторым полуполем.*

Изложим теперь некоторые применения к равномерным структурам и пространствам близости. При этом равномерные структуры мы будем рассматривать только в смысле Вейля, а пространства близости — только такие, для которых соответствующая топология вполне регулярна.

Пусть X — метрическое пространство над полуполем E. Для любой окрестности нуля V в полуполе E мы обозначим через V^* совокупность всех тех точек $(x, y) \in X \times X$, для которых $\varrho(x, y) \in V$. Тогда совокупность $\mathscr{V}$ всех множеств вида V^* образует базу некоторой равномерной структуры на множестве X.

Эту структуру мы будем называть *естественной равномерной структурой* метрического пространства X. Оказывается, что *естественная топология этой равномерной структуры совпадает с естественной топологией метрического пространства X.*

Далее, пусть F — равномерная структура на множестве X. Тогда существует такая метрика $\varrho : X \times X \to E$ над некоторым полуполем E, что естественная равномерная структура получающегося метрического пространства (X, ϱ, E) совпадает с исходной равномерной структурой F. Коротко говоря, *всякая равномерная структура может быть метризована над некоторым полуполем E.*

Доказательство использует известный процесс Фринка-Читтендена построения непрерывных функций. Используя эту метризационную теорему для равномерных структур, можно весьма просто доказать ряд известных теорем о равномерных структурах, а также некоторые новые предложения. Так, например,

всякая равномерная структура может быть пополнена, т. е. может быть включена в качестве подструктуры в некоторую полную структуру;

пусть F — некоторая равномерная структура на множестве X; пространство X (в естественной топологии) тогда и только тогда компактно, когда равномерная структура F вполне ограниченна и полна;

всякая топологическая группа G допускает инвариантную метризацию над некоторым полуполем E, т. е. существует такая метрика $\varrho : G \times G \to E$, что $\varrho(x, y) = \varrho(ax, ay)$ для любых элементов $a, x, y \in G$ (обобщение теоремы Какутани [2]).

Таким образом, мы имеем четыре об'екта: вполне регулярная топология, близость, равномерная структура, метрика (над некоторым полуполем). Между этими об'ектами существуют следующие связи. Всякая метрика ϱ на X индуцирует естественную равномерность на X, которую мы обозначим через $w(\varrho)$, естественную близость $e(\varrho)$ и естественную топологию $t(\varrho)$ на X. Далее, всякая равномерная структура F на X индуцирует естественную близость на X, которую мы обозначим через $e(F)$, и естественную топологию $t(F)$. Наконец, всякая близость δ на X индуцирует естественную топологию $t(\delta)$ на X. Имеют место следующие формулы:

$$t(e(w(\varrho))) = t(e(\varrho)) = t(w(\varrho)) = t(\varrho)\,,$$
$$e(w(\varrho)) = e(\varrho)\,, \quad t(e(F)) = t(F)\,.$$

Кроме того, каждая вполне регулярная топология на X индуцируется некоторой (вообще говоря, не определенной однозначно) близостью на X, каждая близость индуцируется некоторой (вообще говоря, не определенной однозначно) равномерной структурой, а каждая равномерная структура — некоторой (также, вообще говоря, не определенной однозначно) метрикой. Иначе говоря, если мы обозначим через $T(X)$ множество всех вполне регулярных топологий на X, через $E(X)$ — множество всех близостей на X, через $W(X)$ — множество всех равномерных структур на X и через $M(X)$ — множество всех метрик (над произвольными полуполями) на X, то естественные отображения w, e, t, указанные выше:

$$T(X) \xleftarrow{t} E(X) \xleftarrow{e} W(X) \xleftarrow{w} \boldsymbol{M}(X)$$

оказываются во всех случаях отображениями *на все множество*.

В множествах $T(X)$, $E(X)$, $W(X)$ можно ввести естественным образом частичное упорядочение. Мы рассмотрим здесь в качестве примера только частичное упорядочение в множестве $W(X)$. Именно, если F_1 и F_2 — равномерные структуры на X, то мы будем говорить, что $F_1 \geqq F_2$, если $F_1 \supset F_2$(т. е. из $Q \in F_2$ следует, что $Q \in F_1$). Использование метрики над полуполями позволяет легко решить вопрос о существовании максимальной (в смысле указанного упорядочения) равномерной структуры, индуцирующей данную топологию. Именно, пусть

$$\varrho_\alpha : X \times X \to E_\alpha , \quad \alpha \in A ,$$

— семейство метрик, заданных на одном и том же множестве X. Обозначим через E прямое произведение всех полуполей E_α, $\alpha \in A$. Элементом полуполя E является всякая функция f, заданная на A и принимающая значения, удовлетворяющие условию $f(\alpha) \in E_\alpha$ $(\alpha \in A)$. Далее, определим отображение

$$\varrho : X \times X \to E ,$$

принимая за $\varrho(x, y)$ функцию на A, принимающую на α значение $\varrho_\alpha(x, y)$. Легко проверяется, что отображение ϱ представляет собой метрику на X (над полуполем E). Эту метрику мы будем называть *произведением* метрик ϱ_α. Легко проверяется, далее, что

$$w(\varrho) \geqq w(\varrho_\alpha) \quad \text{для любого} \quad \alpha \in A .$$

Наконец, если все метрики ϱ_α индуцируют одну и ту же топологию (или близость, или равномерную структуру), то метрика ϱ индуцирует ту же самую топологию (близость, равномерную структуру). Если теперь мы обозначим через $W(\tau)$ совокупность всех равномерных структур F на X, индуцирующих на X заданную топологию τ, то, выбрав для каждой структуры $F \in W(\tau)$ какую-либо метризацию $\varrho_F : X \times X \to E_F$, удовлетворяющую условию $w(\varrho_F) = F$, мы сможем затем построить произведение ϱ всех метрик ϱ_F $(F \in W(\tau))$. Эта метрика ϱ индуцирует на X ту же самую топологию τ (см. выше) и такую равномерность $w(\varrho)$, которая, в силу сказанного выше, удовлетворяет условию

$$w(\varrho) \geqq F \quad \text{для любого} \quad F \in W(\tau)$$

и, кроме того, индуцирует ту же самую топологию τ:

$$t(w(\varrho)) = t(\varrho) = \tau .$$

Таким образом, $w(\varrho)$ — максимальная равномерная структура, индуцирующая на X топологию τ.

Литература

[1] *М. Я. Антоновский*, *В. Г. Болтянский*, *Т. А. Сарымсаков:* Топологические полуполя. Изд-во СамГУ, Ташкент 1961.

[2] *S. Kakutani*: Über die Metrisation der topologischen Gruppen. Proc. Japan Acad. *12* (1936), 82–84.

ON IMBEDDINGS OF POLYHEDRA INTO EUCLIDEAN SPACES

V. BOLTJANSKI

Moscow

Let X be a topological space and E an Euclidean space. A continuous mapping $f: X \to E$ is said to be *k-regular*, if for all $(k+1)$-tuples of distinct points $x_0, x_1, \ldots, x_k$ of X the points $f(x_0), f(x_1), \ldots, f(x_k)$ are vertices of a k-dimensional simplex in E. For example, the map $f: X \to E$ is 1-regular, iff it is $1-1$; the map f is 2-regular iff the points $f(x_0), f(x_1), f(x_2)$ do not lie on a single straight line for distinct points $x_0, x_1, x_2 \in X$. This definition of a k-regular map was given by K. BORSUK.

Let us denote by $F^n(X)$ the set of all continuous maps $X \to E^n$, where E^n is an n-dimensional Euclidean space. Denote by $R_k^n(X)$ the set of all k-regular maps $X \to E^n$.

In connection with the definitions just given the following two problems arise:

Problem 1. (Borsuk). What is the smallest integer n such that the set $R_k^n(X)$ is non-void for all compact metric spaces X of dimension $\leqq p$? This smallest integer will be denoted by $n(p, k)$.

Problem 2. What is the smallest integer n such that the set $R_k^n(X)$ is dense in the metric space $F^n(X)$ for all compact metric spaces X of dimension $\leqq p$. This smallest integer will be denoted by $n'(p, k)$.

It is clear that

$$n(p, k) \leqq n'(p, k) \text{ for all } p \text{ and } k.$$

The Nöbeling-Pontrjagin imbedding theorem states that $n'(p, 1) \leqq 2p + 1$. Furthermore, the example of van KAMPEN (which is a p-dimensional skeleton of a $(2p + 2)$-dimensional simplex) shows that $n(p, 1) \geqq 2p + 1$. Consequently we have the inequalities

$$2p + 1 \leqq n(p, 1) \leqq n'(p, 1) \leqq 2p + 1$$

and it follows that $n(p, 1) = n'(p, 1) = 2p + 1$. Thus, if $k = 1$ Problem 1 coincides with Problem 2.

It is easy to prove that $n(p, 2) = 2p + 2$. To show this, let X be a p-dimensional compact metric space. Then by the Pontrjagin-Nöbeling theorem, there exists an imbedding map $X \to S^{2p+1}$, where S^{2p+1} is the unit sphere in E^{2p+2}. The composition map $X \to S^{2p+1} \to E^{2p+2}$ is obviously 2-regular (since no three points of a unit sphere can lie on a straight line). Thus we have the equalities $n(p, 1) = 2p + 1$ and $n(p, 2) =$

$= 2p + 2$. These equalities led Borsuk to the conjecture that $n(p, k) = 2p + k$. We shall show immediately that this conjecture is wrong.

We will now state four theorems.

Theorem 1. *The number $n'(p, k)$ is equal to $pk + p + k$.*

The proof is rather complicated; it is given in [1] and uses a generalisation of the notion of intersection number. This generalisation is interesting in its own right.

In virtue of the inequality $n(p, k) \leqq n'(p, k)$, theorem 1 gives us an upper estimate for the number $n(p, k)$:

$$n(p, k) \leqq pk + p + k\,.$$

We will next consider estimates from below for the number $n(p, k)$. In [2], the two following theorems are proved:

Theorem 2. *Let $f: X \to E^q$ be a k-regular map of the p-dimensional polyhedron X into E^q; then*

$$q \geqq \left[\frac{k+1}{2}\right] p + \left[\frac{k}{2}\right].$$

This theorem holds for an arbitrary polyhedron X. But if we take a sufficiently complicated polyhedron (namely, if X is the p-dimensional skeleton of a cube or simplex of large dimension), then we obtain a stronger estimate as given in the following theorem.

Theorem 3. *We have:*

$$n(p, k) \geqq \begin{cases} pk + p + q\left[\dfrac{k}{4}\right] & \text{if } k \text{ is odd}, \\ pk + q\left[\dfrac{k}{4}\right] & \text{if } k \text{ is even}. \end{cases}$$

In particular we have $n(p, 3) \geqq 3p$, which shows that Borsuk's conjecture is wrong. More precisely, Borsuk conjectured that the number k appears in $n(p, k)$ as a summand, but in fact k appears in the estimate of $n(p, k)$ from below as a multiplicative factor: $n(p, k) \geqq pk$.

In [2], we obtained an interesting application of the above theorems to the constructive theory of functions. In order to formulate this application we shall introduce some definitions.

Let X be a compact metric space and $C(X)$ the space of all real-valued continuous functions on X with the usual norm

$$\|f\| = \max_{x \in X} |f(x)|\,.$$

Furthermore, suppose that

$$f_0(x) \equiv 1\,, \quad f_1(x), \ldots, f_m(x)$$

are linearly independent elements in the Banach space $C(X)$. Let us denote by L_m the linear subspace of $C(X)$ generated by the elements $f_0, f_1, \dots, f_m$. In the constructive theory of functions, the following problem of Chebyshev plays an important rôle:

For a given function $\varphi \in C(X)$, find the polynomial of best approximation for the system $(f_0, f_1, \dots, f_m)$; that is, find an element $p^* \in L_m$ such that

$$\|\varphi - p^*\| = \min_{p \in L_m} \|\varphi - p\|.$$

A solution of Chebyshev's problem always exists, but in general it is not unique. The set $V(\varphi)$ of all polynomials giving the best approximation is a convex set in L_m, which is called the polyhedron of best approximation. The number

$$\max_{\varphi \in C(X)} \dim V(\varphi)$$

is called the Chebyshev rank of the system $(f_0, f_1, \dots, f_m)$.

Theorem 4. *Let X be a p-dimensional polyhedron and m a positive integer. Then the Chebyshev rank of any system* $(f_0 \equiv 1, f_1, \dots, f_m)$ *is not less than* $\frac{p-1}{p+1} m - \frac{q}{p+1}$. *Furthermore, there exists a system* $f_0 \equiv 1, f_1, \dots, f_m$ *on X such that its Chebyshev rank is not more than* $\frac{p}{p+1} m + \frac{2p+1}{p+1}$.

In particular, if $\dim X \geqq q$, then for $m \to \infty$ the Chebyshev rank of systems $(f_0 \equiv 1, f_1, \dots, f_m)$ increases at least as quickly the linear function $\lambda m + \mu$, where $\lambda = \frac{p-1}{p+1} > 0$; thus the Chebyshev rank tends to infiinity. In other words, only on one-dimensional polyhedra can there be a system $(f_0 \equiv 1, f_1, \dots, f_m)$ of bounded Chebyshev rank and arbitrary length m.

References

[1] *В. Г. Болтянский:* Отображения комплексов в эвклидовы пространства. Известия Ак. наук СССР, сер. матем., *23* (1959), 871—892.

[2] *В. Г. Болтянский, С. С. Рышков, Ю. А. Шашкин:* О к-регулярных вложениях и их применении к теории приближения функций. Успехи матем. наук, *15,* No 6 (1960), 125—132.

CONCERNING THE DIMENSION OF ANR-SETS

K. BORSUK

Warszawa

I shall understand here by ANR-sets only compact absolute neighbourhood retracts. These sets constitute a class of spaces which is much more general than the class of all finite polytopes. However, the ANR-sets have topological properties similar in many respects to topological properties of polytopes.

In the present communication I intend to give a simple theorem exhibiting a further analogy between the dimensional properties of ANR-sets and of polytopes.

It is a very elementary fact, that a family of n-dimensional disjoint sets lying in an n-dimensional polytope is at most countable. An analogous statement for arbitrary n-dimensional compacta is not true. For instance, the Cartesian product $Q^n \times C$ of the n-dimensional ball Q^n with the Cantor discontinuum C is an n-dimensional compactum which contains a family of $2^{\aleph_0}$ n-dimensional disjoint balls of the form $Q^n \times (x)$, with $x \in C$.

For ANR-spaces an analogous phenomenon is impossible. In fact, we have the following

Theorem. *Let X ba an ANR-set and let $\{K_\alpha\}$ be a family of n-dimensional ANR-sets lying in X and indexed by α which runs over an uncountable set A. If for every two distinct indices $\alpha, \alpha' \in A$ the dimension of the common part of K_α and $K_{\alpha'}$ is less than n, then the dimension of X is greater than* **n**.

In order to prove this theorem, let us assume that X is a subset of the Hilbert space H^ω. Since X is an ANR-set

(1) *There exists a neighbourhood U of X in H^ω and a retraction $r: U \to X$ of U to X.*

Since dim K_α is equal to n, there exists in K_α an infinite n-dimensional chain such that its boundary lies in a compactum $B_\alpha \subset K_\alpha$, and there exists a positive number ε_α such that the boundary of this chain is not homologous to zero in the generalized ball

$$Q_\alpha = \underset{x \in K_\alpha}{E} [\varrho(x, B) < \varepsilon_\alpha].$$

By an infinite chain in K_α we understand here a sequence $\{K_{\alpha,i}\}$ of n-dimensional chains lying in K_α, with coefficients belonging to arbitrary Abelian groups, in general depending on i, and with maximal diameter of simplexes converging to zero when i

tends to infinity. By the boundary of this chain we understand the infinite cycle $\{\partial K_{\alpha,i}\}$.

Hence

(2) $\{\partial K_{\alpha,i}\}$ *lies in* $B_\alpha \subset K_\alpha$ *and* $\{\partial K_{\alpha,i}\} \not\sim 0$ *in* $Q_\alpha = \underset{x \in K_\alpha}{E} [\varrho(x, B_\alpha) < \varepsilon_\alpha]$.

In general, the positive number ε_α depends on α. However, since α runs over the uncountable set A, there exists an $\varepsilon > 0$ such that $\varepsilon_\alpha > \varepsilon$ for an uncountable set of indices α. Consequently, if we replace A by its suitably chosen subset, we can assume that

(3) $$\varepsilon_\alpha > \varepsilon > 0 \textit{ for every } \alpha \in A.$$

The compacta K_α may be considered as points of the space 2^X consisting of all non-empty subcompacta of X. Since 2^X is compact and since A is uncountable, we infer easily that there exists an index β in A and a sequence $\{\alpha_m\}$ of distinct indices such that

(4) $$\lim K_{\alpha_m} = K \quad and \quad \alpha_m \neq \beta \quad for \quad m = 1, 2, \ldots$$

Since K_β is an ANR-set, we infer that

(5) *There exists a neighbourhood* V *of* K *in* H^ω *and a retraction* s *of* V *to* K_β.

Now we see easily that there exists a positive integer n_0 such that for the index $\gamma = \alpha_{m_0}$ every segment $\overline{x\, s(x)}$ (in H^ω) with $x \in K_\gamma$ lies in $U \cap V$ and that the diameter of the set $r(\overline{x\, s(x)})$ is $< \varepsilon$:

$$\overline{x\, s(x)} \subset U \cap V \quad and \quad \delta[r(\overline{x\, s(x)})] < \varepsilon \quad for\ every \quad x \in K_\gamma.$$

Setting

$$f_t(x) = r[(1-t)\,x + t\, s(x)] \quad \text{for every} \quad 0 \leqq t \leqq 1,$$

we see easily that the family of functions $\{f_t\}$ is a homotopical deformation of the set K_γ in the space X to the set K_β.

By (2) and (3), there exists in K_γ an infinite n-dimensional chain $\{K_{\gamma,i}\}$ such that the infinite cycle $\{\partial K_{\gamma,i}\}$ lies in a compactum $B_\gamma \subset K_\gamma$ and it is not homologuous to zero in the ball

$$Q_\gamma = \underset{x \in K_\gamma}{E} [\varrho(x, B_\gamma) < \varepsilon].$$

Let us consider the compactum

$$M = \bigcup_{x \in B_\gamma} (\overline{x\, s(x)}).$$

Since the diameter of the set $r(\overline{x\, s(x)})$ is smaller than ε and since $r(x) = x \in B_\gamma$, we infer that $r(M) \subset Q_\gamma$.

Evidently $f_t(x) \in r(M) \subset Q_\gamma$ for every point $x \in B_\gamma$. We conclude that there exists in the space X an infinite $(n+1)$-dimensional chain $\{\lambda_i\}$ such that

$$\partial \lambda_i = K_{\gamma,i} - s(K_{\gamma,i}) - \mu_i,$$

where $\{\mu_i\}$ is an infinite n-dimensional chain lying in Q_γ. It follows that the sequence $\{K_{\gamma,i} - s(K_{\gamma,i}) - \mu_i\}$ is an infinite n-dimensional cycle lying in the compactum $K_\beta \cup K_\gamma \cap r(M)$ and that this cycle is homologuous to zero in X. Moreover, if we apply the hypothesis that dim $(K_\beta \cap K_\gamma) < n$, we see easily that this cycle is not homologuous to zero in its carrier $K_\beta \cup K_\gamma \cup r(M)$. However the existence of a such infinite cycle implies that the dimension of the space X is greater than n. Thus the proof of the theorem is concluded.

The following **problems** remain open:

1. *Is the theorem true if the notion of ANR-sets in understand in the more general sense, without the hypothesis of compactness?*

2. *Does the theorem remain true if we replace the hypothesis that the uncountable family of sets $\{K_\alpha\}$ consists of ANR-sets, by the weaker hypothesis, that K_α are arbitrary n-dimensional compacta?*

Now I shall present two applications of this theorem: the first to the problem of existence of universal absolute retracts, and the second — to the theory of r-neighbours.

We understand by an universal n-dimensional AR-set every n-dimensional AR-set which topologically contains every other n-dimensional AR-set. Since 1-dimensional AR-sets coincide with the dendrites, that is with locally connected continua which do not contain any simple closed curve, the problem of existence of an 1-dimensional AR-set was solved many years ago by T. Ważewski ([2]), who constructed a dendrite containing topologically every other dendrite. However the question of existence of n-dimensional universal AR-sets, for $n > 1$, has remained open. By a remark due to K. Siekluck, our theorem would allow to solve this problem for $n = 2$ in the negative sense, in case we can construct an uncountable family of 2-dimensional AR-sets with the property that none of them topologically contains any 2-dimensional closed subset of another.

I shall give the idea of a construction of such a family. Consider an arbitrary sequence $\{n_k\}$ of natural numbers greater than 1, and let $P_1 = \Delta$ be a triangle in Euclidean 3-space E^3. By T_1 we understand the triangulation of P_1 consisting of the triangle Δ and all its sides and vertices. Consider a system of n_1 triangles $\Delta_1, \ldots, \Delta_{n_1}$ lying in the interior of the triangle Δ and satisfying the following two conditions:

1. The barycenter b_Δ of Δ is the common vertex of $\Delta_1, \ldots, \Delta_{n_1}$.
2. $\Delta_i \cap \Delta_j = (b_\Delta)$ for $i \neq j$.

Now let ε_1 be a positive number and let $\overline{a_\Delta b_\Delta}$ be a segment of length ε_1, perpendicular to the triangle Δ. Consider the system of $3n_1$ triangles $\Delta'_1, \ldots, \Delta'_{3n_1}$ which are spanned by the point a_Δ and by all sides of the triangles $\Delta_1, \ldots, \Delta_{n_1}$. Let us denote by P_2 the polytope

$$R(\Delta, n_1, \varepsilon_1) = \Delta - \bigcup_{i=1}^{n_1} \Delta_i \cap \bigcup_{j=1}^{3n_1} \Delta'_j .$$

Next consider a triangulation T_2 of this polytope and replace each of the triangles T_2 by the polytope $R(\Delta', n_2, \varepsilon_2)$ where ε_2 is a sufficiently small positive number. Thus we obtain a polytope P_3. By iterating this procedure, we obtain a sequence $\{P_k\}$ of 2-dimensional polytopes in E^3 and it is easy to prove that, by a suitable choice of the triangulations $T_1, T_2, \ldots$ and of the numbers $\varepsilon_1, \varepsilon_2, \ldots$, the sequence $\{P_k\}$ converges to a 2-dimensional AR-set, which we denote by $P(\{n_k\})$.

Now let us consider a sequence $\{w_n\}$ of all rational numbers and let us assign to every real number t the increasing sequence $\{n_k(t)\}$ consisting of all the integers n for which $w_n < t$. Setting

$$\Phi(t) = P(\{n_k(t)\}),$$

one obtains a family consisting of $2^{\aleph_0}$ two-dimensional AR-sets with the property that, for $t \neq t'$, none of the 2-dimensional closed subsets of $\Phi(t)$ is topologically included in $\Phi(t')$. By the preceding theorem, we see at once that none of the 2-dimensional ANR-sets could topologically contain all the sets $\Phi(t)$. Consequently a 2-dimensional universal AR-set does not exist.

The other application of our theorem concerns the theory of r-neighbours. (See [1].) We say that a space X is *r-smaller* than a space Y (in symbols: $X \underset{r}{<} Y$) provided X is homeomorphic to a retract of Y, but Y is not homeomorphic to a retract of X. If $X \underset{r}{<} Y$, but no space Z satisfies the condition $X \underset{r}{<} Z \underset{r}{<} Y$, then we say that X is an r-neighbour of Y on the left. It is easy to show that if X is an r-neighbour on the left of the Euclidean 3-cube Q^3, then X must be a 2-dimensional AR-set, which topologically contains all of the sets $\Phi(t)$. However, by our theorem, this is impossible. Consequently the cube Q^3 has no r-neighbours on the left.

Added in proof. The problem 2 is positively solved recently by K. SIEKLUCKI.

References

[1] *K. Borsuk*: Concerning the classification of topological spaces from the stand-point of the theory of retracts. Fundam. Math. *46* (1959), 321–330.

[2] *T. Ważewski*: Sur les courbes de Jordan ne renfermant aucune courbe simple fermée de Jordan. Ann. Soc. Polon. Math. *2* (1923), 49–170.

DARSTELLUNGEN VON MATRIZENGRUPPEN ÜBER TOPOLOGISCHEN KÖRPERN

H. BOSECK

Berlin

Es sei K ein lokal-bikompakter, nicht zusammenhängender topologischer Körper der Charakteristik O. Mit $\mathfrak{G} = GL(2, K)$ werde die Gruppe der zweireihigen Matrizen

$$g = \left\| \begin{matrix} \alpha & \beta \\ \gamma & \delta \end{matrix} \right\|$$

mit nicht verschwindender Determinante bezeichnet, wobei $\alpha, \beta, \gamma, \delta \in K$ ist. Es sei ferner $G = PGL(2, K) = \mathfrak{G}/\mathfrak{z}$, wobei $\mathfrak{z}$ das Zentrum der Gruppe $\mathfrak{G}$ bezeichnet. Die Gruppe G wird häufig als Gruppe der gebrochenen linearen Transformationen

$$x' = x\bar{g} = \frac{\alpha x + \gamma}{\beta x + \delta}, \qquad x \in K \tag{1}$$

auf dem topologischen Körper K interpretiert.

Auf der additiven Gruppe K^+ des topologischen Körpers K existiert ein invariantes Integral, das mit

$$\int_{K^+} f(x)\,\mathrm{d}x = \int_{K^+} f(x + a)\,\mathrm{d}x, \qquad a \in K$$

bezeichnet wird. Es entsteht die Frage nach dem Verhalten dieses Integrals gegenüber der in (1) angegebenen gebrochenen rationalen Transformation. Diese Frage lässt sich wie folgt beantworten:

Es ist

$$\int_{K^+} f(x\bar{g})\, \beta(x, g)\,\mathrm{d}x = \int_{K^+} f(x)\,\mathrm{d}x \tag{2}$$

mit

$$\beta(x, g) = |\det g|\, |\beta x + \delta|^{-2}. \tag{2'}$$

Hier bezeichnet $|\ |$ den in einem nicht zusammenhängenden topologischen Körper durch eine Bewertung definierten Absolutbetrag, der noch als normiert vorausgesetzt sei.

Eine Darstellung der Gruppe G, die in Analogie zu den Arbeiten von I. M. Gelfand, M. A. Neumark, M. J. Grajew als *quasireguläre Darstellung* bezeichnet werde, lässt sich nun wie folgt definieren: Es sei H der Raum der messbaren, quadratisch integrierbaren Funktionen $\varphi(\xi, s)$, $\xi \in K^+$, $s \in K^\times$, und es sei

$$(3) \qquad T_g \varphi(\xi, s) = \beta^{\frac{1}{2}}(\xi, g)\, \varphi\left(\frac{\alpha\xi + \gamma}{\beta\xi + \delta}, \frac{s \det g}{(\beta\xi + \delta)^2}\right).$$

Die Zuordnung $g \to T_g$ *ist eine unitäre Darstellung von* G *im Raum* H, *die quasireguläre Darstellung.*

Die quasireguläre Darstellung lässt sich in der üblichen Weise zerlegen, indem man die Charaktergruppe $X^\times$ der multiplikativen Gruppe $K^\times$ der Körpers K betrachtet und die Fouriertransformation

$$\psi(\xi, \chi) = \int_{K^\times} \varphi(\xi, s)\, \overline{\chi(s)}\, d^\times s$$

durchführt. Es ist

$$T_g \psi(\xi, \chi) = \beta^{\frac{1}{2}}(\xi, g)\, \chi\left(\frac{\det g}{(\beta\xi + \delta)^2}\right) \psi\left(\frac{\alpha\xi + \gamma}{\beta\xi + \delta}, \chi\right).$$

Aus dieser Gleichung ergibt sich unmittelbar, dass H in eine kontinuierliche direkte Summe von Hilberträumen zerfällt, die alle zu $L^2(K^+)$ isomorph sind.

Die *erste Hauptserie* von Darstellungen der Gruppe G erhält man nun im Raum $L^2(K^+)$ durch die Operatoren

$$T_g^{(\chi)} f(x) = \chi\left(\frac{\det g}{(\beta\xi + \delta)^2}\right) \frac{|\det g|^{\frac{1}{2}}}{|\beta\xi + \delta|} f\left(\frac{\alpha\xi + \gamma}{\beta\xi + \delta}\right).$$

Die Darstellungen $g \to T_g^{(\chi)}$, $\chi \in X^\times$ *der ersten Hauptserie sind unitär, irreduzibel und in ihrer Gesamtheit treu.*

Beim Beweis der Irreduzibilität der Darstellungen der ersten Hauptserie spielt folgender Satz über die Struktur der Charaktergruppe Y^+ der additiven Gruppe K^+ des Körpers K eine Rolle:

Ist $y \in Y^+$, *so sei definitionsgemäss für* $a \in K^+ : y^a(\xi) = y(a\xi)$. *Ist dann* y_0 *ein vom Einscharakter verschiedener Charakter von* K^+ *und* y *beliebig aus* Y^+, *so gibt es ein* $a \in K$ *mit der Eigenschaft* $y = y_0^a$.

Eine unmittelbare Folgerung dieser Aussage ist:

Die Gruppen K^+ *und* Y^+ *sind isomorph.*

Anmerkung. Der volle Text der Arbeit erscheint in der Zeitschrift „Mathematische Nachrichten," Band *24*, Heft 4 (1962).

ARITHMETISCH-TOPOLOGISCHE UNTERSUCHUNGEN AN RINGEN MIT EINGESCHRÄNKTEN MINIMALBEDINGUNGEN

L. BUDACH und H. GRELL

Berlin

I. In einem Ring t gilt der eingeschränkte Produktkettensatz, wenn jede Kette $c_1 \supseteq c_2 \supseteq \ldots \supseteq c_i \supseteq \ldots \supseteq c \neq (0)$ von Idealen c_i, deren jedes c_i aus dem vorhergehenden c_{i-1} durch Idealmultiplikation $c_i = d_i c_{i-1}$ entsteht und die alle ein vom Nullideal verschiedenes Ideal c umfassen, im Endlichen abbricht. Nach Akizuki und Krull sind in t alle von (0) und t verschiedenen Primideale maximal, und jedes (eigentliche, d. h. von (0) und t verschiedene) Ideal wird eindeutiges Produkt oder, was dasselbe ist, eindeutiger Durchschnitt endlichvieler zu verschiedenen Primidealen gehöriger Primärideale von endlichem Exponenten. Umgekehrt ist für die Gültigkeit dieser Idealtheorie die eingeschränkte Produktkettenbedingung notwendig. Die genannten Ringe bilden sogar noch dann, wenn man Nullteilerfreiheit verlangt, eine echte Oberklasse der Ringe mit eingeschränkter Minimalbedingung, die durch Fortfall der Bedingung $c_i = d_i c_{i-1}$ beschrieben sind; sie lassen sich auch kennzeichnen als Ringe mit eigeschränktem Produktkettensatz, in denen jedes Ideal eine endliche Basis hat.

II. Für die zu Beginn von I. genannten Ringe gilt im Fall der Nullteilerfreiheit

Satz 1. *Für ein Primideal p mit $(0) \subset p \subset t$ ist stets $\bigcap_1^\infty p^\nu = (0)$.*

Dieser Satz ist für Noethersche Integritätsbereiche als „Durchschnittssatz" wohlbekannt. Weiter hat man

Satz 2. *Bei $t^2 \subset t$* (t^2 echte Untermenge von t) *ist* $\bigcap_1^\infty t^\nu = (0)$ ($t^2 \subset t$ kann nur eintreten, falls t kein Einselement besitzt, ist aber mit der Nichtexistenz eines Einselementes nicht äquivalent).

Diese Sätze ermöglichen für die genannten Ringe in naheliegender Weise u. a. die Einführung einer „natürlichen" Topologie, die, eben ihnen zufolge, dem Regularitätsaxiom genügt.

III. Für einen Integritätsbereich t mit Gültigkeit der eingeschränkten Minimalbedingung sei $T(t)$ die Menge aller t umfassenden Integritätsbereiche im Quotientenkörper $Q(t)$ von t. Durch die Vorschrift: „$t_1 <_t t_2$, falls die durch t_1 definierte natürliche und auf t eingeschränkte Topologie feiner ist als die entsprechende durch t_2 definierte und auf t eingeschränkte", wird $T(t)$ eine Halbordnung. Bei $t_1, t_2 \in T(t)$

heisse t_1 zu t_2 bezüglich t äquivalent, $t_1 \equiv_t t_2$, falls gleichzeitig $t_1 <_t t_2$ und $t_2 <_t t_1$ gilt. Man kann zeigen, dass dann die Äquivalenzklassen bez. $\equiv_t$ abgeschlossen sind gegenüber den Operationen der Vereinigung endlich und des Durchschnitts sogar unendlich vieler Exemplare einer Klasse. Insbesondere ist der Durchschnitt aller Elemente einer Klasse ebenfalls Element der Klasse. Es gilt:

1. Der genannte Durchschnitt $\tilde{t}$ ist gleich der topologischen Abschliessung von t in einem jeden Exemplar der Klasse. – Neben diese topologische Charakterisierung treten die beiden folgenden, ihr jeweils einzeln gleichwertigen arithmetischen.

2. $\tilde{t}$ ist der grösste t umfassende und in einem beliebigen Exemplar der Äquivalenzklasse enthaltene Integritätsbereich derart, dass die Erweiterungsideale $\tilde{t}p$ sämtlicher Primideale p aus t in $\tilde{t}$ wiederum Primideale vom t-Grade 1 sind.

3. Für einen beliebigen Repräsentanten t' der Äquivalenzklasse ist $\tilde{t}$ der kleinste t umfassende und in t' gelegene Integritätsbereich, über dem t' lokal endlich ist. „Lokalendlich" besagt: Ist für ein beliebiges Primideal p aus $\tilde{t}$ die Menge S_p definiert als das multiplikativ abgeschlossene System aller nicht in p gelegenen Elemente aus t, so ist der Quotientenring t'_{S_p} endlicher $\tilde{t}_p$-Modul, wo $\tilde{t}_p$ der wie üblich aus $\tilde{t}$ durch Aufnahme der in p nicht enthaltenen Elemente in die Nenner gebildete Quotientenring ist.

IV. In einer im vergangenen Jahr in den Londoner Proceedings veröffentlichten Arbeit „Prime Ideals and Integral Dependence" definiert NORTHCOTT verallgemeinerte Dedekindsche Ordnungen als Integritätsbereiche t mit Gültigkeit der eingeschränkten Minimalbedingung, in denen fast alle Primideale p umkehrbar sind, $pp^{-1} = t$ für fast alle p aus t.

Es gilt

4. t ist verallgemeinerte Dedekindsche Ordnung genau dann, falls für jede Kette $t \subseteq t_1 \subseteq t_2 \subseteq \ldots \subseteq \hat{t}$ von Integritätsbereichen t_i, die sämtlichen in der ganzen Abschliessung $\hat{t}$ von t in $Q(t)$ enthalten sind, von einem gewissen Index $i \geqq i_j$ ab die in $Q(t)$ gebildeten Modulquotienten $t_{i+1}/t_i \neq (0)$ sind. – Für eine verallgemeinerte Dedekindsche Ordnung t ist die topologische Abschliessung $\tilde{t}$ von t in der ganzen Abschliessung $\hat{t}$ von t dadurch ausgezeichnet, dass $\hat{t}$ ein endlicher $\tilde{t}$-Modul wird. Nimmt man diese letzte Eigenschaft als charakterisierende Bedingung, so erhält man eine Ringklasse, die eine Verallgemeinerung der Northcottschen verallgemeinerten Dedekindschen Ordnungen darstellt. In diesen Ringen werden die Erweiterungsideale fast aller Primideale aus t ebenfalls Primideale, und zwar vom t-Grad 1. Ein Gegenbeispiel zeigt, daß aus der letzten Bedingung nicht umgekehrt die Umkehrbarkeit des Ausgangsprimideals erschlossen werden kann.

ON HOMOLOGY THEORY OF NON-CLOSED SETS

G. CHOGOSHVILI
Tbilisi

1. Direct systems of compact groups. In homology theory of non-closed sets the approximation of sets by their compact subsets or by their neighbourhoods is of decisive importance. Such approximations lead, in particular, to direct systems of compact groups. The definition of the limit of such systems given below would seem to have proved of some use in homology theory of non-compact spaces [2b, c; 3; 6c, d, f].

Let $\{A_\alpha, \pi_{\alpha\beta}\}$ be a direct system of compact groups A_α with homomorphisms

$$\pi_{\alpha\beta} : A_\alpha \to A_\beta .$$

Let B_α be the character-group of A_α and $\sigma_{\beta\alpha} : B_\beta \to B_\alpha$ a homomorphism, satisfying the permanence relation

$$(a_\alpha, \sigma_{\beta\alpha} b_\beta) = (\pi_{\alpha\beta} a_\alpha, b_\beta) , \quad a_\alpha \in A_\alpha , \quad b_\beta \in B_\beta .$$

Then $\{B_\alpha, \sigma_{\beta\alpha}\}$ is an inverse system of discrete groups, and $\{A_\alpha, \pi_{\alpha\beta}\}$ and $\{B_\alpha, \sigma_{\beta\alpha}\}$ are dually paired to the group κ of real numbers mod 1. Let B be the limit-group of $\{B_\alpha, \sigma_{\beta\alpha}\}$ with *discrete* topology, and A' the usual algebraic limit-group of $\{A_\alpha, \pi_{\alpha\beta}\}$. Then the groups A' and B are paired to κ under a multiplication defined as follows:

$$(a, b) = (a_\alpha, b_\alpha) , \quad \text{where} \quad a_\alpha \in a \in A' , \quad b_\alpha \in b \in B .$$

Let A_0 be the annihilator of B in A'. We use the induced pairing of the factor-group A'/A_0 and the group B to introduce a topology in A'/A_0 as follows: for any finite subset F of B and any nucleus V of κ a nucleus U of A'/A_0 is defined as a set of elements a of A'/A_0 satisfying the condition $(a, F) \in V$. We call the group A'/A_0 in this topology the *general limit-group* of $\{A_\alpha, \pi_{\alpha\beta}\}$, and the compact completion A of A'/A_0, which exists and is unique, the *limit-group* of $\{A_\alpha, \pi_{\alpha\beta}\}$:

$$A = \varinjlim \{A_\alpha, \pi_{\alpha\beta}\} .$$

The group A'/A_0 may be topologically imbedded in the character-group of B as an everywhere dense subgroup of it and, therefore, A and B are dual: $A \mid B$.

Now we can introduce a compact topology in *the direct sum* $\sum A_\alpha$ *of compact groups* A_α. To do this, it is sufficient to consider $\sum A_\alpha$ as the limit in the above sense of the direct system of all groups A'_α with inclusion homomorphisms, where A'_α is the sum of a finite subsystem of the system $\{A_\alpha\}$.

Conversely, we can first define the compact sum $\sum A_\alpha$ of the compact groups A_α, and then the limit of the system $\{A_\alpha, \pi_{\alpha\beta}\}$. To do this, we consider the topology of the usual sum $\sum A_\alpha$ which satisfies the following conditions: a) the inclusion homomorphism

$$i_\alpha : A_\alpha \to \sum A_\alpha$$

is continuous for every α; b) every homomorphism f of $\sum A_\alpha$ in any compact group C is continuous, if the homomorphisms fi_α are continuous; c) in this topology $\sum A_\alpha$ has a compact completion. Such a topology of $\sum A_\alpha$ exists and is unique. The compact completion of $\sum A_\alpha$ will be called the *direct sum of compact groups* A_α and denoted by $\sum A_\alpha$. Now, the factor group $\sum A_\alpha / A_0$, where A_0 is the closure of the subgroup generated by the elements $a_\alpha - \pi_{\alpha\beta} a_\alpha$, is the *limit*

$$\varinjlim \{A_\alpha, \pi_{\alpha\beta}\} .$$

2. Projective and spectral groups of complexes and spaces. Let $\{K_\alpha, <\}$ be a directed system of all finite closed subcomplexes K_α of a complex K, ordered by the inclusion

$$\alpha < \beta \Leftrightarrow K_\alpha \subset K_\beta .$$

The groups of r-chains of K_α over a discrete or compact group of coefficients X, with the homomorphisms $i_{\alpha\beta *}$ induced by the inclusion maps

$$i_{\alpha\beta} : K_\alpha \to K_\beta ,$$

form a directed system of groups

$$\{C_r(K_\alpha, X), i_{\alpha\beta *}\} . \tag{1}$$

On the basis of (1), we construct homology groups of K of two kinds: projective and spectral. *Projective homology groups* are obtained if we first take the limit of the system (1) and then apply the homological functor, or, in notation,

$$H_r \varinjlim \{C_r(K_\alpha, X), i_{\alpha\beta *}\} ,$$

the limit being understood in the sense of § 1. Here, when X is compact, the boundary operator is first defined for the general limit-group and then extended by continuity to the limit-group. *Spectral homology groups* are obtained if, on the contrary, we first apply the homological functor and then take the limit; in notation,

$$\varinjlim \{H_r(K_\alpha, X), i_{\alpha\beta *}\} .$$

Using the inverse system of cochain groups of K_α over a discrete or compact group of coefficients Y

$$\{C^r(K_\alpha, Y), i^*_{\beta\alpha}\} \tag{2}$$

we obtain, similarly, the *projective* and *spectral cohomology groups* of K.

If X and Y are dual, then the projective [spectral] homology group of K over X and the projective [spectral] cohomology group of K over Y are dual not only for a discrete X, but also for a compact X.

From the *theorem on commutativity of limit operator and homology functor,*[1]) now a proposition of homological algebra, it follows that *projective and spectral homology groups are isomorphic for a discrete group of coefficients X*, while *projective and spectral cohomology groups are isomorphic for a compact group of coefficients Y.* Examples show that these isomorphisms are not valid when X is compact and Y discrete.

Making use of the spectral and projective groups of complexes we construct the corresponding (i. e. spectral and projective) homology and cohomology groups of spaces of various types, viz., singular, continuous, Čech, Vietoris, etc. In this way we obtain, on the one hand, the usual singular, Vietoris, etc. groups, every one of these groups being of either the spectral or the projective kind. On the other hand, we obtain new groups which are opposite in kind to the usual groups just mentioned. Moreover, the above definitions, especially that of the limit of direct system of compact groups, makes it possible to construct homology and cohomology groups of spaces not only over a discrete, but over a compact group of coefficients as well. As is known, these latter have not all been previously defined (see, e. g., [8], pp. 166, 184, 185, 188, 223, 233 and [10], p. 393).

Taking the singular complex of a space and its projective and spectral groups, we obtain, apart from the usual singular groups of the space – which are groups of the projective kind – also the *spectral singular groups*, as well as the *projective singular homology groups with compact coefficients.*

The *continuous* homology groups are discrete groups of the spectral kind, but the *projective continuous groups* may also be constructed, as well as the *compact spectral homology groups.*

Spectral and projective groups of nerves of *arbitrary* coverings form direct and inverse systems of compact or discrete groups, whose limit groups (in the sense of § 1) are *Čech groups* of a space; in particular, we obtain *spectral and projective homology groups with compact coefficients.*

Groups of vietorisian complexes of coverings[2]) with homomorphisms, induced by inclusion maps, form inverse and direct systems, whose limit groups are spectral and projective *Vietoris groups* of a space over discrete or *compact* coefficients.

The relations between the spectral and projective groups, stated above for complexes, extend to the groups of spaces in any homology theory – singular, Vietoris, etc. The relations between various theories, established previously for cases when projective and spectral groups coincide (for Čech and Vietoris theories in [7b], for singular and continuous theories in [9], for singular and Čech theories in [13], for Čech and Alexander-Kolmogoroff theories in [6a, e] and [12]), are valid for other

[1]) Proved by P. S. ALEXANDROFF [2a] for sequences and generalised by the present author [6a] for arbitrary systems; cf. [4, 12].

[2]) By the vietorisian of a covering we mean a complex, whose vertices are points of the space, a subset of vertices forming a simplex, if and only if it is contained in an element of the covering.

cases likewise, provided the groups in question are of the same kind – projective or spectral.

Of the various applications which these groups have already received in topology and variational calculus [1; 2b, c; 3; 6b–g; 14; 15], we shall consider here the duality laws, and not only in view of their classical character, but in view also of the distinguished rôle, EDUARD ČECH's investigations play in this field.

3. Duality theorems for spectral groups. Let S^n be an n-sphere, A an arbitrary set of S^n, F_a a compact subset of A and G_a the complement of F_a. Let, further, K be a triangulation of G_a, K_α a finite subcomplex of K, and L_α the triangulated complement in S^n of K_α. The Alexander-Pontrjagin theorem asserts the duality

$$H_r(L_\alpha, X) \mid H_{n-r-1}(K_\alpha, Y)\,, \tag{3}$$

where $H_s(M, Z)$ denotes the s-dimensional homology group of M over a group of coefficients Z, and X and Y are dual, $X \mid Y$. In its original form it was necessary to suppose in this theorem X to be a *discrete* group. But interpreting $H_r(L_\alpha, X)$ as a spectral group, we can extend this theorem to the case when X is *compact*. On carrying out this extension we are faced, for the first time, with the necessity of applying the homological approximations of a set by its compact subsets and, *simultaneously*, the approximations of its complement by the complements of the compact subsets just mentioned. The approximation of L_α by its finite closed subcomplexes $L_{\alpha\tau}$ gives precisely the spectral group $H_r(L_\alpha, X)$ which is the limit of the system

$$\{H_r(L_{\alpha\tau}, X), i_{\tau\sigma *}\}\,, \tag{4}$$

where $i_{\tau\sigma *}$ are the homomorphisms induced by the inclusions $i_{\tau\sigma} : L_{\alpha\tau} \to L_{\alpha\sigma}$, $\tau < \sigma$.

The homology groups $H_{n-r-1}(K_{\alpha\tau}, Y)$ of the complements

$$K_{\alpha\tau} = S^n \setminus L_{\alpha\tau}$$

with the homomorphisms $j_{\sigma\tau *}$, induced by the inclusions $j_{\sigma\tau} : K_{\alpha\sigma} \to K_{\alpha\tau}$, form an inverse system of groups

$$\{H_{n-r-1}(K_{\alpha\tau}, Y), j_{\sigma\tau *}\}\,. \tag{5}$$

Since, by Alexander-Pontrjagin duality theorem in its original form, i. e. when Y is discrete, the groups

$$H_r(L_{\alpha\tau}, X) \quad \text{and} \quad H_{n-r-1}(K_{\alpha\tau}, Y)$$

are dual, systems (4) and (5) are dually paired. Hence the limit-groups of (4) and (5), if the limits are taken in the sense of § 1, are dual. But the limit-group of (5) is isomorphic to the limit-group of the inverse system

$$\{H_{n-r-1}(N_\xi, Y), \omega_{\eta\xi}\}\,, \tag{6}$$

where N_ξ are nerves (or vietorisian complexes) of external open coverings U_ξ of K_α (i. e. U_ξ is a system of open sets of S^n, whose union contains K_α) and $\omega_{\eta\xi}$ are the corresponding homomorphisms of the homology groups. But the external coverings can be substituted in (6) by the internal coverings of K_α (i. e. by the coverings of K_α by *its* open subsets), in virtue of the following lemma of Čech (for proofs of different forms of this lemma under various conditions cf. [5; 11; 14; 15; 6b]):

Čech's lemma. *For any external covering U and any internal covering u of A there exist isomorphic* (i. e. with isomorphic nerves) *external and internal coverings V and, respectively, v of A, which are refinements of U and u, respectively, and satisfy the condition $v = V \cap A$.*

Applying this lemma, *in the case when A is a polyhedron,* to system (6) we conclude at once that the limit-group of (6) is isomorphic to the homology group $H_{n-r-1}(K_\alpha, Y)$ of K_α. Thus, the *Alexander-Pontrjagin duality* (3) *holds also when X is a compact group.*

Let us consider now the cohomology groups $H^r(L_\alpha, Y)$ and $H^{n-r-1}(K_\alpha, X)$; understanding $H^r(L_\alpha, Y)$ as the spectral group of L_α, we see that these cohomology groups are character groups of the corresponding homology groups under discussion, and we obtain the diagram:

$$(7) \qquad \begin{array}{c|c} H_r(L_\alpha, X) & H_{n-r-1}(K_\alpha, Y) \\ \hline H^r(L_\alpha, Y) & H^{n-r-1}(K_\alpha, X) \end{array} \; (\text{with crossing arrows } \nwarrow\nearrow\swarrow\searrow).$$

A *diagram* of this kind has the following sense. It is a quadruple of graded groups which are connected by group multiplications and homomorphisms, denoted by $|$ and $\rightarrow$ respectively, and which are represented as the vertices of a square. The components of each pair of these graded groups are in a certain $1-1$-correspondence, which will be called the *correspondence of the diagram.* We shall consider not only the usual correspondence, when the *difference* of dimensions of the corresponding components is constant (*degree* of correspondence), but also a correspondence, such that the *sum* of dimensions of corresponding components is constant; this constant we call the *σ-degree.*

The corresponding components of any pair of neighbouring groups are paired to κ. We shall consider here the case, when one of the neighbouring groups is discrete, the other compact, and the multiplication is distributive, continuous and orthogonal. The corresponding components of any pair of opposite (non-neighbouring) groups are isomorphic. The multiplications and isomorphisms are *compatible* in the sense that: (a) the composition of any two correspondences of the diagram is a correspondence of the diagram; (b) x and y being corresponding elements of an arbitrary pair of isomorphic groups, and t an element of either of the two other groups of the diagram, $(t, x) = (t, y)$. Diagram (7) has all these properties; its correspondences are of degree 0 and of σ-degree $n - 1$.

By a *directed system of diagrams* $\{\mathscr{D}_\alpha\}$ we mean a set of diagrams $\mathscr{D}_\alpha$ indexed by a directed system $\{\alpha\}$ and satisfying the following conditions:

(a) for each α, β the quadruples of $\mathscr{D}_\alpha$ and $\mathscr{D}_\beta$ are bijective;

(b) for each $\alpha < \beta$ the groups corresponding to each other by the bijection just mentioned are connected by homomorphisms in such a manner, that they form an inverse or direct system of groups; in the sequel these systems will be called systems *generated* by $\{\mathscr{D}_\alpha\}$;

(c) neighbouring systems of groups generated by $\{\mathscr{D}_\alpha\}$ have opposite directions and are paired to κ;

(d) the homomorphisms of opposite systems of groups, generated by $\{\mathscr{D}_\alpha\}$, commute with the isomorphisms of the diagrams $\mathscr{D}_\alpha$ and $\mathscr{D}_\beta$.

The *limit diagram* $\mathscr{D}$ of the system $\{\mathscr{D}_\alpha\}$,

$$\mathscr{D} = \lim \{\mathscr{D}_\alpha\} ,$$

is a quadruple, consisting of the limit groups of the systems generated by $\{\mathscr{D}_\alpha\}$. These limit groups are in the same categories as the groups of corresponding systems, the definition of limit being as in § 1. The correspondances, multiplications, and isomorphisms of $\mathscr{D}$ are defined from those of $\mathscr{D}_\alpha$. For instance, if $p = \{p_\alpha\}$ and $q = \{q_\alpha\}$ are elements of limit-groups, then the multiplication (p, q) is defined as (p_α, q_α), the latter being independent of the choice of α. Now, the compatibility and other properties of diagrams mentioned above can be proved to be valid for $\mathscr{D}$. Thus, $\lim \{\mathscr{D}_\alpha\}$ is a diagram. Degrees of correspondences of $\mathscr{D}$ coincide with those of $\mathscr{D}_\alpha$.

Diagram (7) is a diagram $\mathscr{D}_\alpha$ in the sense just described. If $\alpha < \beta$, i. e. $K_\alpha \subset K_\beta$, the groups of $\mathscr{D}_\alpha$ and $\mathscr{D}_\beta$ are connected by the homomorphisms $i_{\alpha\beta *}, i^*_{\beta\alpha}, j_{\alpha\beta *}, j^*_{\beta\alpha}$, induced by the inclusions

$$i_{\alpha\beta} : K_\alpha \to K_\beta$$

and

$$j_{\beta\alpha} : L_\beta \to L_\alpha .$$

It can be verified that the set of all $\mathscr{D}_\alpha$ with homomorphisms $i_{\alpha\beta *}$, etc., is a directed system of diagrams $\{\mathscr{D}_\alpha\}$. This system homologically approximates to the set $G_a = K$ by its finite closed subcomplexes and to the set F_a by its neighbourhoods.

The limit diagram $\mathscr{D}_a = \{\mathscr{D}_\alpha\}$ consists of the spectral homology and cohomology groups of G_a, $H_{n-r-1}(G_a, Y)$ and $H^{n-r-1}(G_a, X)$ respectively, and of the external groups $H_r(F_a, X)$ and $H^r(F_a, Y)$ of F_a. But applying the lemma of Čech, *in the case when A is a compact set* F_a, we conclude as above, that the latter groups may be considered as usual, i. e. internal, Čech (or Vietoris) groups of F_a. Thus we obtain the diagram $\mathscr{D}_a$:

$$(8) \qquad \frac{H_r(F_a, X)}{H^r(F_a, Y)} \;\; \begin{smallmatrix} \nwarrow\nearrow \\ \swarrow\searrow \end{smallmatrix} \;\; \frac{H_{n-r-1}(G_a, Y)}{H^{n-r-1}(G_a, X)} ,$$

representing the *correlations between the spectral groups of a compact—open pair of complementary sets* (F_a, G_a).

Now let us consider such diagrams for each a, i. e. for each compact subset F_a of A, and let us connect them for each $a < b$, i. e. for each $F_a \subset F_b$, by homomorphisms induced by the inclusions

$$i_{ab} : F_a \to F_b \quad \text{and} \quad j_{ba} : G_b \to G_a .$$

The set of all diagrams $\mathscr{D}_a$ and homomorphisms just mentioned form a directed system of diagrams, giving the internal homological approximation of A by its compact subsets F_a and, simultaneously, the external approximation of B by complements G_a of F_a. The limit diagram

$$\mathscr{D} = \lim \{\mathscr{D}_a\}$$

consists of the homology and cohomology groups of A with compact carriers, $H_r(A, X)$ and $H^r(A, Y)$ respectively, and of the external groups $H_{n-r-1}(B, Y)$ and $H^{n-r-1}(B, X)$ of B. But the lemma of Čech for *arbitrary* A guarantees that the latter groups can be understood not only as limit-groups of the system consisting of groups of neighbourhoods or of groups based on external coverings, but as usual Čech (or Vietoris) groups of B. Here it must be taken into account that these groups must be based not on *finite* coverings of B, as originally defined for the Čech groups [5], but on *all* open coverings of B [2b; 6c, d; 7a; 11]. These groups may be considered also as Vietoris groups [7b] and, when A is a neighbourhood retract (in particular, when A is an infinite polyhedron [6b]) as singular groups (see [13], cf. [6b]). Thus we obtain the diagram $\mathscr{D}$

$$\frac{H_r(A, X)}{H^r(A, Y)} \times \frac{H_{n-r-1}(B, Y)}{H^{n-r-1}(B, X)}, \tag{9}$$

which gives the various forms of the *Alexander-Pontrjagin duality theorem for an arbitrary pair of sets* (A, B). Certain of these forms and their particular cases (theorems for external groups, for the discrete group of coefficients X, for the compact group of coefficients X, etc.) have been obtained by P. S. Alexandroff, N. A. Berikashvili, A. N. Kolmogoroff, K. A. Sitnikov and G. S. Chogoshvili [2b, c; 3; 6b, c, d, f; 14]. The diagram $\mathscr{D}$, especially the compatibility of $\mathscr{D}$, and the way it was obtained above, show the interrelations of these forms with each other, and prove that all of them can be obtained by one and the same method, the chief tools being: *the simultaneous approximations to the sets by compact subsets and their complements, the theory of group systems, and Čech's lemma.*

The duality of the first line of $\mathscr{D}$ – the earliest to have been obtained – gives the Alexander-Pontrjagin theorem in its classical form. Moreover, it is the form from which it is easiest to obtain the duality theorems for non-closed sets obtained previously, namely Eilenberg's theorems relating to cases: (a) when $r = 0$ and n is arbitrary, and (b) when $n = 2$ and A is a homeomorphic image of a linear set (cf. [2b; 6b]).

The proof of the isomorphism of external and internal groups, given by P. S. Alexandroff [2], differs from that sketched above. Alexandroff's proof makes use of the canonical triangulations and transformations, which proved to be very useful in the generalisation of duality theorems for projective groups.

4. Duality theorems for projective groups. The relations which, in this case, constitute the starting point are represented by the following diagram $\mathscr{D}_a$:

$$\frac{H_r(F_a, X)}{H^r(F_a, Y)} \times \frac{H_{n-r}(G_a, Y)}{H^{n-r}(G_a, X)}. \tag{10}$$

Here $H_r(F_a, X)$ and $H^r(F_a, Y)$ are r-dimensional Steenrod's homology and, respectively, cohomology groups of regular cycles and cocycles of F_a, while $H_{n-r}(G_a, Y)$ and $H^{n-r}(G_a, X)$ are projective homology and cohomology groups of $G_a = K$. The isomorphisms and horizontal dualities of (10) are forms of Steenrod's duality theorem [16]. From these forms, Steenrod's original form can be obtained by applying Poincaré's duality theorem to the groups of K. The groups which we obtain by this dualisation form, with the groups of left and right verticals of $\mathcal{D}_a$, two auxiliary diagrams. The vertical dualities of $\mathcal{D}_a$ are ordinary dualities of the homology and cohomology groups. The duality of the right vertical was considered in § 2. The duality of the left vertical is obtained similarly: in each complex participating in the definition of Steenrod's groups we only need interchange chains and cochains, i. e. consider the inverse system of chains and the direct system of cochains of finite open subcomplexes in order to form the corresponding projective groups of the complex; when Y is compact, the limit is taken in the sense of § 1.

The dualities and isomorphisms mentioned above satisfy the conditions of § 3 and, therefore, $\mathcal{D}_a$ is a diagram. Its correspondences are of degree 0 and of σ-degree n.

Consider now the set of all diagrams $\mathcal{D}_a$, ordered by

$$a < b \Leftrightarrow F_a \subset F_b\,,$$

and the set of all homomorphisms of the groups of $\mathcal{D}_a$ and $\mathcal{D}_b$, $a < b$, induced by the inclusions

$$i_{ab} : F_a \to F_b \quad \text{and} \quad j_{ba} : G_b \to G_a\,.$$

These diagrams and homomorphisms form a directed system of diagrams $\{\mathcal{D}_a\}$. To prove this, it is most convinient to use the auxiliary diagrams mentioned above. Supplementary groups of the auxiliary diagrams are connected by homomorphisms induced by canonical transformations (see end of § 3).

The limit diagram of the system $\{\mathcal{D}_a\}$ is

$$\frac{H_r(A, X)}{H^r(A, Y)} \times \frac{H_{n-r}(B, Y)}{H^{n-r}(B, X)}\,. \tag{11}$$

Here $H_r(A, X)$ and $H^r(A, Y)$ are Steenrod's homology and cohomology groups of A with compact carriers. The groups $H_{n-r}(B, Y)$ and $H^{n-r}(B, X)$ are the homology and, respectively, the cohomology groups of B, based on neighbourhoods of B. But, as above, it can easily be shown that these groups coincide with the groups based on external coverings and, consequently, in virtue of Čech's lemma, with projective Čech groups of B. (It is to be noted that there does not exist an invariant definition of the limit groups of systems consisting of supplementary groups of the auxiliary diagrams). Thus, diagram (11) gives the duality theorems for projective groups of arbitrary pairs of sets (A, B). The isomorphism of the groups $H_r(A, X)$ and $H^{n-r}(B, X)$ is the generalisation of Steenrod's duality theorem which coincides with the theorem proved by K. A. Sitnikov, Steenrod's groups being isomorphic to the groups considered by K. A. Sitnikov (see [14], cf. [3; 6g]).

If X is compact, we obtain, from the coincidence of the spectral and projective groups, the coincidence of diagrams (9) and (11) and, therefore, of Steenrod's and Vietoris' groups; in this case the two coinciding theorems constitute the theorem of Alexander-Pontrjagin in its original form.

References

[1] *Альбер, С. И.*: О периодической задаче вариационного исчисления в целом. Успехи мат. наук, *XII* : 4 (1957), 57—124.

[2] *Alexandroff P. S.*: (a) Zur Homologie-Theorie der Kompakten. Comp. Math. *4* (1937), 256–270.

(b) Основные теоремы двойственности для незамкнутых множеств *n*-мерного пространства. Мат. Сборник, *21* (1947), 161—232.

(c) Топологические теоремы двойственности. Труды Мат. Инст. им. Стеклова, *54* (1959), 1—136.

[3] *Берикашвили, Н. А.*: Об аксиоматической теории спектров и о законах двойственности для произвольных множеств. Труды Тбилис. Мат. Инст., *XXIV* (1957), 409—484.

[4] *Cartan H.* and *Eilenberg S.*: Homological Algebra. Princeton, 1956.

[5] *Čech E.*: Théorie générale de l'homologie dans un espace quelconque. Fund. Math. *19* (1932), 149–183.

[6] *Chogoshvili G. S.* (Чогошвили, Г. С.): (a) On the homology theory of topological spaces. Сообщения АН Груз. ССР, *1* (1940), 337—340;

(b) О соотношениях двойственности в топологических пространствах. Диссертация, Москва,1945.

(c) The duality law for retracts. C. R. (Doklady) Acad. Sci. URSS, *51* (1946), 91—94.

(d) О гомологических аппроксимациях и законах двойственности для произвольных множеств. Мат. сб. *28* (1951), 89—118.

(e) Об эквивалентности функциональной и спектральной теории гомологии. Изв. АН СССР, сер. мат.. *15* (1951), 421—438.

(f) Алгебраические методы в теоретико-множественной топологии. Труды Третьего всесоюзного математического съезда, т. 3, Москва (1958), 391—400.

(g) К обобщению закона двойственности Стинрода. Сообщения АН Груз. ССР, *XXI* : 6 (1958), 641—648.

[7] *Dowker C. H.*: (a) Mapping theorems for non-compact spaces. Am. J. Math. *69* (1947), 200–242.

(b) Homology groups of relations. Ann. Math. *56* (1952), 84–95.

[8] *Eilenberg S.* and *Steenrod N.*: Foundations of Algebraic Topology, Princeton 1952.

[9] *Giever J. B.*: On the equivalence of two singular homology theories. Ann. Math. *51* (1950), 178–191.

[10] *Hurewicz W.*, *Dugundji J.* and *Dowker C. H.*: Continuous connectivity groups in terms of limit groups. Ann. Math. *49* (1948), 391–406.

[11] *Kaplan S.*: Homology properties of arbitrary subsets of Euclidean spaces. Trans. Am. Math. Soc. *62* (1947), 248–271.

[12] *Lefschetz S.*: Algebraic Topology, Princeton, 1942.

[13] *Mardešić S.*: Comparison of singular and Čech homology in locally connected spaces. Michigan Math. J. *6* (1959), 151–166.

[14] *Ситников, К. А.*: Комбинаторная топология незамкнутых множеств, I. Мат. сб. *34* (1954), 3—54.

[15] *Смирнов, Ю. М.*: Группы Бетти пересечения бесконечного числа множеств. Докл. АН СССР, *76* (1951), 29—32.

[16] *Steenrod N.*: Regular cycles of compact metric spaces. Ann. Math. *41* (1940), 831 – 851.

COMPLÉTION ET COMPACTIFICATION D'ESPACES SYNTOPOGÈNES

Á. CSÁSZÁR

Budapest

Une théorie de structures générales, appelées structures syntopogènes, embrassant les structures topologiques, les structures uniformes, les structures de proximité et d'autres, a été élaborée par l'auteur dans l'ouvrage [1]. Le terme primitif dont se sert cette théorie est la notion d'ordre semi-topogène; on entend par *ordre semi-topogène* sur un ensemble E une relation binaire $<$ définie pour deux sous-ensembles de E et remplissant les conditions

(O_1) $$0 < 0, \quad E < E;$$

(O_2) $$A < B \quad \textit{implique} \quad A \subset B;$$

(O_3) $$A \subset A' < B' \subset B \quad \textit{implique} \quad A < B.$$

Un *ordre topogène* est un ordre semi-topogène satisfaisant à la condition:

(Q) $A < B$ *et* $A' < B'$ *impliquent* $A \cap A' < B \cap B'$ *et* $A \cup A' < B \cup B'$.

Nous appelons *structure syntopogène* sur E une famille $\mathscr{S}$ d'ordres topogènes sur E vérifiant les axiomes:

(S_1) $<', <'' \in \mathscr{S}$ *implique l'existence de* $< \in \mathscr{S}$ *tel que* $A < B$ *découle de l'une quelconque des conditions* $A <' B$ *et* $A <'' B$;

(S_2) $< \in \mathscr{S}$ *implique l'existence de* $<' \in \mathscr{S}$ *tel que* $A < B$ *entraîne* $A <' C <' B$ *pour un ensemble convenable* C.

Dans un espace topologique E, on introduit un ordre topogène en posant $A < B$ si et seulement si $A \subset \operatorname{Int} B$; la famille $\{<\}$ composée de cet ordre est une structure syntopogène sur E. Dans un espace de proximité E, on définit un ordre topogène $<$ en posant $A < B$ si et seulement si $A \bar{\delta} E - B$; la famille $\{<\}$ constitue de nouveau une structure syntopogène. Enfin, dans un espace uniforme E, on peut faire correspondre à chaque entourage symétrique V un ordre topogène $<_V$ en posant $A <_V B$ si et seulement si $x \in A$, $(x, y) \in V$ entraînent $y \in B$; la famille $\{<_V\}$ de tous ces ordres forme une structure syntopogène sur E.

Dans ce qui suit, nous employons la terminologie et les notations de [1]. Dans § 16 de [1], les questions de complétion d'espaces syntopogènes et de compactification d'espaces topogènes ont été étudiées. Par l'application des méthodes nouvelles et de quelques idées nouvelles, dues en partie à notre collaborateur J. Czipszer, nous avons réussi récemment à donner à la théorie de la complétion et de la compactification une forme plus générale et en même temps plus précise.

Considérons deux ensembles E et E^* et une opération h qui fait correspondre à un sous-ensemble quelconque $A \subset E$ un sous-ensemble $h(A) \subset E^*$ et qui vérifie les conditions suivantes:

(1) $$h(0) = 0\,, \quad h(E) = E^*\,;$$

(2) $$A \subset B \subset E \quad \textit{implique} \quad h(A) \subset h(B)\,.$$

Si $<$ est un ordre semi-topogène sur E, définissons une relation $<^h$ entre deux sous-ensembles de E^* en posant

(3) $A^* <^h B^*$ *si et seulement si il existe deux ensembles A et B tels que*

$$A < B\,, \quad A^* \subset h(A)\,, \quad h(B) \subset B^*\,.$$

La relation $<^h$ est un ordre semi-topogène sur E^*. Par exemple, si f est une application de E^* dans E et si l'on pose $h(A) = f^{-1}(A)$, on aura $<^h = f^{-1}(<)$ (cf. [1], p. 51). De plus, si f est une application biunivoque de E sur un sous-ensemble $E_0^* \subset E^*$ et si l'on a

(4) $$f(A) = E_0^* \cap h(A) \quad \textit{pour} \quad A \subset E\,,$$

on vérifie aisément l'égalité $< \; = f^{-1}(<^h)$.

$\mathscr{S}$ étant une structure syntopogène sur E, la famille

(5) $$\mathscr{S}^h = \{<^{hq} : < \in \mathscr{S}\}$$

(cf. [1], p. 27) est une structure syntopogène sur E^*, satisfaisant à l'égalité

(6) $$\mathscr{S} = f^{-1}(\mathscr{S}^h)$$

(cf. [1], p. 91) si la condition (4) a lieu.

En généralisant une méthode connue de prolongement d'espaces topologiques (v. [3]; [4]; [2], p. 159), on peut définir une méthode générale de prolongement d'espaces syntopogènes de la façon suivante. Dans un espace syntopogène $[E, \mathscr{S}]$ (cf. [1], p. 62), appelons *grilles fondamentales* les grilles (cf. [1], p. 183) de la forme $\{\{x\}\}$ pour $x \in E$, et désignons par f l'application qui fait correspondre à $x \in E$ la grille fondamentale $f(x) = \{\{x\}\}$, par E_0^* l'ensemble des grilles fondamentales, et par E^* un ensemble de grilles dans E contenant E_0^* comme sous-ensemble. Pour $A \subset E$, désignons par $h(A)$ l'ensemble des grilles $x^* \in E^*$ telles qu'il existe un ensemble $X \in x^*$, $X \subset A$. Alors (1), (2) et (4) ont lieu, de sorte qu'en définissant, pour $< \in \mathscr{S}$, $<^h$ d'après (3), et $\mathscr{S}^h$ d'après (5), $\mathscr{S}^h$ sera une structure syntopogène sur E^* satisfaisant à (6). De plus, on vérifie aisément que l'image par f de la grille $x^* \in E^*$ (cf. [1], p. 184) converge vers x^*:

(7) $$f(x^*) \to x^* \quad (\mathscr{S}^h)$$

(cf. [1], p. 185), et que par conséquent E_0^* est dense dans $[E^*, \mathscr{S}^h]$ (cf. [1], p. 221).

En généralisant la terminologie de [2], nous dirons qu'une grille $\mathfrak{R}$ est *ronde* dans un espace syntopogène $[E, \mathscr{S}]$, si $R \in \mathfrak{R}$ implique l'existence de $< \in \mathscr{S}$ et $R' \in \mathfrak{R}$

tels que $R' < R$. Or si, dans la construction précédente, les $x^* \in E^* - E_0^*$ sont des filtres ronds dans $[E, \mathscr{S}]$, on a

$$(8) \qquad f(x^*) = \mathfrak{B}^*(x^*) (\cap) E_0^* \quad pour \quad x^* \in E^* - E_0^*$$

(cf. [1], p. 183), où $\mathfrak{B}^*(x^*)$ désigne le filtre des voisinages (cf. [1], p. 185) du point x^* par rapport à $\mathscr{S}^h$. Si, de plus, les grilles $x^* \in E^* - E_0^*$ sont des filtres ronds qui ne convergent pas dans $[E, \mathscr{S}]$, alors la structure syntopogène $\mathscr{S}^h$ est *relativement séparée* par rapport à E_0 en ce sens que $x^*, y^* \in E^*$, $x^* \neq y^*$ impliquent l'existence de $<^* \in \mathscr{S}^h$ tel que soit $x^* <^* E^* - y^*$, soit $y^* <^* E^* - x^*$ a lieu, sauf le cas où $x^*, y^* \in E_0^*$.

Supposons maintenant que les grilles $x^* \in E^*$ sont comprimées dans $[E, \mathscr{S}]$ (cf. [1], p. 191). On a alors

$$(9) \qquad \mathscr{S}^{hs} \sim \mathscr{S}^{sh}$$

(cf. [1], pp. 75 et 19) et au lieu de (7)

$$(10) \qquad f(x^*) \to x^* \ (\mathscr{S}^{hs}) \quad pour \quad x^* \in E^*,$$

de sorte que E_0^* est dense dans $[E^*, \mathscr{S}^{hs}]$. De plus, si les grilles $x^* \in E^*$ sont des grilles de Cauchy dans $[E, \mathscr{S}]$ (cf. [1], p. 189), on peut remplacer (7) et (10) par

$$(11) \qquad f(x^*) \to x^* \ (\mathscr{S}^{hsb}) \quad pour \quad x^* \in E^*$$

(cf. [1], p. 75), de sorte que E_0^* est dense dans $[E^*, \mathscr{S}^{hsb}]$.

Réciproquement, soient $[E, \mathscr{S}]$ et $[E', \mathscr{S}']$ deux espaces syntopogènes, $E'_0 \subset E'$, $\mathscr{S}'_0 = \mathscr{S}' \mid E'_0$ (cf. [1], p. 94), k un isomorphisme de $[E'_0, \mathscr{S}'_0]$ sur $[E, \mathscr{S}]$ (cf. [1], p. 103) et E'_0 dense dans $[E', \mathscr{S}']$. Désignons par $\mathfrak{B}'(x')$ le filtre des voisinages de $x' \in E'$ par rapport à $\mathscr{S}'$, et posons $\mathfrak{B}'_0(x') = \mathfrak{B}'(x') (\cap) E'_0$. Alors $k(\mathfrak{B}'_0(x'))$ sera, pour $x' \in E' - E'_0$, un filtre rond dans $[E, \mathscr{S}]$, et si l'on désigne par E^* l'ensemble composé de tous ces filtres $k(\mathfrak{B}'_0(x'))$ $(x' \in E' - E'_0)$ et de toutes les grilles fondamentales, puis on construit $\mathscr{S}^h$ de la manière décrite plus haut, alors l'application

$$l(x') = f(k(x')) \quad \text{pour} \quad x' \in E'_0,$$
$$l(x') = k(\mathfrak{B}'_0(x')) \quad \text{pour} \quad x' \in E' - E'_0$$

sera $(\mathscr{S}'^{tp}, \mathscr{S}^{htp})$-continue (cf. [1], pp. 73, 74 et 102), et si l'on suppose encore que $\mathscr{S}'$ est symétrique (cf. [1], p. 62), l sera même $(\mathscr{S}', \mathscr{S}^h)$-continue.

Les méthodes de prolongement d'espaces syntopogènes que nous venons d'esquisser permettent d'obtenir facilement la solution des problèmes de complétion et de compactification. En effet, si $[E, \mathscr{S}]$ est un espace syntopogène quelconque, désignons par E^* l'ensemble composé des grilles fondamentales et des filtres de Cauchy ronds qui ne convergent pas dans $[E, \mathscr{S}^{sb}]$, et construisons $\mathscr{S}^h$ comme plus haut. Alors les structures syntopogènes $\mathscr{S}^h$ et $\mathscr{S}^{hsb}$ sont complètes (cf. [1], p. 193), E_0^* est dense dans $[E^*, \mathscr{S}^{hsb}]$, $\mathscr{S}^h$ est relativement séparée par rapport à E_0^*, et l'on a $\mathscr{S} = f^{-1}(\mathscr{S}^h)$, d'où résulte que f est un isomorphisme de $[E, \mathscr{S}]$ sur $[E_0^*, \mathscr{S}^h \mid E_0^*]$. Convenons d'appeler *complétion* pour un espace syntopogène $[E, \mathscr{S}]$ le triple $(E', \mathscr{S}', f')$ d'un ensemble E', d'une structure syntopogène $\mathcal{S}'$ sur E' et d'une application f' de E sur $E'_0 \subset E'$ jouissant des propriétés: $\mathcal{S}'$ et $\mathcal{S}'^{sb}$ sont complètes, E'_0 est dense dans $[E', \mathcal{S}'^{sb}]$, $\mathcal{S}'$ est relativement séparée par rapport à E'_0 et f' est un isomorphisme de $[E, \mathcal{S}]$ sur $[E'_0, \mathcal{S}' \mid E'_0]$. On peut dire alors que, pour un espace syntopogène quelconque $[E, \mathcal{S}]$, il existe au moins une complétion $(E', \mathcal{S}', f')$ satisfaisant même à l'égalité plus précise $\mathcal{S} = f'^{-1}(\mathcal{S}')$. Si $\mathcal{S}$ est séparée (cf. [1], p. 175), $\mathcal{S}'$ sera également séparée, et si $\mathcal{S}$ est symétrique, parfaite, biparfaite ou symétrique et biparfaite (cf. [1], p. 62), on peut choisir $\mathcal{S}'$ de la manière qu'elle jouisse de la même propriété.

On peut même démontrer que la complétion d'un espace syntopogène est déterminée univoquement à un isomorphisme près. Cela veut dire de façon plus précise que si $(E', \mathcal{S}', f')$ et $(E'', \mathcal{S}'', f'')$ sont deux complétions pour un espace syntopogène $[E, \mathcal{S}]$, alors il existe un isomorphisme g de $[E', \mathcal{S}']$ sur $[E'', \mathcal{S}'']$ tel que $g \mid f'(E) = f'' \circ f'^{-1}$. C'est une conséquence immédiate du théorème d'extension suivant. Soient $[E, \mathcal{S}]$ et $[E', \mathcal{S}']$ deux espaces syntopogènes, $\mathcal{S}'^{sb}$ complète, $E_0 \subset E$ dense dans $[E, \mathcal{S}^{sb}]$ et f_0 une application $(\mathcal{S} \mid E_0, \mathcal{S}')$-continue de E_0 sur un ensemble $E'_0 \subset E'$. Il existe alors une application $(\mathcal{S}, \mathcal{S}')$-continue de E dans E' telle que $f \mid E_0 = f_0$. Cette application est déterminée univoquement si soit $\mathcal{S}'$ est séparée, soit $\mathcal{S}$ est relativement séparée par rapport à E_0, $\mathcal{S}'$ est relativement séparée par rapport à E'_0 et f_0 est un isomorphisme de $[E_0, \mathcal{S} \mid E_0]$ sur $[E'_0, \mathcal{S}' \mid E'_0]$; ces dernières conditions entraînent que f est un isomorphisme de $[E, \mathcal{S}]$ sur $[f(E), \mathcal{S}' \mid f(E)]$ et, si de plus $\mathcal{S}^{sb}$ est complète et E'_0 est dense dans $[E', \mathcal{S}'^{sb}]$, on a encore $f(E) = E'$.

Pour étudier la question de compactification, on considère un espace topogène $[E, \mathcal{T}]$ (cf. [1], p. 62), on désigne par E^* l'ensemble composé des grilles fondamentales et des filtres comprimés ronds qui ne convergent pas dans $[E, \mathcal{T}^s]$, et on construit la structure topogène $\mathcal{T}^h$. On voit alors que $\mathcal{T}^h$ et $\mathcal{T}^{hs}$ sont compactes (cf. [1], p. 195), E^*_0 est dense dans $[E^*, \mathcal{T}^{hs}]$, $\mathcal{T}^h$ est relativement séparée par rapport à E^*_0, et on a enfin $\mathcal{T} = f^{-1}(\mathcal{T}^h)$, de sorte que f est un isomorphisme de $[E, \mathcal{T}]$ sur $[E^*_0, \mathcal{T}^h \mid E^*_0]$. Appelons *double compactification* pour un espace topogène $[E, \mathcal{T}]$ un triple $(E', \mathcal{T}', f')$ d'un ensemble E', d'une structure topogène $\mathcal{T}'$ sur E' et d'une application f' de E sur un sous-ensemble $E'_0 \subset E'$, si $\mathcal{T}'$ et $\mathcal{T}'^s$ sont compactes, E'_0 est dense dans $[E', \mathcal{T}'^s]$, $\mathcal{T}'$ est relativement séparée par rapport à E'_0 et f' est un isomorphisme de $[E, \mathcal{T}]$ sur $[E'_0, \mathcal{T}' \mid E'_0]$. Par conséquent, il existe au moins une double compactification $(E', \mathcal{T}', f')$ pour un espace topogène quelconque $[E, \mathcal{T}]$, de plus, si $\mathcal{T}$ est symétrique ou séparée, $\mathcal{T}'$ jouira de la même propriété. Si $(E', \mathcal{T}', f')$ et $(E'', \mathcal{T}'', f'')$ sont deux doubles compactifications pour $[E, \mathcal{T}]$, il existe un isomorphisme g de $[E', \mathcal{T}']$ sur $[E'', \mathcal{T}'']$ tel que $g \mid f'(E) = f'' \circ f'^{-1}$, ce qu'on peut démontrer à l'aide d'un théorème d'extension semblable à celui que nous avons formulé à propos de la question d'unicité des complétions. On peut l'obtenir en y remplaçant $\mathcal{S}^{sb}$ par $\mathcal{S}^s$, $\mathcal{S}'^{sb}$ par $\mathcal{S}'^s$ et le mot „complète“ par „compacte“.

Les résultats énumérés comprennent, comme cas particuliers, plusieurs théorèmes connus sur la complétion d'espaces uniformes et sur la compactification d'espaces topologiques et d'espaces de proximité. Il est même possible de donner à ceux-ci une forme plus générale que leur formulation généralement connue. Par exemple, si E est un espace uniforme (séparé ou non), on peut ajouter à E des points idéaux de la manière que l'espace E' qui résulte soit un espace uniforme complet contenant E comme sous-espace dense et relativement séparé par rapport à E en ce sens que $x', y' \in E'$, $x' \neq y'$ impliquent qu'il existe un entourage qui ne contient pas le couple (x', y'), sauf si $x', y' \in E$. De plus, si E' et E'' sont deux espaces uniformes du type en question, alors il existe un isomorphisme de E' sur E'' admettant les points de E pour points fixes.

Littérature

[1] *Á. Császár*: Fondements de la topologie générale. Budapest et Paris 1960.
[2] *H. J. Kowalsky*: Topologische Räume. Basel und Stuttgart 1961.
[3] *А. П. Мышкис*: К понятию границы. Матем. сб. *25* (67) (1949), 387—414.
[4] *F. J. Wagner*: Notes on compactification. Indagationes math. *19* (1957), 171—176; 177—181.

FIXED-POINT THEORY ON NEIGHBORHOOD RETRACTS OF CONVEXOID SPACES

A. DELEANU

Bucarest

The author sets up a fixed-point theory on neighborhood retracts of spaces introduced by JEAN LERAY in 1945 under the name of "convexoid spaces". Proofs and further details can be found in Bull. Soc. Math. France *87*, 235—243 and *89*, 223–226.

Leaning heavily on results of J. Leray, a fixed-point index is defined for the retracts of convexoid spaces. Then it is proved that each compact neighborhood retract of a convexoid space consists of a finite number of components, each of which is retract of a convexoid space. Using this fact, a fixed-point index $i_\xi(0)$ is defined for each map ξ of a compact neighborhood retract E of a convexoid space into itself and for each open subset 0 of E such that its boundary contains no fixed point of ξ. The fixed-point index thus defined posesses all the usual properties of this notion.

In this manner, the fixed-point theory of S. Lefschetz is generalized in two directions:

1° It may be applied to spaces which are not absolute neighborhood retracts in the sense of K. BORSUK (there are even acyclic convexoid spaces which are not absolute neighborhood retracts).

2° It studies not only the fixed points in the whole space, but, more generally, the fixed points which lie in an open subset of the space under consideration.

By making use of the notion of the fixed-point index, several fixed-point theorems are established. For instance:

A. *Any acyclic retract of a convexoid space has the fixed-point property.*

B. *Any map ξ of a retract of a convexoid space into itself such that there exists an integer $p > 0$ with the property that ξ^p is homotopic to a constant map has at least one fixed point.*

C. *Let C be a compact space, which is neighborhood retract of a convexoid space, and let ξ be a map of C into itself. If there exists a compact acyclic subset K of C such that*

$$\bigcap_{n>0} \xi^n(C) \subset K,$$

then ξ has at least one fixed point.

MAPPINGS OF PROXIMITY STRUCTURES

C. H. DOWKER

London

We consider proximity structures without the usual requirement of symmetry. Given a function $f : X \to Y$, there are three mappings f^q, f^0 and f^c of the proximity structures of X to those of Y related, respectively, to the notions of continuity, openness and closedness. The mappings f^0 and f^c do not in general preserve symmetry.

We also solve a problem of YU. M. SMIRNOV ([1], page 546) by giving an example of a symmetric proximity space which does not have a finest symmetric uniform structure inducing its proximity structure. The example is the product of two infinite spaces, with the product proximity structure.

A proximity structure in a set X is a relation $<$ in the set of all subsets of X, satisfying the following axioms:

1. $A < B$ implies $A \subset B$.
2. $A \subset B < C \subset D$ implies $A < D$.
3. $A_i < B$ for all $i \in I$, I finite, implies $\bigcup_i A_i < B$; $A < B_i$ for all $i \in I$, I finite implies $A < \bigcap_i B_i$.
4. $A < C$ implies that there exists B such that $A < B < C$.

Taking I void in axiom 3, we see that $\emptyset < A < X$ for every set A in X. A proximity structure $<_1$ is called finer than $<$ if $A < B$ implies $A <_1 B$. A set X has a finest proximity structure: the discrete structure in which $A < B$ whenever $A \subset B$. It also has a least fine proximity structure in which $A < B$ only if $A = \emptyset$ or $B = X$. A set X, together with a proximity structure $<$ in it, is called a proximity space.

The proximity structure $<'$, such that $A <' B$ if and only if $X \setminus B < X \setminus A$, is called the conjugate of $<$. The proximity structure $<$ is called symmetric if $<' =$ $= <$. We shall not assume an axiom of symmetry.

A proximity structure in X induces a topology in X, a set A being a neighbourhood of a point x if $(x) < A$. A finer proximity structure induces a finer topology.

If $f : X \to Y$ is a function and $<$ is a proximity structure in Y, let $A <_1 B$, for A and B in X, if there is some set C in Y such that $f(A) < C$ and $f^{-1}C \subset B$. Then $<_1$ is a proximity structure in X, called $f^{-1}(<)$. If $<$ is symmetric, so is $f^{-1}(<)$. If a given proximity structure $<_0$ in X is finer than $f^{-1}(<)$, f is called a proximally continuous function from $(X, <_0)$ to $(Y, <)$. The inverse image of the topology T induced by $<$

is the topology induced by $f^{-1}(<)$. Hence a proximally continuous function is continuous.

A uniform structure in a set X is a family $V = \{u\}$ of functions from X to the set 2^X of all subsets of X, satisfying the following axioms:

1. For each $x \in X$ and each $u \in V$, $x \in u(x)$.
2. If $u \in V$ and $u < v$ (i. e., $u(x) \subset v(x)$ for all x), then $v \in V$.
3. If $u_i \in V$ for $i \in I$, I finite, then $\bigcap_i u_i \in V$.
4. Given $u \in V$ there exists $v \in V$ such that $v^2 < u$, i. e., if $y \in v(x)$, $v(y) \subset u(x)$.

In axiom 3, $\bigcap u_i$ is the function which assigns to the point x the set $\cap u_i(x)$. The case of axiom 3 when I is void states that the maximal function 1, defined by $1(x) = X$ for all $x \in X$, belongs to V. Thus V is not empty. A uniform structure W is called finer than V if $V \subset W$. There is a finest uniform structure in X consisting of all functions satisfying axiom 1, and there is a least fine uniform structure consisting only of the function 1.

The function v', defined by $v'(x) = \{y : y \in X, x \in v(y)\}$, is called the conjugate of v. The family $V' = \{u'\}$ of conjugates of functions u in the uniform structure V is itself a uniform structure, called the conjugate of V. The uniform structure V is called symmetric if $V' = V$.

A uniform structure V induces a proximity structure $<$ as follows: $A < B$ if there exists $u \in V$ such that $\bigcup_{x \in A} u(x) \subset B$.

If $f : X \to Y$ is a function and V is a uniform structure in Y, there is a uniform structure $f^{-1}V$ in X defined as follows: Let $u \in f^{-1}V$ if there exists $v \in V$ such that for each $x \in X$, $u(x) \supset f^{-1}vf(x)$. If a given uniform structure U in X is finer than $f^{-1}V$, f is called a uniformly continuous function from (X, U) to (Y, V). If V induces the proximity structure $<$, then $f^{-1}V$ induces $f^{-1}(<)$. Hence a uniformly continuous function is proximally continuous.

Given a function $f : X \to Y$ and given a proximity structure $<$ in X, we define the quotient proximity structure $f^q(<)$ to be the finest proximity structure $<_1$ in Y for which $f : (X, <) \to (Y, <_1)$ is proximally continuous. Similarly a quotient topology $f^q(T)$ and a quotient uniform structure $f^q(V)$ can be defined. If $<$ is induced by a uniform structure V in X, $f^q(<)$ is induced by $f^q(V)$. If T is the topology induced by $<$ in X, $f^q(T)$ is finer, and in some cases strictly finer, than the topology induced by $f^q(<)$. If $<$ or V is symmetric, so is $f^q(<)$, respectively $f^q(V)$.

Given a function $f : X \to Y$ and given a proximity structure $<$ in X, we define the open image $f^0(<)$ to be the least fine proximity structure $<_1$ in Y such that $f(A) <_1 f(B)$ whenever $A < B$. The open image of a topology or of a uniform structure is similarly defined. If Y has a given proximity structure $<_0$, f is called proximally open if $<_0$ is finer than $f^0(<)$. Open functions and uniformly open functions are similarly defined. If $<$ induces the topology T, $f^0(<)$ induces $f^0(T)$. If $<$ is induced by a uniform structure V, the proximity structure induced by $f^0(V)$ is finer, and may be strictly finer, than $f^0(<)$. Thus a proximally open function is open, and a uniformly open function is proximally open.

If $<'$ is the conjugate of $<$, $f^0(<')$ is not necessarily the conjugate of $f^0(<)$. In particular, if $<$ is symmetric, $f^0(<)$ need not be symmetric. Similarly, the symmetry of the uniform structure V does not imply symmetry of $f^0(V)$.

Given a function $f : X \to Y$ and given a proximity structure $<$ in X, we define the closed image $f^c(<)$ to be the least fine proximity structure $<_1$ in Y such that $A <_1 Y \setminus f(B)$ whenever $f^{-1}A < X \setminus B$. The closed image of a topology or of a uniform structure is similarly defined. If Y has a given proximity structure $<_0$, f is called proximally closed if $<_0$ is finer than $f^c(<)$. Closed functions and uniformly closed functions are similarly defined. Every uniformly closed function is proximally closed, but it need not be closed.The closed image of a symmetric proximity structure or uniform structure need not be symmetric.

If $u : X \to 2^X$ is any function, we say that a set $A \subset X$ is u-small if, for each pair of points x_1 and x_2 in A, $x_2 \in u(x_1)$. A uniform space (X, V) is called totally bounded if for each $u \in V$ there exists a finite decomposition of X into u-small sets.

If $\{X_\omega, <_\omega\}_{\omega \in \Omega}$ is any family of proximity spaces, the product proximity structure $\Pi <_\omega$ is defined to be the least fine proximity structure in ΠX_ω such that each projection $\pi_\omega : \Pi X_\omega \to X_\omega$ is proximally continuous. The product topology and product uniform structure are similarly defined. If $<_\omega$ induces the topology T_ω, then $\Pi <_\omega$ induces ΠT_ω. If V_ω induces $<_\omega$ and if all but one of the uniform spaces (X, V_ω) are totally bounded, then ΠV_ω induces $\Pi <_\omega$. The hypothesis of total boundedness can not be omitted.

For example, let Z be the space of integers, let U be the uniform structure of finite decompositions of Z and let V be the finest uniform structure of Z. Then U and V induce the same discrete proximity structure $<$ in Z. Since (Z, U) is totally bounded, the symmetric uniform structures $U \times U$, $U \times V$ and $V \times U$ induce the same proximity structure $< \times <$ in Z $\times$ Z. But this proximity structure is strictly less fine than the discrete proximity structure induced by $V \times V$. Since $V \times V$ is the only uniform structure in Z $\times$ Z which is finer than both $U \times V$ and $V \times U$, therefore there is no finest symmetric uniform structure inducing the proximity structure $< \times <$ in Z $\times$ Z.

Reference

[1] *Ю. М. Смирнов:* О пространствах близости. Мат. сб., *31* (1952), 543—574.

CONNEXIONS BETWEEN CONVEXITY OF A METRIC CONTINUUM X AND CONVEXITY OF ITS HYPERSPACES $C(X)$ AND 2^X

R. DUDA

Wrocław

Let X be a continuum with a metric ϱ. We denote by $C(X)$ the hyperspace of all nonvacuous subcontinua of X and by 2^X the hyperspace of all nonvacuous and closed subsets of X, both metrized by the Hausdorff metric ([2], p. 291):

$$\varrho^1(A, B) = \max\left[\sup_{a\in A} \varrho(a, B), \sup_{b\in B} \varrho(A, b)\right]. \tag{1}$$

By virtue of a theorem of Mazurkiewicz ([5], see also [3], th. 2.7) the hyperspaces $C(X)$ and 2^X are continua.

For every subset Z of X and every $\eta \geqq 0$ let $Q(Z, \eta)$ be a generalized solid sphere of centre Z and radius η, i. e.

$$Q(Z, \eta) = \{x : x \in X, \varrho(x, Z) \leqq \eta\}.$$

The formula

$$\varrho^1(A, B) = \inf\{\eta : [A \subset Q(B, \eta)], [B \subset Q(A, \eta)]\} \tag{2}$$

is equivalent to the formula (1) ([3], p. 22).

We use in this paper the notion of convexity in the well known general sense of K. Menger ([6], p. 81): A space X is said to be convex provided that for each two distinct points x, y of X there exists a point $z \in X$ different from x and y which lies between x and y, i. e.

$$\varrho(x, y) = \varrho(x, z) + \varrho(z, y).$$

It is known ([6], p. 89, see also [1]) that in complete convex spaces X each pair of points $x, y \in X$ is joined by a metric segment $\overline{xy}$, i. e. by a subset of X isometric to a segment of the real line with length $\varrho(x, y)$. A space X will be said to be strongly convex provided that each two points $x, y \in X$ are joined by precisely one metric segment.

Let A and B be two subsets of X such that for each pair of points $a \in A$ and $b \in B$ there is at least one segment $\overline{ab}$ in X. We shall call a *junction in X between A and B*, denoting it by $J(A, B)$, the union of these segments, i. e. the set containing with each pair of points $a \in A$ and $b \in B$, at least one segment $\overline{ab}$. We shall call a *bridge in X between A and B*, denoting it by $P(A, B)$, every compact junction in X between A and B.

We shall use the following four lemmas:

Lemma 1. *If X is a metric continuum, A and B closed subsets of X, and $J(A,B)$ a junction in X between A and B, then its closure $\overline{J(A,B)}$ is the bridge in X between A and B.*

Lemma 2. *If X is a metric space, A and B closed subsets of X, $P(A, B)$ a bridge in X between A and B, and if $H \subset P(A, B)$ is closed, then there exist bridges $P(A, H)$ and $P(H, B)$, both contained in $P(A, B)$.*

Lemma 3. *If X is a metric space, A and B closed subsets of X such that there exists a bridge $P(A, B)$ in X between A and B, and if ε is a number such that $0 \leqq \varepsilon \leqq \varrho^1(A, B)$, then the set*

$$H = P(A, B) \cap Q(A, \varepsilon) \cap Q[B, \varrho^1(A, B) - \varepsilon] \tag{3}$$

satisfies the conditions $H \in 2^X$, $\varrho^1(A, H) = \varepsilon$, $\varrho^1(H, B) = \varrho^1(A, B) - \varepsilon$.

Lemma 4. *If X is a convex metric continuum and if every subcontinuum of X is convex, then the following sets are strongly convex: the continuum X, the generalized solid sphere $Q(A, \varepsilon)$ for every continuum $A \subset X$ and every $\varepsilon \geqq 0$, the bridge $P(A, B)$ for every pair of subcontinua A and B of X.*

We have the following six theorems, the proofs of which will be outlined only:

Theorem 1. *If X is a metric continuum, A and B closed subsets of X and if there is a bridge $P(A, B)$, then there exists in 2^X at least one segment between A and B. If, moreover, A and B are subcontinua of X and every subcontinuum of X is convex, then there exists in $C(X)$ at least one segment between A and B.*

In fact, let $A = H_0 \in 2^X$ and $B = H_1 \in 2^X$. By Lemma 3 for $\varepsilon = 2^{-1} \cdot \varrho^1(H_0, H_1)$ there exists a set $H_{1/2}$ defined by formula (3), i. e. such that $H_{1/2} \subset P(H_0, H_1)$ and

$$\varrho^1(H_0, H_{1/2}) = \varrho^1(H_{1/2}, H_1) = 2^{-1} \cdot \varrho^1(H_0, H_1) .$$

By induction and using lemmas 2 and 3, we define a family of closed sets $\{H_{k/2^n}\}$, where $n = 0, 1, \ldots$ and $k = 0, 1, \ldots, 2^n$, with the following properties:

$$H_{2k/2^{n+1}} = H_{k/2^n} \quad \text{for} \quad n = 0, 1, \ldots \quad \text{and} \quad k = 0, 1, \ldots, 2^n ,$$
$$H_{(2k+1)/2^n} \subset P(H_{2k/2^n}, H_{(2k+2)/2^n}) \quad \text{for} \quad k = 0, 1, \ldots, 2^{n-1} - 1 ,$$
$$\varrho^1(H_{k/2^n}, H_{m/2^n}) = \frac{|k-m|}{2^n} \varrho^1(H_0, H_1) \quad \text{for} \quad k, m = 0, 1, \ldots, 2^n .$$

The closure in 2^X of this family is a segment between A and B ([6], p. 87–89).

If, moreover, every subcontinuum of X is convex, $A = H_0 \in C(X)$ and $B = H_1 \in C(X)$, then the set $H_{1/2}$ is a continuum (strongly convex) since, by (3), it is the intersection of three continua which are strongly convex by Lemma 4 ([6], p. 104). Hence $H_{1/2} \in C(X)$. For the same reason each $H_{k/2^n}$, where $n = 0, 1, \ldots$ and $k = 0, 1, \ldots, 2^n$, is a continuum. Therefore the closure in $C(X)$ of the family $\{H_{k/2^n}\}$ is a segment in $C(X)$ between A and B ([6], p. 87–89 and [4], p. 110).

The Theorem 1 implies at once the following

Theorem 2. *If X is a convex metric continuum and every subcontinuum of X is convex, then the hyperspace $C(X)$ is convex.*

The converse implication is an open problem (see p. 145).

Theorem 3. *If X is a metric continuum and at least one of the hyperspaces $C(X)$ and 2^X is convex, then X is convex.*

In fact, let $p \in X$ and $q \in X$. At least one of the hyperspaces $C(X)$ and 2^X being convex by hypothesis, there exists in this hyperspace a segment between (p) and (q), composed of subsets of X. Therefore the inequality $0 \leqq \varepsilon \leqq \varrho^1(p, q)$ implies the existence of a set $Z \subset X$ belonging to this segment and such that $\varrho^1(p, Z) = \varepsilon$ and $\varrho^1(Z, q) = \varrho^1(p, q) - \varepsilon$.

As can be seen easily, each point $z \in Z$ satisfies the equalities $\varrho(p, z) = \varepsilon$ and $\varrho(q, z) = \varrho(p, q) - \varepsilon$. Hence the continuum X is convex.

Theorem 4. *If X is a metric continuum containing isometrically the boundary of a square, then the hyperspace $C(X)$ is not convex.*

In fact, let $K \subset X$ be a continuum isometric with the boundary of the unit square in the plane $0xy$, with opposite vertices $(0, 0)$ and $(1, 1)$. The continuum K is then a union of 4 segments: I with ends $(0, 0)$ and $(0, 1)$, II with ends $(0, 1)$ and $(1, 1)$, III with ends $(1, 1)$ and $(1, 0)$, and IV with ends $(1, 0)$ and $(0, 0)$. Consider the continua $A = \mathrm{I} \cup \mathrm{II} \cup \mathrm{IV}$ and $B = \mathrm{III} \cup \mathrm{II} \cup \mathrm{IV}$. We have

$$Q(A, 4^{-1}) \cap Q(B, 4^{-1}) = Q(\mathrm{II}, 4^{-1}) \cup Q(\mathrm{IV}, 4^{-1}), \tag{4}$$

$$Q(\mathrm{II}, 4^{-1}) \cap Q(\mathrm{IV}, 4^{-1}) = 0. \tag{5}$$

Since $\varrho^1(A, B) = 2^{-1}$, it suffices to prove that there exist no continuum $H \subset X$ such that

$$\varrho^1(A, H) = \varrho^1(H, B) = 4^{-1}. \tag{6}$$

Note first the following implication: each of the inclusions

$$H \subset Q(\mathrm{II}, 4^{-1}) \quad \text{and} \quad H \subset Q(\mathrm{IV}, 4^{-1}) \tag{7}$$

implies both of the inequalities

$$\varrho^1(A, H) > 4^{-1} \quad \text{and} \quad \varrho^1(H, B) > 4^{-1}. \tag{8}$$

Suppose now that there exists a continuum $H \subset X$ satisfying (6). Then by (2) we have $H \subset Q(A, 4^{-1})$ and $H \subset Q(B, 4^{-1})$, whence $H \subset Q(A, 4^{-1}) \cap Q(B, 4^{-1})$. By (4) and (5) there follows one of the inclusions (7), and therefore, by the mentioned implication, the inequalities (8), contrary to (6).

Theorem 5. *If X is a metric continuum, then the hyperspace 2^X is convex if and only if X is convex.*

In fact, if the hyperspace 2^X is convex, then by Theorem 3 the continuum X is also convex. Inversely, if the continuum X is convex, then evidently there exists, by the definition of junction, a junction $J(A, B)$ in X between A and B for each two closed subsets A and B of X. Then by Lemma 1 there exists a bridge $P(A, B)$ in X between A and B, and by Theorem 1 there follows the existence of a segment in 2^X joining A and B. Hence 2^X is convex.

Theorem 6. *If a metric continuum X can be immersed isometrically in Euclidean n-space E^n with $n \geqq 1$, and if the hyperspace $C(X)$ is convex, then X is a segment — and conversely.*

In fact, if X is a segment, then every subcontinuum is a segment or a point and therefore is convex. Hence by Theorem 2 the hyperspace $C(X)$ is also convex.

Conversely, if $C(X)$ is convex, then X is convex by Theorem 3 and contains no boundary of a square by Theorem 4. Therefore dim $X \leqq 1$, because every convex and at least 2-dimensional continuum $X \subset E^n$ contains some square. The only 1-dimensional convex continuum lying isometrically in Euclidean space is a segment, of course.

Problems. 1. *Characterize the family of continua whose hyperspaces of subcontinua are convex.*

This problem was solved for continua isometrically immersible in Euclidean space only: the characteristic property is to be a segment.

Among continua which are not isometrically immersible in Euclidean spaces, the dendrites (i.e. acyclic and locally connected continua), metrized by arc-length have only convex subcontinua and therefore, by Theorem 2, their hyperspaces of subcontinua are convex.

The solution of problem 1 would be obtained from the positive answer to the following problem (see Theorem 2):

2. *Does the convexity of the hyperspace $C(X)$ of a continuum X imply that every subcontinuum of X is convex?*

Remark. Detailed proofs of lemmas and theorems formulated here are contained in the author's article "On convex metric spaces III." Fundamenta Mathematicae *51* (1962).

References

[1] *N. Aronszajn*: Neuer Beweis der streckenverbundenheit vollständiger konvexer Räume. Ergebnisse eines mat. Kolloquiums *4* (1932), 45—56.
[2] *F. Hausdorff*: Grundzüge der Mengenlehre. Leipzig 1914.
[3] *J. L. Kelley*: Hyperspaces of a Continuum. Trans. Amer. Math. Soc. *52* (1942), 22—36.
[4] *C. Kuratowski*: Topologie II. Warszawa 1952.
[5] *S. Mazurkiewicz*: Sur l'hyperespace d'un continu. Fundam. math. *18* (1932), 171—177.
[6] *K. Menger*: Untersuchungen über allgemeine Metrik. Math. Ann. *100* (1928), 75—163.

TWO RESULTS CONCERNING BICONNECTED SETS WITH DISPERSION POINTS

R. DUDA

Wrocław

By a *connected* space I understand a connected space (i. e. space which is not a sum of two nonvacuous, disjoint and closed subsets) containing at least two distinct points. A space X is said to be *biconnected* if it is connected and is not a sum of two nonvacuous, disjoint and connected subsets.

The concept of a biconnected set was introduced by B. KNASTER and C. KURATOWSKI [2]. All their examples contain the so called *dispersion point* (i. e. a point p contained in every connected subset). No connected space can have more than one dispersion point [1]. Using the continuum hypothesis, however, E. W. MILLER [6] proved, that there exists a biconnected set which contains no dispersion point.

In what follows I only consider biconnected spaces with dispersion points. Many interesting results are known about them [1], [2], [3], [4], [5], [7] and [8]. I want to supply them with two new results.

I. *For every metric, separable and biconnected space Y there exist a biconnected space X with a dispersion point and a continuous function f that maps X onto Y.*

A space X is said to be *minimally biconnected* if it is a biconnected space with a dispersion point p, and every quasi-component of $X - (p)$ consists of exactly one point.

B. KNASTER [4] constructed minimally biconnected spaces of arbitrary dimension $n = 1, 2, \ldots$ J. H. ROBERTS [7] proved that the set R of all rational points of Hilbert space is homeomorphic with the plane minimally biconnected set whose dispersion point is removed.

Knaster posed the following problem: does there exist a biconnected set with a dispersion point which contains no minimally biconnected set?

If the continuum hypothesis is true, the answer is affirmative. Namely, I prove that:

II. *If the continuum hypothesis is true, there exists a plane biconnected set X with a dispersion point p such that, for every biconnected subset $B \subset X$, the set $B - (p)$ contains $2^{\aleph_0}$ quasi-components each of which is of power $2^{\aleph_0}$.*

Remark. The proofs of the above results are contained in an article to appear in "Rozprawy Matematyczne".

References

[1] *J. R. Kline*: A theorem concerning connected point sets. Fund. Math. *3* (1922), 238–239.
[2] *B. Knaster* et *C. Kuratowski*: Sur les ensembles connexes. Fund. Math. *2* (1921), 206–255.
[3] *B. Knaster* et *C. Kuratowski*: Sur quelques propriétés topologiques des fonctions derivées. Rend. del Circ. Math. di Palermo, *59* (1925), 382–386.
[4] *B. Knaster*: Sur les coupures biconnexes des espaces euclidiens de dimension $n > 1$ arbitraire. Recueil Math. de Moscou *19* (61) (1946), 7–18 (in Russian with French summary).
[5] *A. Lelek*: Ensembles σ-connexes et le théorème de Gehman. Fund. Math. *47* (1959), 265–276.
[6] *E. W. Miller*: Concerning biconnected sets. Fund. Math. *29* (1937), 123–133.
[7] *J. H. Roberts*: The rational points in Hilbert space. Duke Math. Journ. *23* (1956), 489–491.
[8] *R. L. Wilder*: A point set which has no true quasi-components and which becomes connected upon the addition of a single point. Bull. of Amer. Math. Soc. *33* (1927), 423–427.

ON THE TOPOLOGICAL PRODUCT OF DISCRETE λ-COMPACT SPACES

P. ERDÖS and A. HAJNAL

Budapest

In a previous paper [1] we investigated general intersection properties of abstract sets and applied our results to topological products of discrete spaces. In the present paper after restating some of our old results we solve one of the problems left open in [1] and state some old and new problems.

A topological space $\mathscr{X}$ is said to be κ-compact if every family $\mathscr{M}$ of closed subsets of it with void intersection contains a subfamily $\mathscr{M}' \subseteq \mathscr{M}$, $\overline{\overline{\mathscr{M}'}} < \aleph_\kappa$ with void intersection. 0-compactness means ordinary compactness (bicompactness in the sense of P. S. ALEXANDROFF and P. URYSON who introduced this terminology).

1-compact spaces are the Lindelöf spaces.

The symbol $\mathbf{T}(m, \lambda) \rightarrow \kappa$ will denote the following statement: If $\mathscr{F}$ is a family of discrete λ-compact topological spaces, $\overline{\overline{\mathscr{F}}} = m$, then the topological product of the elements of $\mathscr{F}$ is κ-compact. $\mathbf{T}(m, \lambda) \nrightarrow \kappa$ denotes the negation of the above statement.

Tychonov's classical theorem can be stated as $\mathbf{T}(m, 0) \rightarrow 0$ for every cardinal number m.

If we use the generalised continuum hypothesis a theorem of J. Łos can be stated as:

(1) $$\mathbf{T}(\aleph_{\alpha+1}, 1) \nrightarrow \alpha \quad \text{for every} \quad \alpha \geqq 1$$

provided $\aleph_\alpha$ is regular and of measure 0.[1]) (See [2].)

We proved

(2) $$\mathbf{T}(\aleph_{\alpha+n}, \alpha + 1) \nrightarrow \alpha + n$$

for every ordinal number α and for every $1 \leqq n < \omega$.

It is easy to see that (2) is best possible but it gives no information if $n \geqq \omega$. In [1] we proposed among others the following problems:

(3) $$\mathbf{T}(\aleph_\omega, 1) \rightarrow \omega\ ?$$

(4) $$\mathbf{T}(\aleph_{\omega+2}, 1) \rightarrow \omega + 2\ ? \quad (\text{or } \mathbf{T}(\aleph_{\omega+1}, 1) \rightarrow \omega + 1\ ?).$$

We can not answer (4) ($\mathbf{T}(\aleph_{\omega+2}, 1) \nrightarrow \omega + 1$ follows from (1)). But we shall prove that the answer to (3) is negative.

[1]) The cardinal number m is said to be of measure o, if every two valued σ-measure defined on all subsets of a set S, $\overline{\overline{S}} = m$ vanishes identically provided $M(\{x\}) = 0$ for every $x \in S$.

Before we give the (simple) proof we would like to state a few problems most of which have been already stated in [1]. First we need some definitions:

The family $\mathscr{F}$ of sets is said to possess property **B** if there exists a set B such that

$$F \cap B \neq 0 \quad \text{and} \quad F \nsubseteq B \quad \text{for every} \quad F \in \mathscr{F}.$$

$\mathscr{F}$ is said to possess property $\mathbf{B}(s)$ if there is set B such that

$$1 \leqq \overline{\overline{F \cap B}} < s \quad \text{for every} \quad F \in \mathscr{F}.$$

If $\overline{\overline{F}} = p$ for every $F \in \mathscr{F}$ we briefly write $p(\mathscr{F}) = p$. The family $\mathscr{F}$ is said to possess property $\mathbf{C}(\xi r)$ if $\overline{\overline{F_1 \cap F_2}} < r$ for every $F_1 \neq F_2 \in \mathscr{F}$.

Let $\mathbf{M}(m, p, r) \to \mathbf{B}(s)$ briefly denote the following statement:

Every family $\mathscr{F}$, $\overline{\overline{\mathscr{F}}} = m$, $p(\mathscr{F}) = p$ which possesses property $\mathbf{C}(r)$ possesses property $\mathbf{B}(s)$ too.

$\mathbf{M}(m, p, r) \nrightarrow \mathbf{B}(1)$ denotes then negation of this statement. (2) was deduced from the following result of [1]

(5) $\quad \mathbf{M}(\aleph_{\alpha+n}, \aleph_\alpha, r) \to \mathbf{B}((r-1)(n+1)+2), \quad \omega > r, n, \quad r \geqq 1, \quad n \geqq 0$

and

$$\mathbf{M}(\aleph_{\alpha+n}, \aleph_\alpha, r) \nrightarrow \mathbf{B}((r-1)(n+1)+1), \quad \omega > r, n, \quad r \geqq 1, \quad n \geqq 0.$$

(See Theorems 8 and 10 of [1].)

Namely it is easy to see that if there exists a family $\mathscr{F}$, $\overline{\overline{\mathscr{F}}} = \aleph_\beta$, $p(\mathscr{F}) = \aleph_\alpha$ and an integer s such that every subfamily $\mathscr{F}'$ of power $< \aleph_\beta$ of $\mathscr{F}$ possesses property $\mathbf{B}(s)$ but $\mathscr{F}$ does not possess property $\mathbf{B}(s)$ then we have $\mathbf{T}(\aleph_\beta, \alpha + 1) \nrightarrow \beta$.

The results of [1] show that the investigation of the symbol $\mathbf{M}(m, p, r) \to \mathbf{B}(s)$ can not lead to the existence of such families for $\beta \geqq \alpha + \omega$.

Perhaps question of the following type can lead to new results in this direction.

Does there exist a family $\mathscr{F}$, $p(\mathscr{F}) = \aleph_\alpha$, $\overline{\overline{\mathscr{F}}} = \aleph_{\alpha+\gamma}$ and an integer valued function $l(F)$, defined for every $F \in \mathscr{F}$ satisfying the following conditions:

If $\mathscr{F}' \nsubseteq \mathscr{F}$, $\mathscr{F}' < \aleph_{\alpha+\gamma}$ then there exists a set B' such that $1 \leqq \overline{\overline{F \cap B'}} < l(F)$ for every $F \in \mathscr{F}'$.

If $F \cap B \neq 0$ for every $F \in \mathscr{F}$ then $\overline{\overline{F \cap B}} \geqq l(F)$ for at least one $F \in \mathscr{F}$.

If $\alpha = 0$, $\gamma < \omega$ the existence of such a family follows from (5). The simplest cases where we do know the answer are $\alpha = 0$, $\gamma = \omega$ or $\gamma = \omega + 1$. It is obvious that a positive solution of this problem for $\alpha = 0$, $\beta = \omega + 1$ would fournish a proof of

$$\mathbf{T}(\aleph_{\omega+1}, 1) \nrightarrow \omega + 1.$$

Here are some problems which would all have been consequences of $\mathbf{T}(\aleph_2, 1) \to 2$ (which we know is false). The answer to these questions is probably negative but we can not disprove them.

Let $\mathscr{F}$ be a family, $\overline{\overline{\mathscr{F}}} = \aleph_2$, $p(\mathscr{F}) = \aleph_0$ such that every $\mathscr{F}' \subseteq \mathscr{F}$, $\overline{\overline{\mathscr{F}'}} \leqq \aleph_1$ possesses property **B**. Does then $\mathscr{F}$ necessarily possess property **B** too?

A family $\mathscr{F}$ is said to have property **G** if there exists a function $f(F) \in F$ defined for every F of $\mathscr{F}$ such that $f(F_1) \neq f(F_2)$ for $F_1 \neq F_2 \in \mathscr{F}$.

Let $\mathcal{F}$ be a family ($\overline{\overline{\mathcal{F}}} = \aleph_2$, $p(\mathcal{F}) = \aleph_0$) such that every $\mathcal{F}' \subseteq \mathcal{F}$, ($\overline{\overline{\mathcal{F}'}} \leqq \aleph_1$) possesses property **G**. Does then $\mathcal{F}$ necessarily possess property **G** too? This problem is due to W. Gustin.

Let there be given a graph $\mathcal{G}$ of power $\aleph_2$. Suppose that every subgraph of power $\leqq \aleph_1$ of it has chromatic number $\leqq \aleph_0$ (i. e. its vertices can be coloured with $\aleph_0$ colours so that two vertices of the same colour are never connected). Is it then true that $\mathcal{G}$ has chromatic number $\leqq \aleph_0$?

Let there be given a graph $\mathcal{G}$ of power $\aleph_2$. Suppose that for every subgraph $\mathcal{G}'$ of $\mathcal{G}$ of power $\leqq \aleph_1$ its edges can be directed in such a way that the number of edges emanating from an arbitrary vertex is finite. Is it true that the same holds for the graph $\mathcal{G}$? (This would not follow from $\mathbf{T}(\aleph_2, 1) \to 2$.)

Now we are going to outline the solution of problem (3).

Using the generalized continuumhypothesis we can prove the following theorem:

Suppose that $\aleph_{\alpha+\gamma}$ *is singular* $cf(\gamma) \leqq \omega$ (*cf* = *cofinal*) *then*

$$\mathbf{T}(\aleph_{\alpha+\gamma}, \alpha + 1) \not\to \alpha + \gamma .$$

We give the proof of the simplest case $\alpha = 0, \gamma = \omega, (cf(\gamma) = 0)$.

By (2) for every $\omega > n \geqq 1$ there exists a family $\mathcal{F}_n$, $\overline{\overline{\mathcal{F}}}_n = \aleph_n$, $p(\mathcal{F}) = \aleph_0$ such that the topological product $\aleph_n$ of the discrete spaces $F \in \mathcal{F}_n$ is not n-compact, i. e. there exists a family $\mathcal{M}_n$ of closed subsets of X_n such that $\mathcal{M}_n$ has a void intersection and $\mathcal{M}' \subseteq \mathcal{M}$, $\overline{\overline{\mathcal{M}'}} < \aleph_n$ implies that $\mathcal{M}'$ has a non-void intersection.

Let $J = \{1, \ldots, n, \ldots\}$ be the set of integers and consider the space $\mathcal{X} = J \times J_1 \times \ldots \times J_n \times \ldots$.

Let $\mathcal{M}_n^*$ be the following system of subsets of $\mathcal{X}$: $U \in \mathcal{M}_n^*$ if and only if there exists an $U' \in \mathcal{M}_n$ such that $U = J \times \mathcal{X}_1 \times \ldots \times \mathcal{X}_{n-1} \times U' \times \mathcal{X}_{n+1} \times \ldots \cup \cup J_n \times \mathcal{X}_1 \times \ldots \times \mathcal{X}_n \times \ldots$ where $J_n \subseteq J$, $J_n = \{n, n+1, \ldots\}$. It is obvious that $\mathcal{M}_n^*$ consists of closed subsets of $\mathcal{X}$. Put $\mathcal{M} = \bigcup_{n=1}^{\infty} \mathcal{M}_n^*$. Considering that the $\mathcal{M}_n$'s have a void intersection it follows that $\mathcal{M}$ has a void intersection and it is easy to verify that $\mathcal{M}' \subseteq \mathcal{M}$, $\overline{\overline{\mathcal{M}'}} < \aleph_\omega$ implies that $\mathcal{M}'$ has a non-void intersection. Hence $\mathcal{X}$ is the topological product of $\aleph_\omega$ discrete 1-compact spaces and is not ω-compact.

In the general case the proof becomes a little more complicated since instead of J and the sets J_n we have to use a system which proves $\mathbf{T}(\aleph_{cf(\gamma)}, \alpha + 1) \not\to cf(\gamma)$ and as to the existence of the systems corresponding to the $\mathcal{M}_n$'s we have to refer to Łos's theorem.

For singular $\aleph_{\alpha+\gamma}$ the simplest unsolved problem is the following:

$$\mathbf{T}(\aleph_{\omega_{\omega+1}}, 1) \to \omega_{\omega+1} \,?$$

Our proof for $\mathbf{T}(\aleph_{\omega_{\omega+1}}, 1) \not\to \omega_{\omega+1}$ breaks down since we can not even prove

$$\mathbf{T}(\aleph_{\omega+1}, 1) \not\to \omega + 1$$

References

[1] *P. Erdös* and *A. Hajnal*: On a property of families of sets. Acta Math. Acad. Sci. Hung. *12* (1961), 87–123.

[2] *J. Łos*: Linear equations and pure subgroups. Bull. Acad. Polon. Sci. Math. *7* (1959), 13–18.

NULLDIMENSIONALE RÄUME

J. FLACHSMEYER

Berlin

Aus einer in Vorbereitung befindlichen Arbeit (die voraussichtlich in den „Abhandlungen aus dem Mathematischen Seminar der Universität Hamburg" erscheinen wird) über den genannten Gegenstand sollen hier einige Punkte berührt werden. Dabei sind 0-dimensionale Räume im Sinne der kleinen induktiven Dimension ind $X = 0$ gemeint, d. h. solche, für die die offenabgeschlossenen Mengen eine offene Basis bilden.

1. Ein Hausdorffscher 0-dimensionaler Raum X gestattet zu je zwei verschiedenen Punkten eine Zerlegung in offene Mengen, die die Punkte trennt. Diese Zerlegungseigenschaft ist äquivalent damit, dass die Quasikomponenten einpunktig sind, also der Raum total-zusammenhangslos ist. Welche Bedingung muss nun noch zu der totalen Zusammenhangslosigkeit dazukommen, damit Äquivalenz zur Nulldimensionalität erreicht wird?

Satz 1. *Ein Hausdorffscher Raum X ist 0-dimensional genau dann, wenn er total-zusammenhangslos und lokal-peripher-kompakt ist.*

Die lokal-periphere Kompaktheit stellt eine von L. Zippin angegebene Abschwächung der lokalen Kompaktheit dar, es wird nämlich zu jedem Punkt nur die Existenz beliebig kleiner offener Umgebungen mit kompakter Begrenzung verlangt.

Eine weitere Bedingung, welche die 0-dimensionalen Räume als Spezialfälle unter den lokal-peripher-kompakten aussondert, gibt die nachstehende Aussage an.

Satz 2. *Ein lokal-peripher-kompakter Hausdorffschen Raum ist 0-dimensional genau dann, wenn jede endliche, offene, peripher-kompakte Überdeckung eine endliche, offen-abgeschlossene Verfeinerung besitzt, deren Elemente disjunkt sind.*

Der in der Formulierung vorkommende Begriff einer peripher-kompakten Überdeckung steht für eine Überdeckung, gebildet aus Überdeckungselementen mit kompakter Begrenzung. Weil in kompakten Räumen jede Überdeckung peripher-kompakt ist, so sagt also Satz 2 in diesem Falle die wohlbekannte Übereinstimmung von kleiner induktiver Dimension 0 und Überdeckungsdimension 0 aus.

2. Wir gehen jetzt zu Betrachtungen in kompakten Hausdorffschen Erweiterungen vollständig regulärer Räume über.

0-dimensionale Hausdorffsche Räume besitzen als vollständig reguläre Räume kompakte Hausdorffsche Erweiterungen. Wir fragen, wann ist solch eine Erweiterung bX selbst wieder 0-dimensional.

Im Hinblick auf den folgenden 3. Punkt beschränken wir uns auf eine funktionale Kennzeichung.

Satz 3. *bX sei eine kompakte Hausdorffsche Erweiterung des vollständig regulären Raumes X. γ bezeichne den Ring der beschränkten, reellen, stetigen Funktionen von X, die sich auf bX stetig fortsetzen lassen. bX ist* 0*-dimensional genau dann, wenn der Unterring der Funktionen aus γ, die nur endlich viele Werte annehmen, bezüglich gleichmässiger Konvergenz in γ dicht liegt.*

Diese Tatsache kann man leicht aus der Beziehung ablesen, dass für das kompakte bX die kleine induktive Dimension ind $bX = 0$ gleichbedeutend mit der Überdeckungsdimension dim $bX = 0$ und dies wiederum gleichbedeutend mit der analytischen Dimension ad $C^*(bX) = 0$ (vergl. über analytische Dimension das Buch von Gillman-Jerison: Rings of continuous functions, van Nostrand 1960). Ein direkter Beweis, der von der Theorie der analytischen Dimension unabhängig ist, kann unter Benutzung folgender beider Beweiselemente geführt werden. Die Dichtigkeit des Unterringes der reellen, stetigen Funktionen aus γ, die nur endlich viele Werte annehmen, ist äquivalent mit der Bedingung: Je zwei bezüglich γ vollständig separierte Mengen A, B von X, für die es also ein $f \in \gamma$ gibt mit $\overline{f(A)} \cap \overline{f(B)} = 0$, lassen sich schon durch eine Funktion aus γ, deren Bildmenge endlich ist, in der angegebenen Weise trennen. Weiter sind nun zwei Mengen A, B aus X bezüglich γ vollständig separiert genau dann, wenn die abgeschlossenen Hüllen von A und B in bX disjunkt sind.

Der angeführte Satz gestattet auch eine funktionale Erzeugung der ganzen Skala aller 0-dimensionalen Hausdorffschen kompakten Erweiterungen von X. Dazu betrachte man alle Unterringe $\mathfrak{C}$ mit Eins des Ringes $C^*(X)$ aller stetigen, reellen, beschränkten Funktionen von X, die aus Funktionen gebildet werden, die nur endliche Bildmengen haben. Ist $\mathfrak{C}$ solch ein Unterring von $C^*(X)$ und ist ausserdem die von $\mathfrak{C}$ erzeugte schwache Topologie auf X mit der ursprünglichen identisch, so liefert der Strukturraum der von $\mathfrak{C}$ in $C^*(X)$ erzeugten Banach-Algebra $\mathscr{B}(\mathfrak{C})$ eine 0-dimensionale kompakte Erweiterung. Jede wird auf diese Weise erhalten.

3. Wir bemühen uns jetzt um eine inner-topologische Übersicht über die Skala der 0-dimensionalen kompakten Hausdorffschen Erweiterungen. Das kann wie folgt geschehen.

Wegen der Nulldimensionalität von X gibt es Basen $\mathfrak{B}$ aus offen-abgeschlossenen Mengen. Wir betrachten zu einer solchen Basis $\mathfrak{B}$ das System $\mathscr{U}(\mathfrak{B})$ der endlichen Überdeckungen mit Basiselementen aus $\mathfrak{B}$. Dabei setzen wir jetzt immer voraus, dass zu einer Basis die Grundmenge des Raumes adjungiert sei. Eine Überdeckung $\alpha \in \mathscr{U}(\mathfrak{B})$ bestimmt sodann eine Äquivalenzrelation R_α, indem zwei Punkte von X genau dann äquivalent sind, wenn mit dem einen Punkt auch stets der andere in demselben Überdeckungselement von α liegt. Die Quotientenräume X/R_α formieren sich zu einem inversen Spektrum $(X/R_\alpha, \pi_\alpha^\beta)_{R_\alpha}$, $\alpha \in \mathscr{U}(\mathfrak{B})$, sofern man die R_α bezüglich der Verfeinerungsbeziehung richtet und dann unter π_α^β im Falle, dass R_β feiner als R_α ist, die kanonische Abbildung von X/R_β auf X/R_α versteht. Dieses Spektrum — wir nennen es ein Zerlegungsspektrum — liefert mit seinem Grenzraum bX eine 0-dimensionale kompakte Erweiterung von X, denn jeder Quotientenraum X/R_α ist ein endlicher diskreter Raum.

Satz 4. *Ausgehend von einer offenen Basis offen-abgeschlossener Mengen eines 0-dimensionalen Hausdorffschen Raumes konstruiert man mittels der aus Basiselementen gebildeten endlichen Überdeckungen ein Zerlegungsspektrum von X. Der Grenzraum dieses Zerlegungsspektrum ist eine kompakte 0-dimensionale Hausdorffsche Erweiterung von X.*

Unterscheidet man zwei Erweiterungen nicht, sobald es eine Homöomorphie zwischen ihnen gibt, welche die Punkte von X festlässt, so kann man folgendes aussprechen.

Satz 5. *Für einen 0-dimensionalen Hausdorffschen Raum liefert die spektrale Erzeugung von kompakten Erweiterungen aus Basen offen-abgeschlossener Mengen, die mit je zwei Mengen auch deren Vereinigung und mit jeder Menge auch deren Komplement enthalten, eine eineindeutige Entsprechung zwischen solchen Basen und den 0-dimensionalen kompakten Hausdorffschen Erweiterungen.*

Die in Rede stehenden Basen bilden in bezug auf die beiden Operationen der symmetrischen Differenz und des Durchschnittes eine Boolesche Algebra. Der Stonesche Darstellungsraum von dieser Algebra ist gerade gleich dem von dieser Basis auf dem oben beschriebenen spektralen Wege erzeugten kompakten Raum.

L'ESPACE DES COURBES N'EST QU'UN SEMI-ESPACE DE BANACH

M. FRÉCHET

Paris

1. Pour essayer de faire d'un espace dont chaque élément est une courbe, un espace de Banach, il est naturel de généraliser les définitions relatives à l'espace euclidien de la manière suivante.

On prendra:

pour l'élément neutre, Θ, une courbe réduite à un point fixe;

pour la norme $\|\xi\|$ d'une courbe ξ, le maximum de la distance de Θ aux points de ξ;

pour le produit par scalaire, $a \,.\, \xi$, l'homothétique de ξ, dans le rapport a, avec Θ pour centre d'homothétie.

Théorème 1. *Il n'existe aucune définition de la somme qui, combinée avec les trois definitions précédentes, fasse d'un espace de courbes, un espace de Banach.*

2. Il est naturel de généraliser la définition de la somme de deux vecteurs de la façon suivante.

Soient deux paramètres *intrinsèques*, t, t' (variant de 0 à 1) définissant les positions de deux points M, M' des courbes ξ, η.[1])

Soit $\overline{ON}$, la somme géométrique des vecteurs $\overline{OM}$, $\overline{OM'}$. *La somme* $\xi + \eta$ des courbes ξ, η, sera, par définition, la courbe décrite par le point N, quand t croît et que *t' reste égal à t.*

Nous prendrons pour espace des courbes, soit l'ensemble $\mathfrak{C}$ des arcs de courbes continues orientées, soit une famille $\mathfrak{F}$ de courbes continues orientées. Nous supposerons que la famille $\mathfrak{F}$ et la paramètrisation intrinsèque, p, choisie satisfont aux quatre conditions suivantes:

A. La famille $\mathfrak{F}$ contient au moins une courbe réduite à un point.

B. Si ξ appartient à $\mathfrak{F}$, il en est de même du produit par scalaire $a \,.\, \xi$.

C. Si ξ, η appartiennent à $\mathfrak{F}$, il en est de même de leur somme $\xi + \eta$.

D. Soient N un point de $a \,.\, \xi$ et M un point de ξ. Si M, N se correspondent dans l'homothétie de ξ à $a \,.\, \xi$, N correspond à la même valeur du paramètre intrinsèque que M.

---

[1]) Quand il s'agit de l'espace R, des courbes *rectifiables*, le choix d'un paramètre intrinséque parait s'imposer: on prendra $t = \beta/L$, β étant l'abscisse curviligne $\widehat{AM}$ du point M et L la longueur de ξ.

(Les conditions A, B, C, D sont vérifiées par les exemples simples, connus, d'espaces de courbes.)

Théorème 2. *Quand les conditions* A, B, C, D *sont vérifiées par un espace de courbes, les définitions précédentes de l'élément neutre, de la norme, du produit par scalaire et de la somme, vérifient les axiomes de Banach, sauf, peut-être, les axiomes*

3° $(\xi + \eta) + \zeta = \xi + (\eta + \zeta)$.

4° *Si* $\xi + \eta = \xi + \zeta$, *on a* $\eta = \zeta$.

Et, d'après le Théorème 1, *l'un au moins de ces axiomes n'est pas vérifié: Par contre, sont vérifiées deux conséquences plus faibles de ces deux axiomes, à savoir*

16° bis $\|\xi - \eta\| \leqq \|\xi - \zeta\| + \|\zeta - \eta\|$;

4° bis $\xi - \eta = \Theta$ *a pour conséquence* $\xi = \eta$.

Définition. Nous appellerons *semiespace de Banach*, tout espace où les axiomes 16° bis et 4° bis sont vérifiés ainsi que les axiomes de Banach, sauf peut-être 3°, 4°.

Application. Nous avons défini en 1925 la différentielle de $Y = F(X)$ quand X et Y appartiennent à deux espaces de Banach (distincts ou non).

Théorème 3. 1° *On peut étendre cette définition au cas où X et Y appartiennent à deux* semi-*espaces de Banach distincts ou non.*

2° *Dans ce cas plus général, plusieurs propriétés importantes de la différentielle classique sont conservées.*

Exemples d'espaces de courbes. 1° L'exemple le plus simple est l'espace des courbes rectifiables. Pour cet espace, on voit immédiatement que les conditions A, B, D, sont vérifiées et on démontre facilement qu'il en est de même de la condition C.

2° Quand on prend pour famille $\mathfrak{F}$ l'ensemble $\mathfrak{C}$ de toutes les courbes continues orientées, le choix d'un paramètre intrinséque ne parait plus s'imposer. Nous en avons proposé un exemple, pour lequel, on voit immédiatement que les conditions A, B, C, D sont vérifiées.

Pour ces deux espaces de courbes, la somme de deux lignes polygonales est aussi une ligne polygonale. Ce résultat facilite le choix de deux contre-exemples simples, montrant que *pour ces deux espaces, ni* 3°, *ni* 4° *ne sont vérifiées.*

Remarque. Il existe une autre paramétrisation intrinséque des courbes continues orientées, définie postérieurement par Marston Morse et qui lui atendu service en Calcul des Variations. Dès lors, il en existe une infinité d'autres.

On trouvera plus de détails sur les mêmes sujets, dans nos 5 Notes aux *Comptes-Rendus*, présentées à l'Académie des Sciences:

11 Janvier 1960: L'espace des courbes est-il un espace de Banach, 248—249.
20 Avril 1960: L'espace des courbes n'est pas un espace de Banach, 2787—2790.
26 Septembre 1960: L'espace dont chaque élément est une courbe n'est qu'un semi-espace de Banach, 1258—1260.
24 Octobre 1960: Exemples de semi-espaces de Banach, 1702—1703.
23 Janvier 1961: La différentielle sur deux semi-espaces de Banach, 481—482.

A CONTRIBUTION TO THE DESCRIPTIVE THEORY OF SETS AND SPACES

Z. FROLÍK
Praha

In the present note the following kinds of spaces are investigated: bianalytic spaces (Baire sets of compact spaces; for the definition of Baire sets see 1.10 and 1.5), Borelian spaces (one-to-one continuous images of bianalytic spaces), analytic spaces (continuous images of bianalytic spaces), one-to-one continuous images of closed subspaces of the space of all irrational numbers, and continuous images of the space of all irr. numbers. As an introduction one can make use of [6] and [9]. For historical notes see Section 5. It should be noted that the notation, terminology and results of Section 1 are used without references, the proofs of most results of Section 3 do not depend upon Section 2, and Section 4 essentially depends upon the preceding sections. The proofs of Section 2 are relatively brief because they are similar to those of [6].

For convenience, all spaces under consideration are supposed to be completely regular.

1. NOTATION AND TERMINOLOGY

1.1. exp H always denotes the family of all subsets of the set H.

1.2. Let f be a mapping of H onto L. If $\mathcal{M} \subset \exp H$, then $f[\mathcal{M}]$ denotes the family of all $f[M]$, $M \in \mathcal{M}$. If $\mathcal{M} \subset \exp L$, then $f^{-1}[\mathcal{M}]$ denotes the family of all $f^{-1}[M]$, $M \in \mathcal{M}$.

1.3. If $\mathcal{M} \subset \exp H$ and $N \subset H$, then $\mathcal{M} \cap N$ $(= N \cap \mathcal{M})$ denotes the family of all $M \cap N$, $M \in \mathcal{M}$.

1.4. A centered family of sets is a family $\mathcal{M}$ with the finite intersection property, i.e. the intersection of any finite subfamily of $\mathcal{M}$ is non-void.

1.5. For any family $\mathcal{M} \subset \exp H$, $\mathcal{B}^*(\mathcal{M})$, $\mathcal{B}(\mathcal{M})$, $\mathcal{B}_*(\mathcal{M})$ denote, respectively, the smallest families containing $\mathcal{M}$ and closed under following operations:

(a) countable unions and complementation,
(b) countable unions and countable intersections,
(c) countable intersections and countable disjoint unions.

1.6. By a complemented part of a family of sets $\mathcal{M}$ is meant the following family

$$\text{compl. p. } \mathcal{M} = \{M : M \in \mathcal{M}, (L - M) \in \mathcal{M}\},$$

where L is the union of $\mathcal{M}$. An $\mathcal{M}$ will be called complemented if

$$\text{compl. p. } \mathcal{M} = \mathcal{M} .$$

1.7. The letters S and Σ will always be used to denote the set of all finite sequences and infinite sequences, respectively, of positive integers. S_n, $n = 1, 2, \ldots$, denotes the set of all $s \in S$ of length n. We shall write $s \prec \sigma$ if s is a section of σ, i. e., if $s = \{s_1, \ldots, s_n\}$ and $\sigma = \{\sigma_i\}$, then $s_i = \sigma_i$ for all $i \leqq n$.

1.8. A determining system[1]) in a family $\mathcal{M}$ of sets is a mapping $M = \{M(s)\}$ of S to $\mathcal{M}$ such that

(1) $$M(\{s_1, \ldots, s_n, k\}) \subset M(\{s_1, \ldots, s_n\}) .$$

The nucleus of the determining system M is the set

(2) $$\mathcal{A}(M) = \mathcal{A}(\{M(s)\}) = \bigcup_{\sigma \in \Sigma} \bigcap_{s \prec \sigma} M(s) .$$

The nuclei of determining systems in $\mathcal{M}$ will be called $\mathcal{M}$-Souslin sets or Souslin with respect to $\mathcal{M}$. The family of all $\mathcal{M}$-Souslin sets will be denoted by $\mathcal{A}(\mathcal{M})$. It is well known that

(3) $$\mathcal{A}(\mathcal{A}(\mathcal{M})) = \mathcal{A}(\mathcal{M}) ,$$

that means, the family of all $\mathcal{M}$-Souslin sets is closed under the Souslin operation. Of course, by the Souslin operation is meant the operation leading from M to $\mathcal{A}(M)$.

1.9. By a space is meant a completely regular topological space. The letters T, X, Y, Z always denote spaces. For any X, $\mathsf{F}(X)$, $\mathsf{Z}(X)$ and $\mathsf{K}(X)$ denote, respectively, the family of all closed sets of X, zero-sets of X and compact sets contained in X. Of course, zero-sets of X are sets of the form $f^{-1}(0)$, where f is a real-valued continuous function on X. The closure in X of $M \subset X$ will be denoted by $\overline{M}^X$ or merely $\overline{M}$. If $\mathcal{M} \subset \exp X$, then $\overline{\mathcal{M}}^X$ or merely $\overline{\mathcal{M}}$, will be used to denote the family of all $\overline{M}^X$, $M \in \mathcal{M}$.

1.10. The elements of $\mathcal{B}^*(\mathsf{F}(X))$ will be called Borel subsets of X. According to M. Katětov [13], the elements of $\mathcal{B}^*(\mathsf{Z}(X)$ will be called the Baire sets of X. The family $\mathcal{B}(\mathsf{Z}(X)$ is complemented, for complements of zero-sets are countable unions of zero-sets. Thus

(4) $$\mathcal{B}(\mathsf{Z}(X)) = \mathcal{B}^*(\mathsf{Z}(X)) .$$

If X is metrizable, or more generally, perfectly normal, then $\mathsf{Z}(X) = \mathsf{F}(X)$ and hence

(5) $$\mathcal{B}^*(\mathsf{F}(X)) = \mathcal{B}(\mathsf{Z}(X)) .$$

To my knowledge, it is not known whether (5) implies that X is perfectly normal (this is a problem of M. Katětov [13]).

1.11. By a perfect mapping of X onto Y is meant a continuous and closed mapping of X onto Y such that the preimages of points are compact. If f is a perfect map-

[1]) By a determining system in $\mathcal{M}$ is usually meant a mapping of S to $\mathcal{M}$ and the determining system satisfying (1) is called regular.

ping of X onto Y, and $M \subset X$ is either closed in X or $f^{-1}[f[M]] = M$, then the restriction of f to M is a perfect mapping.

1.12. A class **D** of spaces will be called F-hereditary if closed subspaces of spaces from **D** belong to **D**. **D** will be called productive (countably productive, finitely productive) if the topological product of any (countable, finite) indexed family of spaces from **D** belongs to **D**.

1.13. Let $\mu = \{\mathcal{M}\}$ be a collection of coverings of X. An μ-Cauchy family is a centered family $\mathcal{N}$ of subsets of X such that $\mathcal{N} \cap \mathcal{M} \neq \emptyset$ for all $\mathcal{M}$ in μ. The collection μ is said to be *complete* if the intersection of $\overline{\mathcal{N}}$ is non-void for every μ-Cauchy family $\mathcal{N}$.

One can prove the following results (the proofs may be found in [7]): Let f be a mapping of X onto Y. If f is perfect and μ is a complete collection in Y, then $f^{-1}[\mu] = \{f^{-1}[\mathcal{M}]\}$ is complete in X. If f is continuous and one-to-one and μ is complete in X, then $f[\mu] = \{f[\mathcal{M}]\}$ is complete in Y.

2. ANALYTIC AND BIANALYTIC SPACES

In the classical descriptive theory of sets, and also in that presented here, the space of irrational numbers plays an important rôle. It is well known that the space of all irrational numbers is homeomorphic with the product space $\Sigma = N^N$, where N is the discrete space of positive integers. Thus Σ is the set of all infinite sequences of positive integers with the topology of pointwise convergence. Setting

$$f(\sigma) = \frac{1}{\sigma_1 + 1/(\sigma_2 + \ldots)}$$

we obtain a homeomorphism of Σ onto the space of all irrational numbers of the interval $\langle 0, 1 \rangle$.

In the classical theory, continuous images of Σ, if metrizable, are called analytic sets. G. Choquet first showed that continuous images of spaces belonging to $\mathcal{B}(\mathbf{K}(X))$ for some X (K-analytic spaces in his terminology), if metrizable, are analytic sets.

In [6] and [8] an internal characterisation of K-analytic (analytic in our terminology) is given. Here we make use of another definition, formally similar to that of analytic sets.

Definition 1. A space X will be called *analytic* if there exists a continuous compact multi-valued mapping of Σ onto X. The class of all analytic spaces will be denoted by **A** and the family of all $A \subset X$, $A \in \mathbf{A}$, by $\mathbf{A}(X)$.

By a multivalued mapping of X onto Y is meant a mapping f of X into exp Y such that the union of all $f(x)$ is Y. A mapping f will be called continuous, if for any $x \in X$ and any open set $U \supset f(x)$ there exists a neighborhood V of x with

$$y \in V \Rightarrow f(y) \subset U .$$

Setting

$$f^{-1}[M] = \{x : x \in X, f(x) \subset M\},$$

we can say that f is continuous if and only if $f^{-1}[U]$ is open for any open U. The composition $h = g \circ f$ of two multi-valued mappings f and g is defined as follows:

$$h(x) = \bigcup \{g(y) : y \in f(x)\}.$$

Clearly the composition of two continuous multi-valued mappings is continuous. f will be called compact, if all sets $f(x)$ are compact. It is easy to prove that the image of a compact (resp. Lindelöf) space under a continuous compact multi-valued mapping is a compact (Lindelöf) space. From this fact one can deduce at once that the composition of two continuous compact multivalued mappings is a continuous compact multi-valued mapping. Next, it is easy to prove that the Cartesian product of (compact) continuous mappings is a (compact) continuous mapping. Finally, if T is closed in X and f is a compact continuous mapping of X onto Y, then setting

$$g(x) = f(x) \cap T,$$

we obtain a compact continuous mapping of X onto T.

Theorem 1. *The class* **A** *is* F-*hereditary, countably productive and closed under compact continuous multi-valued mappings, in particular, under continuous mappings. Every analytic space is a Lindelöf space, and consequently normal.*

Proof. The first and the third assertions follow from Definition 1 and the above remarks. The second assertion follows from the obvious fact that the topological product of a countable number of copies of Σ is a copy of Σ. Finally, any analytic space is a Lindelöf space, for Σ is a a Lindelöf space.

Now we shall give an internal characterization of analytic spaces.

Definition 2. Let $M = \{M(s)\}$ be a determining system (see 1.8) in exp X. An M-Cauchy family (in X) is a centered family $\mathcal{M}$ of subsets of X such that $M(s) \in \mathcal{M}$ for all $s < \sigma$, where σ is an element of Σ. The system M will be called *complete* (in X) if the intersection of $\overline{\mathcal{M}}$ is non-void for every M-Cauchy family $\mathcal{M}$. An *analytic structure* in a space X is a complete determining system M in X such that

(1) $$\mathcal{A}(M) = X.$$

In [6] the following useful result is proved:

Lemma 1. *A determining system M in* exp X *is complete in X if and only if all sets*

(2) $$M(\sigma) = \bigcap_{s<\sigma} \overline{M(s)}$$

are compact, and for any $\sigma \in \Sigma$ and open $U \supset M(\sigma)$ there exists an $s < \sigma$ with $\overline{M(s)} \subset U$.

Now, for each s in S, put

(3) $$\Sigma(s) = \{\sigma : s < \sigma\}.$$

Either from Lemma 1 or directly from Definition 1 it follows at once that $\{\Sigma(s)\}$ is an analytic structure in Σ.

Let f be a compact, continuous multi-valued mapping of Σ onto X. Set

$$M(s) = \bigcup \{f(x) : x \in \Sigma(s)\} . \tag{4}$$

By Lemma 1, $M = \{M(s)\}$ is an analytic structure in X. Conversely, let M be an analytic structure in X. For each $\sigma \in \Sigma$ set

$$f(\sigma) = M(\sigma) , \tag{5}$$

where the $M(\sigma)$ are defined by (2). By Lemma 1, the multi-valued mapping f is continuous. Thus we have proved the following

Theorem 2. *A space X is analytic if and only if there exists an analytic structure in X.*

Now we shall prove the following

Theorem 3. *The following conditions on a space X are equivalent*:

(a) *X is analytic.*

(b) *X is $\mathsf{F}(Y)$-Souslin for any $Y \supset X$.*

(c) *X is $\mathsf{K}(Y)$-Souslin for some $Y \supset X$.*

Proof. First, from Lemma 1 it follows immediately that if M is a complete determining system in X, then also $\{\overline{M(s)}\}$ is a complete determining system. Next, if M is complete in X, then, clearly, M is also complete in any $Y \subset X$. Finally, if M is an analytic structure in X and $Y \supset X$, then

$$\mathscr{A}(\{\overline{M(s)}^Y\}) = X .$$

Thus (a) implies (b). Obviously (b) implies (c). Finally, obviously, every determining system consisting of compact sets is complete. Thus (c) implies (a).

Theorem 4. *For any space we have*

$$\mathscr{A}(\mathbf{A}(X)) = \mathbf{A}(X) . \tag{6}$$

If X is analytic, then

$$\mathbf{A}(X) = \mathscr{A}(\mathsf{F}(X)) . \tag{7}$$

Proof. The second assertion is an immediate consequence of the first and Theorems 1 and 3. By Theorem 3 and property (3), Section 1, of $\mathscr{M}$-Souslin sets, (6) is true for compact X. Now let X be any space and let K be a compactification of X. Since

$$\mathbf{A}(X) = X \cap \mathbf{A}(K) ,$$

(6) follows from the corresponding property of K.

Let $M = \{M(s)\}$ be an analytic structure in X. Put

$$F(s) = \bigcup \{M(\sigma) : \sigma \in \Sigma(s)\} .$$

Thus also $F = \{F(s)\}$ is an analytic structure in X and

$$(8) \qquad F(s_1, \ldots, s_n) = \bigcup_{k=1}^{\infty} F(s_1, \ldots, s_n, k)\,.$$

Such structures will be called regular.

Theorem 5. *If X and Y are disjoint analytic subspaces of a space T, then there exists a Baire set B in T with*

$$(9) \qquad X \subset B \subset T - Y\,.$$

Remark. The preceding result is a generalization of the famous Luzin's first separation principle.

Corollary 1. For any space we have

$$\mathscr{B}(\mathsf{Z}(X)) \supset \text{compl. p. } \mathbf{A}(X)\,.$$

If X is analytic, then

$$\text{compl. p. } \mathbf{A}(X) = \mathscr{B}(\mathsf{Z}(X))\,.$$

Corollary 2. If $\{X_n\}$ is a disjoint sequence of analytic subspaces of X, then there exists a disjoint sequence $\{B_n\}$ of Baire sets of X with $B_n \supset X_n$.

Proof of Theorem 5. Let $\{X(s)\}$, $\{Y(s)\}$ be regular analytic structures in X and Y, respectively. Supposing (9) is true for no Baire set B, one can construct, by induction, a σ and a τ in Σ such that

$$(10) \qquad X(\{\sigma_1, \ldots, \sigma_n\}) \subset B \subset T - Y(\{\tau_1, \ldots, \tau_n\})$$

for no Baire set B and no $n = 1, 2, \ldots$ The sets

$$X(\sigma) = \bigcap_{s<\sigma} \overline{X(s)}\,, \quad Y(\tau) = \bigcap_{t<\tau} \overline{Y(t)}$$

are compact and disjoint. Thus there exists a Baire set Z in T (in fact, a zero-set) with

$$(11) \qquad X(\sigma) \subset \operatorname{int} Z = U\,, \quad Y(\tau) \subset \operatorname{int}(T - Z) = V\,.$$

By Lemma 1 there exists an i such that

$$X(\{\sigma_1, \ldots, \sigma_i\}) \subset U\,, \quad Y(\{\tau_1, \ldots, \tau_i\}) \subset V\,.$$

It follows that (10) is true for $B = Z$ and $n = i$. This contradiction establishes the Theorem 5.

Definition 3. A space X will be called *bianalytic* if X is a Baire set of some compact space.

Theorem 6. *The images and the preimages under perfect mappings of bianalytic spaces are bianalytic.*

Proof. Let f be a perfect mapping of X onto Y. There exists a continuous mapping g of the Čech-Stone compactification $\beta(X)$ of X onto $\beta(Y)$ such that f is a restriction of g. It is well known that

$$g[\beta(X) - X] = \beta(Y) - Y\,.$$

By Theorem 1, X (respectively, $\beta(X) - X$) is analytic if and only if Y (respectively, $\beta(Y) - Y$) is such. Since clearly bianalytic space X is a Baire set of $\beta(X)$ (by the Čech-Stone mapping theorem), the proof is complete.

Remark. The union of two bianalytic subspaces of a space may fail to be bianalytic. A one-to-one continuous image of a bianalytic space may fail to be bianalytic. Indeed, let N be a countable infinite discrete space and let x be a point of $\beta(N) - N$. Clearly, $N \cup (x)$ is a one-to-one continuous image of N. Next, N is bianalytic and $N \cup (x)$ is not, because $\beta(N) - (N \cup (x))$ is not a Lindelöf space. Further, $N \cup (x)$ is the disjoint union of two bianalytic spaces N and (x).

3. BORELIAN SPACES

Definition 4. A Borelian structure in a space X is a complete sequence $\{\mathcal{M}_n\}$ (see 1,13) of *countable disjoint* coverings of X satisfying the following two conditions.
(1) (a) If $M_n, N_n \in \mathcal{M}_n$ and $M_k \neq N_k$ for some k, then

$$\bigcap_{n=1}^{\infty} \overline{M}_n \cap \bigcap_{n=1}^{\infty} \overline{N}_n = \emptyset .$$

(b) $\mathcal{M}_{n+1}$ refines $\mathcal{M}_n$, $n = 1, 2, \ldots$

Definition 5. A space X will be called *Borelian* if in X there exists a Borelian structure. $\mathbf{B}$ will be used to denote the class of all Borelian spaces and $\mathbf{B}(X)$ to denote the family of all $B \subset X$, $B \in \mathbf{B}$.

From the definition we have at once the following

Lemma 2. *If $\{\mathcal{M}_n\}$ is a Borelian structure in X and $M \in \mathcal{M}_k$, then $\{M \cap \mathcal{M}_{k+n}\}$ is a Borelian structure in M.*

Let $\{\mathcal{M}_n\}$ be a Borelian structure in X. By induction one can construct determining system $\{M(s)\}$ in X such that

$$s \in S_n , \quad M(s) \neq \emptyset \Rightarrow M(s) \in \mathcal{M}_n , \tag{2}$$

$$M(s_1, \ldots, s_n) = \bigcup_{k=1}^{\infty} M(s_1, \ldots, s_n, k) . \tag{3}$$

Clearly $\{M(s)\}$ is an analytic structure in X. Let f be the corresponding multi-valued mapping of Σ onto X (for the definition see Section 2, (2) and (5)). Clearly

$$\sigma \neq \tau \Rightarrow f(\sigma) \cap f(\tau) = \emptyset . \tag{4}$$

Any multi-valued mapping satisfying (4) will be called *disjoint*.

Conversely, let f be a compact, continuous and disjoint multi-valued mapping of Σ onto X. Put

$$M(s) = \{f(\sigma) : s \prec \sigma\} .$$

It is easy to see that $\{\mathcal{M}_n\}$,

(5) $$\mathcal{M}_n = \{M(s) : s \in S_n\},$$

is a Borelian structure in X.

By Lemma 1, $\{M(s)\}$ is an analytical structure in X. Clearly, all $\mathcal{M}_n$ are disjoint. Thus $\{\mathcal{M}_n\}$ is a complete sequence of disjoint coverings. Finally, let $\sigma \neq \tau$. The sets $f(\sigma)$ and $f(\tau)$ being compact and disjoint, we can choose disjoint open sets U and V with

$$f(\sigma) \subset U, \quad f(\tau) \subset V.$$

By Lemma 1, there exist $s, t \in S_n$, $s \prec \sigma$, $t \prec \tau$, with $\overline{M(s)} \subset U$ and $\overline{M(t)} \subset V$. Thus (a) is fulfilled. Clearly also (b) is fulfilled. We have proved the following

Theorem 7. *A space X is Borelian if and only if there exists a compact and continuous disjoint multi-valued mapping of Σ onto X.*

Theorem 8. *The class of all Borelian spaces is* F*-hereditary, countably productive and closed under compact and continuous disjoint multi-valued mappings. In particular, one-to-one continuous images and perfect preimages of Borelian spaces are Borelian.*

The proof follows at once from Theorem 7 and from the properties of multi-valued mappings.

Lemma 3. *Let f be a compact and continuous disjoint multivalued mapping of X onto Y. There exists a space T, a one-to-one continuous mapping g of T onto Y, and a perfect mapping h of T onto a closed subset of X, such that*

(6) $$f = g \circ h^{-1}$$

where h^{-1} is the inverse of h, i. e.

$$h^{-1}(x) = h^{-1}[(x)].$$

Conversely, if g is one-to-one continuous and h is perfect, then the mapping f (given by (6)) is a compact and continuous disjoint multi-valued mapping.

Proof. The second assertion is obvious. Let f be a mapping which satisfies the assumptions of the first assertion. Let $\mathfrak{J}$ be the smallest topology in the set Y containing the topology of the space Y (that means, open sets of Y) and all sets $f[U]$ with U open in X, where, of course,

(7) $$f[U] = \bigcup \{f(x) : x \in U\}.$$

Let T be the set Y with the topology $\mathfrak{J}$. Clearly the identity mapping g of T onto Y is continuous. Now, since f is disjoint, for any t in T there exists one and only one point x of X with $t \in f(x)$. Put $h(t) = x$. Clearly (5) holds. It remains to prove that h is perfect. First, h is continuous, because, by definition of $\mathfrak{J}$, all sets of the form

$$g^{-1}[U] = f[U],$$

where U is open in X, belong to $\mathfrak{J}$. Since f is compact and $g^{-1}(x) = f(x)$, the inverses of points are compact. Finally, if F is closed in T, then $T - F = U$ is open in T. To prove $h[F]$ is closed in X it is sufficient to show that

$$V = f^{-1}[U] = \{x : f(x) \subset U\}$$

is open in X. Let $x \in V$. By definition of the topology $\mathfrak{T}$ of T, there exists an open set V_1 in X and open set U_1 in Y with

$$f(x) \subset U_1 \cap f[V_1] \subset U .$$

By continuity of f the set $f^{-1}[U_1]$ is open in X and by definition of the topology of T, also $V_1 = f[f^{-1}[V]]$ is open in X. Clearly

$$x \in V_1 \cap f^{-1}[U_1] \subset f^{-1}[U] .$$

Thus x is an interior point of $f^{-1}[U]$. Since x is arbitrary, $f^{-1}[U]$ is open. The proof is complete.

In view of Lemma 3, Theorem 7 may be restated as follows.

Theorem 9. *A space X is Borelian if and only if X is a one-to-one continuous image of a space which admits a perfect mapping onto a closed subspace of the space Σ of irrational numbers.*

Now we shall investigate $\mathbf{B}(X)$ for any X. First we shall prove the following

Theorem 10. *For any space X we have*

$$\mathscr{B}_*(\mathbf{B}(X)) = \mathbf{B}(X) . \tag{8}$$

Proof. We must show that $\mathbf{B}(X)$ is closed under countable intersections and countable disjoint unions. Let $\{Y_k\}$ be a disjoint sequence of Borelian subspaces of X and let $\{\mathscr{M}_n(k)\}_{n=1}^{\infty}$ be a Borelian structure in Y_k. It is easy to see that $\{\mathscr{M}_n\}$ is a Borelian structure in the union of all X_k, where

$$\mathscr{M}_n = \bigcup_{k=1}^{\infty} \mathscr{M}_n(k) .$$

The only one, perhaps, not entirely trivial point is the validity of condition (a) in Definition 4. We must show that

$$\bigcap_{k=1}^{\infty} \overline{M}_n^X = \bigcap_{n=1}^{\infty} \overline{M}_n^{Y_k} ,$$

where $M_n \in \mathscr{M}_n(k)$, $n = 1, 2, \ldots$ But this follows from Lemma 1, for any Borelian structure may be considered as an analytical structure (see the first part of the proof of Theorem 7).

Now let $\{Y_k\}$ be an arbitrary sequence of Borelian subspaces of X. Let Y be the intersection of all Y_k and let $\{\mathscr{M}_n(k)\}_{n=1}^{\infty}$ be a Borelian structure in Y_k. Clearly

$$\{Y \cap \mathscr{M}_n(k)\} \tag{9}$$

is a complete collection of countable coverings of Y. Let $\mathscr{M}_i$ be the family of all sets of the form

$$Y \cap \bigcap \{M_n(k) : k \leqq i, n \leqq i\}$$

where $M_n(k) \in \mathcal{M}_n(k)$. Obviously, $\{\mathcal{M}_i\}$ is a complete sequence of countable disjoint coverings of Y, which satisfies condition (b) of Definition 4. To prove that condition (a) is also satisfied, let us suppose $M_n, N_n \in \mathcal{M}_n$, $n = 1, 2, \ldots$, and $M_k \neq N_k$. By construction of the sequence $\{\mathcal{M}_n\}$, there exist decreasing sequences $\{N_n(i)\}_{n=1}^{\infty}, \{\mathcal{M}_n(i)\}_{n=1}^{\infty}$, $i = 1, 2, \ldots$, where $N_n(i)$, $M_n(i) \in \mathcal{M}_n(i)$, such that

$$M_n(n) \supset M_n\,, \quad N_n(n) \supset N_n\,. \tag{10}$$

If all N_n and M_n are non-void, the sequences $\{M_n(i)\}$, $\{N_n(i)\}$ are uniquely determined by (10) and

$$\begin{aligned} M_n &= \bigcap \{M_i(j) : i \leqq n,\ j \leqq n\}\,, \\ N_n &= \bigcap \{N_i(j) : i \leqq n,\ j \leqq n\}\,. \end{aligned} \tag{11}$$

Since $M_k \neq N_k$, there exist an i and an $j \leqq k$, with

$$M_i(j) \neq N_i(j)\,.$$

$\{\mathcal{M}_j\}$ being a Borelian structure, we have

$$\bigcap_{n=1}^{\infty} \overline{M}_n(j) \cap \bigcap_{n=1}^{\infty} \overline{M}_n(j) = \emptyset\,,$$

and consequently, in view of (11), (1) holds. The proof is complete.

Remark. In general the family $\mathbf{B}(X)$ is not closed under countable unions. Even a σ-compact space may fail to be a Borelian space. For example, let K be an uncountable compact space with only one accumulation point, say x, and let X be the topological product of K and the discrete space N of positive integers. Identifying the points of the set $(x) \times N = y$ we obtain the quotient space Y. We shall prove that Y is not a Borelian space. Let us suppose that $\{\mathcal{M}_n\}$ is a Borelian structure Y. By Lemma 2, any set from

$$\mathcal{M} = \bigcup_{n=1}^{\infty} \mathcal{M}_n \tag{12}$$

is a Borelian space, and consequently, a Lindelöf space. Thus any $M \in \mathcal{M}$ either contains y or is countable. Therefore the set

$$Y_0 = \bigcup \{M : M \in \mathcal{M},\ y \notin M\}$$

must be countable. The set $Y - Y_0$ is, by definition of Borelian structures, compact. But this is impossible for we can choose

$$y_n \in (K \times (n)) - Y_0$$

and clearly, the set of all y_n has no accumulation point in Y.

Theorem 11. *For any space X we have*

$$\mathbf{B}(X) \subset \mathcal{B}_*(\mathsf{F}(X) \cap \mathcal{B}(\mathsf{Z}(X)))\,. \tag{13}$$

More precisely, $\mathbf{B}(X)$ is contained in the family consisting of all countable intersections of countable disjoint unions of sets of the form $F \cap Z$, $F \in \mathsf{F}(X)$, $Z \in \mathcal{B}(\mathsf{Z}(X))$ and obviously this family is contained in the right side of (13).

Proof. Let Y be a Borelian subspace of X and let $\{\mathcal{M}_n\}$ be a Borelian structure in Y. By Lemma 2, all sets from (12) are Borelian spaces, and consequently, by Corollary 2 to Theorem 5, there exist Baire sets $B(M) \supset M$ in X such that the families

$$\{B(M) : M \in \mathcal{M}_n\} \tag{14}$$

are disjoint. Put

$$F(M) = B(M) \cap \overline{M}^X .$$

Since $\{\mathcal{M}_n\}$ is a complete sequence, we have

$$\bigcup_{\{M_n\}} \bigcap_{n=1}^{\infty} \overline{M}_n = Y, \tag{15}$$

where $\{M_n\}$ runs over all sequences with $M_n \in \mathcal{M}_n$. The coverings $\{F(M) : M \in \mathcal{M}_n\}$ are disjoint, because the coverings (14) are disjoint, and consequently,

$$\bigcup_{\{M_n\}} \bigcap_{n=1}^{\infty} F(M_n) = \bigcap_{n=1}^{\infty} \bigcup \{F(M); M \in \mathcal{M}_n\} . \tag{16}$$

Clearly the set on the right side of (16) contains X and the set on the left side of (16) is contained in the left side of (15), and consequently, in X. It follows that

$$\bigcap_{n=1}^{\infty} \bigcup \{F(M) : M \in \mathcal{M}_n\} = Y,$$

which establishes Theorem 11.

Remark. The above proof of Theorem 11 depends essentially upon the theory of analytic spaces. Indeed, the existence of (14) follows from Theorem 5. Making use of the same trick as in the proof of Theorem 5 one can prove the existence of Baire sets (14) directly.

Now we shall prove the following useful

Theorem 12. *If X is a Borelian space, then*

$$\mathsf{B}(X) = \mathcal{B}_*(\mathsf{F}(X) \cup \mathcal{B}(\mathsf{Z}(X))) . \tag{17}$$

More precisely, $\mathsf{B}(X)$ *coincides with the family described in Theorem* 11.

Proof. By Theorem 11 the inclusion $\subset$ holds. To prove the converse inclusion, by Theorem 10 it is sufficient to prove

$$X \in \mathsf{B} \Rightarrow \mathcal{B}(\mathsf{Z}(X)) \subset \mathsf{B}(X) . \tag{18}$$

It is easy to see that (18) follows from

$$Y \text{ compact} \Rightarrow \mathcal{B}(\mathsf{Z}(Y)) \subset \mathsf{B}(Y) . \tag{19}$$

Indeed, let Y be the Čech-Stone compactification of a Borelian space X. Since any bounded real-valued continuous functions on X has a continuous extension on Y, we have

$$\mathsf{Z}(X) = X \cap \mathsf{Z}(Y)$$

and consequently,

$$\mathcal{B}(\mathsf{Z}(X)) = X \cap \mathcal{B}(\mathsf{Z}(Y)) . \tag{20}$$

On the other hand obviously

(21) $$\mathbf{B}(X) = \{B : B \subset X,\ B \in \mathbf{B}(Y)\}\,.$$

Combining (19), (20) and (21) we obtain

(22) $$\mathscr{B}(\mathsf{Z}(X)) \subset \mathbf{B}(X)$$

which establishes (18). It remains to prove (19). This follows from lemmas 4 and 5.

Lemma 4. *Every cozero-set N of a compact space Y is a Borelian space.*

Proof. Let f be a real-valued continuous function on Y with

$$N = \{x : f(x) \neq 0\}\,.$$

Let g be the restriction of f to N. The mapping g is perfect because f is such. By Theorem 8 it is sufficient to show that $g[N]$ is a Borelian space. Let E, R, I denote the spaces of all real, rational and irrational numbers, respectively. The subspace $R \cap g[N]$ is countable, and hence, Borelian. The set $g[N] \cap I$ is closed in I because

$$\overline{g[N]}^{E} \subset I \cup (0)$$

and $0 \notin I$. By Theorem 8, the space $g[N] \cap I$ is Borelian. By Theorem 10, the space

$$g[N] = (g[N] \cap R) \cup (g[N] \cap I)$$

is Borelian.

Lemma 5. *Let $\mathsf{N}(X)$ denote the family of all cozero-sets of a space X. Then*

(23) $$\mathscr{B}_*(\mathsf{N}(X)) = \mathscr{B}(\mathsf{N}(X)) = \mathscr{B}(\mathsf{Z}(X))\,.$$

Proof. I cannot prove (23) without the Borel classification of Baire sets. A proof, making use of the Borel classification, may be found, for example, in [13], p. 255.

Corollary 1. Every bianalytic space is Borelian.

Corollary 2. If X is a perfectly normal Borelian space, in particular a metrizable Borelian space, then

(24) $$\mathbf{B}(X) = \mathscr{B}(\mathsf{Z}(X))\,.$$

Remark. Conversely, from (24) it follows at once that X is perfectly normal. Combining Corollary 2 of Theorem 12 and Corollary 1 of Theorem 5 we obtain

(25) $$\mathbf{B}(X) = \mathscr{B}(\mathsf{Z}(X)) = \text{compl. p. } \mathbf{A}(X)$$

for any perfectly normal space X.

Theorem 13. *The class of all Borelian spaces is the smallest class of spaces containing all bianalytic spaces and closed under one-to-one continuous mappings.*

Proof. By Corollary 1 every bianalytic space is Borelian and by Theorem 8 a one-to-one continuous image of a Borelian space is a Borelian space. Thus the class of all one-to-one continuous images of bianalytic spaces is contained in $\mathbf{B}$. By Theorem 9, if X is a Borelian space, then there exists a space T, a one-to-one continuous mapping of T onto X, and a perfect mapping of T onto a closed subspace B of Σ. The space B is bianalytic because B is a G_δ in the closed unit interval of real numbers, and open sets of metrizable spaces are Baire sets. By Theorem 6, the space T is bianalytic.

Theorem 14. *Y is a Borelian space if and only if there exists a complete sequence* $\{\mathcal{M}_n\}$ *of countable disjoint coverings of Y consisting of analytic subspaces of Y.*

Proof. By Lemma 2, if $\{\mathcal{M}_n\}$ is a Borelian structure in Y, then all sets belonging to the union of all $\mathcal{M}_n$ are Borelian spaces, and consequently, analytic spaces. Conversely, let $\{\mathcal{M}_n\}$ be a complete sequence of countable disjoint coverings of Y consisting of analytic subspaces of Y. By the proof of Theorem 11, for any space X containing Y we have

$$Y \in \mathcal{B}_*(\mathsf{F}(X) \cup \mathcal{B}(\mathsf{Z}(X))) . \tag{26}$$

By Theorem 12, Y is a Borelian space.

In [9] other proofs of the theorems of this section are sketched. The space Σ and multi-valued mappings may be eliminated. Using Borelian structures one can prove Theorem 9 directly. Theorem 9 follows from the following two lemmas.

Lemma 6. *X is the preimage under a perfect mapping of a closed subspace of* Σ *if and only if there exists a Borelian structure* $\{\mathcal{M}_n\}$ *in X such that all sets belonging to*

$$\mathcal{M} = \bigcup_{n=1}^{\infty} \mathcal{M}_n \tag{27}$$

are open.

Lemma 7. *Any Borelian space is an one-to-one continuous image of a space which has a Borelian structure* $\{\mathcal{M}_n\}$ *such that the sets belonging to* (27) *are open.*

Next, Theorem 10 and 11 depend neither on Σ nor on multi-valued mappings. Moreover, one can prove Theorem 11 without the theory of analytic spaces (see the Remark following the proof of Theorem 11).

In the proof of Theorem 12 the space Σ is used to prove that any cozero-set of a compact space is a Borelian space. We need only the fact that Σ is a Borelian space. In this case the use of Σ is very convenient.

Making use of the following lemma and Lemma 7 one can prove Theorem 12 without Theorem 9.

Lemma 8. *Let* $\{\mathcal{M}_n\}$ *be a complete sequence of disjoint open coverings of a space X. Then*

$$X = \bigcap_{n=1}^{\infty} \bigcup \overline{\mathcal{M}}_n^K \tag{28}$$

where K is the Čech-Stone compactification of X, and all sets from $\bigcup_{n=1}^{\infty} \overline{\mathcal{M}}_n^K$ *are closed and open in K, in particular, all these sets are zero-sets in K.*

Proof. The sets from (27) are closed in X. Thus their closures in K are open and closed. Clearly all the families $\overline{\mathcal{M}}_n^K$ are disjoint. It follows that

$$\bigcap_{n=1}^{\infty} \bigcup \overline{\mathcal{M}}_n^K = \bigcup_{\{M_n\}} \bigcap_{n=1}^{\infty} \overline{M}_n^K . \tag{29}$$

But the set on the right side of (29) is X and hence (28) holds.

We conclude this section by the following

Theorem 15. *A space X is analytic if and only if X is a continuous image of a bianalytic space. Moreover, every analytic space is a continuous image of a space which admits a perfect mapping onto a closed subspace of Σ.*

The complete proof can be found in [6]. Here we give only a suggestion. Let $\{M(s)\}$ be an analytic structure in X and let K be a compactification of X. Let π be the projection of the product space $Y = K \times \Sigma$ onto K. Consider the subspace

$$T = \bigcap_{n=1}^{\infty} \bigcup \{\overline{M(s)} \times \Sigma(s) : s \in S_n\}$$

of Y. It is easy to see that $\pi[T] = X$ and that $\{\mathcal{M}_n\}$ is a Borelian structure in T, such that all sets belonging to (27) are open, where

$$\mathcal{M}_n = T \cap \{\overline{M(s)} \times \Sigma(s) : s \in S_n\} .$$

4. METRIZABLE BORELIAN AND ANALYTIC SPACES

For convenience, metrizable Borelian (analytic) spaces will be called *classical Borelian* (*classical analytic*) spaces. Since every metrizable Lindelöf space is separable, every classical analytic space is separable.

Theorem 16. *The following conditions on a metrizable space X are equivalent:*

(a) *X is Borelian.*

(b) *X is bianalytic.*

(c) *X is a Baire set of some complete metrizable separable space.*

(d) *X is separable, and if X is contained in a metrizable space Y, then X is a Baire set of Y.*

In the classical theory the following theorem plays the fundamental rôle:

Theorem 17. *Every classical Borelian space is an one-to-one continuous image of a closed subspace of the space Σ of irrational numbers. Every classical analytic space is a continuous image of Σ.*

The classical theory makes use of this theorem instead of Borelian and analytic structures. Thus this theorem loses its importance in our presentation.

First we shall prove the following two results:

Theorem 18. *A space X is a continuous image of Σ if and only if there exists an analytical structure $\{M(s)\}$ in X such that the sets*

(1) $M(\sigma) = \bigcap_{s<\sigma} \overline{M(s)}$

contain at most one point.

Theorem 19. *A space X is an one-to-one continuous image of a closed subspace of Σ if and only if there exists a Borelian structure $\{\mathcal{M}_n\}$ in X such that*

(2) *the sets* $\bigcap_{n=1}^{\infty} \overline{M}_n$ *contain at most one point.*

Proof. In both theorems the conditions are clearly necessary. Conversely, let f be the multivalued mapping of Σ onto X corresponding to the analytic structure $\{M(s)\}$. Let F be the set of all σ with non-void images. Since f is continuous, F is closed in Σ. For each σ in F let $g(\sigma)$ be the element of $f(\sigma)$. Then g is a continuous mapping of F onto X. It is well known and easy to prove that any closed subset of Σ is a continuous image of Σ, moreover, a retract of Σ. The proof of Theorem 18 is complete. The proof of sufficiency of the condition of Theorem 19 can be proved analoguously.

Remark. The fact that every non-void closed subset F of Σ is a retract of Σ can be proved as follows:

There exists a mapping f of S to F such that $f(s) \in F \cap \Sigma(s)$ if possible. Put $g(\sigma) = \sigma$ for $\sigma \in F$. If $\sigma \notin F$ and $\Sigma(\sigma_1) \cap F = \emptyset$, put $g(\sigma) = f(\sigma_1)$. In the remaining case there exists an n with

$$\Sigma(\{\sigma_1, \ldots, \sigma_n\}) \cap F \neq \emptyset, \quad M(\{\sigma_1, \ldots, \sigma_{n+1}\}) \cap F = \emptyset .$$

Put $g(\sigma) = f(\{\sigma_1, \ldots, \sigma_n\})$. It is easy to see that g is a retraction of Σ to F. Indeed, if $F \cap \Sigma(s) \neq \emptyset$, then $g[\Sigma(s)] \subset F \cap \Sigma(s)$ and in the other case $g[M(s)]$ is a one point set of F.

The part of Theorem 17 concerning classical analytic spaces follows easily from 18. Indeed, if $\{M(s)\}$ is an analytical structure in a metrizable space X and if ϱ is a metric generating the topology of X, then one can construct a determining system $\{F(s)\}$ in X, such that $\mathscr{A}(F) = X$ and

(a) if $s \in S_n$, then the diameter of $F(s)$ is less than $1/n$.

(b) $\{F(s)\}$ is a refinement of $\{M(s)\}$, i. e. for each $\sigma \in \Sigma$ there exists a τ in Σ such that

$$F(\{\tau_1, \ldots, \tau_n\}) \subset M(\{\sigma_1, \ldots, \sigma_n\}) .$$

By (b), $\{F(s)\}$ is an analytic structure in X and by (a) the sets $F(\sigma)$ contain at most one point.

The proof of the second part of Theorem 17 is more difficult. Let $\mathbf{B}_1$ be the class of all one-to-one continuous images of closed subspaces of Σ and let $\mathbf{B}_1(X) = \{Y : Y \subset X, Y \in \mathbf{B}_1\}$. Using Borelian structures satisfying (2), we obtain at once

(3) $\mathscr{B}_*(\mathbf{B}_1(X)) = \mathbf{B}_1(X)$.

Indeed, the proof of Theorem (10) is applicable. Next

(4) $\mathbf{B}_1$ is countably productive and F-hereditary. Indeed, the topological product of a countable number of copies of Σ is homeomorphic to Σ. From (3) and (4) one can deduce at once

(5) Any complete metrizable separable space belongs to $\mathbf{B}_1$.

Indeed, clearly the Euclidean line belongs to $\mathbf{B}_1$ (as a union of Σ and a coutable set); by (4) closed subspace of the topological product of the coutable number of Euclidean lines belong to $\mathbf{B}_1$. Finally, it is well known that any complete metrizable separable space is homeomorphic with a closed subspace of this topological product.

Now let K be a metrizable compact space. Every open subspace of K is a complete metrizable separable space, and hence, every open subspace of K belongs to $\mathbf{B}_1(K)$. By Lemma 5 (Section 3) and (3) we have

$$\mathbf{B}_1(K) \supset \mathscr{B}(\mathsf{Z}(K)) .$$

We have proved that Baire sets of compact metrizable spaces belong to $\mathbf{B}_1$. The proof is complete.

5. REMARKS

Classical Borelian spaces are precisely those spaces which belong to

$$\mathscr{B}(\mathbf{K}(X)) \tag{1}$$

for some metrizable space. It seems that this fact led V. ŠNEJDER to introduce the spaces which belong to (1) for some space X (called K-Borelian by G. CHOQUET) and their continuous images which coincide by analytic spaces (by Theorem 15).

In [2] G. Choquet showed the relation between analytic spaces (K-analytic in his terminology) and the so-called K-Souslin spaces (spaces which are $\mathbf{K}(X)$-Souslin for some X). In [3] he proved the essential part of Theorem 15 and showed that a metrizable space X is analytic if and only if X is a classical analytic space (using classical results). M. SION independently reproved all Choquet's results from [3]. Further, he tried to prove the invariance of K-Borelian spaces under one-to-one continuous mappings. He proved that a one-to-one continuous image of a K-Borelian space X is K-Borelian under certain drastic assumption on a σ-compact space containing X. It seems that this problem is still unsolved.

In [8] the author introduced analytic structures, and using these, reproved all Choquet's results and proved some, it seems, new results. In [10] he introduced bianalytic spaces, proved Theorem 5 and gave the first internal characterization of classical Borelian spaces. In [9] and [6] somewhat other proofs of some results of the present note are given.

References

[1] *Bourbaki*: Topologie générale. Chapitre 9. Paris 1958.
[2] *G. Choquet*: Theory of Capacities. Ann. Inst. Fourier, *5* (1953–1954), 131–295.
[3] *G. Choquet*: Ensembles K-analytiques et K-Sousliniens. Ann. Inst. Fourier, *IX* (1959), 75–81.
[4] *E. Čech*: On Bicompact Spaces. Ann. of Math. *38* (1937), 823–844.
[5] *Z. Frolík*: On Almost Realcompact Spaces. Bull. Acad. Pol., *9* (1961), 247—250.
[6] *Z. Frolík*: On Analytic Spaces. Bull. Acad. Pol., *9* (1961), 721—725.
[7] *Z. Frolík*: A Generalization of Realcompact Spaces. To appear in Czech. Math. J.
[8] *Z. Frolík*: On Descriptive Theory of Sets and Spaces. To appear in Czech. Math. J.
[9] *Z. Frolík*: On Borelian and Bianalytic Spaces. Czech. Math. J. *11(86)*, (1961), 629—631.
[10] *Z. Frolík*: On Bianalytic Spaces. To appear in Czech. Math. J.
[11] *Z. Frolík*: Generalizations of the G_δ-property of Complete Metric Spaces. Czech. Math. J. *10* (85), 1960, 359–379.

[12] *M. Katětov*: Measures in Fully Normal Spaces. Fund. Math. *38* (1951), 73—84.
[13] *K. Kuratowski*: Topologie I. Warszawa 1952.
[14] *M. Sion*: On Analytic Sets in Topological Spaces. Trans. Amer. Math. Soc., *96* (1960), 341—354.
[15] *M. Sion*: Topological and Measure Theoretic Properties of analytic sets. Proc. Amer. Math. Soc. *11* (1960), 769—776.
[16] *V. E. Šnejder*: Continuous Images of Souslin and Borel Sets. Dokl. Akad. Nauk SSSR *50* (1945), 77—79.
[17] *V. E. Šnejder*: Descriptive Theory of Sets in Topological Spaces. Ibid. 81—83.

ALGEBRAIC PROPERTIES OF FUNCTION SPACES

T. GANEA

Bucureşti

Let X be an H-space with multiplication $\mu : X \times X \to X$ and inversion $\nu : X \to \to X$. The basic commutator map is the composition

$$\varphi : X^2 \xrightarrow{\Delta} X^2 \times X^2 \xrightarrow{1^2 \times \nu^2} X^2 \times X^2 \xrightarrow{\mu \times \mu} X \times X \xrightarrow{\mu} X$$

in which $X^2 = X \times X$, Δ is the diagonal map and 1 is the identity map; the commutator map of weight $n + 1$ is the composition

$$\varphi_{n+1} : X^{n+1} = X^n \times X \xrightarrow{\varphi_n \times 1} X \times X \xrightarrow{\varphi} X$$

in which φ_n is the commutator map of weight $n \geqq 1$ with $\varphi_1 = 1$. The nilpotency class nil X is defined as the least integer $n \geqq 0$ for which φ_{n+1} is nullhomotopic; if no such integer exists, we put nil $X = \infty$. Next, for any space X define $\cup$-long X as the least integer $n \geqq 0$ such that for any commutative coefficient field the cup product of any $n + 1$ singular cohomology classes of positive dimension vanishes; also, let wcat X denote the least integer $n \geqq 1$ for which the composition

$$X \xrightarrow{\Delta} X^n \xrightarrow{p} X^{(n)}$$

is nullhomotopic (the symbol $X^{(n)}$ stands for the smashed n-fold product).

Let X be a Hausdorff space with base-point $a \in X$ and let G be an arbitrary H-space with unit $e \in G$. The compact-open topologized space $(G, e)^{(X,a)}$ of all continuous maps $(X, a) \to (G, e)$ is an H-space, and the main result of this paper consists of the inequalities

$$\cup\text{-long } X \leqq \sup \text{nil}\,(G, e)^{(X,a)} \leqq \text{wcat } X - 1$$

in which G ranges over all H-spaces. The second inequality improves a result due to G. W. Whitehead (Comment. Math. Helv. *28* (1954), 320—328). Proofs and further details may be found in a joint paper by I. Berstein and the present author (Illinois J. Math. *5* (1961), 99—130).

REMOTE POINTS IN βR

L. GILLMAN

Rochester

The results presented here were obtained jointly with N. J. FINE.[1])

It seems natural to conjecture that each point p in βR is a limit point of a suitable increasing or decreasing sequence in R – that is, that $p \in \mathrm{cl}_{\beta R} D$ for some discrete subset D of R that is closed in R. (As usual, βX denotes the Stone-Čech compactification of X, and R denotes the real line.) However, this is false. In fact (as was pointed out by W. F. EBERLEIN several years ago), it is easy to find a point in βR that is not a limit point of any closed subset of R that has finite Lebesgue measure.

Our present question is: does there exist a point in βR that is not in the closure of any discrete subset of R (closed or not). The problem seems surprisingly difficult. If we assume the continuum hypothesis [CH], then we can find such a "remote" point. (But we do not know whether [CH] is necessary.) An equivalent formulation in terms of subsets of R itself is: [CH] there exists a "z-ultrafilter" on R no member of which is nowhere dense. (A z-ultrafilter is a maximal family of zero-sets with the finite intersection property. On the real line, zero-sets – i. e., sets of zeros of continuous real-valued functions – are the same as closed sets.)

More generally, we have:

Theorem. *Let X be a completely regular* (*Hausdorff*) *space such that* (a) *the set of all isolated points does not admit a Ulam* 2-*valued measure, and* (b) *there exists a family $\mathscr{U}$ of $\aleph_1$ dense open sets such that every dense open set in X contains a member of $\mathscr{U}$. Then X admits an unbounded continuous real-valued function if and only if there exists a z-ultrafilter $\mathscr{A}$ on X such that $\bigcap \mathscr{A}$ is void and every dense open set contains a member of $\mathscr{A}$.*

Hypothesis (a) holds, in particular, if the cardinal of the set of isolated points of X is smaller than the first strongly inaccessible cardinal. In the proof of necessity, this hypothesis is not used at all. (Other portions of the theorem may also be stated more generally.)

Our result about remote points in βR follows easily from [CH] and the theorem. If we consider the subspace consisting of the rationals and one remote point, we get:

---

[1]) The complete article appears in the Proceedings of the American Mathematical Society, *13* (1962), 29—36.

Corollary. [CH] *There exists a countable, completely regular space without isolated points, one of whose points is not a limit point of any discrete set.*

Finally, it can be shown [CH] that the set of all remote points is actually dense in $\beta R - R$.

A NOTION OF UNIFORMITY FOR *L*-SPACES OF FRECHET

A. GOETZ
Wrocław

Let be given a set X and a relation $\xi\, \boldsymbol{n}\, \xi'$ between sequences $\xi = \{x_n\}$ and $\xi' = \{x'_n\}$ of elements of X (called nearness relation) which satisfies the following conditions:

(i) $\xi\, \boldsymbol{n}\, \xi$;
(ii) if $\xi\, \boldsymbol{n}\, \xi'$, then $\xi'\, \boldsymbol{n}\, \xi$;
(iii) if $\xi\, \boldsymbol{n}\, \xi'$ and $\xi'\, \boldsymbol{n}\, \xi''$, then $\xi\, \boldsymbol{n}\, \xi''$;
(iv) $\{x\}\, \boldsymbol{n}\, \{x'\}$ if and only if $x = x'$;[1])
(v) if $\{x_i\}\, \boldsymbol{n}\, \{x'_i\}$, then $\{x_{i_n}\}\, \boldsymbol{n}\, \{x'_{i_n}\}$ for every sequence $\{i_n\}$ of indices;
(vi) if every sequence $\{i_k\}$ of natural numbers contains a subsequence $\{i'_n\}$, such that $\{x_{i'_n}\}\, \boldsymbol{n}\, \{x'_{i'_n}\}$, then $\{x_n\}\, \boldsymbol{n}\, \{x'_n\}$.

X with the relation $\boldsymbol{n}$ is called a UL^*-space. The relation $\boldsymbol{n}$ is called sometimes a UL^*-structure in X.

By setting $x = \lim x_n$ iff $\{x_n\}\, \boldsymbol{n}\, \{x\}$, X becomes an L^*-space of Fréchet.

A natural order may be introduced into the set of all UL^*-structures of the given set X by setting $\boldsymbol{n} \leqq \boldsymbol{m}$ iff $\xi\, \boldsymbol{n}\, \xi'$ implies $\xi\, \boldsymbol{m}\, \xi'$.

Theorem. *The set of all UL^*-structures of X form an absolutely multiplicative semilattice. Its subsemilattice consisting of all UL^*-structures, which induce the same convergence, is a lattice and contains the least and the largest elements.*

Theorem. *The lattice of UL^*-structures of X inducing a convergence, for which X is compact, contains a single element.*

The UL^*-structure enables to introduce for Fréchet spaces some notions known for metric spaces or generally for uniform spaces: the notion of uniform convergencs of sequences of functions, of uniform continuity of functions, of Cauchy sequencee and completeness.

A function $f(x)$ is called uniformly continuous if $\{x_n\}\, \boldsymbol{n}\, \{x'_n\}$ implies $\{f(x_n)\}\, \boldsymbol{m}\, \{f(x'_n)\}$, where $\boldsymbol{n}$ is the nearness relation in the domain of the function and $\boldsymbol{m}$ the nearness relation in the set of values of the function.

A sequence $\{f_n\}$ of functions with values in an UL^*-space is said to converge uniformly to f if for each sequence $\{x_n\}$ $\{f_n(x_n)\}\, \boldsymbol{m}\, \{f(x_n)\}$.

---

[1]) $\{x\}$ denotes the constant sequence ($x_n = x$, $n = 1, 2, \ldots$).

For functions defined in a UL^*-space X with values in a metric space (or more generally in a special kind of UL^*-spaces) the following theorem holds.

Theorem. *The limit of a uniformly convergent sequence of uniformly continuous functions is a uniformly continuous function.*

A sequence $\{x_n\}$ is called a Cauchy sequence if $\{x_n\}$ **n** $\{x_{i_n}\}$ for every subsequence $\{x_{i_n}\}$. X is complete iff all Cauchy sequences are convergent.

The questions of completeness and completion of UL^*-spaces are still open.

The paper is to be published in "Colloquium Mathematicum", *9* (1962).

ARITHMETICA TOPOLOGICA

S. W. GOLOMB

Pasadena

The topology D for the positive integers is obtained when those arithmetic progressions $\{an + b\}$ with $(a, b) = 1$ are taken as a basis for the open sets. This topology is connected and Hausdorff, but is neither regular, compact, nor locally compact. In the topology D, there is a simple proof of the existence of infinitely many primes, and Dirichlet's theorem on primes in arithmetic progressions is equivalent to the assertion that the primes form a dense subset of the integers. The interior of the set of primes is empty.

Let $Q = \{q_i\}$ be an infinite subset of the primes, and let $g(x)$ denote the number of members of Q which do not exceed x. Call Q *rare* if $\sum 1/q_i$ converges and call Q *sparse* if $g(x) = o(x/\log x)$. The causal relation between rarity and sparsity is settled, and it is shown that a certain condition on the structure of Q implies both that Q is *nowhere dense* (as a topological subset of the integers) and that Q is *sparse* (in the purely metric-analytic sense), although neither nowhere-density alone nor sparsity alone implies the other. It thus becomes possible not merely to formulate prime density problems and other sieve method problems in purely topological terms, but to solve problems of the type treated in [8] without resort to computation. Thus many of the results in [8] have been improved and extended by viewing them in their topological setting.

The topological viewpoint is useful not merely to formulate and solve traditional problems of prime number theory, but also to suggest problems of an essentially different character. Thus, one can form "Cantor Sets" of integers and examine the density of the primes contained therein.

I. A CONNECTED TOPOLOGY FOR THE INTEGERS

A topology D for the positive integers is obtained when those arithmetic progressions $\{an + b\}$ with $(a, b) = 1$ are taken as a basis for the open sets. They form a basis because the intersection of two such progressions is of the same type, or empty, as is easily verified. Note that every nonempty open set, being a union of arithmetic progressions, must be infinite.

This topology furnishes an interesting proof of

Theorem 1. *The number of primes is infinite.*

Proof. If p is prime, the progression $\{np\}$ is closed, since its complement is

$$\{np + 1\} \cup \{np + 2\} \cup \ldots \cup \{np + (p - 1)\},$$

a union of open sets. Consider the union $X = U_p\{ap\}$ extended over all primes. If this is a finite union of closed sets, then X is closed. But the complement of X is $\{1\}$, which is neither empty nor infinite. Since the complement of X is not open, X cannot be closed, the union is not a finite one, and the number of primes is infinite.

(A similar proof, in a stronger and very disconnected topology, was given by H. FURSTENBERG [2].)

Theorem 2. *The topology D is Hausdorff.*

Proof. Given distinct positive integers s and t, choose a prime p (by Theorem 1) which exceeds $\max(s, t)$. Then $\{pn + s\}$ and $\{pn + t\}$ are disjoint open sets which separate s and t.

Theorem 3. *The topology D is connected.*

Proof. Suppose the integers could be represented as the union of two disjoint nonempty open sets O_1 and O_2. Let $\{a_1n + b_1\}$ be a basis set in O_1, and let $\{a_2n + b_2\}$ be a basis set in O_2. Let α be a multiple of a_1. If α were in O_2, we would have $\alpha = An_0 + B$, where $\{An + B\} \subset O_2$. Since $(A, B) = 1$, we would have $(\alpha, A) = 1$, and hence $(a_1, A) = 1$. But then $\{a_1n + b_1\}$ and $\{An + B\}$ would intersect infinitely often, contradicting disjointness of O_1 and O_2. Thus all multiples of a_1 must belong to O_1. Similarly the multiples of a_2 must belong to O_2. But then the *common* multiples of a_1 and a_2 must belong to both O_1 and O_2, which contradicts disjointness.

A proof of the connectedness of the topology D, without reference to number theory, was presented by MORTON BROWN at the April 1953 meeting of the American Mathematical Society in New York [1].

Theorem 4. *The topology D is not regular.*

Proof. Suppose that open coverings are given for the closed set $\{2n\}$ and for the point $\{1\}$ outside it. Any open covering of $\{1\}$ not intersecting $\{2n\}$ must include a progression $\{en + 1\}$, where e is even. That is, $e \in \{2n\}$. Let $\{an + b\}$ be the member of the open covering of $\{2n\}$ which contains e, so that $e = an_0 + b$. Since $(a, b) = 1$, we have $(a, e) = 1$, whereby $\{an + b\}$ intersects $\{en + 1\}$ infinitely often. Thus the closed set $\{2n\}$ and the point $\{1\}$ cannot have disjoint open neighborhoods.

Theorem 5. *The topology D is not compact.*

Proof. The union $\bigcup_p \{np - 1\}$ extended over all primes is an infinite open covering for the positive integers. Since the omission of any progression $\{nq - 1\}$ leaves the number $q - 1$ uncovered, the Heine-Borel property fails.

Actually, the topology D is not even locally compact, because every locally compact Hausdorff space is regular. For a proof of this, as well as for the more basic definitions of point-set topology, the reader is referred to [5].

Dirichlet's theorem, which asserts that every progression $\{an + b\}$ with $(a, b) = 1$ contains infinitely many primes, has an elegant formulation in terms of the topology D.

Theorem 6. *Dirichlet's theorem is equivalent to the assertion that the primes are a dense subset of the integers in the topology D.*

Proof. Assume first the validity of Dirichlet's theorem. Then every nonempty open set contains primes, so that the primes are a dense subset of the integers. Conversely, assume that the primes are a dense subset. Then every nonempty open set, and in particular all the progressions $\{an + b\}$ with $(a, b) = 1$, must contain primes. It is well known [4] that if every such progression contains at least one prime, then every such progression contains infinitely many primes. (In topological terminology: "If the closure of the primes is the integers, then the derived set of the primes is the integers.")

Although it is quite unlikely that a complete topological proof of Dirichlet's theorem could be given without the introduction of powerful new ideas and methods, the attempt should be well worth the effort. In particular, if the proof that works for the rational integers should also be valid in other rings of algebraic integers (where the corresponding topology, based on residue classes of ideals, is introduced), the enrichment of number theory would be enormous. Thus, the corresponding theorem for the Gaussian integers would imply infinitely many Gaussian primes in the progression $\{n + i\}$, and hence infinitely many rational primes of the form $n^2 + 1$, a classical unsolved problem.

Another familiar fact capable of topological formulation is

Theorem 7. *In the topology D, the interior of the set of primes is empty.*

Proof. If there were an open set consisting entirely of primes, there would be a progression $\{an + b\}$ with $1 \leqq b \leqq a$ consisting entirely of primes. But with

$$n_0 = a + b + 1\,, \quad an_0 + b = (a + b)(a + 1)\,,$$

which is composite.

It is interesting to consider also the topology D' for the positive integers, which has as a basis those progressions $\{an + b\}$ with $(a, b) = 1$ for all $n > N$. (Here N is allowed to assume all values.) This topology may appear *stronger* than D, although it is in fact equivalent to D. Moreover, certain theorems related to Eratosthenes' sieve are readily seen in terms of D'. In particular,

Theorem 8. *The set of positive integers m such that* $6m - 1$ *and* $6m + 1$ *are a pair of "prime twins" is closed in D', and hence in D.*

Proof. It is known [3], [10], that the numbers m in question are precisely those positive integers not expressible in the form $6ab \pm a \pm b$ for any $a \geqq 1$ and $b \geqq 1$. Thus the *complement* of our set is

$$\bigcup_{b \geqq 1} \{(6b \pm 1)\, a \pm b\}\,,$$

where each progression is restricted to $a \geqq 1$, and is open because $(6b \pm 1, b) = 1$. The union is open in D', because it is a union of open sets. Thus the integers m for which $6m - 1$ and $6m + 1$ are both prime form a closed set.

II. RARITY AND SPARSITY

Let $Q = \{q_i\}$ be an infinite subset of the primes, and let $g(x)$ denote the number of members of Q which do not exceed x. Call Q *rare* if $\sum 1/q_i$ converges, and call Q *sparse* if $g(x) = o\,(x/\log x)$ [7]. In this section the causal relation between rarity and sparsity is settled in the negative, i. e.:

Theorem 9. *Rarity is unnecessary and insufficient for sparsity.*

Proof. Four examples suffice to establish this Theorem. (The most surprising of these is the fourth.)

1. The set of all primes, $P = \{p_i\}$, is neither sparse nor rare. (Trivial.)
2. The subset $Q_{rs} = \{p_{n!}\}$ is both sparse and rare. (Trivial.)
3. Define $Q_s = \{q_n\}$ recursively by $q_1 = 2$, and

$$q_{n+1} = \max\left[p_{\pi(q_n)+1}\,,\ p_{\pi(n\log n\log\log n)}\right].$$

Since $p_{\pi(y)}$ is the largest prime not exceeding y, and since $p_n \sim n \log n$, we see that $q_n \sim n \log n \log \log n$, so that

$$\sum \frac{1}{q_n} > k \sum 1/n \log n \log\log n = \infty\,, \quad \text{while} \quad g(x) \sim x/\log x \log\log x = o(x/\log x)\,.$$

The use of the Prime Number Theorem here can easily be replaced by more elementary results. (See also the last paragraph of this paper.)

4. Let

$$Q_r = \bigcup_{i=1}^{\infty} \bigcup_{j=1}^{2^{2^i}-i} p_{\pi(2^{2^i})+j}\,.$$

That is, after each value $x = 2^{2^i}$, the set Q_r contains the next 2^{2^i-i} primes. Using the elementary (Chebycheff) results: $\pi(x) < ax/\log x$ and $p_n < bn \log n$, we have, letting $c = a \log_2 e + 1$,

$$p_{\pi(2^{2^i})+2^{2^i}-i} < b[\pi(2^{2^i}) + 2^{2^i-i}] \log [\pi(2^{2^i}) + 2^{2^i-i}] <$$
$$< bc\,\frac{2^{2^i}}{2^i}\,[\log c + (2^i - i) \log 2] < k\,.\,2^{2^i}\,,$$

where k is independent of i.

Hence,

$$\sum_{q\in Q_r} \frac{1}{q} \leqq \sum_{i=1}^{\infty} \frac{2^{2^i-i}}{2^{2^i}} = \sum_{i=1}^{\infty} \frac{1}{2^i} = 1 < \infty\,,$$

while for $x = k\,.\,2^{2^i}$, which includes arbitrarily large values of x,

$$g(x) = g(k\,.\,2^{2^i}) \geqq 2^{2^i-i} = \frac{x/k}{\log (x/k)} \log 2 > d\,\frac{x}{\log x}\,,$$

for some absolute constant $d > 0$. This precludes $g(x) = o(x/\log x)$.

Thus the supposition that rarity is a stronger condition than sparsity is false, at least in the case of sets of primes with sufficiently irregular distribution. However, rarity *does* imply

$$\liminf_{x\to\infty} \frac{g(x)}{x/\log x} = 0\,,$$

but this is a weaker condition than sparsity, which can be rephrased

$$\lim_{x\to\infty} \frac{g(x)}{x/\log x} = 0\,.$$

In some sense the *intersection* of the rarity and sparsity conditions is the requirement

$$\liminf_{x\to\infty} \frac{g(x)}{x/\log x} = 0\,.$$

A somewhat more general approach is to define a "moment-generating function" for Q by

$$g(x, s) = \sum_{q\leqq x} q^{-s}\,.$$

The rarity *vs.* sparsity problem then becomes one of the interrelationship between the asymptotic behaviors of the two "moments" $g(x, 0)$ and $g(x, 1)$.

III. SPARSITY AND TOPOLOGICAL DENSITY

Definition. Let $A = \{an + b\}$ be any arithmetic progression. Define the *π-measure on A by*

$$\pi(A) = \begin{cases} 0 & \text{if } (a, b) > 1\,, \\ 1/\varphi(a) & \text{if } (a, b) = 1\,, \end{cases}$$

where $\varphi(a)$ is Euler's function.

(For the empty set Φ, define $\pi(\Phi) = 0$.)

If A and B are two progressions, so too is $A \cap B$. The formula $\pi(A \cup B) = = \pi(A) + \pi(B) - \pi(A \cap B)$ may be used to extend the definition of π-measure to all *finite* unions of arithmetic progressions.

Theorem 10. *As a measure, $\pi(A)$ is finitely additive but not absolutely additive.*

Proof. By the principle of cross-classification,

$$\pi\Big(\bigcup_{i=1}^{n} A_i\Big) = \sum \pi(A_i) - \sum \pi(A_i \cap A_j) + - \ldots + (-1)^{n+1}\, A_1 \cap A_2 \cap \ldots \cap A_n\,.$$

To show that this measure is not absolutely additive, consider the set of progressions $A_i = \{p_i n\}$, where p_i is the *i-th* prime, $i = 1, 2, 3, \ldots$, and define $A_0 = \{qn + 1\}$ for any odd prime q. Although $\pi(A_i) = 0$ for $i \geqq 1$, and though $\pi(A_0) = 1/(q - 1)$ where q may be arbitrarily large, yet $\bigcup_{i=0}^{\infty} A_i = Z$, the set of *all* integers, and $\pi(Z) = 1$.

Note. By the asymptotic form of Dirichlet's Theorem, the number of primes in a progression $A = \{an + b\}$ which do not exceed x, denoted by $\pi(x; a, b)$, satisfies

$$\lim_{x \to \infty} \frac{\pi(x; a, b)}{x/\log x} = \pi(A).$$

Hence an equivalent *definition* for π-measure would be

$$\pi(A) = \lim_{x \to \infty} \frac{\pi(x, A)}{x/\log x},$$

or even more suggestively,

$$\pi(A) = \lim_{x \to \infty} \frac{\pi(x, A)}{\pi(x)},$$

and this definition generalizes to *any* set A.

Definition. Any set A having π-measure 0 will be called *sparse*, and any subset of a sparse set is also called sparse, and defined to have π-measure 0. (When this definition is restricted to sets of *primes*, it clearly coincides with the definition of sparsity given in Section II of this paper.)

Theorem 11. *The set A will be called essentially sparse if $\pi(Z - A) = 1$. Essential sparsity is equivalent to sparsity.*

Proof.

$$\pi(Z - A) = \lim_{x \to \infty} \frac{\pi(Z - A, x)}{\pi(x)} = \lim_{x \to \infty} \frac{\pi(Z, x) - \pi(A, x)}{\pi(x)} = \lim_{x \to \infty} \left(1 - \frac{\pi(A, x)}{\pi(x)}\right),$$

which is 1 if and only if

$$\pi(A) = \lim \frac{\pi(A, x)}{\pi(x)} = 0.$$

Definition. Relative to the topology D, a subset S of the integers Z is called *nowhere dense* if there is no non-empty open set in the closure of S.

Theorem 12. *If S is a nowhere dense subset of Z, then S may or may not be sparse, and conversely.*

Proof. The empty set is *both* nowhere dense and sparse; the set of all primes is *neither*.

Let $\{A_i\}$ be the denumerable collection of all the basis sets $\{a_i n + b_i\}$. From each A_i, pick a prime $s_i > 2^i$, and let $S = \{s_i\}$. Then S contains at least one, and hence infinitely many (*cf.* Theorem 6) members of every non-empty open set, and is therefore dense in D. However,

$$\pi(S) = \lim_{x \to \infty} \frac{\pi(x, S)}{\pi(x)} \leqq \lim_{x \to \infty} \frac{\log_2 x}{x/\log x} = 0,$$

so that S is both dense and sparse.

Finally, from each progression A_i it is possible to remove a "small" subprogression B_i so that most of the primes of A_i are still in $A_i - B_i$, and so that $\mathscr{S} = Z - \bigcup B_i$

is a set which is nowhere dense, yet has $\pi(\mathcal{S})$ arbitrarily close to 1. Care must be exercised in the choice of B_i to prevent the infinite union $\bigcup B_i$ from containing too many (or even all) of the primes. This can be done by assuring that the smallest prime in B_i exceeds 2^i, along with

$$\pi(x, B_i) < \frac{1}{N \,.\, 2^i} \frac{x}{\log x}$$

for all $x > 1$ and suitable large N. The remaining details are left as an exercise.

Note that the last set $\mathcal{S}$ is a kind of *Cantor set*. By removing smaller and smaller "intervals" B_i, one is left with a set which is nowhere dense, which is perfect (*i. e.* $\mathcal{S}$ is the set of its own limit points), but which has "measure" arbitrarily close to 1. This is an example of the way in which topological notions can be used to exhibit sets of primes which are more pathological than those previously studied.

Theorem 13. *If Q is a set of primes such that, with only finitely many exceptions, $Q \subset A_i = \{a_i n + b_i\}$ for arbitrarily large values of a_i, then Q is both sparse and nowhere dense.*

Proof. To show sparsity, let $\varepsilon > 0$ be given, and pick a_i so large that

$$\frac{1}{\varphi(a_i)} < \varepsilon/4 \quad (\text{using } \varphi(n) \to \infty \text{ as } n \to \infty)\,.$$

There are only finitely many – say t – members of Q which do not belong to $A_i = \{a_i n + b_i\}$, by the hypothesis. Pick x_1 so large that

$$\frac{t}{x_1/\log x_1} < \varepsilon/2\,.$$

Pick x_2 so large that for all $x \geqq x_2$,

$$\frac{\pi(x, A_i)}{x/\log x} \leqq \frac{2}{\varphi(a_i)} < \frac{\varepsilon}{2}\,.$$

Pick $x_0 = \max(x_1, x_2)$. Then

$$\frac{\pi(x, Q)}{x/\log x} \leqq \frac{t}{x/\log x} + \frac{\pi(x, A_i)}{x/\log x}\,,$$

for all $x > x_0$, whence

$$\pi(Q) = \lim_{x \to \infty} \frac{\pi(x, Q)}{x/\log x} < \varepsilon$$

for all $\varepsilon > 0$, and $\pi(Q) = 0$.

To show that Q is nowhere dense, assume the contrary. Then there would be a progression B such that *every* subprogression of B satisfying the relative-prime condition has non-empty intersection with Q. Let $\pi(B) = \beta$. By hypothesis, with only finitely many exceptions (say t exceptions), $Q \subset A_i$ with $\pi(A_i) < \frac{1}{2}\beta$. Thus $\pi(B - A_i) \geqq \frac{1}{2}\beta$, where $B - A_i$ denotes the intersection of B with the complement of A_i. Any open progression in $B - A_i$ (and there must be at least one) can be decomposed into more than t disjoint open subprogressions, with only t members of Q available to be in them, contradicting the assumption that Q could be dense in B.

An immediate application of Theorem 13 is to the improvement of Theorem 4 in [8], which asserts that if P_n is any particular prime factor of $F_n = 2^{2^n} + 1$, then the set $\{P_n\}$ has "intermediate density", a weaker condition than sparsity.

Theorem 14. *The set of all prime factors of all the Fermat numbers* $F_n = 2^{2^n} + 1$ *form a sparse set of primes.*

Proof. As shown in [8], every prime factor of F_n belongs to $A_n = \{2^{n+1}K + 1\}$. Since $A_1 \supset A_2 \supset A_3 \supset \ldots$ with $\Pi(A_n) \to 0$, Theorem 13 applies, and asserts that the set of all prime factors of the F_n are a *sparse* set, and are also nowhere dense.

Using the concepts of the present paper, Theorem 3 of [8] can also be strengthened. Let Q be the set of odd primes defined inductively by starting with $3 \varepsilon Q$, and placing each subsequent prime into Q if and only if it fails to be congruent to 1 modulo any of the previously chosen members of Q. In [8] it was shown that Q has "intermediate density", defined as

$$\liminf_{x \to \infty} \frac{\| q \in Q, q \leqq x \|}{x/\log x} = 0 .$$

A review of the proof, however, shows that Q must be either *rare* or *sparse*, and as shown in Section II of this paper, each of these conditions is stronger than the intermediate density condition.

Using very powerful analytic methods, ERDÖS has recently shown [9] that $q_n \sim n \log n \log \log n$, where q_n is the n-th member of Q. It is unlikely that topological methods will ever replace analysis in obtaining results of this depth.

References

[1] *M. Brown*: A Countable Connected Hausdorff Space. Bull. Amer. Math. Soc., *59* (1953), 367.
[2] *H. Furstenberg*: On the Infinitude of Primes. Amer. Math. Monthly, *62* (1955), 353.
[3] *S. W. Golomb*: Problem E 969. Amer. Math. Monthly, *58* (1951), 338.
[4] *R. Spira*: Problem E 1218. Amer. Math. Monthly, *63* (1956), 342.
[5] *J. L. Kelley*: General Topology. New York 1955.
[6] *S. W. Golomb*: A Connected Topology for the Integers, Amer. Math. Monthly, *66*, No. 8, October (1959), 663–666.
[7] *S. W. Golomb*: Advanced Problem 4970. Amer. Math. Monthly, *68*, No. 5, May (1961), 511.
[8] *S. W. Golomb*: Sets of Primes with Intermediate Density. Mathematica Scandinavica, *3* (1955), 264–274.
[9] *P. Erdös*: On a Problem of S. Golomb. Australian Math. Soc. Jour. vol. II, Part I, April (1961), 1–8.
[10] *W. J. Leveque*: Topics in Number Theory. Vol. I, p. 69, problem 4, Addison-Wesley (1956).

EINE NATÜRLICHE TOPOLOGISIERUNG DER POTENZMENGE EINES TOPOLOGISCHEN RAUMES

G. GRIMEISEN

Stuttgart

1. Gegeben sei ein topologischer Raum (E, τ), unter τ wie üblich eine additive ($\tau(X \cup Y) = \tau X \cup \tau Y$), extensionale ($X \subseteq \tau X$), idempotente ($\tau^2 = \tau$) Abbildung der Menge $\mathfrak{P}E$ aller Teilmengen von E (der Potenzmenge von E) in die Menge $\mathfrak{P}E$, die die leere Menge $\emptyset$ festläßt ($\tau\emptyset = \emptyset$), verstanden.

Ist $(f(i))_{i\in I}$, kürzer (f, I), eine Familie von Elementen $f(i)$ von E, wir sagen: eine *Familie über E*, und $\mathfrak{a}$ ein Filter über deren Indexbereich I, so nennen wir das Paar $(f, \mathfrak{a})$, ausführlicher $(f, I, \mathfrak{a})$ oder $f(i)_{i\in I,\mathfrak{a}}$, nach G. Nöbeling [13] eine *gefilterte Familie über E*. Die Menge aller Limespunkte von $(f, \mathfrak{a})$ bezüglich der Topologie τ nennen wir mit J. Schmidt [14] den *Limes* $\mathrm{Lim}_\tau(f, \mathfrak{a})$ von $(f, \mathfrak{a})$. (Statt „$X \in \mathrm{Lim}_\tau(f, \mathfrak{a})$" sagt Bourbaki [3] „$x$ est valeur limite de f suivant $\mathfrak{a}$".) Ist $(g, \mathfrak{b})$ eine gefilterte Familie über $\mathfrak{P}E$, so bezeichnen wir wie üblich (siehe etwa G. Choquet [4] oder G. Nöbeling [13]) den *Limes inferior* von $(g, \mathfrak{b})$ bezüglich τ mit $\liminf_\tau(g, \mathfrak{b})$. Wir bemerken, dass für jede gefilterte Familie $(f, I, \mathfrak{a})$ über E $\mathrm{Lim}_\tau(f, \mathfrak{a}) = \liminf_\tau \{f(i)\}_{i\in I,\mathfrak{a}}$ gilt.

Lim_τ ist ein Operator mit der Klasse aller gefilterten Familien über E als Definitionsbereich und Werten in der Menge $\mathfrak{P}E$. Die Zuordnung $(g, \mathfrak{b}) \to \mathfrak{P}(\liminf_\tau(g, \mathfrak{b}))$ ($(g, \mathfrak{b})$ eine gefilterte Familie über $\mathfrak{P}E$) werde mit $\mathfrak{P}\liminf_\tau$ bezeichnet. $\mathfrak{P}\liminf_\tau$ ist ein Operator mit der Klasse aller gefilterten Familien über $\mathfrak{P}E$ als Definitionsbereich und Werten in der Menge $\mathfrak{P}\mathfrak{P}E$. Wir stellen die Frage nach der Existenz einer Topologie σ der Menge $\mathfrak{P}E$ mit der Eigenschaft

$$\mathfrak{P}\liminf_\tau = \mathrm{Lim}_\sigma .$$

2. Die Lösung des Problems ordnet sich in eine Theorie der Limesräume ein: Gegeben sei eine (abstrakte) Menge E. Wir nennen eine Abbildung Lim, die jeder gefilterten Familie $(f, \mathfrak{a})$ über E eine bestimmte Teilmenge $\mathrm{Lim}(f, \mathfrak{a})$ von E zuordnet, einen *Limesoperator* – das Paar (E, Lim) einen *Limesraum* – wenn Lim nachfolgenden Axiomen (Lim 1), (Lim 2) und (Lim 3) genügt.

(Lim 1): *Ist $(f, I, \mathfrak{a})$ eine gefilterte Familie über E und $x \in E$, so gilt $x \in \mathrm{Lim}(f, \mathfrak{a})$ genau dann, wenn es zu jeder Menge $S \subseteq E$, für die $f(i) \in S$ für $\mathfrak{a}$-konfinal viele $i \in I$ gilt, eine gefilterte Familie $(g, K, \mathfrak{b})$ über E gibt mit $g(K) \subseteq S$ und $x \in \mathrm{Lim}(g, \mathfrak{b})$.*

Dabei bedeute für irgendeine Aussageform $H(i)$ in der Variablen i, sinnvoll für alle $i \in I$, nach G. Nöbeling [13] „$H(i)$ gilt für $\mathfrak{a}$-konfinal viele $i \in I$" dasselbe wie „in jeder Menge $A \in \mathfrak{a}$ gibt es ein Element i derart, dass $H(i)$ gilt" und später übrigens (wie in [7]) „$H(i)$ gilt für $\mathfrak{a}$-fast alle $i \in I$" dasselbe wie „es gibt eine Menge $A \in \mathfrak{a}$ derart, dass $H(i)$ für alle $i \in A$ gilt".

(Lim 2): $$x \in \operatorname{Lim} \langle x \rangle \textit{ für alle } x \in E\,.$$

Mit $\langle x \rangle$ bezeichnen wir die spezielle gefilterte Familie $(f, I, \mathfrak{a})$, in der $I = \{x\}$, $\mathfrak{a} = \{I\}$, $f(x) = x$ ist (also die konstante Folge).

(Lim 3): *Ist $(f, I, \mathfrak{a})$ eine gefilterte Familie über E und zu jedem $i \in I$ $(g_i, \mathfrak{b}_i)$ eine gefilterte Familie über E, so gilt mit*

$$f(i) \in \operatorname{Lim} (g_i, \mathfrak{b}_i) \textit{ für alle } i \in I$$

stets auch

$$\operatorname{Lim} (f, \mathfrak{a}) \subseteq \operatorname{Lim} \Big(\mathop{\mathsf{S}}_{i \in I} g_i, \ {}^{\mathfrak{a}}\!\mathop{\mathsf{S}}_{i \in I} \mathfrak{b}_i \Big)\,.$$

Die in (Lim 3) vorkommende gefilterte Familie $\big(\mathop{\mathsf{S}}_{i \in I} g_i, {}^{\mathfrak{a}}\!\mathop{\mathsf{S}}_{i \in I} \mathfrak{b}_i \big)$ nennen wir in [8] auch die *durch* $\mathfrak{a}$ *gefilterte Summe* ${}^{\mathfrak{a}}\!\mathop{\mathsf{S}}_{i \in I} (g_i, \mathfrak{b}_i)$ *der gefilterten Familien* $(g_i, \mathfrak{b}_i)$ (diese seien ausführlich, unter Betonung der Indexbereiche, etwa mit $(g_i, K_i, \mathfrak{b}_i)$ bezeichnet); sie ist eine modifizierte Verallgemeinerung des Begriffs der Diagonalfolge einer Doppelfolge und wird folgendermassen definiert: Wir verstehen (siehe [7] und [8])

(a) unter der *direkten Summe* $\mathop{\mathsf{S}}_{i \in I} K_i$ *der Mengen* K_i die Menge aller geordneten Paare (j, k) mit $j \in I$ und $k \in K_j$;

(b) unter der *direkten Summe* $\mathop{\mathsf{S}}_{i \in I} g_i$ *der Abbildungen* g_i die Abbildung

$$(j, k) \rightarrow g_j(k) \quad ((j, k) \in \mathsf{S} K_i)\,;$$

(c) unter dem *j-ten Schnitt* $q_j X$ (mit $j \in I$) *einer Menge* $X \subseteq \mathsf{S} K_i$ die Menge aller $k \in K_j$ mit $(j, k) \in X$;

(d) unter der *durch* $\mathfrak{a}$ *gefilterten Summe* ${}^{\mathfrak{a}}\!\mathop{\mathsf{S}}_{i \in I} \mathfrak{b}_i$ *der Filter* $\mathfrak{b}_i$ die Menge aller $X \subseteq \mathsf{S} K_i$ mit der Eigenschaft, daß $q_j X \in \mathfrak{b}_j$ für $\mathfrak{a}$-fast alle $j \in I$.

${}^{\mathfrak{a}}\mathsf{S}\mathfrak{b}_i$ ist ein Filter über der Menge $\mathsf{S} K_i$, nach (b) folglich $(\mathsf{S} g_i, {}^{\mathfrak{a}}\mathsf{S}\mathfrak{b}_i)$ – ausführlicher $(\mathsf{S} g_i, \mathsf{S} K_i, {}^{\mathfrak{a}}\mathsf{S}\mathfrak{b}_i)$ geschrieben – eine gefilterte Familie über E.

Wir bemerken, daß (Lim 1) eine inhaltliche Zusammenfassung des die Teilfolge betreffenden Axioms von M. Fréchet [5] (in der Theorie der Limesräume) mit dem dieses in gewisser Weise umkehrenden Axiom von P. Urysohn (siehe P. Alexandroff-P. Urysohn [1] und P. Urysohn [15]) darstellt. (Lim 2) geht auf M. Fréchet [5] zurück, (Lim 3) ist nichts anderes als die filtertheoretische Fassung des „Theorem on iterated limits" von G. Birkhoff [2] und J. L. Kelley [11], welches in einer konventionellen Sprechweise besagt, daß man (in topologischen Räumen) iterierte Grenzübergänge stets in einfache, nicht iterierte Grenzübergänge verwandeln kann.

(E, Lim) sei ein Limesraum. Ist $X \subseteq E$, so sei $\tau_{\mathrm{Lim}} X$ die Menge aller $y \in E$ mit der Eigenschaft, daß es zu y eine gefilterte Familie $(f, I, \mathfrak{a})$ über E gibt mit $f(I) \subseteq X$ und $y \in \mathrm{Lim}\,(f, \mathfrak{a})$. Der so definierte Operator τ_{Lim} ist eine Topologie, anders ausgedrückt:

Satz 1. (E, τ_{Lim}) *ist ein topologischer Raum.*

Beweis in [9].

Im Sinne von Abschnitt 1 ist also der Operator $\mathrm{Lim}_{\tau_{\mathrm{Lim}}}$ bezüglich der Topologie τ_{Lim} definiert. Wesentlich ist nun

Satz 2. $\mathrm{Lim} = \mathrm{Lim}_{\tau_{\mathrm{Lim}}}$.

Beweis in [9].

Während der Beweis von Satz 1 inhaltlich wie der des entsprechenden Satzes bei Kelley [11] (p. 74 f.) verläuft, benutzt derjenige von Satz 2, anders als bei Kelley [11] (p. 75), wo an der entsprechenden Stelle das „Theorem on iterated limits" wesentlich verwendet wird, von den Axiomen (Lim 1) bis (Lim 3) nur das erste. Daran liegt es, daß man eine Theorie der Limesräume auch allein auf das Axiom (Lim 1) bzw. auf die beiden Axiome (Lim 1) und (Lim 2) aufbauen kann, die dann der Theorie der nichtidempotenten und nichtextensionalen bzw. der nichtidempotenten „Topologien" genau entspricht.

3. Damit haben wir die Hilfsmittel zur Lösung des aufgeworfenen Problems zusammengestellt. Wir gehen wie in Abschnitt 1 von einem topologischen Raum (E, τ) aus. Dann gilt zunächst, als eine wichtige Rechtfertigung obiger Theorie der Limesräume,

Satz 3. (E, Lim_τ) *ist ein Limesraum, und es gilt* $\tau = \tau_{\mathrm{Lim}_\tau}$.

Beweis in [9].

Dabei sei τ_{Lim_τ} wie τ_{Lim} in Abschnitt 2, mit Lim_τ anstelle Lim, definiert. Topologische Räume und Limesräume entsprechen einander also eineindeutig.

Hier interessiert besonders

Satz 4. $(\mathfrak{P}E, \mathfrak{P}\,\lim\inf_\tau)$ *ist ein Limesraum.*

Beweis in [9].

Mittels des Limesoperators $\mathfrak{P}\,\lim\inf_\tau$ bezüglich $\mathfrak{P}E$ als Grundmenge (in Abschnitt 2: Lim bezüglich E als Grundmenge) definieren wir den Operator $\tau_{\mathfrak{P}\lim\inf_\tau}$ (wie τ_{Lim} in Abschnitt 2) und setzen $\tau_{\mathfrak{P}\lim\inf_\tau} = \sigma(\tau)$. Die Verknüpfung der Sätze 1 bis 4 liefert das angestrebte Ergebnis, nämlich den

Satz 5. $(\mathfrak{P}E, \sigma(\tau))$ *ist ein topologischer Raum, es gilt* $\mathfrak{P}\,\lim\inf_\tau = \mathrm{Lim}_{\sigma(\tau)}$, *und* $\sigma(\tau)$ *ist die einzige Topologie* σ *von* $\mathfrak{P}E$ *mit der Eigenschaft* $\mathfrak{P}\,\lim\inf_\tau = \mathrm{Lim}_\sigma$.

4. Eine andere Topologisierung von $\mathfrak{P}E$ bei gegebenem topologischen Raum (E, τ) wird von G. Choquet [4] (siehe insbesondere p. 91, remarque) angegeben: Ist $(g, K, \mathfrak{b})$ eine gefilterte Familie über $\mathfrak{P}E$, so sei $\Phi_\tau(g, \mathfrak{b})$ das System aller $X \in \mathfrak{P}(\lim\inf_\tau(g, \mathfrak{b}))$ mit der Eigenschaft, dass für jede Umgebung U von X bezüglich τ die Inklusion $g(k) \subseteq U$ für $\mathfrak{b}$-fast alle $k \in K$ gilt. An die Stelle unseres Operators $\mathfrak{P}\,\lim\inf_\tau$ tritt im wesentlichen (G. Choquet arbeitet mit Relationen) der Operator Φ_τ. Mittels Φ_τ

wird, auf dem Weg über eine geeignete Konzeption des Limesraums, eine Topologie σ_{Φ_τ} von $\mathfrak{P}E$ definiert. Es fehlen jedoch (unseres Wissens) Sätze, die unseren Sätzen 2 und 5 entsprächen.

Gewöhnlich beschränkt man sich aber auf die Topologisierung eines Teiles von $\mathfrak{P}E$, nämlich auf diejenige der Menge 2^E aller abgeschlossenen Teilmengen von E. Ausser den historischen Ansätzen bei F. HAUSDORFF [10] (Zugrundelegung einer Metrik von E) und deren Weiterentwicklung bei C. KURATOWSKI [12] (Einführung des $(2^E)_L$-Raumes) ist die schon zitierte Arbeit von G. CHOQUET [4] (p. 87) zu erwähnen, in der u. W. zum erstenmal (bei dieser Problemstellung) auf eine Metrik von E verzichtet wird und statt gewöhnlicher Folgen gefilterte Familien verwendet werden, und schließlich, als u. W. neueste Note, die von Z. FROLÍK [6]. Wesentliches Hilfsmittel zur Metrisierung oder Topologisierung von 2^E ist in diesen Arbeiten der topologische Limes einer Folge oder verallgemeinerten Folge von Elementen aus 2^E.

Literatur

[1] *P. Alexandroff* und *P. Urysohn*: Une condition nécessaire et suffisante pour qu'une classe ($\mathscr{L}$) soit une classe ($\mathscr{D}$). C. R. Acad. Sci. *177* (1923), 1274–1277.
[2] *G. Birkhoff*: Moore-Smith convergence in general topology. Ann. Math. *38* (1937), 39–56.
[3] *N. Bourbaki*: Topologie générale, Chap. I–II. 2. Aufl. Actual. Sci. Industr. *1142* (1951).
[4] *G. Choquet*: Convergences. Ann. Univ. Grenoble *23* (1948), 57–112.
[5] *M. Fréchet*: Sur quelques points du calcul fonctionnel. Rend. Circolo mat. Palermo *22* (1906), 1–74.
[6] *Z. Frolík*: Concerning topological convergence of sets. Czechoslovak Math. J. *10* (*85*), (1960), 169–180.
[7] *G. Grimeisen*: Gefilterte Summation von Filtern und iterierte Grenzprozesse. I. Math. Ann. *141* (1960), 318–342.
[8] *G. Grimeisen*: Gefilterte Summation von Filtern und iterierte Grenzprozesse. II. Math. Ann. *144* (1961), 386–417.
[9] *G. Grimeisen*: Zur Stufenhebung bei topologischen Räumen. Math. Ann. *147* (1962), 95–109.
[10] *F. Hausdorff*: Grundzüge der Mengenlehre. Leipzig 1914.
[11] *J. L. Kelley*: General topology. New York 1955.
[12] *C. Kuratowski*: Topologie. Bd. 1. 4. Aufl. Warszawa 1958.
[13] *G. Nöbeling*: Grundlagen der analytischen Topologie. Berlin 1954.
[14] *J. Schmidt*: Eine Studie zum Begriff der Teilfolge. Jahresber. Dtsch. Math. Ver. *63* (1960), 28–50.
[15] *P. Urysohn*: Sur les classes ($\mathscr{L}$) de M. Fréchet. Enseign. math. *25* (1926), 77–83.

LINEARIZATION OF MAPPINGS

J. DE GROOT
Amsterdam

A brief discussion of two theorems in this area.

Let M be a metrizable space and G a compact topological transformation group of homeomorphisms of M onto M. It is clear when such a pair G, M is called (topologically) equivalent to a pair G^*, M^*.

Theorem I. *To every pair G, M there corresponds an equivalent pair G^*, M^* where M^* is embedded in some suitable real Hilbert space H^* and the action of G^* on M^* can be extended over all of H^* in such a way that G^* acts as a (compact) group of unitary homeomorphisms of H^* onto H^*.*

Briefly: *the action of G on M is linearized by a group of unitary transformations in Hilbert space.*

Sketch of the proof. M may be thought of as being embedded into a bounded subset of some real Hilbert space H. Introduce an orthogonal coordinate system in H, and a point $x \in H$ will have coordinates $(x)_\alpha$, α running through some index-set A. We define for every $x \in H$ a map

$$\tau : x = (x)_\alpha \to x^* = (gx)_\alpha\,, \quad \alpha \in A\,, \quad g \in G\,,$$

where gx is the image of x under g in M and $(gx)_\alpha$ is thought of as a functional depending on the two variables g and α. Observe that τ is one-one. We will embed the set $\{x^*\} = M^*$ into a Hilbert space H^*. In order to define H^* we proceed as follows.

The vector space $\mathbf{V}$ will consist of all finite linear combinations of points x^* over the real field, where addition and multiplication with a real scalar are defined in the natural way. For two such vectors $\mathbf{v}$ and $\mathbf{w}$

$$\mathbf{v} = \sum_{j=1}^{n} a_j (gx_j)_\alpha\,, \quad \mathbf{w} = \sum_{j=1}^{n} b_j (gy_j)_\alpha$$

we define an inner product

$$(\mathbf{v}, \mathbf{w}) = \int_G \sum_\alpha (\mathbf{v} \,.\, \mathbf{w})\, \mathrm{d}g\,.$$

Observe that this makes sense. Thus the vector space $\mathbf{V}$ becomes an, in general, still incomplete Hilbert space. Its completion will be H^*. One can prove that τ is a topological map of M onto M^*, while the action of

$$G^* = \tau G \tau^{-1} \quad \text{on} \quad M^*$$

is defined in a natural way over all of H^*. The invariance of integration shows that G^* acts in this way as a group of unitary transformations.

Two unsolved problems:

1° If G is locally compact, can we find a G^* of bounded linear operators?

2° The same question, if G is a compact semigroup of continuous mappings of M into itself.

If P is a topological product of an infinite number, say m copies of one and the same topological space T, every permutation of these m copies induces in a natural way, an autohomeomorphism of P.

In the same way every *immutation* (an immutation is defined as a map of a set – in our case of power m – into itself) defines, in the natural way, a continuous map of P into itself. If T is a vector space, such an immutation is a linear map.

A family of immutations of a given set generates a semigroup of immutations. Conversely, if some semigroup is given, we may add a unit element to the semigroup. The set of all left (or right) multiplications carried out on the elements of the latter semigroup defines a semigroup of immutations (on the set of elements of the semigroup) which is isomorphic (anti-isomorphic) to the latter semigroup. In particular a free semigroup F of power m with identity element may be represented isomorphically by the corresponding free immutation semigroup of left immutations.

In the sequel let P be a product of m segments. The free semigroup F may be represented as a set of immutations of the m segments, inducing a free semigroup of continuous maps of P into itself. We might call these maps "linear" (since we can extend the segments to real lines). This defines the pair F, P.

Take a set of free generators φ of F. How does such a φ look like as immutation, i.e. as coordinate transformation on the m coordinates x_α of P? For every such φ there corresponds a splitting of the m coordinate-indices α into m countable sets of indices β, i, where β is an index-set of power m and $i = 1, 2, 3, \ldots$ ad inf. The corresponding coordinate transformation induced by φ is given by

$$(*) \qquad y_{\beta,i} = x_{\beta,i+1} \quad \text{for all pairs } \beta, i\,.$$

Every completely regular space R of weight $\leqq m$ admits a topological embedding into P. We might say P is a universal space regarding the family of spaces R. Now let, moreover, be given a set S of m arbitrary continuous mappings of R into itself. Without loss of generality we may assume that S is a semigroup with identity element. This defines the pair S, R.

Theorem II. *Any pair S, R admits a universal linearization by means of the pair F, P.*

Explicitly: it is possible to embed R in such a way into P, that the action of F onto P, restricted to the embedded R, coincides with the action of S onto the embedded R. So, in particular the action of any $s \in S$ on the embedded R can be extended over all of P.

Every such an extension map is a "linear" map of type (*).

Remarks. Analogous results hold for sets S of power different from m. The action of F on the embedded R is not effective, in general. A corresponding theorem holds for autohomeomorphism groups S. In this case F is a free group and i runs through all integers in the equations (*).

Indication of proof. Set up a one to one correspondence

$$\varphi \leftrightarrow s \quad (s \neq e)$$

between the free generators of F and the elements ($\neq e$) of S. This correspondence induces a homomorphic map ω of F onto S.

The elements of F will be denoted by ψ and F will also serve as an index-set. We can write

$$P = \prod_{\substack{\lambda \in L \\ \psi \in F}} I_{\lambda,\psi},$$

where $L$is an index set of power m and every $I_{\lambda,\psi}$ is a segment. A point $x \in P$ has coordinates $x_{\lambda,\psi}$

$$x = (x_{\lambda,\psi})_{\substack{\lambda \in L \\ \psi \in F}} \quad (0 \leqq x_{\lambda,\psi} \leqq 1).$$

For every fixed element $\gamma \in F$ we determine a "linear" map γ of P into itself by the following immutation ($x\gamma$ denotes the image of x under γ)

$$x\gamma = (x\gamma_{\lambda,\psi})_{\substack{\lambda \in L \\ \psi \in F}} \stackrel{\text{def}}{=} (x_{\lambda,\gamma\psi})_{\substack{\lambda \in L \\ \psi \in F}}.$$

Furthermore, one may think R to be contained topologically (this is a preliminary embedding) in the subspace of P spanned by the segments $I_{\lambda,\varepsilon}$ ($\lambda \in L$, $\varepsilon =$ identity-index of F). So a point $y \in R$ has coordinates

$$y = (y_{\lambda,\psi})$$

with

$$y_{\lambda,\psi} = 0 \quad \text{if} \quad \psi \neq \varepsilon, \quad \psi \in F.$$

The final embedding $R^* = \{y^*\}$ of R is determined by a map τ of R into P:

$$\tau\colon\ y \to y^* = (y^*_{\lambda,\psi})_{\substack{\lambda \in L \\ \psi \in F}} \stackrel{\text{def}}{=} (y\ \omega(\psi)_{\lambda,\varepsilon})_{\substack{\lambda \in L \\ \psi \in F}}, \tag{1}$$

where $y\ \omega(\psi)$ is the image of y under $s = \omega(\psi)$, so a point of R in its first embedding.

One can show that τ is a homeomorphism, while moreover the action of an element $\gamma \in F$ on R^* coincides with the action of $\omega(\gamma)$ on R. Moreover, it appears that the requirements of theorem II are fulfilled.

Some other results:

J. de Groot: Every continuous mapping is linear. Notices Amer. Math. Soc. *6* (1959), 754.

A. H. Copeland Jr. and *J. de Groot*: Linearization of a homeomorphism, Math. Ann. *144* (1961), 80–92.

SOME RELATIONS BETWEEN TOPOLOGICAL AND ALGEBRAIC PROPERTIES OF TOPOLOGICAL GROUPS

S. HARTMAN

Wrocław

Several theorems are known about the mutual dependence between topological and algebraic properties of groups, especially of abelian topological groups. E. g. the equivalence of connexity and divisibility in compact abelian groups, or the algebraic characterization of the abelian groups which admit a compact topology (A. HULANICKI).

The following are some results of this kind which I obtained in the last years in cooperation with other authors:

I. The property of a topological group G to be generated by an arbitrary neighbourhood of the unit element e is, in the case of a locally compact group, not only necessary but also sufficient for G to be connected. Compact divisible groups have a stronger property, namely they are unions $\bigcup_{x \in U} [x]$ of cyclic subgroups, U being an arbitrary neighbourhood of e [1]. Since all connected compact groups (even non-abelian) are divisible [2], they may be represented in this manner.

II. A subgroup H of an abelian group G is called pure if the equation $nx = a$ $(a \in H)$ is soluble in H whenever it is soluble in G. Denote by K the class of abelian groups G such that either G itself or its character group $\hat{G}$ is generated by a compact neighbourhood of e. Then, for every $G \in K$, the closed subgroup $H \subset G$ is pure if and only if each (continuous) character of H of finite order can be extended to a character of the whole group G without raising its order. The assumption $G \in K$ cannot be dropped [3].

III. If $\aleph_{\alpha+1} = 2^{\aleph_\alpha}$ for every ordinal α, then it can be proved that:

(a) an infinite compact abelian[1]) group of cardinality $\leqq 2^{2^{\mathfrak{m}}}$ contains a dense subset of cardinality $\leqq \mathfrak{m}$,

(b) for an infinite locally compact abelian group of cardinality $\leqq 2^{2^{\mathfrak{m}}}$ the following conditions are equivalent:

(1) there are more than $\mathfrak{m}$ disjoint neighbourhoods in G,

(2) every dense subset of G has cardinality $> \mathfrak{m}$,

(3) G can be homomorphically and continuously mapped onto a discrete group of cardinality $> \mathfrak{m}$,

---

[1]) From recent results communicated during the Symposion by Prof. P. S. ALEXANDROV it follows that the assumption of commutativity can be dropped.

(4) G can be continuously mapped onto an isolated space of cardinality $> \mathfrak{m}$.

These conditions are satisfied if G contains an isolated subgroup of cardinality $> \mathfrak{m}$. The converse is not true [4].

References

[1] *S. Hartman* and *C. Ryll-Nardzewski*: Zur Theorie der lokal kompakten abelschen Gruppen. Colloq. Mat. *4* (1957), 157–188.

[2] *Jan Mycielski*: Some Properties of Connected Compact Groups. Colloq. Mat. *5* (1958), 162–166.

[3] *S. Hartman* et *A. Hulanicki*: Les sous-groupes purs et leurs duals. Fundam. Math. *45* (1957), 71–77.

[4] *S. Hartman* et *A. Hulanicki*: Sur les ensembles denses de puissance minimum dans les groupes topologiques. Colloq. Mat. *6* (1958), 187–191.

TOPOLOGISCHE UNTERGRUPPENRÄUME

G. HELMBERG

Innsbruck

Es sei X eine kompakte Hausdorffsche topologische Gruppe und $\mathfrak{X} = \{X_\varrho : \varrho \in R\}$ die Menge der abgeschlossenen Untergruppen von X. Ist μ'_ϱ das normierte Haarsche Maß auf X_ϱ und ordnet man jeder Untergruppe $X_\varrho \in \mathfrak{X}$ das durch $\mu_\varrho(E) = \mu'_\varrho(E \cap X_\varrho)$ definierte Borel-Maß auf X zu, dann wird dadurch die Menge $\mathfrak{X}$ eineindeutig auf eine schwach abgeschlossene Untermenge $\mathfrak{X}^*$ der Einheitskugel in dem zum Banachraum $\mathfrak{C}$ aller stetigen komplexwertigen Funktionen auf X konjugierten Raum $\mathfrak{C}^*$ abgebildet (siehe [2]). Überträgt man die auf $\mathfrak{X}^*$ relativierte schwache Topologie in $\mathfrak{C}^*$ auf $\mathfrak{X}$, dann wird $\mathfrak{X}$ zu einem kompakten Hausdorffschen Raum, in dem für beliebige Netze (Moore-Smith-Folgen) $\mathfrak{N} = \{X_\sigma : \sigma \in S\}$ von Untergruppen die Beziehung $\lim_{\sigma \in S} X_\sigma = X_0$ gleichbedeutend ist mit

$$\lim_{\sigma \in S} \int f \, d\mu_\sigma = \int f \, d\mu_0 \quad \text{für alle} \quad f \in \mathfrak{C}.$$

Das Ziel der vorliegenden Arbeit ist eine Charakterisierung dieser Topologie $\mathfrak{T}$ in $\mathfrak{X}$ ohne Rückgriff auf $\mathfrak{C}$ und $\mathfrak{C}^*$, sowie eine Übertragung dieser Überlegungen auf abstrakte (nicht topologische) Gruppen.

Für ein Netz $\mathfrak{N}$ in $\mathfrak{X}$ seien die unteren und oberen abgeschlossenen Limites $\underline{\mathrm{Fl}}\, X_\sigma$ und $\overline{\mathrm{Fl}}\, X_\sigma$ erklärt wie bei F. Hausdorff. Mit Hilfe von Netzen läßt sich $\mathfrak{T}$ folgendermaßen charakterisieren: Ein Netz $\mathfrak{N}$ in $\mathfrak{X}$ konvergiert dann und nur dann in der Topologie $\mathfrak{T}$, wenn $\underline{\mathrm{Fl}} X_\sigma = \overline{\mathrm{Fl}}\, X_\sigma$. Falls $\mathfrak{N}$ konvergiert, gilt weiter

$$\underline{\mathrm{Fl}}\, X_\sigma = \overline{\mathrm{Fl}}\, X_\sigma = \lim_{\sigma \in S} X_\sigma \in \mathfrak{X}.$$

Ist $\mathfrak{G}$ die Menge aller Untergruppen aus $\mathfrak{X}$, die Häufungspunkte des Netzes $\mathfrak{N}$ sind, dann gilt $\underline{\mathrm{Fl}}\, X_\sigma = \cap\, \mathfrak{G}$ und $\overline{\mathrm{Fl}}\, X_\sigma = \cup\, \mathfrak{G}$. Diese Aussagen bleiben richtig, wenn an Stelle von $\mathfrak{X}$ die Menge $\mathfrak{Y}$ aller abgeschlossenen Normalteiler von X in der auf $\mathfrak{Y}$ relativierten Topologie $\mathfrak{T}$ tritt. Der Unterraum $\mathfrak{Y}$ fällt für eine abelsche Gruppe X mit dem Raum $\mathfrak{X}$ zusammen und wird bei Einführung der Komplexmultiplikation in X als Verknüpfung zu einer kompakten Halbgruppe.

Für eine beliebig gegebene Untergruppe $X_0 \in \mathfrak{X}$, eine beliebige offene Umgebung V der Einheit in X und eine endliche Menge von Elementen $x_1, \ldots, x_n \in X_0$ sei die Untermenge $\mathfrak{U}(X_0; x_1, \ldots, x_n; V)$ von $\mathfrak{X}$ definiert durch

$$\mathfrak{U}(X_0; x_1, \ldots, x_n; V) = \{X_\varrho \in \mathfrak{X} : X_\varrho \cap V x_i \neq 0 \quad (i = 1, \ldots, n),\ X_\varrho \subset V X_0\}.$$

Dann ist die Familie aller Untermengen $\mathfrak{U}(X_\varrho; X_{\varrho 1}, \ldots, X_{\varrho n}; V)$ von $\mathfrak{X}$ $(X_\varrho \in \mathfrak{X}$, $x_{\varrho i} \in X_\varrho$ für $i = 1, \ldots, n$, V eine offene Umgebung der Einheit in $X)$ ein vollständiges Umgebungssystem für die Topologie $\mathfrak{T}$ in $\mathfrak{X}$. Mit Rücksicht auf die Definition von $\mathfrak{T}$ kann dieser Satz auch folgendermaßen formuliert werden: Es seien $X_0 \in \mathfrak{X}$, $f_i \in \mathfrak{C}$ $(i = 1, \ldots, m)$ und $\varepsilon > 0$ beliebig gegeben. Dann gibt es eine endliche Menge von Elementen $x_j \in X_0$ $(j = 1, \ldots, n)$ und eine offene Umgebung V der Einheit in X derart, daß aus $X_\varrho \in \mathfrak{U}(X_0; x_1, \ldots, x_n; V)$ die Ungleichungen $|\int f_i \, d\mu_\varrho - \int f_i \, d\mu_0| < \varepsilon$ für $i = 1, \ldots, m$ folgen. Umgekehrt existiert zu jeder Untermenge $\mathfrak{U}(X_0; x_1, \ldots, x_n; V)$ von $\mathfrak{X}$ eine endliche Anzahl von Funktionen $f_i \in \mathfrak{C}$ $(i = 1, \ldots, m)$ und eine reelle Zahl $\varepsilon > 0$ derart, daß aus

$$\left| \int f_i \, d\mu_\varrho - \int f_i \, d\mu_0 \right| < \varepsilon \quad \text{für} \quad i = 1, \ldots, m$$

die Beziehung $X_\varrho \in \mathfrak{U}(X_0; x_1, \ldots, x_n; V)$ folgt.

Dieser Satz kann verwendet werden, um für eine konkrete Gruppe X den Untergruppenraum $\mathfrak{X}$ zu identifizieren. Beispielsweise ist der Untergruppenraum der eindimensionalen Torusgruppe homöomorph zu einer konvergenten Punktfolge (der die Folge der Untergruppen endlicher Ordnung entspricht) zusammen mit ihrem Grenzpunkt (dem die ganze Gruppe X entspricht). In der zweidimensionalen Torusgruppe bilden die abgeschlossenen nicht diskreten Untergruppen eine kompakte Teilmenge von $\mathfrak{X}$, die mit der ersten Ableitung von $\mathfrak{X}$ zusammenfällt. In der relativierten Topologie ist dieser Unterraum von $\mathfrak{X}$ homöomorph mit der Einpukt-Kompaktifizierung der Menge aller Gitterpunkte einer Halbene, wobei dem Punkt im Unendlichen wieder die Gruppe X entspricht. Der Untergruppenraum der Diedergruppe der eindimensionalen Torusgruppe ist homöomorph mit einer gegen den gemeinsamen Mittelpunkt konvergierenden Folge konzentrischer Kreise, zusammen mit einer getrennt davon liegenden konvergenten Punktfolge samt Grenzpunkt (die dem Untergruppenraum des eindimensionalen Torus entspricht). Den Punkten eines Kreises entsprechen die Dieder-Untergruppen einer bestimmten, endlichen Ordnung von X, dem gemeinsamen Mittelpunkt wieder die ganze Gruppe X.

Unter Heranziehung fastperiodischer Kompaktifizierungen einer abstrakten Gruppe X können diese Resultate auf nicht topologische Gruppen folgendermaßen übertragen werden: Es sei $\mathfrak{A}$ ein voller Modul fastperiodischer Funktionen auf X und (X', φ) eine $\mathfrak{A}$-Kompaktifizierung von X, d. h. eine kompakte Hausdorffsche topologische Gruppe X' zusammen mit einem Homomorphismus φ von X auf eine dichte Untergruppe von X' derart, daß $\mathfrak{A} = \{g \circ \varphi : g \in \mathfrak{C}'\}$ (siehe [1]). Ferner sei $\mathfrak{X} = \{X_\varrho : \varrho \in R\}$ die Menge aller Untergruppen von X und $\mathfrak{X}'$ der Untergruppenraum von X'. Für $f \in \mathfrak{A}$ sei $M_\varrho(f)$ der über X_ϱ erstreckte Mittelwert der auf X_ϱ beschränkten (und daher auf X_ϱ fastperiodischen) Funktion f. Schreibt man $X_\varrho \equiv X_\sigma$ für: $M_\varrho(f) = M_\sigma(f)$ für alle $f \in \mathfrak{A}$, dann ist dadurch in der Menge $\mathfrak{X}$ eine Äquivalenzrelation definiert. Die X_ϱ enthaltende Äquivalenzklasse sei mit X''_ϱ bezeichnet und die Menge aller Äquivalenzklassen mit $\mathfrak{X}''$.

Eine nicht negative reellwertige Funktion aus $\mathfrak{A}$, die in der Einheit von X einen positiven Wert annimt, soll Umgebungsfunktion heißen. Es seien $X_0 \in \mathfrak{X}$, sowie $x_i \in X_0$ $(i = 1, \ldots, n)$ und eine Umgebungsfunktion $f \in \mathfrak{A}$ beliebig gegeben. Die Untermenge $\mathfrak{U}(X_0; x_1, \ldots, x_n; f)$ von $\mathfrak{X}$ sei definiert durch

$$\mathfrak{U}(X_0; x_1, \ldots, x_n; f) = \{X_\varrho \in \mathfrak{X} : \sup_{x_\rho \in X_\rho} f(x_\varrho x_i^{-1}) > 0 \quad (i = 1, \ldots, n),$$

$$\inf_{x_\rho \in X_\rho} [\sup_{x_0 \in X_0} f(x_\varrho x_0)] > 0\}.$$

Da die Menge $\mathfrak{U}(X_0; x_1, \ldots, x_n; f)$ mit jeder Untergruppe X_ϱ auch alle Untergruppen der Äquivalenzklasse X''_ϱ enthält, kann sie auch als Untermenge von $\mathfrak{X}''$ aufgefaßt werden. Dies sei durch die Schreibweise $\mathfrak{U}(X''_0; x_1, \ldots, x_n; f)$ hervorgehoben.

Die Familie aller Untermengen $\mathfrak{U}(X''_\varrho; x_{\varrho 1}, \ldots, x_{\varrho n}; f)$ von $\mathfrak{X}''$ $(X_\varrho \in \mathfrak{X}, x_{\varrho i} \in X_\varrho$ für $i = 1, \ldots, n, f$ eine Umgebungsfunktion in $\mathfrak{A})$ ist ein vollständiges Umgebungssystem für eine Hausdorffsche Topologie in $\mathfrak{X}''$. Ist $\mathfrak{N} = \{X''_\varrho : \sigma \in S\}$ ein in dieser Topologie konvergentes Netz in $\mathfrak{X}''$, dann ist $\lim_{\sigma \in S} X''_\sigma = X''_0$ gleichbedeutend mit

$$\lim_{\sigma \in S} M_\sigma(f) = M_0(f) \quad \text{für alle} \quad f \in \mathfrak{A}.$$

In dieser Topologie ist $\mathfrak{X}''$ homöomorph zu einem Unterraum des topologischen Untergruppenraumes $\mathfrak{X}'$ der $\mathfrak{A}$-Kompaktifizierungsgruppe X' von X. Dieser Unterraum braucht jedoch, wie Beispiele zeigen, weder kompakt noch dicht in $\mathfrak{X}'$ zu sein.

Eine Arbeit über topologische Untergruppenräume, die auch die Beweise der angeführten Resultate enthält, erscheint demnächst im Journal für reine und angewandte Mathematik (siche [3]).

Literatur

[1] *Nöbeling G.* und *Bauer H.*: Allgemeine Approximationskriterien mit Anwendungen. Jahresber. Dtsch. Math. Ver. *58* (1956), 54–72.

[2] *Wendel J. G.*: Haar measure and the semigroup of measures on a compact group. Proc. Amer. Math. Soc. *5* (1954), 923–929.

[3] *Helmberg G.*: Topologische Untergruppenräume. Journal f. d. reine u. angew. Math. *208* (1961), 164—180.

THE SPACE OF MINIMAL PRIME IDEALS OF A COMMUTATIVE RING

M. HENRIKSEN and M. JERISON
Lafayette

1. Introduction. Our interest in the space of minimal prime ideals of a commutative ring arises from the special features of this space in case the ring is $C(X)$, the ring of all continuous real-valued functions on a topological space X. For instance, if X is the one-point compactification of a countable discrete space N, then the space of minimal prime ideals of $C(X)$ is homeomorphic with βN, the Stone-Čech compactification of N. This was pointed out by C. W. Kohls [4], who initiated the study of minimal prime ideals in rings $C(X)$.

It should be noted at the outset that a *minimal* prime ideal means a prime ideal that contains no smaller prime ideal. Thus, in an integral domain, the only minimal prime ideals is (0). The following lemma provides a key tool for the study of such ideals in an arbitrary ring, which we always assume to be commutative.

1.1. Lemma. *A proper prime ideal P of a ring A is minimal if and only if for each $x \in P$ there exists $a \in A \sim P$ such that ax is nilpotent.*

It is easy to see that the stated condition is sufficient for minimality of P. To prove necessity, one assumes that the condition is violated and uses a standard argument involving Zorn's lemma to construct a prime ideal contained properly in P.

2. *The space $\mathscr{P}(A)$.* Let $\mathscr{P}$, or more precisely $\mathscr{P}(A)$, denote the set of all minimal prime ideals in a ring A. The *hull* of a set $S \subset A$ is

$$h(S) = \{P \in \mathscr{P} : S \subset P\} .$$

The *kernel* of a set $\mathscr{S} \subset \mathscr{P}$ is

$$k(\mathscr{S}) = \bigcap\{P : P \in \mathscr{S}\} .$$

A topology is defined in $\mathscr{P}$ by means of a closure operation: The *closure* of $\mathscr{S}$ is the set $h\,k(\mathscr{S})$. Evidently, the family of sets $\{h(a) : a \in A\}$ is a base for the closed sets in $\mathscr{P}$.

2.1. Theorem. *Let I be an ideal of A. The mapping τ defined by*

$$\tau(P) = P \cap I , \quad P \in h(I)$$

is a homeomorphism of the subspace $h(I)$ of $\mathscr{P}(A)$ onto a subspace of $\mathscr{P}(A/I)$.

The proof of this theorem is straightforward. In case I is the ideal of all nilpotents in A, then $h(I)$ is all of $\mathscr{P}(A)$ and the image under τ is all of $\mathscr{P}(A/I)$. Consequently, we lose no generality in studying topological properties of $\mathscr{P}(A)$ if we assume that A has no nonzero nilpotent.

For any $S \subset A$, we denote the *annihilator of S by $\mathfrak{A}(S)$*:

$$\mathfrak{A}(S) = [a \in A : as = 0 \text{ for all } s \in S].$$

2.2. Theorem. *For any element a in a ring without nonzero nilpotent, $h(\mathfrak{A}(a)) = \mathscr{P} \sim h(a)$. Thus, besides being closed by definition, the sets $h(a)$ and $h(\mathfrak{A}(a))$ are open.*

This theorem follows directly from Lemma 1.1 which, for rings without nonzero nilpotent, simply says: a prime ideal P is minimal if and only if for all $x \in P$, $\mathfrak{A}(x) \not\subset P$.

2.3. Corollary. *$\mathscr{P}$ is a Hausdorff space with a base of open-and-closed sets.*

2.4. Corollary. *An element in a ring without nonzero nilpotent belongs to some minimal prime ideal if and only if it is a divisor of zero.*

Additional useful properties of annihilators and hulls of elements are:

2.5. Lemma. *For all x, y, z in a ring without nonzero nilpotent,*

(i) $h(x) = h(\mathfrak{A}\,\mathfrak{A}(x))$;

(ii) $\mathfrak{A}\,\mathfrak{A}(xy) = \mathfrak{A}\,\mathfrak{A}(x) \cap \mathfrak{A}\,\mathfrak{A}(y)$;

(iii) $\mathfrak{A}(z) = \mathfrak{A}(x) \cap \mathfrak{A}(y)$ *if and only if* $h(z) = h(x) \cap h(y)$;

(iv) $\mathfrak{A}\,\mathfrak{A}(y) = \mathfrak{A}(x)$ *if and only if* $h(y) = h(\mathfrak{A}(x))$.

3. *Compactness of $\mathscr{P}$.* A striking difference between the space $\mathscr{P}(\mathfrak{A})$ and more familiar spaces of ideals of a ring A (see, e. g. [1]) is that compactness of $\mathscr{P}(A)$ is wholly unrelated to the presence of a unity in A. Instead, compactness of $\mathscr{P}(A)$ hinges upon the existence of a kind of complement in the sense that for each element x of A there shall exist $x' \in A$ such that $\mathfrak{A}\,\mathfrak{A}(x') = \mathfrak{A}(x)$. This condition is sufficient for compactness; we have been able to prove that it is necessary only under the additional restriction stated next.

3.1. Definition. *A ring A is said to satisfy the annihilator condition (or is an a. c. ring) if A has no nonzero nilpotent and for every x, $y \in A$, there exists $z \in A$ such that $\mathfrak{A}(z) = \mathfrak{A}(x) \cap \mathfrak{A}(y)$.*

It is difficult to find a ring without nonzero nilpotent that is not a. c. Professor HARLEY FLANDERS *provided the following example which, moreover, has a unity.*

3.2. Example. Let K be an algebraically closed field and $\Lambda = K \times K \times K$. In the ring K^{Λ} of all K-valued functions on Λ, let F be the subring of functions that are 0 except on a finite subset of Λ. Define x, $y \in K^{\Lambda}$ by

$$x(a, b, c) = a\,, \quad y(a, b, c) = b\,, \quad ((a, b, c) \in \Lambda)\,,$$

and let A be the smallest subring of K^{Λ} that contains F, x, y, and the constants. In the ring A, $\mathfrak{A}(x) \cap \mathfrak{A}(y)$ is not the annihilator of any single element.

3.3. Theorem. *The following conditions on a ring A without nonzero nilpotent are equivalent:*

(a) *A is a. c. and $\mathscr{P}(A)$ is compact.*

(b) *For each $x \in A$ there exists $x' \in A$ such that $\mathfrak{A}\,\mathfrak{A}(x') = \mathfrak{A}(x)$.*

Proof. (a) implies (b). For a given $x \in A$, the existence of x' will follow from compactness of $h(x)$ only. By Theorem 2.2,

$$\bigcap\{h(y) \cap h(x) : y \in \mathfrak{A}(x)\} = h(\mathfrak{A}(x)) \cap h(x) = \emptyset .$$

Hence, there exist $y_1, \ldots, y_n \in \mathfrak{A}(x)$ such that

$$h(y_1) \cap \ldots \cap h(y_n) \cap h(x) = \emptyset ,$$

which implies $h(y_1) \cap \ldots \cap h(y_n) = h(\mathfrak{A}(x))$. Since A is a. c., there exists $x' \in A$ such that $\mathfrak{A}(x') = \mathfrak{A}(y_1) \cap \ldots \cap \mathfrak{A}(y_n)$. By Lemma 2.5, we have, $h(x') = h(\mathfrak{A}(x))$ and hence $\mathfrak{A}\, \mathfrak{A}(x') = \mathfrak{A}(x)$.

Now assume (b). That A is a. c. follows from Lemma 2.5 (ii), if we set $z = (x'y')'$. To prove that $\mathscr{P}(A)$ is compact, we need

3.4. Lemma. *Let A satisfy* (b). *An ideal I in A is contained in some minimal prime ideal of A if (and only if) every member of I is a divisor of* 0. *In particular, a prime ideal in A is minimal if and only if each of its members is a divisor of* 0. (*Cf. Corollary* 2.4).

To prove this lemma, we use Zorn's lemma to embed I in a prime ideal P each of whose members is a divisor of 0. Suppose that P is not minimal. Then there exists $x \in P$ such that $\mathfrak{A}(x) \subset P$. The element x' such that $\mathfrak{A}\, \mathfrak{A}(x') = \mathfrak{A}(x)$ clearly belongs to $\mathfrak{A}(x)$, and so $x' \in P$. Hence $x + x' \in P$. But $h(x') = h(\mathfrak{A}(x)) = \mathscr{P} \sim h(x)$, that is, every minimal prime ideal contains exactly one of x and x'. Thus, $h(x + x') = \emptyset$, so by Corollary 2.4, $x + x'$ is not a divisor of 0. This contradicts $x + x' \in P$.

To complete the proof of the theorem, let $\{h(x_\alpha)\}$ be a family of basic closed sets in $\mathscr{P}$ with empty intersection. If I is the ideal generated by $\{x_\alpha\}$, then $h(I) = \bigcap h(x_\alpha) = \emptyset$. By the lemma, I contains a nondivisor of 0, say e. Then there exist $x_{\alpha_1}, \ldots, x_{\alpha_n}$ and $a_1, \ldots, a_n$ in A such that $e = \sum_{i=1}^{n} a_i x_{\alpha_1}$, and we have

$$\bigcap_{i=1}^{n} h(x_{\alpha_i}) \subset h(e) = \emptyset .$$

4. *Countable compactness and basic disconnectivity of* $\mathscr{P}$.

4.1. Definition. *A ring A is said to satisfy the countable annihilator condition* (*or is a c. a. c. ring*) *if A has no nonzero nilpotent and for each sequence $\{x_n\}$ in A, there exists $x \in A$ such that* $\mathfrak{A}(x) = \bigcap_{n=1}^{\infty} \mathfrak{A}(x_n)$.

Obviously, every c. a. c. ring is a. c. Any ring $C(T)$ is a c. a. c. ring, as follows: $x(t) = \sum_{n=1}^{\infty} 2^{-n} \min(|x_n(t)|, 1)$ for all $t \in T$.

4.2. Lemma. *If B is a set in any ring A, then in the space $\mathscr{P}(A)$, the closure of* $\bigcup\{h(\mathfrak{A}(b)) : b \in B\}$ *is* $h(\mathfrak{A}(B))$.

4.3. Corollary. *If for every $B \subset A$, there exists $x \in A$ such that $\mathfrak{A}(B) = \mathfrak{A}(x)$, then $\mathscr{P}(A)$ is extremally disconnected.*

The hypothesis of this corollary is an obvious strengthening of the countable annihilator condition. If only c. a. c. is assumed, the most that might be expected of $\mathscr{P}(A)$ is that it be basically disconnected – a countable analogue of extremal disconnectivity – which is defined in [2] as follows: a space X is *basically disconnected* if every zero-set in X has a closed interior. However, c. a. c. by itself is not sufficient to make $\mathscr{P}(A)$ basically disconnected. Our most general result in this direction is

4.4. Theorem. *If A is a c. a. c. ring and $\mathscr{P}(A)$ is locally compact, then $\mathscr{P}(A)$ is basically disconnected.*

Next, we have a property of all c. a. c. rings.

4.5. Theorem. *If A is a c. a. c. ring, then $\mathscr{P}(A)$ is countably compact.*

A cluster point for an arbitrary sequence $\{P_n\}$ in such a $\mathscr{P}(A)$ is constructed as follows: Let $\mathscr{U}$ be an ultrafilter on the integers with void intersection. For each $x \in A$, let $E(x) = \{n : x \in P_n\}$. Then the set $\{x \in A : E(x) \in \mathscr{U}\}$ is a minimal prime ideal of A and is a cluster point of $\{P_n\}$. The countable annihilator condition is used only in the proof of minimality.

5. *Minimal prime ideals of Φ-algebras.* An archimedean lattice-ordered algebra over the real field with a unity element 1 that is also a weak order unit is called a *Φ-algebra*. As was shown in [3], a Φ-algebra is a natural generalization of a ring $C(X)$, especially if one is concerned with spaces of ideals. If A is a Φ-algebra, then the space $\mathscr{M}(A)$ of all maximal l-ideals (an l-ideal I is a ring ideal such that $b \in I$ and $|a| \leqq |b|$ implies $a \in I$) of A is a compact Hausdorff space. The set

$$A^* = \{a \in A : |a| \leqq \lambda \,.\, 1 \text{ for some real } \lambda\}$$

of bounded elements of A is also a Φ-algebra, and $\mathscr{M}(A^*)$ is homeomorphic with $\mathscr{M}(A)$. It is also true that $\mathscr{P}(A^*)$ is homeomorphic with $\mathscr{P}(A)$. Any Φ-algebra A is isomorphic with a Φ-algebra of extended real-valued, continuous functions on the space $\mathscr{M}(A)$ that are real-valued on a dense subset of $\mathscr{M}(A)$. The isomorphism carries A^* onto a subalgebra of $C(\mathscr{M}(A))$.

Each minimal prime ideal of A is contained in a unique maximal l-ideal. Thus, there is a mapping ι of $\mathscr{P}(A)$ *onto* $\mathscr{M}(A)$, which is automatically continuous. We shall state the properties of this mapping for the case $A = C(X)$, where X is a compact Hausdorff space; in view of the remarks of the preceding paragraph, this entails little loss of generality. Also, we use the well-known homeomorphism between X and $\mathscr{M}(C(X))$ and regard ι as a mapping of $\mathscr{P}$ onto X – for $P \in \mathscr{P}$, $\iota(P)$ is the unique point in X where all functions in P vanish.

5.1. Theorem. (a) *ι is one-one if and only if X is an F-space* [2, p. 208].

(b) *ι is a homeomorphism if and only if X is basically disconnected.*

(c) *In case X is an F-space, $\mathscr{P}$ is compact if and only if X is basically disconnected.*

Any $C(X)$ is an a. c. ring, in fact, a c. a. c. ring. Condition (b) of Theorem 3.3 is therefore necessary and sufficient in order that $\mathscr{P}(C(X))$ be compact. In terms of the behavior of functions, this condition says:

(b′) For each $f \in C(X)$, there exists $f' \in C(X)$ such that

$$Z(f) \cup Z(f') = X \quad \text{and} \quad \operatorname{int}[Z(f) \cap Z(f')] = \emptyset .$$

($Z(f)$ denotes the zero-set of f.) A more easily verified sufficient, but not necessary, condition for $\mathscr{P}(C(X))$ to be compact is given next.

5.2. Theorem. *If, for every $f \in C(X)$, the support of f is a zero-set, in particular if X is perfectly normal, then $\mathscr{P}(C(X))$ is compact.*

We conclude with some illuminating examples.

5.3. A space Γ such that $\mathscr{P}(C(\Gamma))$ is locally compact, but not compact. Let W^* be the totally ordered space of ordinal numbers less than or equal to the first uncountable ordinal, ω_1. Γ is the quotient space of W^* obtained by identifying ω_0 with ω_1. A function $f \in C(\Gamma)$ for which (b′) fails may be defined as follows: $f(n) = 1/n$ if $0 < n < \omega_0, f(\gamma) = 0$ otherwise. Hence $\mathscr{P}(C(\Gamma))$ is not compact. It is locally compact, however.

5.4. A space X such that $\mathscr{P}(C(X))$ is compact but for which the hypothesis of Theorem 5.2 is not satisfied. Let N^* denote the totally ordered space of ordinals less than or equal to ω_0. With Γ as in 5.3, X is the complement in $\Gamma \times N^*$ of the set $\{(m, n) : m < \omega_0, n < \omega_0\}$.

5.5. A space X such that no open set in $\mathscr{P}(C(X))$ has compact closure. Let $X = \beta N \sim N$, where N is a countable discrete space. We do not know whether $\mathscr{P}(C(X))$ is basically disconnected.

References

[1] *L. Gillman*: Rings with Hausdorff structure space. Fundam. Math. *45* (1957), 1–16.

[2] *L. Gillman* and *M. Jerison*: Rings of continuous functions. D. Van Nostrand Co., Princeton 1960.

[3] *M. Henriksen* and *D. Johnson*: On the structure of a class of archimedean lattice-ordered algebras. Fundam. Math. *50* (1961), 73–94.

[4] *C. W. Kohls*: Prime ideals in rings of continuous functions. II. Duke Math. J., *25* (1958), 447–458.

SOME APPLICATIONS OF COMPACTNESS IN HARMONIC ANALYSIS

E. HEWITT

Seattle

The discovery in 1922 of the concept of compact Hausdorff space (бикомпактное Хаусдорфово пространство) by P. S. Aleksandrov and P. S. Uryson [1] is a landmark in contemporary abstract analysis. Of course the idea of compactness did not begin with this memoir: notions and techniques involving compactness had been used with great effectiveness for many decades prior to 1922; but the final formulation of the concept of compactness, so elegant in its simplicity and so far-reaching in its applications, is the work of Aleksandrov and Uryson.

Two comments on axiomatics may be in order. First, for the purposes of contemporary analysis, compactness has little interest without Hausdorff separation. Real- and complex-valued continuous functions are essential for the work of the analyst, and these (barring constants) may well be absent in a non-Hausdorff compact space. Thus a minimal infinite T_1-space (a subset is closed if and only if it is finite or the entire space) is compact but is interesting to analysts only as a curiosity.[1]) Second, the many generalizations of compactness that have been put forward in recent years may in the future prove valuable for analysis. Thus Lindelöf (finally $\aleph_1$-compact) spaces are frequently useful already; and other notions of this genre may well be used by future workers. Nevertheless, definite limitations exist in the usefulness of non-compact (or non locally compact) spaces, as we will show.

The purpose of this essay is to demonstrate the central rôle of compactness in harmonic analysis. Two theorems from functional analysis, however, are so important to harmonic analysis, and so clearly illustrate the importance of compactness, that they should be cited.

The first of these is the Stone-Weierstrass approximation theorem [1]. Let X be a compact Hausdorff space, and let $\mathfrak{C}(X)$ be the algebra of all *complex*-valued continuous functions on X, where addition and multiplication are as usual pointwise, and where $\|f\|_u = \max\{|f(x)| : x \in X\}$ for $f \in \mathfrak{C}(X)$. Let $\mathfrak{S}$ be a subalgebra of $\mathfrak{C}(X)$ that: (a) separates points of X; (b) is closed under complex conjugation; (c) has the property that for all $x \in X$, there is a $\varphi \in \mathfrak{S}$ such that $\varphi(x) \neq 0$. Then the subalgebra $\mathfrak{S}$ is dense in the topology of $\mathfrak{C}(X)$ induced by the norm $\| \ \|_u$. A proof of a special case, immediately adaptable to the general case, appears in [12]. It would be hard to overstate the

[1]) The closed unit disk in the complex plane receives this topology as the maximal ideal space of a certain Banach algebra of analytic functions: see I. M. Gel'fand and G. E. Šilov [5].

importance of the Stone-Weierstrass theorem. We cite a few applications: to the proof of Fubini's theorem in one of its forms; to computing characters of compact Abelian groups;[2]) to computing irreducible unitary representations of compact non-Abelian groups. The Stone-Weierstrass theorem exhibits a complete dichotomy between the compact and noncompact situations. If X is *any* noncompact, nonvoid, completely regular space, then one can find a subalgebra $\mathfrak{S}$ of $\mathfrak{C}(X)$ satisfying the hypotheses of the Stone-Weierstrass theorem that is not dense in the uniform topology of $\mathfrak{C}(X)$. This is shown in [10].

Our second classical theorem from functional analysis is F. Riesz's representation theorem. Let X now be a *locally* compact Hausdorff space; let $\mathfrak{C}_{00}(X)$ denote the space of all complex-valued continuous functions on X each of which vanishes outside of some compact subset of X (this compact set depending upon the function); let $\mathfrak{C}_{00}^{r}(X)$ denote the real-valued functions in $\mathfrak{C}_{00}(X)$; and $\mathfrak{C}_{00}^{+}(X)$ the nonnegative functions in $\mathfrak{C}_{00}^{r}(X)$. Let I be any linear functional on $\mathfrak{C}_{00}(X)$ that assumes nonnegative real values for all functions in $\mathfrak{C}_{00}^{+}(X)$.[3]) Then there exists a set-function ι defined for all subsets of X having the following properties:

(1) $0 \leqq \iota(A) \leqq \infty$ for all $A \subset X$;

(2) if A^{-} is compact, then $\iota(A)$ is finite;

(3) ι is countably additive on a σ-algebra $\mathscr{S}$ of subsets of X that contains all closed sets;

(4) for all $f \in \mathfrak{C}_{00}(X)$, the identity

$$I(f) = \int_X f(x)\, d\iota(x)$$

obtains.

Thus the functional I is representable as the integral with respect to a *countably* additive measure. The rôle played by countable additivity in integration theory is vital. Without it, Fubini's theorem and Lebesgue's theorem on dominated convergence fail utterly. A close examination of the proof of Riesz's representation theorem shows that compactness of the sets $\{x \in X : f(x) \neq 0\}^{-}$ is the key to proving that ι is countably additive on $\mathscr{S}$ (see [14], § 11). It is not clear what to say of Riesz's theorem for non locally compact X, since (as in the case of the rational numbers with their usual topology) 0 may be the only function in $\mathfrak{C}_{00}(X)$. However, we can consider a linear functional I on $\mathfrak{C}(X)$ that is nonnegative and real on $\mathfrak{C}^{+}(X)$, where X is any completely regular space and $\mathfrak{C}(X)$ is the space of all bounded continuous complex-valued functions on X. It is an easy matter to prove that

$$I(f) = \int_X f(x)\, d\iota(x) \quad \text{for} \quad f \in \mathfrak{C}(X),$$

[2]) If G is a compact Abelian group and $\mathbf{Y}$ is a subgroup of the character group $\mathbf{X}$ of G such that $\mathbf{Y}$ separates points of G, then $\mathbf{Y} = \mathbf{X}$.

[3]) Note that we suppose no continuity property for I; the condition $I(\mathfrak{C}_{00}^{+}(X)) \subset [0, \infty[$ is a replacement for continuity.

where now ι is a nonnegative set function on all subsets of X that is *finitely* additive on an algebra of subsets of X that contains all sets

$$\{x \in X : f(x) = 0\} \quad [f \in \mathfrak{C}(X)] .$$

Glicksberg [6] has shown that every such ι is countably additive if and only if X is pseudo-compact.[4])

We pass to some of the applications of compactness in harmonic analysis proper. We shall see that compactness enters not only as an essential hypothesis in many situations, but also as parts of definitions, and as a technique in proving existence theorems.

Abstract harmonic analysis as we know it today could not exist without Haar measure, which we will now describe. Let G be a group and f any function on G. For a, b in G, we denote by ${}_af, f_b$ and ${}_af_b$, respectively, the functions $x \to f(ax)$, $x \to f(xb)$, $x \to f(axb)$, on G. Now suppose that G is a locally compact T_0 group.[5])

Then there exists a linear functional I on $\mathfrak{C}_{00}(G)$ with the following properties:

(i) $I(f)$ is real and nonnegative for $f \in \mathfrak{C}_{00}^{+}(G)$;
(ii) $I({}_af) = I(f)$ for all $a \in G$ and $f \in \mathfrak{C}_{00}(G)$;
(iii) $I \neq 0$.

Such a functional is called a *left Haar integral* on $\mathfrak{C}_{00}(G)$, and the measure λ corresponding thereto by F. Riesz's theorem is called a *left Haar measure.* (It is easy to show that $I(f)$ is strictly positive for $f \neq 0, f \in \mathfrak{C}_{00}^{+}(G)$.) A. Weil's original proof of the existence of a Haar integral [18] made use of compactness in the form of Tihonov's theorem; but H. Cartan [2] shortly after the publication of [18] gave a strictly constructive proof of the existence and uniqueness (up to a multiplicative constant, naturally) of the left Haar integral. Compactness enters in Cartan's proof only in producing a certain partition of unity and in establishing some elementary inequalities. Nevertheless, local compactness is "nearly" essential for proving the existence of Haar measure. If a group G admits an invariant measure and if a certain technical restriction holds, then G is a subgroup of a locally compact group $\tilde{G}$, and G in a certain sense is "large" in $\tilde{G}$. The details are given in P. R. Halmos [9]. It should be pointed out that a finitely additive invariant measure exists on every locally bounded T_0 group (a topological group is locally bounded if it has a neighborhood V of the identity such that a finite number of translates of an arbitrary neighborhood of the identity cover V). This fact was proved by A. A. Markov [15].

The theory of almost periodic functions provides another excellent illustration of the uses of compactness. Consider any T_0 topological group G and any function $f \in \mathfrak{C}(G)$. For $a \in G$, let D_af be the following function on $G \times G : (x, y) \to f(xay)$.

[4]) We recall that a completely regular space X is said to be pseudo-compact if every continuous real-valued function on X is bounded. Such spaces need not be compact: see [11].

[5]) It is well known that a T_0 group is completely regular and that a locally compact T_0 group is normal.

It is elementary, although not completely trivial, to show that the following assertions are equivalent: $\{_af : a \in G\}^-$ is compact in $\mathfrak{C}(G)$; $\{f_b : b \in G\}^-$ is compact in $\mathfrak{C}(G)$; $\{_af_b : a, b \in G\}^-$ is compact in $\mathfrak{C}(G)$; $\{D_af : a \in G\}$ is compact in $\mathfrak{C}(G \times G)$. (In all cases we use the uniform topology in $\mathfrak{C}$.) A function satisfying one and hence all of these properties is called *almost periodic*. Here compactness (ordinary sequential compactness, it is true, since $\mathfrak{C}(G)$ is a metric space) is a part of the definition. There is a complete theory of almost periodic functions. The space $\mathfrak{A}(G)$ of almost periodic functions on G admits a unique nonnegative left invariant mean value (whose existence is proved by wholly elementary arguments), which is right and inversion invariant. Functions in $\mathfrak{A}(G)$ are uniform limits of linear combinations of coefficients of finite-dimensional continuous unitary representations of G; and so on.

A promising generalization of almost periodicity was advanced a few years ago by W. F. Eberlein [3]. Topologize $\mathfrak{C}(G)$ not with the uniform topology but with the weak topology based on linear functionals in the conjugate space $\mathfrak{C}^*(G)$. Say that a function $f \in \mathfrak{C}(G)$ *is weakly almost periodic* if $\{_af : a \in G\}^-$ or $\{f_b : b \in G\}^-$ is compact in the weak topology for $\mathfrak{C}(G)$ (the two conditions are equivalent). One may then ask if the space of weakly almost periodic functions for a locally compact G admits an invariant mean value. For Abelian G, it is trivial that there is such a mean, since the space of all bounded functions admits an invariant mean in this case. For non-Abelian G, the problem seems to be unsolved. (For partial results, see Glicksberg and de Leeuw [7].)

Our third illustration of the uses of compactness in abstract harmonic analysis is the proof of the famous theorem of I. M. Gel'fand and D. A. Raĭkov [4]. (See also [8].) Let G be a topological group. A *continuous unitary representation* of G is a mapping $x \to U_x$ of G into the group of unitary operators on some Hilbert space $\mathscr{H}$ such that $U_{xy} = U_xU_y$ for all $x, y \in G$ and such that $x \to \langle U_x\xi, \eta\rangle$ is a continuous function on G for all $\xi, \eta \in \mathscr{H}$. A unitary representation U is *irreducible* if there is no closed subspace $\mathscr{S}$ of $\mathscr{H}$ distinct from $\{0\}$ and $\mathscr{H}$ such that $U_x(\mathscr{S}) \subset \mathscr{S}$ for all $x \in G$. The Gel'fand-Raĭkov theorem asserts that if G is locally compact, then for every x in G different from the identity, there is an irreducible unitary representation U of G such that U_x is not the identity operator. This theorem implies at once the Peter-Weyl theorem and the fact that a locally compact Abelian group admits sufficiently many continuous characters. In addition it has inspired an immense amount of research on computing the irreducible unitary representations (for the most part infinite-dimensional) of the classical groups.

The proof of the Gel'fand-Raĭkov theorem is somewhat technical. There are two versions of it, one based on positive-definite functions on G, another based on the following considerations. Let $\mathfrak{L}_1(G)$ denote the Banach space of all Borel (let us say) measurable complex-valued functions f on the locally compact group G for which

$$\|f\|_1 = \int_G |f(x)| \, d\lambda(x) < \infty ,$$

where λ denotes a left Haar measure on G. For f, g in $\mathfrak{L}_1(G)$, define the function $f * g$ (convolution, Faltung, or свертка) by

$$f * g(x) = \int_G f(xy)\, g(y^{-1})\, \mathrm{d}\lambda(y)\,, \quad \text{for} \quad x \in G\,.$$

It can be shown that $f * g(x)$ exists and is a complex number for λ-almost all $x \in G$, that the function $f * g$ defined in this fashion is in $\mathfrak{L}_1(G)$, and that the inequality

$$\|f * g\|_1 \leqq \|f\|_1 \cdot \|g\|_1$$

obtains for all f, g in $\mathfrak{L}_1(G)$. With pointwise linear operations and multiplication defined as convolution, $\mathfrak{L}_1(G)$ is thus a (complex) Banach algebra.

In addition, the algebra $\mathfrak{L}_1(G)$ admits an involution. For $x \in G$ let

$$\Delta(x) = \int_G f_{x^{-1}}(y)\, \mathrm{d}\lambda(y) \Big/ \int_G f(y)\, \mathrm{d}\lambda(y)\,,$$

where f is any nonzero function in $\mathfrak{C}_{00}^+(G)$; Δ is continuous and positive and satisfies the relation $\Delta(xy) = \Delta(x)\,\Delta(y)$ for all x, y in G. (The fact that Δ depends on x alone follows from the uniqueness of left Haar measure.) Now for $f \in \mathfrak{L}_1(G)$, let $f^\sim$ be defined by

$$f^\sim(x) = \overline{f(x^{-1})}\, \frac{1}{\Delta(x)}\,.$$

The mapping $f \to f^\sim$ is an involution on $\mathfrak{L}_1(G)$.

A linear functional p on $\mathfrak{L}_1(G)$ is called *positive* if $p(f^\sim * f)$ is real and nonnegative for all $f \in \mathfrak{L}_1(G)$. A proof of the Gel'fand-Raĭkov theorem can be given that depends upon a close analysis of positive functionals on $\mathfrak{L}_1(G)$, their connection with representations of $\mathfrak{L}_1(G)$ by operators on Hilbert spaces, and the connection of these with continuous unitary representations of G itself. The subspace $\mathfrak{H}$ of $\mathfrak{L}_1(G)$ consisting of all functions such that $f = f^\sim$ is a real Banach space. The set P of all positive functionals p on $\mathfrak{L}_1(G)$ such that $p(f^\sim) = p(f)$ and $|p(f)| \leqq p(f^\sim * f)^{\frac{1}{2}}$ for all $f \in \mathfrak{L}_1(G)$ is a compact convex subset of the (real!) conjugate space $\mathfrak{H}^*$. By the Kreĭn-Mil'man theorem, P is the ($*$-weak) closure of the convex hull of its own extreme points. The extreme points of P correspond to irreducible representations of $\mathfrak{L}_1(G)$, and so in a certain sense every representation of $\mathfrak{L}_1(G)$ can be approximated by irreducible representations. Finally, the mapping $\varphi \to f * \varphi = T_f\varphi$ of $\mathfrak{L}_2(G)$ into itself is a bounded linear operator for all $f \in \mathfrak{L}_1(G)$ and the mapping $f \to T_f$ is a faithful representation of $\mathfrak{L}_1(G)$ by operators on the Hilbert space $\mathfrak{L}_2(G)$. Note too that $(T_f)^\sim = T_{f^\sim}$, where $T^\sim$ denotes the adjoint operator to T.

The facts just outlined give a proof of the Gel'fand-Raĭkov theorem. The crux of the proof is of course the Kreĭn-Mil'man theorem: and this theorem depends wholly upon compactness.

For a compact group G, the function spaces $\mathfrak{C}(G)$, $\mathfrak{L}_2(G)$, and $\mathfrak{L}_1(G)$ are Banach algebras under convolution. Their structure is completely known: all maximal ideals and closed ideals in these algebras have been identified. Here one may say that compactness has registered another success. For noncompact locally compact G, very little is known of the detailed structure of $\mathfrak{L}_1(G)$ ($\mathfrak{C}(G)$ and $\mathfrak{L}_2(G)$ are not algebras in this case). Another Banach algebra can be defined for every locally compact G. Let $\mathfrak{C}_0(G)$ be the Banach space of all continuous complex-valued functions f on G such that for every $\varepsilon > 0$, the set $\{x : x \in G, |f(x)| \geqq \varepsilon\}$ is compact. Let $\mathcal{M}(G)$ denote the conjugate space of $\mathfrak{C}_0(G)$. It is convenient to use F. Riesz's theorem to represent elements of $\mathcal{M}(G)$ as measures. Then for μ, ν in $\mathcal{M}(G)$ and $f \in \mathfrak{C}_0(G)$, let

$$\mu * \nu(f) = \iint_{GG} f(xy)\, \mathrm{d}\nu(y)\, \mathrm{d}\mu(x)\,.$$

This definition is an extension of the definition of convolution for functions in $\mathfrak{L}_1(G)$ (regard functions in $\mathfrak{L}_1(G)$ as measures absolutely continuous with respect to left Haar measure). The algebra $\mathcal{M}(G)$ has been extensively studied (for example, see [16] and [13]), but its detailed structure remains a nearly complete mystery, even for the simplest compact infinite groups. A complete analysis of $\mathcal{M}(G)$ even for compact Abelian groups G would be of the greatest interest. The analysis of $\mathcal{M}(G)$ for general G and of $\mathfrak{L}_1(G)$ for noncompact G would seem to be one of the most important problems now open in harmonic analysis.

In conclusion, we remark that most of the matters discussed in this essay are treated in detail in a forthcoming book [14].

Bibliography

[1] *P. S. Alexandrov* and *P. S. Uryson*: Mémoire sur les espaces topologiques compacts. Verhandel. Koninkl. Nederl. Akad. Wetensch. Afd. Natuurkunde, Amsterdam, 1 sectie XIV (1929), No *1*, 1–96.

[2] *Henri Cartan*: Sur la mesure de Haar. C. R. Acad. Sci. Paris *211* (1940), 759–762.

[3] *W. F. Eberlein*: Abstract ergodic theorems and weak almost periodic functions. Trans. Amer. Math. Soc. *67* (1949), 217–240.

[4] *И. М. Гельфанд, Г. Е. Шилов:* Неприводимые унитарные представления локально бикомпактных групп. Матем. сб. *13* (55), (1943), 301–316.

[5] *I. M. Gel'fand* und *G. E. Šilov*: Über verschiedene Methoden der Einführung der Topologie in die Menge der maximalen Ideale eines normierten Ringes. Matem. sb. *9* (51) (1941), 25–38.

[6] *Irving Glicksberg*: The representation of functionals by integrals. Duke Math. J. *19* (1952), 253–261.

[7] *I. Glicksberg* and *Karel Deleeuw*: Applications of almost periodic compactifications. Acta Mathematica *105* (1961), 63–97.

[8] *Roger Godement*: Les fonctions de type positif et la théorie des groupes. Trans. Amer. Math. Soc. *63* (1948), 1–84.

[9] *Paul R. Halmos*: Measure theory. D. Van Nostrand Co., Inc., New York, 1950.

[10] *Edwin Hewitt*: Certain generalizations of the Weierstrass approximation theorem. Duke Math. J. *14* (1947), 419–427.

[11] *Edwin Hewitt*: Rings of real-valued continuous functions. I. Trans. Amer. Math. Soc. *64* (1948), 45–99.

[12] *Edwin Hewitt*: The rôle of compactness in analysis. Amer. Math. Monthly *67* (1960), 499–516.

[13] *Edwin Hewitt* and *Shizuo Kakutani*: A class of multiplicative linear functionals on the measure algebra of a locally compact Abelian group. Illinois J. of Mathematics *4* (1960), 553–574.

[14] *Edwin Hewitt* and *Kenneth A. Ross*: Abstract harmonic analysis. Volume I. Structure and integration theory. To be published by Springer-Verlag, Berlin-Göttingen-Heidelberg 1962.

[15] *A. A. Markov*: On mean values and exterior densities. Matem. sb. *4* (46) (1938), 165–191.

[16] *Ю. А. Шрейдер:* Строение максимальных идеалов в кольцах со сверткой. Матем. сб. *27* (69) (1950), 297–318.

[17] *M. H. Stone*: Applications of the theory of Boolean rings to general topology. Trans. Amer. Math. Soc. *41* (1937), 375–481.

[18] *André Weil*: L'intégration dans les groupes topologiques et ses applications. Actualités Sci. et Ind. 869. Hermann et Cie, Paris 1940.

REMARKS ON TRANSFINITE DIAMETERS[1])

E. HILLE

New Haven

1. Introduction. The *transfinite diameter* is a set function introduced by MIHÁLY FEKETE in 1923. It was originally defined for bounded closed sets in the complex plane. It coincides with the *Čebyšev constant* and with the *logarithmic capacity* of the set. If the set is a continuum and its complement is connected, then the transfinite diameter also coincides with the *exterior conformal mapping radius.* It is possible to define similar notions in any Euclidean space and even in arbitrary metric spaces.

In this direction G. PÓLYA and G. SZEGÖ took up the study of the three dimensional case and various other extensions in 1931. The important investigations of F. LEJA started in 1933; he examined in particular the conformal mapping aspects of the problem, various associated sequences of polynomials, extensions to the space of two complex variables, aed to general metric spaces. Elliptic and hyperbolic metrics for complex numbers were considered by M. TSUJI (1947). The notion of capacity has been much extended by G. CHOQUET, but he does not seem to have considered possible connections with transfinite diameters.

There is an extensive abstract theory of mean values going back to A. N. KOLMOGOROFF and M. NAGUMO (1930) that has an important bearing on our problem.

2. Transfinite diameters. The general notion of a transfinite diameter involves four essential elements:

[1] *A metric space X.*
[2] *An averaging* (mean value) *process* $\mathscr{A}$.
[3] *An extremal problem.*
[4] *A limiting process.*

Let E be a *compact* set in X. Take any n, $n > 1$, points $P_1, P_2, \ldots, P_n$ in E and form the distances

$$(1) \qquad \delta_{jk} = d(P_j, P_k)\,, \quad 1 \leqq j < k \leqq n\,,$$

which are

$$N = \tfrac{1}{2}n(n-1)$$

in number. This is the first step.

[1]) This research was supported in part by a grant (DA-ORD-12) from the U. S. Army Research Office (Durham).

The second step involves the averaging process $\mathscr{A}$. Here it is convenient to impose the conditions of Kolmogoroff:[2])

(i) *$\mathscr{A}$ assigns a positive average to every finite set of positive numbers* $\{x_j\}$.

(ii) *$A(x_1, x_2, \ldots, x_m)$ is a continuous symmetric function of its arguments and A is strictly increasing as a function of each of them.*

(iii) $A(x, x, \ldots, x) = x$.

(iv) $A(x_1, x_2, \ldots, x_k, x_{k+1}, \ldots, x_m) = A(y, y, \ldots, y, x_{k+1}, \ldots, x_m)$
if $y = A(x_1, \ldots, x_k)$.

As a consequence of (ii) and (iii) we have the important inequality

$$\min x_j \leqq A(x_1, x_2, \ldots, x_m) \leqq \max x_j , \tag{2}$$

where equality holds if and only if all x_j are equal.

It should be observed that $A(x_1, \ldots, x_m)$ decreases to a nonnegative limit if one or more of the variables decreases to zero, so we can define $A(0, x_2, \ldots, x_m)$ by continuity. It is clear that $A(0, 0, \ldots, 0) = 0$, but it may happen that A is zero if one of its arguments is zero. In particular this happens for what in Section 4 below is called the *natural averaging process in E_n* as soon as $n > 1$. It is clear that in (ii) we must restrict ourselves to strictly positive values of the argument.

A. N. Kolmogoroff and M. Nagumo proved that conditions (i)–(iv) imply that A has a particular form: there exists a continuous strictly monotone function $F(u)$ such that

$$m\, F[A(x_1, x_2, \ldots, x_m)] = \sum_{j=1}^{m} F(x_j) . \tag{3}$$

We shall not use this representation. For our purposes it is just as convenient, if not more so, to work merely with the assumptions (i)–(iv). Since mean values defined by (3) have already been used in the theory of transfinite diameters by F. Leja, we cannot expect to produce any new results, but the method of proof based on the abstract postulates offers some advantages.

We return to the set of N numbers δ_{jk} and apply $\mathscr{A}$ to this set. We write

$$A(\delta_{11}, \delta_{12}, \ldots, \delta_{n-1,n}) = \mathscr{A}(\delta_{jk}) . \tag{4}$$

It follows from (2) that

$$0 < \mathscr{A}(\delta_{jk}) \leqq \delta(E) , \tag{5}$$

where $\delta(E)$ is the point set theoretical diameter of the set E and equality holds if and only if $\delta_{jk} = \delta(E)$ for all j and k. It follows that the set $\{\mathscr{A}(\delta_{jk})\}$ is bounded when the points P_j range over E. The set has a supremum and, since E is compact, there is at least one choice of the points for which

$$\mathscr{A}(\delta_{jk}) = \sup \mathscr{A}(\delta_{pq}) \equiv \delta_n(E) . \tag{6}$$

[2]) I am indebted to Professors C. T. Ionescu Tulcea and Shizuo Kakutani for reminding me of the literature on mean values. I had rediscovered some of the results. [I am also indebted to Professors Z. Frolík and V. Jarník whose valuable observations led to a revision of the manuscript in November 1961.]

We have $\delta_2(E) = \delta(E)$ and for all $n > 1$

$$0 < \delta_n(E) \leqq \delta(E). \tag{7}$$

M. Fekete worked with the geometric mean, G. Pólya and G. Szegö mostly with the harmonic mean. Other cases have been considered by them and by F. Leja.

Next we show that the sequence $\{\delta_n(E)\}$ is never increasing. To prove this, let us choose $n + 1$ points P_j such that $\delta_{n+1}(E)$ is the $\mathscr{A}$-average of the distances $d(P_j, P_k)$. It is immaterial if we take the $\frac{1}{2}n(n + 1)$ distances $d(P_j, P_k)$ with $j < k$ or the $n(n + 1)$ distances with $j \neq k$. This follows from (iv). We choose the second alternative and proceed to separate the elements into groups in two different ways. First we separate the δ_{jk} into $n + 1$ groups of n elements each, the elements in the j-th group being the distances from P_j to the other points. Let the average of the distances from P_j to the other points be denoted by η_j so that

$$A(\delta_{j,1}, \ldots, \delta_{j,j-1}, \delta_{j,j+1}, \ldots, \delta_{j,n+1}) = \eta_j. \tag{8}$$

By property (iv) we can replace each element in the j-th group by η_j. In other words, $\delta_{n+1}(E)$ is the average of $\eta_1, \eta_2, \ldots, \eta_{n+1}$, each repeated n times. Using (iv) again, we see we can contract this average to the average of $\eta_1, \eta_2, \ldots, \eta_{n+1}$ taken singly so that

$$\delta_{n+1}(E) = A(\eta_1, \eta_2, \ldots, \eta_{n+1}). \tag{9}$$

We can now apply (2) which says that either all the η's are equal to each other and hence to δ_{n+1} or else

$$\min \eta_j < \delta_{n+1}(E) < \max \eta_j. \tag{10}$$

Next we group the $n(n + 1)$ quantities δ_{jk} in a different manner. We separate the $2n$ elements involving a distance from P_j in one group and lump the remaining $n(n - 1)$ distance into the other. The average of the first $2n$ elements is η_j by (iv) and (8), while the average of the remaining elements is at most δ_n by the definition of the latter. It follows that $\delta_{n+1}(E)$ cannot exceed the $\mathscr{A}$-average of $n(n - 1)$ quantities δ_n and $2n$ quantities η_j, or again contracting with the aid of (iv)

$$\delta_{n+1} \leqq A(\delta_n, \delta_n, \ldots, \delta_n, \eta_j, \eta_j), \tag{11}$$

where δ_n is repeated $n - 1$ times. Here we want to apply (2). Either all the η's are equal to δ_{n+1} in which case the inequality gives

$$\delta_{n+1} \leqq A(\delta_n, \delta_n, \ldots, \delta_n, \delta_{n+1}, \delta_{n+1}), \tag{12}$$

or we can find an $\eta_j < \delta_{n+1}$. For this value of j, formula (11) again gives (12), but now as a strict inequality. Next, either $\delta_n = \delta_{n+1}$ or

$$A(\delta_n, \delta_n, \ldots, \delta_n, \delta_{n+1}, \delta_{n+1}) < \max(\delta_n, \delta_{n+1}).$$

In the latter case

$$\delta_{n+1} < \max(\delta_n, \delta_{n+1})$$

which implies that

$$\delta_{n+1} < \delta_n.$$

Thus, in any case

(13) $$\delta_{n+1}(E) \leqq \delta_n(E)$$

as asserted.

We can now define

(14) $$\delta_0(E) \equiv \lim_{n\to\infty} \delta_n(E)$$

as the *transfinite diameter of E with respect to the average* $\mathscr{A}$.

The set function $\delta_0(E)$ has important properties of monotony and continuity.

I. *If E_1 and E_2 are compact and if $E_1 \subset E_2$, then*

$$\delta_0(E_1) \leqq \delta_0(E_2)\,.$$

This follows from the definition: any average of distances between points of E_1 is also an average of distances between points of E_2 so that the supremum of $\mathscr{A}(\delta_{jk})$ with respect to E_1 for a given n cannot exceed the corresponding supremum with respect to E_2. It may very well happen that $\delta_0(E_1) = \delta_0(E_2)$ even though E_1 is a very small subset of E_2. Thus if ∂E denotes the (outer) boundary of E, we often have the relation

(15) $$\delta_0(\partial E) = \delta_0(E)\,.$$

II. *If E_ε is the set of points whose distance from E does not exceed ε, and if E and E_ε are compact, then*

(16) $$\lim_{\varepsilon\to 0} \delta_0(E_\varepsilon) = \delta_0(E)\,.$$

This is essentially a consequence of the continuity and monotony properties of A. The argument given by M. Fekete for the plane case carries over with minor modifications.

3. Čebyšev functions. The original problem of Fekete is closely related to the theory of Čebyšev polynomials. Similar structures can be introduced in any metric space and for any averaging process satisfying the above conditions.

Let E be a compact set in a metric space X. Let $P_1, P_2, \ldots, P_n$, and P be arbitrary points of X and form the average of the distances from P to the points P_j. Set

(17) $$f(p) \equiv A[d(P, P_1), d(P, P_2), \ldots, d(P, P_n)]\,.$$

For fixed points $P_1, P_2, \ldots, P_n$, not necessarily distinct, this is a continuous function of P which tends to a nonnegative limit when P approaches any one of the points P_j. The function $f(P)$ has a supremum on the given compact set E and this value is reached for at least one choice of P in E. As the points P_j range independently of each other over X, the corresponding maxima $m[f]$ form a set of nonnegative real numbers. This set has an infimum which may be zero. In any case the infimum is attained, that is, there is at least one choice of base points $Q_1, Q_2, \ldots, Q_n$ such that if

(18) $$\check{C}_n(P) \equiv A[d(P, Q_1), d(P, Q_2), \ldots, d(P, Q_n)]\,,$$

then

$$\max_{P \in E} \check{C}_n(P) = \min \max_{P \in E} f(P) \equiv M_n(E) . \tag{19}$$

We call $\check{C}_n(P)$ a Čebyšev function for E of order n. It is immaterial for our purposes if $\check{C}_n(P)$ is unique. In the case studied by Fekete

$$\check{C}_n(P) = |T_n(z)|^{1/n} ,$$

where $T_n(z)$ is the unique Čebyšev polynomial for E of degree n.

The numbers $M_n(E)$ are nonnegative and they do not exceed $\delta(E)$ for any n. In order to prove that the sequence $\{M_n(E)\}$ tends to a limit, we find it convenient to impose an additional, possibly redundant, condition on the averaging process $\mathscr{A}$.

(v) *The average of n entries a and one entry b tends to a when n becomes infinite.*

Let us denote this average by a_n. Then *the sequence* $\{a_n\}$ *is monotone.* To fix the ideas, suppose that $0 < a < b$, so that the sequence becomes *strictly decreasing.* We note first that for all n

$$a < a_n < b .$$

We now form

$$a_n = A(a, \ldots, a, b) = A(a, a_{n-1}, a_{n-1}, \ldots, a_{n-1}) .$$

In the first average, a occurs n times, in the second a_{n-1} occurs $n - 1$ times. Equality between the two averages follows from (iv). We now observe that the second average is less than a_{n-1} by inequality (2) since $a < a_{n-1}$. It follows that

$$a_n < a_{n-1} \quad \text{if} \quad a < b . \tag{20}$$

Thus the sequence $\{a_n\}$ is strictly decreasing so that it has a limit $\geqq a$; condition (v) asserts that the limit equals a.

We now return to the numbers $M_n(E)$. They satisfy two important inequalities, namely

$$M_{n+1} \leqq A[M_n, M_n, \ldots, M_n, \delta(E)] , \tag{21}$$

$$M_{m+n} \leqq \max (M_m, M_n) . \tag{22}$$

Here M_n is repeated n times in (21) and m, n are arbitrary positive integers. For the proof we form functions of type (17) involving the base points of the Čebyšev functions under consideration. In the first case, let

$$F(P) \equiv A[d(P, Q_1), \ldots, d(P, Q_n), d(P, Q)] ,$$

where $Q_1, \ldots, Q_n$ are the base points of $\check{C}_n(P)$ and Q is an arbitrary point in E. Since, by (iv)

$$F(P) = A[\check{C}_n(P), \ldots, \check{C}_n(P), d(P, Q)] ,$$

we see that the maximum of $F(P)$ on E cannot exceed the right member of (21). On the other hand, this maximum is at least equal to M_{n+1}. This proves (21). In the second case we form

$$G(P) \equiv A[d(P, P_1), \ldots, d(P, P_m), d(P, Q_1), \ldots, d(P, Q_n)] = \\ = A[\check{C}_m(P), \ldots, \check{C}_m(P), \check{C}_n(P), \ldots, \check{C}_n(P)]$$

with obvious notation. The maximum of $G(P)$ on E is at least equal to M_{m+n} and at most equal to

$$A(M_m, \ldots, M_m, M_n, \ldots, M_n) \leqq \max(M_m, M_n) .$$

This gives (22).

Suppose now that the positive numbers $\{c_k\}$ satisfy

(23) $$c_{m+n} \leqq \max(c_m, c_n)$$

for all m and n. Such a sequence need not be convergent. Thus if

$$c_k = \alpha_m \text{ for } k = 2^m p, \quad m = 0, 1, 2, \ldots, \quad p = 1, 3, 5, \ldots,$$

where $\{\alpha_m\}$ is a never increasing sequence of positive numbers, then $\{c_k\}$ satisfies (23) and there are infinitely many limit points if there are infinitely many distinct α's. In any case we have

(24) $$\lim_{m\to\infty} c_{2m-1} = \limsup c_n \equiv \beta .$$

To prove this we note first that (23) implies that $c_n \leqq c_1$ for all n, so such a sequence is necessarily bounded. Next, if there is a γ, $0 < \gamma$, and an integer j such that

$$c_j < \gamma , \quad c_{j+1} < \gamma ,$$

then $c_n < \gamma$ for all large n. It suffices that $n > j^2$. Now if $\delta > 0$ is given, we can find an N as large as we please such that

$$\beta - \delta < c_N , \quad \beta = \limsup c_n .$$

From

$$\beta - \delta < c_N \leqq \max(c_k, c_{N-k}) ,$$

it follows that either c_k or c_{N-k} exceeds $\beta - \delta$, where $k = 1, 2, \ldots, N-1$. Since δ and N are arbitrary, we conclude that

$$\beta \leqq c_k$$

holds for at least half the positive integers. Moreover, since $c_j < \beta$, $c_{j+1} < \beta$, implies $c_n < \beta$ for all large n, either

(25) $$\beta \leqq c_{2m} \quad \text{for all } m ,$$

or

(26) $$\beta \leqq c_{2m-1} \quad \text{for all } m .$$

In the second case, (24) obviously holds.

Now if c_n has a unique limit, the latter must coincide with β and (24) holds a fortiori. In order to prove that (24) is always true, it is enough to show that (26) always holds. Suppose, then, that there is an odd integer $2k + 1$ such that

$$c_{2k+1} < \beta .$$

By (23) we have then for every positive integer p

$$c_{(2k+1)p} < \beta .$$

This, however, implies that neither (25) nor (26) can hold for all m and we have seen that at least one of them must be true. This contradiction shows that (26) is always true and this proves (24).

We can apply this analysis to the case $c_k = M_k(E)$. In view of the inequality (22) we see that

$$\lim_{m\to\infty} M_{2m-1}(E) = \limsup_{n\to\infty} M_n(E) \equiv \beta \,. \tag{27}$$

We shall show that condition (21) together with (v) implies the existence of

$$\lim_{n\to\infty} M_n(E) = \chi(E) \tag{28}$$

and the inequality

$$M_n(E) \geqq \chi(E) \tag{29}$$

for all n. In view of (27) it is sufficient to prove (29) in order to obtain (28).

We know that (29) holds for all odd values of n. Suppose there is an even value, $2k$ say, such that

$$M_{2k}(E) = \gamma < \beta \,.$$

In view of (22) we have then also

$$M_{2^pk}(E) \leqq \gamma\,, \quad p = 1, 2, 3, \ldots \tag{30}$$

We now use (21) with $n = 2^pk$ and we replace $\delta(E)$ by a larger number η. We have then certainly $\gamma < \eta$ and (21) gives

$$M_{2^pk+1}(E) < A(\gamma, \gamma, \ldots, \gamma, \eta)\,,$$

where γ is repeated 2^pk times. By (27) the left member tends to β when $p \to \infty$ and by condition (v) the limit of the right member is $\gamma < \beta$. This contradiction shows that (30) cannot hold for any k and p. It follows that (29) holds and this implies the uniqueness of the limit of $M_n(E)$.

We call this limit $\chi(E)$ the *Čebyšev constant* of E.

If A satisfies (i)–(iv) we have also

$$\chi(E) \leqq \delta_0(E)\,. \tag{31}$$

This is proved as follows. We choose $P_1, P_2, \ldots, P_n$ in E so that

$$\delta_n = \delta_n(E) = \mathscr{A}(\delta_{jk})$$

and then P_{n+1} also in E such that

$$A[d(P_{n+1}, P_1), \ldots, d(P_{n+1}, P_n)] =$$
$$= \max_{P\in E} A[d(P, P_1), \ldots, d(P, P_n)] \geqq M_n(E)\,.$$

By the definition of δ_{n+1} and property (iv) we have

$$\delta_{n+1} \geqq A(\delta_{11}, \ldots, \delta_{n-1,n}, \delta_{1,n+1}, \ldots, \delta_{n,n+1}) =$$
$$= A(\delta_n, \ldots, \delta_n, M_n, \ldots, M_n)\,,$$

where δ_n is repeated $\frac{1}{2}n(n-1)$ times and M_n occurs n times. By (2)

$$\delta_{n+1} \geqq \min(\delta_n, M_n) = M_n$$

since $\delta_n \geqq \delta_{n+1}$. This gives (31) when $n \to \infty$.

For most of the known cases equality holds in (31), but it is not always true.

4. Euclidean spaces. Let $\mathscr{X} = \mathscr{E}_n$ be the Euclidean space of n dimensions, $n \geqq 1$, with its natural metric. We may ask if there is also a *natural averaging* process in such a space. This question is too vague to admit of an answer, but we could possibly accept a process $\mathscr{A}$ as natural in $\mathscr{E}_n$, if it gives $\delta_0(S) = R$ for a sphere S of radius R. Such an average exists and it is defined by formula (3) where the function $F(u) = F_n(u)$ is defined as follows:

$$F_n(u) = \begin{cases} u\,, & n = 1\,, \\ \log \dfrac{1}{u}\,, & n = 2\,, \\ \dfrac{1}{u^{n-2}}\,, & n > 2\,. \end{cases} \tag{32}$$

Even without using the results of A. N. Kolmogoroff and M. Nagumo, we can prove that such an averaging process $\mathscr{A}_n$ satisfies conditions (i)–(iv). If $n = 2$, $\mathscr{A}_2$ is the geometric mean used by M. Fekete and for $n = 3$, $\mathscr{A}_3$ is the harmonic mean considered by G. Pólya and G. Szegö. In both cases it is known that $\delta_0(S) = R$ for a "sphere" of radius R.

For $n = 1$ the following result is obtained. *If S is a closed set, contained in the interval $[a, b]$ and containing the points a and b, then the transfinite diameter with respect to $\mathscr{A}_1$, that is, the arithmetic mean, is given by*

$$\delta_0(E) = \tfrac{1}{2}(b - a)\,. \tag{33}$$

A "sphere" in this case is an interval, so we have $\delta_0(S) = R$ as desired. In this case the boundary of E consists of the two points a and b and $\delta_0(\partial E)$ is also given by (33) so that formula (15) holds. The proof of (33) is elementary. We have

$$\delta_n(E) = \max \sum_{k=1}^{n} (n - 2k + 1)\, x_k\,, \tag{34}$$

where $b \geqq x_1 \geqq x_2 \geqq \ldots \geqq x_n \geqq a$ and each x_k belongs to E. The maximum is reached for $x_k = a$ or b according as $n - 2k + 1 < 0$ or > 0. In the limit we obtain (33).

For $n > 3$ we have to delve into the theory of hyperspherical harmonic functions and related theories of capacity. The Čebyšev function for the sphere S in $\mathscr{E}_n$ with radius R and center at the origin is

$$\check{C}_n(P) = d(P, 0) \tag{35}$$

for all n so that $\chi(S) = R$. This is with respect to the average $\mathscr{A}_n$. On the other hand, the integral

$$\omega_n^{-1} \int_{\partial S} [d(P, Q)]^{2-n} \, dQ \,, \tag{36}$$

extended over the surface of the sphere whose area is ω_n, represents a harmonic function of P (with respect to the n dimensional Laplace operator) provided $d(P, Q) > R$ and the value of this function is

$$[d(P, Q)]^{2-n} .$$

It follows that the double integral

$$\omega_n^{-2} \int_{\partial S} \int_{\partial S} [d(P, Q)]^{2-n} \, dP \, dQ = R^{2-n} . \tag{37}$$

But this is the *energy integral* corresponding to the *equilibrium distribution* on the sphere and it has been proved by Otto Frostman [4] that the the minimum value of the energy, corresponding to the equilibrium distribution, equals the transfinite diameter with respect to the average $\mathscr{A}_n$. Frostman gives this only for $n = 3$ but the argument extends to higher dimensions.

We have no assurance that the average $\mathscr{A}_n$ is the only choice for which $\delta_0(S) = R$ even though this seems plausible. There are some results of Frostman's for averages $\mathscr{A}_\alpha$, where α need not be an integer, which enable us to compute $\delta_0(S)$ for S in E_n even if $\alpha \neq n$. It seems likely that Frostman's assumption $n = 3$ can be generalized.

References

[1] *G. Choquet*: Theory of Capacities. Annales de l'Institut Fourier, *5* (1953—54), 131—295.

[2] *M. Fekete*: Über die Verteilung der Wurzeln bei gewissen algebraischen Gleichungen mit ganzzahligen Koeffizienten. Math. Zeitschrift, *17* (1923), 228—249.

[3] *M. Fekete*: Über den transfiniten Durchmesser ebener Punktmengen, I, II. Math. Zeitschrift, *32* (1930), 108—114, 215—221. III. Ibid., *33* (1933), 635—646.

[4] *O. Frostman*: Potentiel d'Équilibre et Capacité des Ensembles avec quelques Applications à la Théorie des Fonctions. Thèse, Lund, 1935.

[5] *E. Hille*: Analytic Function Theory. Vol. II, Chapter 16, Ginn, Boston 1961.

[6] *A. N. Kolmogoroff*: Sur la notion de la moyenne. Atti della Reale Accademia Nazionale dei Lincei, (*6*) *12*, (1930), 388—391.

[7] *F. Leja*: Sur la définition du diamètre et de l'écart transfini d'un ensemble. Annales de la Société Polonaise de Mathématique, *12* (1934), 29—34.

[8] *F. Leja*: Généralisation de certaines fonctions d'ensemble. Annales de la Société Polonaise de Mathématique, *16* (1937), 41—52.

[9] *F. Leja*: Teoria Funkcji Analitycznych. Chapter XI, Bibliography. Biblioteka Matematyczna, Vol. 14, Warszawa 1957.

[10] *M. Nagumo*: Über eine Klasse der Mittelwerte. Japanese Journal of Mathematics, *7* (1930), 71—79.

[11] *G. Pólya* and *G. Szegö*: Über den transfiniten Durchmesser (Kapazitätskonstante) von ebenen und räumlichen Punktmengen. Journal für die reine und angewandte Mathematik, *165* (1931), 4–39.

[12] *M. Tsuji*: Potential Theory in Modern Function Theory. Chapter III, Bibliography, Maruzen, Tokyo 1959.

MAZUR'S THEOREM

J. R. ISBELL

Seattle

Introduction. A linear topological space A is said to *satisfy Mazur's theorem* if every sequentially continuous linear functional on A is continuous. The original theorem of S. MAZUR,[1]) completed by V. PTÁK,[2]) concerns the space $C(X)$ of all continuous real-valued functions on a completely regular space X, in the topology of pointwise convergence. $C(X)$ satisfies Mazur's theorem if and only if X is functionally closed. Moreover, in any case the sequentially continuous linear functionals on $C(X)$ are precisely the finite linear combinations of evaluations at points of the Hewitt completion of X (the completion with respect to $C(X)$).

X can be removed from this description; if $C(X)^*$ is the space of all continuous linear functionals on $C(X)$, in the weak * topology, then the space of all sequentially continuous functionals is the Hewitt completion $\upsilon[C(X)^*]$. This follows from a general theorem of H. H. CORSON:[3]) if A is any linear space, in the weak topology induced by a dual space A^*, and A^* carries the weak* topology, then υA^* is the space of all linear functionals φ on A which are continuous on countable subsets. The case $A = C(X)$ is special in that every sequentially continuous functional is countably continuous.

The question remains for general A, particularly in the weak topology induced by a dual space A^*, when does A satisfy Mazur's theorem? One hopes for an answer in terms of A^*. Of course, since $(A^*)^* = A$, there is such an answer in principle. It seems unlikely that a purely topological property of A^* (as in Corson's theorem) will suffice.

The theorem of Mazur and Pták has been generalized to vector lattices of functions [4] and to spaces of differentiable functions (E. S. Thomas[4])); it will be here extended to many rings of functions. In each case, for a space (lattice or ring) of functions A on a σ-compact[5]) space X, A satisfies Mazur's theorem. However, if we drop the side conditions, there is a countable-dimensional space A of continuous functions on a compactum X (a Cantor set) which does not satisfy Mazur's theorem.

[1]) Unpublished, 1946. Stated in [1], p. 74.

[2]) Unpublished, about 1956.

[3]) See Theorem 1 below.

[4]) Unpublished thesis, University of Washington, 1961.

[5]) In this paper *compact* means bicompact Hausdorff. A σ-compact space is a regular space which is a countable union of compact sets.

Corson's theorem. Let A and A^* be dual real or complex linear spaces as in the Introduction. H. H. Corson has published [3] a proof of the following theorem for the special case that A is a Banach space in the weak topology. The statement in [3] is also a little overspecialized. The theorem in its present form is again due to Corson, and the changes in the proof are quite minor.

Theorem 1. *A is functionally closed if and only if every countably continuous linear functional on A^* is continuous. Moreover, in any case the countably continuous linear functionals on A^*, in the topology induced by A^*, form the Hewitt completion of A.*

The proof depends mainly on the following theorem of Bockstein [2]. Let $P = \prod S_\alpha$ be an arbitrary topological product of separable metrizable spaces; let U and V be disjoint open subsets of P. Then for some countable set I of indices α, the projection of P upon $\prod_{\alpha \in I} S_\alpha$ maps U and V into disjoint open sets.

Bockstein's theorem yields the

Corollary. *Let D be a dense subset of a product $\prod S_\alpha$ of separable metrizable spaces; let g be a continuous real-valued function on D. Then there is a countable set I of indices α such that if π denotes the projection from D into $\prod_{\alpha \in I} S_\alpha$, g is constant on each inverse set $\pi^{-1}(p)$.*

The proof is rather straightforward, using a countable basis for the real line; it is done in [3].

Proof of Theorem 1. Let p be any point of the Hewitt completion υA. Each function f in A^* has a unique continuous extension $\hat{f}$ over υA; and putting $\varphi(f) = \hat{f}(p)$, it is easy to see that we have a countably continuous linear functional φ (which is continuous only if $p \in A$).

Conversely, let φ be a countably continuous linear functional on A^*. For any countable subset K of A^*, the smallest closed linear subspace S containing K is separable, and it is not hard to see that $\varphi \mid S$ is continuous. By the Hahn-Banach theorem, then, φ coincides on K with at least one continuous linear functional, which is represented by some a in A. Let $F(K)$ be the set of all such a. As K varies, the sets $F(K)$ form a filter base for a filter $\mathfrak{F}$. It will suffice to show that $\mathfrak{F}$ is a Cauchy filter in the uniformity induced by all continuous real-valued functions on A.

Choose a Hamel basis B for A^*. The space of all linear functionals on A^* is a product of lines $P = \prod_{\alpha \in B} R_\alpha$, containing A as a dense subspace. By the corollary to Bockstein's theorem, every continuous real-valued function g on A is determined by a countable set of coordinates $K \subset B$. In the set $F(K)$, all points have the same α-th coordinates for $\alpha \in K$; thus $g[F(K)]$ is a single point, and $\mathfrak{F}$ contains small sets with respect to g. This completes the proof.

Let us note how Corson's theorem and Pták's theorem imply that the space of all sequentially continuous functionals on $C(X)$ is $\upsilon[C(X)^*]$. From Corson's theorem, this is the space of all countably continuous functionals. From Pták's theorem, every sequentially continuous functional φ is a finite combination of evaluations at points of υX. Since those evaluations are countably continuous, so is φ.

Examples. The main counterexample shows that when A is an arbitrary space of continuous functions on a compact space X, in the topology of pointwise convergence, A need not satisfy Mazur's theorem – even if X is metric, and A countable-dimensional, so that the whole dual space A^* generated by X is metric. Actually the fact that A can be taken countable-dimensional is obvious, since X compact $\Rightarrow$ A^* σ-compact $\Rightarrow$ every countably continuous linear functional on A is continuous (by Corson's theorem). Thus once we have a discontinuous, sequentially continuous functional φ on some such A, perhaps not countable-dimensional, φ must be discontinuous on some countable subset and thus on some countable-dimensional subspace.

Then I shall describe an example in which A is not countable-dimensional, but is one of the familiar Banach spaces in an unusual topology. Specifically let A be the sequence space l_1 of all real sequences $\{a_n\}$ with $\sum |a_n| < \infty$. Let l_∞ denote the Banach dual space of all bounded sequences $\{x_n\}$, coupled to A by $(a, x) = \sum a_n x_n$. In l_∞ let X denote the set of all sequences of 0's and 1's; let A^* denote the linear space generated by X. Topologized by A, X is a Cantor set and A^* is a σ-compact non-metrizable space. Clearly A^* is a proper subspace of l_∞. If A is topologized by A^*, the functionals in $l_\infty - A^*$ are not continuous; hence, by Corson's theorem, they are not countably continuous.

However, every functional in l_∞ is sequentially continuous on A. To prove this, let $x \in l_\infty$; let (a^n) be a sequence in A such that (a^n, x) does not converge to 0. It will suffice to exhibit a functional $s \in X$ such that (a^n, s) does not converge to 0. We may suppose for convenience that $(a^n, x) = 1$ for all n; and clearly we may suppose that for each m, $a^n_m \to 0$. Also, for convenience, suppose that $\|x\| = \sup |x_n| = 1$. Now since $(a^1, x) = 1$, there is a finite set S_1 of indices such that $|\sum_{m \in S_1} a^1_m| > \frac{3}{4}$. There is a larger finite set T_1 such that $\sum_{m \text{ non} \in T_1} |a^1_m| < \frac{1}{4}$. Put $n_1 = 1$. Recursively, having finite sets $S_1, \ldots, S_k, T_1, \ldots, T_k$, and indices $n_1, \ldots, n_k$, such that $S_i \cap T_{i-1} = \emptyset$,

$$\Big|\sum_{m \in S_i} a^{n_i}_m\Big| > \tfrac{3}{4}, \quad \text{and} \quad \sum_{m \in T_{i-1}} |a^{n_i}_m| + \sum_{m \text{ non} \in T_i} |a^{n_i}_m| < \tfrac{1}{2}, \quad \text{for} \quad i = 1, \ldots, k,$$

there is n_{k+1} so great that for all n this great, $\sum_{m \in T_k} |a^n_m| < \frac{1}{4}$. Then S_{k+1} disjoint from T_k and T_{k+1} containing $S_{k+1} \cup T_k$ can be found to complete the recursion. Finally that s such that $s_m = 1$ for m in $\cup S_k$, $s_m = 0$ otherwise, gives $|(a^n, s)| > \frac{1}{4}$ for the infinite sequence of indices $n = n_k$.

Let us glance at another example in which A^* is generated by a complete (necessarily non-compact) subset X but A^* is not even functionally closed, so that A is very far from satisfying Mazur's theorem. In the theorems of Mazur, Pták, Isbell [4] and Thomas, completeness of X always implies Mazur's theorem for A.

Let X consist of $\aleph_1$ pairs of points (p_α, q_α). Let A be the family of all real-valued functions f on X such that for some constant c, for all but finitely many α, $f(q_\alpha) =$

$= f(p_\alpha) + c$. The weak uniformity induced on X by A consists of all countable coverings; so X is complete. But clearly the functional $\varphi(f) = c$ is well-defined, countably continuous, and discontinuous.

Special results and problems. Now that we know that Mazur's theorem is closely related to completeness in many important special cases but not in general, it becomes very interesting to look at the proofs in the special cases, and to see if they apply, or why they fail, in other interesting special cases. The unpublished proofs of Mazur and Pták, together with related unpublished proofs of L. Schwartz[6]) and S. Mrowka,[7]) are apparently very specialized (for $C(X)$, except for Schwartz's result, which concerns C^∞ functions on a manifold). My proof [4] involves a rather long chain of lemmas on "patching" functions by means of lattice operations, and a notion of *support* which permits convergence arguments showing that a sequentially continuous functional is supported by a finite set and is therefore continuous.

My student E. S. Thomas has modified my patching arguments and, using the same notion of support and the same convergent filter of sets, has proved the following: Let X be a set and A a linear family of real-valued functions on X. Suppose (1) for every $f \in A$ and every uniformly continuous C^∞ function g of one real variable, gf is in A. Further, regard X as a topological and uniform space in the weak uniformity induced by A, and suppose (2) every function locally coinciding with functions in A is in A. Then A satisfies Mazur's theorem if and only if X is complete. This result of course contains the Mazur-Pták theorem and a good theorem on differentiable manifolds. It also provides an interesting addition to the theorem of [4], applied to spaces $C(\mu X)$ of all uniformly continuous functions.

In a different direction, H. H. Corson has pointed out a device for deducing Mazur's theorem for a space A when it is known for a suitable space B. The lemma, properly formulated, has a trivial proof.

Corson's Lemma. Suppose B is a linear family of functions on a set X and A is a linear subfamily of B which is dense in some topology satisfying the first axiom of countability and finer than the topology J of pointwise convergence on X. Then with respect to J, every sequentially continuous linear functional on A has a unique sequentially continuous extension over B; and A satisfies Mazur's theorem if and only if B does.

From this lemma and the theorem of [4] one can prove:

Corollary. *Let A be a linear algebra of real-valued functions determining the topology of a Lindelöf space X, not all vanishing at any point, and such that X is a countable union of subsets on which all the functions in A are bounded. Then in the topology of pointwise convergence on X, A satisfies Mazur's theorem.*

This applies in particular to the space of real polynomials in one variable, in the topology of pointwise convergence on any infinite subset X of the real line. However,

[6]) See [5], p. 69.

[7]) See [1], p. 75.

the question is open if we take for X, say, the unit disc in the complex plane. A more interesting, equally open question: does Mazur's theorem hold for the space A of complex polynomials in the topology of pointwise convergence on the unit disc?

One concluding remark. The method of [4] may yet yield further results, even for examples (such as the complex polynomials) in which there is a proper Šilov boundary. However, for this it would be necessary to modify the notion of *support* for a functional. In [4] this is defined in terms of the usual notion of *support* for a function, which is clearly inappropriate for analytic functions. One may say, for a space A of functions on a set X, that a subset S of X *supports* a sequentially continuous linear functional φ on A when for every sequence $\{f_n\}$ in A converging to zero pointwise on S, $\varphi(f_n)$ converges to zero. For the applications in [4] and Thomas' thesis, this notion is equivalent to the other one.

Note (added in proof). I find the results of Mazur[1]) and Mrówka[7]) were published; see S. Mrówka, Studia Math *21* (1961), 1–14. My paper [4] and Thomas' thesis[4]) are combined in one paper submitted to Proc. Amer. Math. Soc.

References

[1] *П. С. Александров:* О некоторых результатах в теории топологических пространств, полученных за последние 25 лет. Успехи матем. наук *15* (1960), 25—95.

[2] *M. Bockstein*: Un théorème de séparabilité pour les produits topologiques. Fundam. Math. *35* (1948), 242–246.

[3] *H. H. Corson*: The weak topology of a Banach space. Trans. Amer. Math. Soc. (to appear).

[4] *J. R. Isbell*: Mazur's Theorem, I. Proc. Amer. Math. Soc. (to appear).

[5] *L. Schwartz*: Théorie des distributions, Tome I. Act. Sci. Ind. 1091, Paris 1950.

ON A CATEGORY OF SPACES

M. KATĚTOV

Praha

If X is a set, let $E(X)$ denote the linear space of all "formal linear combinations" $\Sigma\lambda_i x_i$ where λ_i are numbers (real or complex), $x_i \in X$. A topology λ on $E(X)$ under which $E(X)$ is a locally convex topological linear space (abbreviated: LC-space, LC-topology) will be called a Λ-structure on X, and the pair (X, λ) will be called a Λ-space. If (X_1, λ_1), (X_2, λ_2) are Λ-spaces, then a mapping φ of X_1 into X_2 will be called Λ-continuous (or a Λ-mapping or simply a morphism) if the linear extension of φ is a continuous (with respect to λ_1, λ_2) mapping of $E(X_1)$ into $E(X_2)$. If λ_1, λ_2 are Λ-structures on X, then λ_1 is finer than λ_2 (λ_2 is coarser than λ_1) if the identity mapping of (X, λ_1) onto (X, λ_2) is Λ-continuous.

In the following, definitions and propositions (as well as some examples) are given in the form of short remarks, some of them formulated somewhat loosely. A full exposition is to be submitted to the *Czechoslovak Mathematical Journal*.

1. Several years ago, V. EFREMOVIČ suggested the investigation of properties of metric spaces invariant under mappings satisfying (in both directions) the Lipschitz condition. This suggestion may be carried out as follows. Two metrics ϱ_1, ϱ_2 on X are called L-equivalent if, for some positive α, β,

$$\alpha\, \varrho_1(x, y) \leqq \varrho_2(x, y) \leqq \beta\, \varrho_1(x, y) \quad \text{for all} \quad x, y \in X\,;$$

a set consisting of all L-equivalent metrics is called a quasi-metric; a pair (X, q), q being a quasi-metric on X, is called an L-space. Some simple properties of L-spaces have been examined by the present author (to appear in the Proceedings of the *Conference on Functional Analysis*, Warsaw 1960). Since every metric on X may by extended [1] to a norm on $E(X)$, L-spaces may be considered as a special case of Λ-spaces.

2. Let $\mathscr{A}$, $\mathscr{B}$, $\mathscr{C}$ be categories. If $S : \mathscr{A} \to \mathscr{C}$, $T : \mathscr{B} \to \mathscr{C}$ are covariant functors, then a category may be obtained in the following way: objects (morphisms) are pairs (a, b), (α, β) of objects (morphisms) from $\mathscr{A}$, $\mathscr{B}$ satisfying the conditions $Sa = Tb$, $S\alpha = T\beta$. If $\mathscr{A}$, $\mathscr{B}$, $\mathscr{C}$ are respectively the categories of all sets, all LC-spaces, all linear spaces, and $S : \mathscr{A} \to \mathscr{C}$, $T : \mathscr{B} \to \mathscr{C}$ are natural functors ($SX = E(X)$, TY is the underlying linear space), then we obtain, essentially, the category of all Λ-spaces. Instead of the "fusing" of categories, as just described, a kind of "transfer of structures" may be considered. Let $\mathscr{A}$, $\mathscr{B}$, $\mathscr{C}$ be categories, the objects of $\mathscr{C}$ being those of $\mathscr{B}$

endowed with certain structures. If $S : \mathscr{A} \to \mathscr{B}$ is a covariant functor, we may consider a category whose objects are pairs (a, μ), a being an object from $\mathscr{A}$, μ a structure on Sa, and morphisms corresponding precisely to those morphisms $\alpha : a \to a'$ of $\mathscr{A}$ for which $S\alpha$ is a morphism for $\mathscr{C}$ mapping (Sa, μ) to (Sa', μ').

3. For any Λ-space X, denote by $\hat{E}(X)$ the completion of $E(X)$, and by $E'(X)$ the linear space (topologized in a suitable way) of continuous linear forms on $E(X)$.

As already mentioned, a metric on a set X induces, in a way described in [1], a norm, hence a topology on $E(X)$, and therefore a Λ-structure on X (of course, two L-equivalent metrics induce, in this sense, the same Λ-structure). Some trivial examples: if X is discrete, $\varrho(x, y) = 1$ for $x \neq y$, then

$$\hat{E}(X) \cong l\,, \quad E'(X) \cong m\,;$$

if X is an interval, then $\hat{E}(X) \cong L$, $E'(X) \cong M$ ($\cong$ means isometric isomorphism).

Another class of Λ-spaces may be obtained as follows. A linear system Φ of real functions on X induces, under certain conditions, a weak LC-topology on $E(X)$; along with it, we may consider the corresponding "strong" topology, or some intermediate topologies. In particular, r-differentiable ($r = 1, 2, \ldots, \infty$) manifolds may be treated in this way; with $r = \infty$ and an appropriate topology for $E(X)$, $\hat{E}(X)$ consists, essentially, of distributions on X.

4. We shall use, for convenience, the expressions u-structure, δ-structure, t-structure to denote, respectively, a uniform structure, a proximity structure, a topology; the same convention is adopted, of course, for spaces. The letters u, δ, t will be used as generic symbols for a structure of the corresponding kind, and the letter c will stand for u, δ or t (in both meanings). The letter λ will be used as a generic symbol for a Λ-structure.

Every λ on X induces, in a natural way, for $c = u, \delta, t$, a c-structure on X denoted by $c(\lambda)$. If γ is a c-structure, then we denote by $\Lambda(\gamma)$ the set of all λ for which $c(\lambda) = \gamma$.

A Λ-space $X = (X, \lambda)$ as well as its structure λ will be called, respectively, weak, bounded, totally bounded if the topology of $E(X)$ is weak, X is bounded, is totally bounded as a subset of $E(X)$.

The following assertions are, for the most part, paraphrases of well known theorems:

(a) $\Lambda(u)$ always contains a finest structure;

(b) $\Lambda(u)$ does not necessarily contain a weak structure;

(c) $\Lambda(\delta)$ contains, in general, no finest structure (example: $N \times N$ imbedded in $\beta N \times \beta N$);

(d) $\Lambda(t)$ always contains a finest structure as well as a totally bounded weak structure (induced by the set of all bounded continuous functions);

(e) $\gamma = u, \delta$ is bounded (totally bounded) if and only if $\Lambda(\gamma)$ contains a bounded (totally bounded) λ (for the definition of boundedness and total boundedness of γ see [3], [4]).

5. Let $\mathscr{A}$, $\mathscr{B}$ be categories. We shall say that $\mathscr{B}$ is a retract of $\mathscr{A}$ if there exist covariant functors $S : \mathscr{A} \to \mathscr{B}$, $T : \mathscr{B} \to \mathscr{A}$ such that $S \circ T$ is the identity functor. It is easy to see that, for $c = u, \delta, t$, the category of all c-spaces is a retract of that of all Λ-spaces. Indeed, for $c = u$, we may put $T(X, u)$ equal to the Λ-space with the finest λ inducing u. As for $c = \delta, t$, it is only a matter of re-wording well known results to prove that the category of δ-spaces is a retract of that of u-spaces (observe that $T(X, \delta) = (X, u)$ with the coarsest u such that $\delta(u) = \delta$), and so on.

6. Let (X_i, ϱ_i), $i = 1, 2$, be metric spaces. The following definition of the direct product of the corresponding Λ-spaces (X_i, λ_i) appears, at the first sight, to be natural and convenient:

$$(X_1, \lambda_1) \times (X_2, \lambda) = (X_1 \times X_2, \lambda)$$

with λ induced by the metric

$$\varrho(x, y) = \varrho_1(x_1, y_1) + \varrho_2(x_2, y_2)\,.$$

Unfortunately, it may happen that, for some $f_i \in E'(X_i)$, the linear form $f_1 \otimes f_2$ on

$$E(X_1) \otimes E(X_2) = E(X_1 \times X_2)$$

is not continuous (this corresponds to the trivial fact that the product of two Lipschitz functions is not necessarily Lipschitz).

Therefore, it is necessary to look for more appropriate definitions of $X_1 \times X_2$. The following one seems to be convenient. Let (X_i, λ_i) be Λ-spaces. The topology of

$$E(X_1 \times X_2) = E(X_1) \otimes E(X_2)$$

will be determined by the following condition: a linear mapping φ of $E(X_1) \otimes \otimes E(X_2)$ into a normed linear space is continuous if and only if the corresponding bilinear mapping $\varphi(\xi_1, \xi_2)$, $\xi_i \in E(X_i)$, is equicontinuous in ξ_1 (ξ_2) for every bounded subset of X_2 (X_1). It is to be noted, however, that, under this definition, the product of L-spaces is not necessarily an L-space; it seems therefore appropriate to assign to a non-bounded metric space X instead of an L-space (as described at the beginning of the present note) a Λ-space defined as follows: a linear mapping of $E(X)$ into a normed linear space is continuous if and only if it is Lipschitz on every bounded set $A \subset X$.

Finally, we may add that the topology for $E(X_1) \otimes E(X_2)$ described in the above definition of the product of two Λ-spaces is, in general, intermediate between the topologies of the inductive and projective products of $E(X_1)$ and $E(X_2)$ introduced by A. GROTHENDIECK.

References

[1] *R. Arens* and *J. Eells*: On embedding uniform and topological spaces. Pacif. J. Math. *6* (1956), 397–403.

[2] *A. Grothendieck*: Produits tensoriels topologiques et espaces nucléaires. Memoirs of the American Math. Soc. *16* (1955), 1–185.

[3] *J. Hejcman*: The boundedness in uniform spaces and topological groups. Czechosl. Math. J. *9* (84) (1959), 544–563.

[4] *M. Katětov*: Über die Berührungsräume. Wiss. Z. Humboldt-Univ. Berlin, Math.-Nat. R. *9* (1959-60), 685–691.

НЕКОТОРЫЕ ТЕОРЕМЫ О ТОПОЛОГИЧЕСКОМ ВЛОЖЕНИИ

ЛЮДМИЛА КЕЛДЫШ

Москва

1.

Мы рассматриваем некоторые непрерывные разбиения E^n_f эвклидова пространства E^n на точки и континуумы и изучаем вопрос о вложении пространства разбиения $f(E^n)$ в эвклидово пространство E^m, где $m \geqq n$. Предполагается, что каждый невырожденный элемент ξ (т. е. содержащий более одной точки) разбиения E^n_f есть *клеточно вложенный в* E^n континуум.

Определение. Континуум $K \subset E^n$ называется клеточно вложенным в E^n, если во всякой его окрестности U найдется другая окрестность Q такая, что:

$$K \subset Q \subset \bar{Q} \subset U$$

и $\bar{Q}$ — замыкание Q есть n-мерный топологический куб. Такую окрестность Q мы называем *клеточной окрестностью* K.

Заметим, что из теорем доказанных М. Брауном [4] легко следует, что свойство континуума быть клеточно вложенным в E^n эквивалентно свойству быть точечно-подобным, т. е. дополнение к нему $E^n \setminus K$ гомеоморфно дополнению к точке $E^n \setminus \{p\}$.

Пусть P — множество $\{\xi\}$ всех невырожденных элементов разбиения E^n_f, а $P^* = f^{-1}(P) = \bigcup \xi$. Мы рассматриваем следующие случаи:

Случай a) P — компакт и $\dim P = 0$.

Случай b) P — произвольное счетное множество.

Бинг построил непрерывное разбиение пространства E^3 удовлетворяющее условию a) такое, что все невырожденные элементы — ручные простые дуги, а пространство разбиения $f(E^3)$ не вложимо в E^3 [1], и непрерывное разбиение E^3, удовлетворяющее условию b), где все невырожденные элементы разбиения — клеточно вложенные в E^n континуумы, а $f(E^3) \not\subset E^3$ [2].

Мы указываем достаточные условия для того, чтобы в случае a) или в случае b) имело место: $f(E^n) = E^n$, и показываем, что в обоих случаях a) и b) имеет место $f(E^n) \subset E^{n+1}$.

Определение. Множество $A \subset E^n$ называется *клеточно разделенным* в E^n, если для каждой его компоненты K в каждой ее окрестности U найдется клеточная окрестность Q такая что (гр. $Q) \cap A = \Lambda$. (Через гр. Q обозначается граница множества Q).

Рассмотрим сначала случай а).

2.

Теорема 1. *Пространство $f(E^n)$ непрерывного разбиения E^n на компоненты клеточного разделенного в E^n компакта P^* и точки $x \in E^n \setminus P^*$ гомеоморфно E^n.* Заметим что в случае $n = 3$ эта теорема следует из теоремы Харрольда [5].

Компакт P^* можно представить в виде:

$$P^* = \bigcap_{k=1}^{\infty} \bigcup_{r=1}^{R_k} U_r^k,$$

где $P^* \cap$ гр. $U_r^k = \Lambda$, $\overline{U}_r^k \subset U_\varrho^{k-1}$, и $\overline{U}_r^k \cap \overline{U}_{r'}^k = \Lambda$ для $r \neq r'$, причем U_r^k – область в E^n, вообще говоря, не клеточная. Каждая компонента ξ компакта P^* есть пересечение:

$$\xi = \bigcap_{k=1}^{\infty} U_{r_k}^k ; \quad \overline{U}_{r_k}^k \subset U_{r_{k-1}}^{k-1} .$$

В нашем случае в каждое покрытие $\{U_r^k\}$, $r = 1, 2, \ldots R_k$ компакта P^* можно вписать покрытие $\{Q_m^k\}$, $m = 1, \ldots M_k$, где каждый $\overline{Q}_m^k$ – топологический куб, (гр. $Q_m^k) \cap P^* = \Lambda$ и для каждой компоненты ξ найдется Q_m^k такой, что

$$\xi \subset Q_m^k \subset \overline{Q}_m^k \subset U_r^k .$$

При этом возможно $Q_m^k \cap Q_{m'}^k \neq \Lambda$ для некоторых m и m'. Рассматривая такие покрытия, можно построить последовательность гомеоморфизмов $\varphi_k : E^n \to E^n$ так, что для каждой компоненты ξ компакта P^*:

$$\operatorname{diam} \varphi_k(\xi) < 1/k$$

и последовательность $\varphi_1, \varphi_2, \ldots, \varphi_k, \ldots$ равномерно сходится к заданному непрерывному отображению $f : E^n \to E^n$.

Теорема 2. *Если $f(E^n)$ – пространство непрерывного разбиения E^n на точки и клеточно вложенные в E^n континуумы, которые являются компонентами компакта P^*, то $f(E^n) \subset E^{n+1}$.*

Для доказательства мы строим вложение (гомеоморфное отображение) Φ пространства E^n в E^{n+1} так, что множество $\Phi(P^*)$ клеточно разделено в E^{n+1}. Пространство непрерывного разбиения E_ψ^{n+1} пространства E^{n+1} на точки и компоненты $\Phi(P^*)$ в силу теоремы 1 гомеоморфно E^{n+1}. А непрерывное отображение $\Psi\Phi : E^n \to E^{n+1}$ топологически эквивалентно f, следовательно, $f(E^n) \subset E^{n+1}$.

Для построения вложения Φ мы определяем на E^n действительную функцию F так, что F постоянна на каждом элементе ξ разбиения и $F[\xi] \neq F[\xi']$, если $\xi \neq \xi'$. Положим $F[\xi] = t_\xi$. $\Phi(E^n)$ есть график функции F, т. е. множество точек $\{x, F(x)\}$, $x \in E^n$. Множество $\Phi(P^*)$ представимо в виде:

$$\Phi(P^*) = \bigcap_{k=1}^{\infty} \bigcup_{m=1}^{R_{k+1}} (Q^k_{mx} \times i^{k+1}_r); \quad \overline{U}^{k+1}_r \subset Q^k_m$$

где $\overline{Q}^k_m$ топологический куб из покрытия $\{Q^k_m\}$, а $\bar{i}^{k+1}_r$ – сегмент оси Ot, причем

$$\bar{i}^{k+1}_m \cap \bar{i}^{k+1}_{r'} = \Lambda \quad \text{для} \quad m \neq m' \quad \text{и} \quad \bar{i}^{k+1}_m \subset \bar{i}^k_\varrho .$$

Следовательно, $(\overline{Q}^k_m \times \bar{i}^{k+1}_r) \cap (\overline{Q}^k_{m'} \times \bar{i}^{k+1}_{r'}) = \Lambda$ для $r \neq r'$и $\Phi(\xi) = \xi \times t_\xi$ для $\xi \in P$.

3.

Аналогичные теоремы имеют место в случае b).

Теорема 3. *Пусть E^n_f непрерывное разбиение E^n на точки и счетное множество D континуумов ξ_i, причем множество $D^* = \bigcup_{i=1}^{\infty} \xi_i$ клеточно разделено в E^n. Тогда $f(E^n)$ гомеоморфно E^n.*

Доказательство этой теоремы основано на следующей лемме.

Пусть в условиях теоремы 3 $\overline{Q}$ – топологический n-мерный куб такой, что

$$D^* \cap \text{гр. } Q = \Lambda .$$

Тогда для любого $\varepsilon > 0$ существует гомеоморфизм $\varphi : E^n \to E^n$ такой, что $\varphi(x) = x$ для $x \in E^n \setminus Q$, и $\operatorname{diam} \varphi(\xi_i) < \varepsilon$ для $\xi_i \subset Q$.

С помощью этой леммы строится последовательность гомеоморфизмов E^n на себя $\varphi_1, \varphi_2, \ldots, \varphi_k, \ldots$, такая, что

$$\operatorname{diam} \varphi_k(\xi_i) < 1/k \quad \text{для} \quad \xi_i \in D ,$$

которая равномерно сходится к непрерывному отображению $f : E^n \to E^n$ определенному заданным непрерывным разбиением.

Теорема 4. *Пространство $f(E^n)$ непрерывного разбиения E^n на точки и счетное множество клеточно вложенных в E^n континуумов топологически вкладывается в E^{n+1}.*

Аналогично случаю теоремы 2, строится топологическое вложение Φ пространства E^n в E^{n+1} так, что множество $\bigcup_{i=1}^{\infty} \Phi(\xi_i)$ клеточно разделено в E^{n+1}. В силу теоремы 3, пространство $\Psi(E^{n+1})$ непрерывного разбиения E^{n+1} на точки и континуумы $\Phi(\xi_i)$ гомеоморфно E^{n+1}, а $\Psi\, \Phi(E^n)$ есть вложение $f(E^n)$ в E^{n+1}.

Для построения вложения Φ мы строим на E^n действительную функцию F так, что:

1. F постоянна на каждом ξ_i;
2. Для каждого ξ_i существует окрестность U_i в E^n такая, что $F(x) > F(x')$, если $x \in \xi_i$, $x' \in U_i \setminus \xi_i$. $\Phi(E^n)$ есть график функции F, т. е. множество точек $\{x, F(x)\}$, $x \in E^n$.

Пусть $F(\xi_i) = t_i$; в силу 2 имеем:

$$(U_i \times t_i) \cap \Phi(E^n) = \xi_i \times t_i .$$

Пусть Q — произвольная клеточная окрестность ξ_i содержащаяся в U_i. Граница области $Q \times t_i$ в гиперплоскости $t = t_i$ не пересекается в $\Phi(E^n)$. Следовательно, для достаточно малого $\varepsilon < 0$ топологическое произведение (гр. Q_i) $\times [t_i - \varepsilon, t_i + \varepsilon]$ также не пересекается с $\Phi(E^n)$. При этом, в силу 1) и счетности множества D, ε можно выбрать так, что гиперплоскости $t = t_i - \varepsilon$ и $t = t_i + \varepsilon$ не пересекают множества $\bigcup_{i=1}^{\infty} \Phi(\xi_i)$. Тогда

$$V = Q \times (t_i - \varepsilon, t_i + \varepsilon)$$

есть клеточная окрестность континуума $\xi_i \times t_i$ в E^{n+1}, причем

$$\text{(1)} \qquad (\text{гр. V}) \cap \Big(\bigcup_{i=1}^{\infty} \Phi(\xi_i)\Big) = \Lambda .$$

Так как Q произвольная клеточная окрестность ξ_i содрежащаяся в U_i, а ε — произвольное положительное число, то V — сколь угодно малая окрестность $\Phi(\xi_i)$ и (1) означает, что множество $\Phi(D^*)$ клеточно разделено в E^{n+1}.

4.

В заключение рассмотрим вопрос о вложении пространства непрерывного разбиения E^n на точки и *конечное число произвольных компактов*. Р. Г. Бинг и М. Л. Куртис [3] построили непрерывное разбиение E^3_f пространства E^3 на точки и девять окружностей такое, что пространство разбиения $f(E^3)$ не вложимо в E^4. Имеет место

Теорема 5. *Пространство непрерывного разбиения E^n на точки и конечное число произвольных компактов топологически вкладывается в E^{n+2}.*

Пусть $K_1, K_2, \ldots, K_r$ — все невырожденные элементы разбиения E^n_f.

Мы строим топологическое вложение Φ пространства E^n в E^{n+2}, определив на E^n пару непрерывных функций $u = \varphi(x)$, $v = \psi(x)$, $x \in E^n$, следующим образом:

$$\text{(2)} \qquad \varphi(x) = i/r \quad \text{для} \quad x \in K_i , \quad i = 1, 2, \ldots, r ; \quad 0 \leqq \varphi(x) \leqq 1 .$$

$$\text{(3)} \qquad \psi(x) = 0 \quad \text{для} \quad x \in \bigcup_{i=1}^{r} K_i ; \quad 1 \geqq \psi(x) > 0 \quad \text{для} \quad x \in E^n \setminus \bigcup_{i=1}^{r} K_i .$$

$\Phi(E^n)$ есть график этой системы функций в пространстве E^{n+2}, т. е. множество точек $\{x, \varphi(x), \psi(x)\}$, где $x \in E^n$. В силу (3) пересечение $\Phi(E^n)$ с $(n + 1)$-мерной гиперплоскостью пространства E^{n+2} определенной уравнением $v = 0$ есть $\bigcup_{i=1}^{r} \Phi(K_i)$, где

$$\Phi(K_i) = K_i \times u_i , \quad u_i = i/r .$$

Для каждого компакта $\Phi(K_i)$ выберем содержащий его и лежащий в n-мерной гиперплоскости определенной уравнениями $u = u_i$, $v = 0$ n-мерный шар Δ_i^n.

$$\Phi(K_i) \subset \Delta_i^n .$$

В силу (3) имеем

$$\Phi(E^n) \cap \Delta_i^n = \Phi(K_i) . \tag{4}$$

Пусть E_ψ^{n+2} — непрерывное разбиение пространства E^{n+2} на точки и шары Δ_i^n. Очевидно, что $\Psi(E^{n+2}) = E^{n+2}$, следовательно, $\Psi\Phi(E^n) \subset E^{n+2}$. Но в силу (4) — на $\Phi(E^n)$ разбиение E_ψ^{n+2} индуцирует разбиение на точки и компакты $\Phi(K_i)$, т. е. оно топологически эквивалентно непрерывному разбиению E_f^n, следовательно, $\Psi\Phi(E^n)$ есть топологическое вложение $f(E^n)$ в E^{n+2}.

В силу теоремы Дайера [6] для непрерывного разбиения E_f^n пространства E^n на клеточно вложенные континуумы имеем всегда

$$\dim f(E^n) \leqq n .$$

Следовательно,

$$f(E^n) \subset E^{2n+1} .$$

Правдоподобно, однако, что $f(E^n)$ вложимо в пространство E^m, где m значительно меньше чем $2n + 1$.

Вопрос 1. В пространство E^m какой наименьшей размерности $m > n$ вложимо произвольное непрерывное разбиение E^n на точки и клеточно вложенные в E^n континуумы?

Вопрос 2. В пространство E^m какой наименьшей размерности $m > n$ вложимо всякое непрерывное разбиение E^n на точки и *нульмерное* множество P клеточно вложенных в E^n континуумов, если P некомпактно и несчетно?

Литература

[1] *R. H. Bing*: A decomposition of E^3 into points and tame arcs such that the decomposition space is topologically different from E^3. Ann. of Math., *65* (1957), 484—498.

[2] *R. H. Bing*: Point-like decompositions of E^3. Notices Am. Math. Soc. 7, *50* (1960), 576—144.

[3] *R. H. Bing* and *M. L. Curtis*: Imbedding decompositions of E^3 in E^4. Proc. Amer. Math. Soc., *11* (1960), 149—155.

[4] *M. Brown*: A proof of the generalized Schoenflies theorem. Bull. Am. M. S., *66* (1960), 74—76.

[5] *O. G. Harrold*: A sufficient condition that a monotone image of the three-sphere be a topological three-sphere. Proc. Am. Math. Soc., *9* (1958), 846—850.

[6] *E. Dyer*: Certain transformations which lower dimension. Ann. Math., *63* (1956), 15—19.

DESCRIPTIONS OF ČECH COHOMOLOGY[1])

J. L. KELLEY

Berkeley

E. H. SPANIER [5] proved that, for compact spaces, a form of the Alexander-Kolmogoroff homology theory suggested by A. D. WALLACE was isomorphic to the Čech theory. W. HUREWICZ, J. DUGUNDJI and C. H. DOWKER [4] established this result for paracompact spaces, and Dowker [3] later proved isomorphism for arbitrary topological spaces. P. ALEXANDROFF has an unpublished proof of the same theorem. The purpose of this note, largely methodological, is to outline in some detail a proof of isomorphism for paracompact spaces. It is remarkable that the proof is completely elementary and non-combinatorial in character. The corresponding development for homology with coefficients in a sheaf is sketched without proof in the last section.

Čech Cohomology. We review the definition of the Čech cohomology groups of a space X with coefficient group G in order to establish the notation. Suppose $U = \{U(i)\}_{i \in I}$ is an (indexed) open cover of X. For each $(q + 1)$-tuple $s = (s_0, s_1, \ldots, s_q)$ of members of the index set I, we let $|U(S)|$ be the intersection $\bigcap\{U(s_i) : i = 0, 1, \ldots, q\}$, and we define the nerve of the cover $U = \{U(i)\}_{i \in I}$ to be the complex with q-dimensional simplices $K_q(U) = \{s : |U(s)| \text{ non-void}\}$. The q-dimensional cochain group $C^q(U)$ is $\{f : f \text{ is a function on } K_q(U) \text{ to } G\}$, and the usual coboundary operator on $C^q(U)$ to $C^{q+1}(U)$ then defines the cohomology groups $H^q(U)$ of the cover.

If $V = \{V(j)\}_{j \in J}$ is also an open cover of X then we say that V is a refinement of U iff $V(j) \subset U(n_j)$ for some suitably chosen function n on J to I. We call n a refining function; n induces a refining map on $K_q(V)$ to $K_q(U)$, which in turn induces a chain map on $C^q(U)$ to $C^q(V)$, and this chain map induces a refining homomorphism of $H^q(U)$ into $H^q(V)$. This homomorphism is independent of the particular refining function n which is chosen. The Čech cohomology group $H^q(X)$ is defined to be the inductive limit (direct limit), under the refining homomorphisms, of the groups $H^q(U)$ for all open covers U of X.

Small Simplex Cohomology (Vietoris Type). There is a special sort of cover which is of particular interest to us. Suppose that N is an open subset of the product $X \times X$ which contains the diagonal $\Delta = \{(x, x) : x \in X\}$. For each member x of X we define $N[x]$ to be $\{y : (x, y) \in N\}$ and we denote by N^* the cover $\{N[x] : x \in X\}$. Thus the space X itself is the index set for the cover N^*. It is known that, in case X is paracom-

[1]) This work was supported by a National Science Foundation Grant 18974.

pact, every open cover has a refinement which is of the form N^*. In other words, the class of covers of the form N^* is cofinal in the class of all open covers of X. The class of open neighborhoods of Δ is directed by $\subset$, and we notice that if M and N are open neighborhoods of the diagonal and $M \subset N$ then the cover M^* is a refinement of the cover N^*. Moreover, if $M \subset N$ then there is a natural choice for the refining function which carries the index set X of M^* into the index set X of N^*, namely the identity. The set $K_q(M^*)$ of q-simplices of the cover M^* is in fact a subset of $K_q(N^*)$, and the induced refining chain map of $C^q(N^*)$ into $C^q(M^*)$ is restriction; that is the image of $f \in C^q(N^*)$ is $f \mid K_q(M^*)$. It follows from these facts that the Čech group $H^q(X)$ is isomorphic to the inductive limit under the homomorphism induced by restriction of $H^q(N^*)$ for neighborhoods N of the diagonal in $X \times X$.

The preceding description of Čech cohomology has a natural geometric interpretation. If we agree that a simplex $(x_0, x_1, \ldots, x_q)$ with vertices in X is N-small if $\bigcap\{N[x_i] : i = 0, 1, \ldots, q\}$ is non-void, then $K_q(N^*)$ is just the set of N-small q-simplices, so that the cohomology theory may be called a "small simplex" theory.

Alexander-Kolmogoroff Cohomology. We next need the fact "cohomology commutes with inductive limit". More precisely: let $C^q(X)$ be the inductive limit, under the restriction maps, of $C^q(N^*)$ for N a neighborhood of the diagonal in $X \times X$. The coboundary operator on the cochain groups $C^q(N^*)$ induces a coboundary operator on $C^q(X)$, and thus defines a cohomology group which we may denote $^*H^q(X)$. It is not hard to see that $^*H^q(X)$ is isomorphic to the Čech group $H^q(X)$, since each is isomorphic to a group which can be described informally as $\{f : f \in C^q(N^*)$ for some N, and for some M the restriction of f to $K_q(M)$ is a cocycle$\}$ modulo the equivalence relation $\{(f, g) :$ for some neighborhood P of the diagonal, $f \mid K_q(P) - g \mid K_q(P)$ is a coboundary$\}$.

We are now very close to the Alexander-Kolmogoroff cohomology theory. The set $K_q(N^*)$ is the subset of the set $X^{(q+1)}$ consisting of all $(q + 1)$-tuples of points of X which are N-small. Thus $K_q(N^*)$ is a neighborhood of the diagonal $\Delta^{(q+1)} = \{(x_0, x_1, \ldots, x_q) : x_i = x_0$ for all $i\}$, and we shall refer to $K_q(N^*)$ as the N-neighborhood of $\Delta^{(q+1)}$. The inductive limit $C^q(X)$ of the groups $C^q(N^*)$ is then, by reason of the definition of the inductive limit, the set $\{(f, N) : f$ on the N-neighborhood of $\Delta^{(q+1)}$ to $G\}$, modulo the equivalence relation: (f, N) is equivalent to (g, M) iff for some $P, f = g$ on the P-neighborhood of $\Delta^{(q+1)}$. Because the space X is paracompact, the family of N-neighborhoods of $\Delta^{(q+1)}$ is a base for the family of all neighborhoods of $\Delta^{(q+1)}$, and consequently $C^q(X)$ is isomorphic to the family F^q of all functions f, each defined on some neighborhood of $\Delta^{(q+1)}$ to G, modulo the subset of all functions f which vanish on some neighborhood of $\Delta^{(q+1)}$. (The isomorphism carries each equivalence class belonging to $C^q(X)$ into the equivalence class containing it.) Finally, each equivalence class of F^q clearly contains members with domain equal to $X^{(q+1)}$. Whence: The Čech cohomology group $H^q(X)$ is isomorphic to the cohomology group of the chain complex with q-dimensional cochain group equal to the group of all functions on $X^{(q+1)}$ to G, modulo the subgroup consisting of functions zero on some neighborhood of the diagonal $\Delta^{(q+1)}$. This is the Alexander-Kolmogoroff cohomology theory.

Cohomology with Coefficients in a Sheaf. Essentially the same reasoning as that given above yields a description of Alexander-Kolmogoroff type for the Čech cohomology group of a paracompact space X with coefficients in a sheaf $\mathscr{J}$ of Abelian groups over X. Let Σ be the set of all sections of $\mathscr{J}$, where sections are added pointwise, the domain of the sum of two sections being the intersection of the domains. Let C^q be the set of all functions f on $X^{(q+1)}$ to Σ with the property that for each member x of X there is a neighborhood U of x such that if $s \in U^{(q+1)}$ then U is a subset of domain of $f(s)$. Let R^q be the equivalence relation: $R^q = \{(f, g) :$ for $x \in X$ there is a neighborhood U of x such that $f(s) \mid U = g(s) \mid U$ for $s \in U^{(q+1)}\}$. The quotient C^q/R^q inherits an addition from Σ, and with the natural coboundary operator, the q-th cohomology group of the chain complex with q-th cochain group C^q/R^q is isomorphic to the Čech group $H^q(X, \mathscr{J})$.

There are several variations of the above description which pretty evidently give the same cohomology groups. R. Deheuvels [2] has a related description of $H^q(X, \mathscr{J})$ in terms of objects which are "locally" functions on $X^{(q+1)}$.

Finally, the group C^q/R^q has a natural representation as a family of functions on X. We may describe this representation in terms of the construction above as follows. For each $x \in X$ define the equivalence relation R^x_q to be $\{(f, g)$: for some neighborhood U of x, if $s \in U^{(q+1)}$ then $f(s) \mid U = g(s) \mid U\}$. Clearly $R^q = \bigcap\{R^x_q : x \in X\}$, and the natural map F such that $F(f/R^q)(x) = f/R^q_x$ is therefore an isomorphism. The family of all functions $F(f/R^q)$ might well be called the group $\mathscr{A}^q$ of Alexander cochains on X. It evidently has the property: if a and b belong to $\mathscr{A}^q$ and $a(x) = b(x)$ then $a \mid U = b \mid U$ for some neighborhood U of x. It is true, but not obvious, that a function b which locally belongs to $\mathscr{A}^q$, in the sense that every point of X has a neighborhood in which b agrees with some member of $\mathscr{A}^q$, necessarily belongs to $\mathscr{A}^q$. In brief, $\mathscr{A}^q$ is a complete carapace in the sense of H. Cartan [1].

References

[1] *Cartan H.*: Seminaire Cartan, Paris 1950–51.

[2] *Deheuvels R.*: Cohomologie d'Alexander-Čech à coefficients dans un faisceau sur un espace topologique quelconque Application. C. R. Acad. Sci., Paris, *238* (1954), 1089–91.

[3] *Dowker C. H.*: Homology groups of relations. Ann. of Math., *56* (1952), 84–95.

[4] *Hurewicz W.*, *Dugundji J.* and *Dowker C. H.*: Continuous connectivity groups in terms of limit groups. Ann. of Math., *49* (1948), 391–406.

[5] *Spanier E. H.*: Cohomology theory for general spaces. Ann. of Math., *49* (1948), 407–427.

EXOTIC TOPOLOGIES FOR LINEAR SPACES

V. KLEE

Seattle[1])

0. Introduction

This is an elementary study of the structure of topological linear spaces (t. l. s.), with special emphasis on those which are *not* locally convex (l. c.). It was motivated in part by the following question of ALEX and WENDY ROBERTSON: If a t. l. s. admits a separating family of continuous linear functionals, is the same true of its completion? We hoped also to discover some sort of "structure theorems" about general t. l. s. Those t. l. s. which are not l. c. are generally regarded as mathematical curiosities rather than as objects of serious interest, probably because they have so little connection with interesting problems in analysis.[2]) But even though they may be quite "pathological" as t. l. s., surely they are unusually "smooth" as topological groups, and thus it is irritating (at least to the author) that so little is known about them. The present approach is not conspicuously successful and the irritation is only slightly ameliorated. Several unsolved problems are posed. We are able to answer (negatively) the Robertsons' question, and in doing so are led to the amusing notion of the orthogonality of two topologies. (Two topologies τ_1 and τ_2 for the same set are said to be *orthogonal* provided every nonempty τ_1-open set meets every nonempty τ_2-open set.)

The prefix "*h*-" before a topology or uniformity will indicate that it fulfills the Hausdorff separation axiom. A topology τ for a (real) linear space L will be called *admissible* provided (L, τ) is a t. l. s. For technical reasons, it is convenient here to consider all admissible topologies rather than merely the admissible *h*-topologies. Seven types of admissible topology seem especially worthy of study, and these will now be defined.

An admissible topology will be called *weak* provided every neighborhood of the origin 0 contains a linear subspace of finite deficiency, *convex* provided every neighborhood of 0 contains a convex neighborhood of 0, and *nearly convex* provided each point of $L \sim \mathrm{cl}\,\{0\}$ can be separated from 0 by a continuous linear functional. It will

[1]) Research supported in part by a fellowship from the Alfred P. Sloan Foundation and in part by a grant from the National Science Foundation, U. S. A. (NSF-G18975).

[2]) A conspicuous exception is the space S of all measurable functions on [0, 1], in the metric topology corresponding to convergence in measure — $d(f, g) = \int_0^1 |f - g|/(1 + |f - g|)$. There are a few other exceptions.

be called *nearly exotic* provided L admits no nontrivial continuous linear functional, and *exotic* provided no proper closed neighborhood of 0 contains an absorbing convex set. We follow IVES [5] in calling a set $X \subset L$ *β-convex* provided X is starshaped from $0([0, 1] X = X)$ and $\beta(X + X) \subset 2X$; a set is *semiconvex* provided it is β-convex for some $\beta > 0$. (Alternatively, we could use a similar notion due to M. LANDSBERG [11, 12]). An admissible topology will be called *semiconvex* provided every neighborhood of 0 contains a semiconvex neighborhood of 0, and *strongly exotic* provided no proper closed neighborhood of 0 contains an absorbing semiconvex set. These are the seven types of topology to be studied here, and the terms are applied to the space (L, τ) as well as to the topology τ. Since an admissible topology is nearly convex if and only if each point of $L \sim \operatorname{cl}\{0\}$ can be separated from 0 by a convex neighborhood of 0, we might define analogously the notion of a *nearly semiconvex* topology, but this seems to be of only marginal interest while the other types of topology do appear in connection with well-known t. l. s.

Note that for every linear space L, the concrete topology $\{\emptyset, L\}$ has all the properties mentioned above except that of being an h-topology. Every infinite-dimensional normed linear space is convex but not weak. For $0 < p < 1$, the space l^p is nearly convex and semiconvex but not convex and the space L^p is semiconvex and exotic but not strongly exotic. (These spaces are discussed in [3, 5, 10, 11, 12, 14].) The space S is strongly exotic, as can be seen by adapting the proof of S. MAZUR and W. ORLICZ [14] that S is nearly exotic. (Ives [5] has a more detailed discussion of the space S and a related example.) If J is an $\aleph_0$-dimensional dense subspace of $L^p(0 < p < 1)$ or of S, then J (in the relative topology) is nearly exotic but it is not exotic and in fact admits no nonconcrete exotic topology, for the finest admissible topology in an $\aleph_0$-dimensional space is known to be convex [7]. The space J is semiconvex in the first case (for L^p) but not in the second (for S).

In the sequel, L will always denote a (real) linear space, E a t. l. s., and E^* the space of all continuous linear functionals on E. The real number space will be denoted by R. The symbol I' will denote the set of indices $\{a, w, c, sc, nc, ne, e, se\}$, with $I = I' \sim \{a\}$. For $\iota \in I$, Γ_ι will denote the class of all t. l. s. which are (in order) weak, convex, semiconvex, nearly convex, nearly exotic, or strongly exotic. For a linear space L and $\iota \in I$, $\sigma_\iota L$ will denote the supremum of all topologies τ for which $(L, \tau) \in \Gamma_\iota$; $\sigma_a L$ is the supremum of all admissible topologies for L.

Proofs will sometimes be abbreviated or omitted. For basic results on t. l. s., sometimes employed here without specific reference, N. BOURBAKI [2] and G. KÖTHE [10] are recommended; for topology, N. Bourbaki [1].

1. Some characterizations

For a t. l. s. E, E_h will denote the corresponding h. l. s. The following obvious fact can often be used to reduce considerations to h. l. s.:

1.1. Remark. *For each* $\iota \in I$, $E \in \Gamma_\iota$ *if and only if* $E_h \in \Gamma_\iota$.

The following characterization is hardly surprising:

1.2. Proposition. *A t. l. s. E is weak if and only if every neighborhood of* 0 *contains a set of the form* $\bigcap_1^j f_i^{-1}]-1, 1[$ *for* $f_i \in E^*$.

Proof. For the "only if" part, consider an arbitrary neighborhood U of 0. Let V be a neighborhood of 0 such that $V + \operatorname{cl} V \subset U$, F a subspace of finite deficiency in V, and φ the natural homomorphism of E onto the quotient space $Q = E/\operatorname{cl} F$. Then Q is finite-dimensional and φV is a neighborhood of the origin in Q, so there exist $g_i \in Q^*$ such that $\bigcap_1^j g_i^{-1}]-1, 1[\subset \varphi V$. With $f_i = g_i \varphi$ we have $f_i \in E^*$ and

$$\bigcap_1^j f_i^{-1}]-1, 1[\subset \varphi^{-1}\varphi V \subset V + \operatorname{cl} F \subset U .$$

The next result was stated by MACKEY [13], and can be deduced almost at once from the fact that $\dim E^* > \aleph_0$ when E is an infinite-dimensional normed linear space.

1.3. Proposition. *If E is convex and* $\dim E^* \leqq \aleph_0$, *then E is weak.*

The following remark is useful:

1.4. Lemma. *In a t. l. s. E of the second category, a closed absorbing set X has nonempty interior; if X is semiconvex,* $0 \in \operatorname{int} X$.

Proof. Since $E = \bigcup_{n=1}^\infty nX$ and each set nX is closed, some nX has an interior point p and then $n^{-1}p \in \operatorname{int} X$. Now suppose further that X is semiconvex, whence $\beta(X + X) \subset X$ for some $\beta > 0$, and let $Y = X \cap -X$. Then Y has an interior point q and $0 = \beta q + \beta(-q) \in \beta(\operatorname{int} Y + \operatorname{int} Y) \subset \operatorname{int} \beta(Y + Y) \subset \beta(X + X) \subset X$.

Using 1.2, 1.4, and the Hahn-Banach theorem, we find

1.5. Proposition. *Every weak topology is convex; every convex topology is semiconvex and nearly convex. Every strongly exotic topology is exotic and every exotic topology is nearly exotic. Every nearly exotic topology of the second category is exotic.*

In connection with 1.5, recall the examples in the Introduction. For 1.6 below, recall the definition of orthogonality of two topologies.

1.6. Theorem. *An admissible topology for L is* $\left\{\begin{array}{l}\text{nearly exotic}\\ \text{exotic}\\ \text{strongly exotic}\end{array}\right\}$ *if and only if it is orthogonal to every* $\left\{\begin{array}{l}\text{weak}\\ \text{convex}\\ \text{semiconvex}\end{array}\right\}$ *topology for L.*

Proof. For the "only if" part for Γ_{ne}, suppose L admits a weak topology τ_2 which fails to be orthogonal to the admissible topology τ_1. Then there exist nonempty disjoint τ_i-open sets U_i in L with $0 \in U_2$. Let F be a subspace of finite deficiency contained in U_2, F_1 the τ_1-closure of F, and G a subspace supplementary to F_1 in L. Then G is a h. l. s., $0 < \dim G < \aleph_0$, and (L, τ_1) is the direct sum of F_1 and G. This implies that τ_1 is not nearly exotic.

It is easily seen that if τ_1 is not exotic, then it is not orthogonal to the convex topology $\sigma_c L$. Now assume, on the other hand, the existence of a convex topology τ_2 for L not orthogonal to τ_1. Let U_i be nonempty disjoint τ_i-open sets with $0 \in U_2$, let C be a convex τ_2-neighborhood of 0 such that $C \subset U_2$, let V_1 be a nonempty τ_1-open set whose τ_1-closure lies in U_1, and let W denote the τ_1-closure of the set $L \sim V_1$. Then W is a τ_1-closed neighborhood of 0 and $0 \in C \subset W \neq L$, so τ_1 is not exotic. This takes care of Γ_e, and the argument for Γ_{se} is essentially the same.

By 1.6, a weak topology for L must be orthogonal to every nearly exotic topology for L. We have been unable to decide in general whether this property characterizes the weak topologies. To prepare for a partial result in that direction, we recall two notions of D. T. FINKBEINER and O. M. NIKODYM [4]. *A* set $C \subset L$ is a *Hamel body* provided there is a basis $B \subset L$ such that $C = \operatorname{conv}(B \cup - B)$. A set is *linearly bounded* provided its intersection with each line lies in some segment.

1.7. Proposition. *A linear space L is of countable dimension if and only if every symmetric linearly bounded convex body in L is contained in a Hamel body.*

Proof. Suppose first that $\dim L > \aleph_0$. Let X be a basis for L and let U be the set of all points of the form $\sum_{x \in X} (fx)\, x$ where f is a finitely supported real-valued function on X and $\sum_{x \in X} (fx)^2 \leqq 1$. Then U is a symmetric linearly bounded convex body in L, and we claim that no Hamel body contains U.

Suppose U lies in a Hamel body C determined by a basis B for L. Let L_1 denote the space L as normed by the gauge functional of C, L_2 the same space as normed by the gauge functional of U, and note that the identity mapping T in L is a continuous linear transformation of L_2 onto L_1. Since the set B is uncountable, there exists a finite number n for which the set $B \cap nU$ is infinite. Let M denote the linear extension of $B \cap nU$ and let M_i denote the normed linear space obtained by restricting to M the norm of L_i. Since $C = \operatorname{conv}(B \cup - B)$, we have $C \cap M \subset nU$ and thus the restriction T' of T to M is a linear homeomorphism of M_2 onto M_1. Then of course T' can be extended to a linear homeomorphism which carries the completion of M_2 onto that of M_1, and this is impossible for the first completion is reflexive (being an l^2 space) and the second is not (being an l^1 space). The "only if" part of 1.7 has been established.

To complete the proof of 1.7, we must show that if E is an $\aleph_0$-dimensional normed linear space with unit cell $U = \{x \in E : \|x\| \leqq 1\}$, then U is contained in some Hamel body in E. Let the sequence x_α form a Hamel basis for E. It is not difficult to produce a sequence f_α in E^* such that $f_i x_j = 0$ for $i \neq j$, and always $f_i x_i > 0$ and $\sup f_i C = 2^{-i}$. Let G denote the linear space of all eventually-zero sequences of real numbers and for each $x \in E$ let

$$\varphi x = (f_1 x, f_2 x, \ldots) \in G .$$

Then φ is an algebraic isomorphism of E onto G, and since always $\sup f_i U = 2^{-i}$ it is easy to see that the set φU lies in the Hamel body C determined by the natural basis $\{\delta_i\}_1^\infty$ of G. Thus $\varphi^{-1} C$ is a Hamel body containing U and the proof of 1.7 is complete.

1.8. Theorem. *A convex topology for a linear space L is weak if and only if it is orthogonal to every nearly exotic topology for L.*

Proof. Only the "if" part requires discussion. Suppose the convex topology τ is not weak, whence there is a symmetric closed convex neighborhood U of 0 which contains no subspace of finite deficiency. The union L' of all lines through 0 which lie in U is a subspace of infinite deficiency, and thus there are supplementary linear subspaces L_1 and L_2 of L for which $L' \subset L_1$ and $\dim L_2 = \aleph_0$. It is easily verified that $U \subset L_1 + (U \cap L_2)$ and that the set $U \cap L_2$ is a symmetric linearly bounded convex body in L_2, whence by 1.7 it lies in some Hamel body C in L_2.

Let η be a nearly exotic h-topology for an $\aleph_0$-dimensional space J and V a non-empty η-open subset of J whose closure misses 0. Since the finest admissible topology $\sigma_a J$ for J is convex [7], there exists an absorbing convex set W in J such that $W \cap \cap V = \emptyset$. It is evident that W must contain a Hamel body C' in J [4] and that there is an algebraic isomorphism T of J onto L_2 which carries C' onto C. Now let ζ be the family of all subsets of L of the form $L_1 + TY$ for η-open $Y \subset J$. Then ζ is nearly exotic because η is nearly exotic. However, the set $L_1 + TV$ is ζ-open and misses the τ-open set U, so τ is not orthogonal to every nearly exotic topology for L and the proof of 1.8 is complete.

Are there characterizations of convex or semiconvex topologies which have a similar relationship to 1.7? Of course there exist nonconvex admissible topologies which are orthogonal to every exotic topology, for an $\aleph_0$-dimensional space admits no nonconcrete exotic topologies. However, it may be that an admissible topology τ is coarser than a convex topology if and only if τ is orthogonal to every exotic topology. This would imply that an admissible topology of the second category is convex if and only if it is orthogonal to every exotic topology, and weak if and only if it is orthogonal to every nearly exotic topology.

2. Preservation of type

The following two assertions are easily verified:

2.1. Proposition. *For each $\iota \in I$, if the t. l. s. E is the direct sum or product of the t. l. s. E_α, then $E \in \Gamma_\iota$ if and only if $E_\alpha \in \Gamma_\iota$ for all α.*

2.2. Proposition. *Let σ denote the supremum of admissible topologies τ_α for a linear space L. If $\iota \in I \sim \{ne\}$ and $(L, \tau_\alpha) \in \Gamma_\iota$ for all α, then $(L, \sigma) \in \Gamma_\iota$.*

In particular, $(L, \sigma_\iota L) \in \Gamma_\iota$ for each $\iota \in I \sim \{ne\}$. This fails for $\iota = ne$, and it seems conceivable even that $\sigma_{ne} L = \sigma_a L$ when L is infinite-dimensional. We have been unable to settle this, but shall prove the following:

2.3. Theorem. *If L is infinite-dimensional, the topology $\sigma_{ne} L$ is finer than the topology $\sigma_w L$.*

Proof. Let f be a nontrivial linear functional on L. We wish to show that f is continuous for the topology $\sigma_{ne}L$, and shall in fact describe two nearly exotic h-topologies ζ_1 and ζ_2 for L such that f is continuous for the topology sup (ζ_1, ζ_2).

Note that an $\aleph_0$-dimensional linear space admits a nearly exotic h-topology, whence the same is true of every infinite-dimensional linear space (for it may be regarded as the direct sum of a family of its $\aleph_0$-dimensional subspaces).

Let τ be a nearly exotic h-topology for the space L under consideration. Let $y \in L$ with $fy = 2$ and consider the following two topologies τ_1 and τ_2 for the space $L \times R$: a set is τ_1-open (resp. τ_2-open) provided it has the form $U \times \{0\} + R(0,1) = U \times R$ (resp. $U \times \{0\} + R(y, 1)$) for some τ-open set $U \subset L$. Then τ_1 and τ_2 are both nearly exotic topologies for $L \times R$. For each $x \in L$, let $\xi x = (x, fx) \in L \times R$ and let ζ_i be the topology for L which is determined by specifying that ξ shall be a homeomorphism of L onto ξL in its relative topology ζ_i' induced by τ_i. Since ξL is dense in $L \times R$ under the topology τ_i, each topology ζ_i is a nearly exotic topology for L. Although the τ_i are not h-topologies, it is easily verified that the topologies ζ_i' (and hence ζ_i) do satisfy the separation axiom. To show that f is continuous for the topology sup (ζ_1, ζ_2), it suffices to produce τ_i-neighborhoods V_i of 0 in $L \times R$ such that $(x, r) \in V_1 \cap V_2$ implies $r \neq 1$, for then the functional $f\xi^{-1}$ fails to assume the value 1 on the set $V_1 \cap V_2 \cap \xi L$, the same must be true of f on the set $\xi^{-1}(V_1 \cap L) \cap \cap\, \xi^{-1}(V_2 \cap L)$, and since the latter set is a sup (ζ_1, ζ_2)-neighborhood of 0 in L it follows readily that f is continuous. Let U be a τ-neighborhood of 0 in L such that $y \notin U - U$, and suppose

$$(z, 1) \in (U \times \{0\} + R(0, 1)) \cap (U \times \{0\} + R(y, 1))\,.$$

Then we have $z \in U$ and $z \in U + y$, whence $y \in U - U$ and the contradiction completes the proof of 2.3.

2.4. Theorem. *For $1 \leqq j \leqq 5$, let A_j denote the set of all $\iota \in I$ such that whenever F is a subspace of a t. l. s. E*

1) *then $E \in \Gamma_\iota$ implies $F \in \Gamma_\iota$;*
2) *and F is dense in E, then $E \in \Gamma_\iota$ implies $F \in \Gamma_\iota$;*
3) *and $\dim E/F < \aleph_0$, then $E \in \Gamma_\iota$ implies $F \in \Gamma_\iota$;*
4) *and F is dense in E, then $F \in \Gamma_\iota$ implies $E \in \Gamma_\iota$;*
5) *and $\dim E/F < \aleph_0$, then $F \in \Gamma_\iota$ implies $E \in \Gamma_\iota$.*

Then $A_1 = \{w, c, sc, nc\}$, $A_2 = A_1 \cup \{ne\} = I \sim \{e, se\}$, $A_3 = I$, $A_4 = I \sim \{nc\}$, and $A_5 = \{w, c, sc\}$.

Proof. The assertion about A_1 is obvious, as is the fact that $A_1 \cup \{ne\} \subset A_2$. To see that $\{e, se\} \subset I \sim A_2$, recall that the space S is strongly exotic and admits a dense subspace J of countable dimension, but J cannot be exotic for the topology $\sigma_a J$ is convex [7].

Note that if F is a dense subspace of E and U is a neighborhood of 0 in F, then cl U is a neighborhood of 0 in E. It follows at once that $\{c, sc\} \subset A_4$. To see that $w \in A_4$, recall the characterization 1.2 and the fact that every continuous linear functional on F can be extended to one on E. That $\{ne, e, se\} \subset A_4$ follows at once from the relevant definitions. Thus $A_4 \supset I \sim \{nc\}$. In § 3 we give an example of a dense subspace F_0 of a h. l. s. E_0 such that F_0 is nearly convex but E_0 is not, thereby showing that $nc \notin A_4$ and completing the discussion of A_4. Let $x \in E_0 \sim F_0$ with $fx = 0$ for all $f \in E^*$; then the pair $F, F + Rx$ shows that $nc \notin A_5$.

For A_3 and A_5 it suffices to consider the case in which $\dim E/F = 1$. Then F must be dense or closed in E, and in the latter event E is the direct sum of F and a line. Thus the remaining assertions about A_5 are evident and for A_3 it remains only to show that $\{e, se\} \subset A_3$.

Suppose E is exotic and F is a (necessarily dense) hyperplane in E but F is not exotic. By 1.6, the topology of F cannot be orthogonal to every convex topology for F, and hence there exist a neighborhood U of 0 in E and a nonempty convex set $C \subset \subset F \sim U$ such that C is equal to its own core relative to F. Let V be a symmetric starshaped neighborhood of 0 in E such that $V + V \subset U$ and let $v \in V \sim F$. Then

$$C +]-v, v[\subset C + V \subset (F \sim U) + V \subset E \sim V.$$

Since the set $C +]-v, v[$ is convex and equal to its own core relative to E, it follows from 1.6 that E is not exotic and the contradiction implies that $e \in A_3$. A similar argument shows that $se \in A_3$ and completes the proof of 2.4.

The relationship of a t. l. s. to its $\aleph_0$-dimensional subspaces seems worthy of study. A. Pełczyński has asked whether every infinite-dimensional metric linear space has an $\aleph_0$-dimensional subspace which admits a nontrivial continuous linear functional, and in the other direction we inquire whether a nearly exotic space must have a nearly exotic $\aleph_0$-dimensional subspace. We may ask also whether membership of E in Γ_ι is implied by that of every $\aleph_0$-dimensional subspace of E. This is trivially the case for $\iota = ne$, and also for $\iota = e$ and $\iota = se$ since the only exotic topologies of countable dimension are concrete. It is not the case for $\iota = c$ or $\iota = sc$, for if $\dim L > \aleph_0$ the topology $\sigma_a L$ is not semiconvex even though its restriction to each $\aleph_0$-dimensional subspace is convex. The question is of interest for $\iota \in \{w, nc\}$, and also for $\iota \in \{c, sc\}$ under additional restrictions on the space. We can report only the following partial results:

2.5. Proposition. *A semiconvex space is weak if and only if all its $\aleph_0$-dimensional subspaces are weak.*

2.6. Proposition. *Suppose $\aleph$ is an infinite cardinal number, $\aleph'$ is the first cardinal $> \aleph$ which is the limit of a sequence of its predecessors, and E is a metric linear space with $\aleph \leqq \dim E < \aleph'$. Then E is convex, semiconvex, or nearly convex if and only if all its $\aleph$-dimensional subspaces have the corresponding property.*

Proofs. For 2.5, we consider a symmetric semiconvex neighborhood U of 0 in E and denote by F the union of all lines through 0 which lie in U. It can be verified (using semiconvexity) that F is a linear subspace of E and hence admits a supplementary subspace M. Since $U \cap M$ contains no lines through 0, either M is finite-dimensional or M is not weak, and this completes the proof of 2.5.

For 2.6, let Z denote the interval $[\aleph, \aleph'[$ of cardinal numbers, and for $\iota \in \{c, sc, nc\}$ let Z_ι denote the set of all $\zeta \in Z$ such that whenever E is a metric linear space of dimension ζ and all $\aleph$-dimensional subspaces of E are members of Γ_ι, then $E \in \Gamma_\iota$. We wish in each case to show that $Z_\iota = Z$. Suppose $Z \sim Z_\iota$ is nonempty and let δ be the first member of $Z \sim Z_\iota$. Let E be a metric linear space of dimension δ, all of whose $\aleph$-dimensional subspaces are members of Γ_ι, and let B be a Hamel basis for E. Let B be well-ordered in such a way that for each $b \in B$, the set P_b of all predecessors of b in B is of cardinality $< \delta$, and for each $b \in B$ let E_b denote the linear extension of P_b in E. From the definition of δ it follows that $E_b \in \Gamma_\iota$ for each $b \in B$, and also that no countable set is cofinal in B.

Now for the case $\iota = nc$, we wish to show that each point $p \in E \sim \{0\}$ can be separated from 0 by a continuous linear functional, whence $E \in \Gamma_{nc}$, $\delta \in Z_\iota$, and the contradiction shows that $Z = Z_\iota$. For each $b \in B$, let φb denote the supremum of the set of all numbers $r \geqq 0$ such that $\operatorname{conv}(N_r \cap E_b) \subset E \sim \{p\}$, where $N_r = \{x \in E : d(x, 0) \leqq r\}$. Then φ is an antitone mapping of B into $[0, \infty]$, and always $\varphi b > 0$ since $E_b \in \Gamma_{nc}$. Since B admits no cofinal sequence it is clear that $\inf \varphi B = 2\varepsilon > 0$ and then $\operatorname{conv} N_\varepsilon \subset E \sim \{p\}$, whence the Hahn-Banach theorem guarantees the existence of $f \varepsilon E^*$ with $fp \neq 0$. This completes the discussion for Γ_{nc}. For Γ_c the reasoning is similar, with the set $E \sim \{p\}$ replaced by an arbitrary neighborhood of 0.

For Γ_{sc}, we consider an arbitrary neighborhood U of 0 in E, and for each $b \in B$ let ψb denote the set of all $(\beta, r) \in]0, 1] \times]0, \infty[$ such that $\operatorname{conv}_\beta (N_r \cap E_b) \subset U$, where $\operatorname{conv}_\beta$ denotes the β-convex hull [5]. Each set ψb is nonempty, for $E_b \in \Gamma_{sc}$, and it is clear that if $(\beta, r) \in \psi b$, $\beta' \in]0, \beta]$, and $r' \in]0, r]$, then $(\beta', r') \in \psi b$. Choose sequences β_α and r_α in $]0, 1]$ such that $\beta_\alpha \searrow 0$ and $r_\alpha \searrow 0$. We claim that for sufficiently large i, $(\beta_i, r_i) \in \bigcap_{b \in B} \psi b$. (Then of course $\operatorname{conv}_{\beta_i} N_{r_i} \subset U$ and the semiconvexity of E is established.) Suppose the contrary, whence for each i there exists b_i having $(\beta_i, r_i) \notin \psi b$. Then with $b' \in B$ and $b_i < b'$ for all i, it follows that $\psi b'$ is empty, a contradiction completing the proof of 2.6.

2.7. Theorem. *For $j = 1, 2$, let B_j denote the set of all $\iota \in I$ such that whenever η is a continuous linear transformation of the t. l. s. E onto the t. l. s. F*

1. *then $E \in \Gamma_\iota$ implies $F \in \Gamma_\iota$;*

2. *and η is open or F of the second category, then $E \in \Gamma_\iota$ implies $F \in \Gamma_\iota$.*

Then $B_1 = \{w, ne, e, se\}$ and $B_2 = I \sim \{nc\}$.

The relevant proofs and examples are rather straightforward and will be left for the reader. Use 1.4 when F is of the second category. In [8] there are described a separable metric linear space E and supplementary closed linear subspaces M_1 and M_2 of E such that E is nearly convex but both the quotient spaces E/M_i are nearly exotic. Of course this cannot happen if E is complete. However, we do not know (in the setting of 2.7) whether near convexity of E implies that of F when η is continuous and open *and* F is of the second category. Note that if E is convex and η continuous, then

F cannot be exotic unless its topology is concrete, but F can be a nearly exotic t. l. s., as we see by letting J be an $\aleph_0$-dimensional dense subspace of S, η the identity mapping on J, $E = (J, \sigma_a J)$, and F the space J in the relative topology inherited from S.

3. Orthogonality and completeness

Two uniform structures for the same set will be called *orthogonal* provided the topologies which they generate are orthogonal.

3.1. Proposition. *Suppose $\mathscr{U}_1$ and $\mathscr{U}_2$ are orthogonal uniformities for a set X such that $(X, \sup(\mathscr{U}_1, \mathscr{U}_2))$ is a complete uniform space. Then for any two points x_1 and x_2 of X, the $\mathscr{U}_1$-closure of $\{x_1\}$ meets the $\mathscr{U}_2$-closure of $\{x_2\}$.*

Proof. Let $\mathscr{B}$ be the family of all sets of the form $U_1|x_1| \cap U_2|x_2|$ for $U_i \in \mathscr{U}_i$. Since $\mathscr{U}_1$ and $\mathscr{U}_2$ are orthogonal, each member of $\mathscr{B}$ is nonempty and it follows that $\mathscr{B}$ is the base of a filter $\mathscr{F}$. We claim that $\mathscr{F}$ is a Cauchy filter for the uniformity $\sup(\mathscr{U}_1, \mathscr{U}_2)$. Indeed, consider an arbitrary member V of $\sup(\mathscr{U}_1, \mathscr{U}_2)$, containing the set $V_1 \cap V_2$ for certain $V_i \in \mathscr{U}_i$. Let W_i be a member of $\mathscr{U}_i$ such that $W_i = W_i^{-1}$ and $W_iW_iW_iW_i \subset V_i$, and let $p \in Z = W_1|x_1| \cap W_2|x_2|$. For each $q \in Z$ we have $(p, x_i) \in W_i$ and $(x_i, q) \in W_i$, whence $(p, q) \in W_iW_i$. It follows that

$$Z \times Z \subset W_iW_iW_iW_i \subset V_i,$$

whence $Z \times Z \subset V_1 \cap V_2$. Thus $\mathscr{F}$ is a Cauchy filter for $\sup(\mathscr{U}_1, \mathscr{U}_2)$ and by hypothesis must converge to a point $z \in X$. Since each neighborhood $U_i'|z|$ (for $U_i' \in \mathscr{U}_i$) must contain $U_i|x_i|$ for some $U_i \in \mathscr{U}_i$, it is clear that z lies in the $\mathscr{U}_i$-closure of $\{x_i\}$ and this completes the proof.

3.2. Corollary. *If a linear space L is complete under the supremum of two orthogonal admissible topologies τ_1 and τ_2, then L is the linear sum of the τ_1-closure of $\{0\}$ and the τ_2-closure of $\{0\}$.*

3.3. Proposition. *Two convex topologies for a linear space are orthogonal if and only if there is no nontrivial linear functional which is continuous in both topologies.*

The result 3.3 follows at once from the separation theorem for convex bodies. The result 3.4 below is well-known and can be proved in simpler ways (cf. Theorem 15 of Mackey [13]), but the reader may find it instructive to base a proof on 3.1 and 3.3.

3.4. Proposition. *A weak h. l. s. E is complete if and only if no proper subspace of E* separates the points of E.*

For a uniform space $(X, \mathscr{U})$, the corresponding h-uniform space will be denoted by $(X, \mathscr{U})_h$ and the completion of $(X, \mathscr{U})_h$ by $(X, \mathscr{U})_c$.

3.5. Theorem. *If $\mathscr{U}_1$ and $\mathscr{U}_2$ are orthogonal uniformities for a set X, the space $(X, \sup(\mathscr{U}_1, \mathscr{U}_2))_c$ is uniformly isomorphic with the product space $(X, \mathscr{U}_1)_c \times$ $\times (X, \mathscr{U}_2)_c$.*

Proof. Let $\mathscr{U}_0 = \sup(\mathscr{U}_1, \mathscr{U}_2)$ and for $i = 0, 1$, or 2 let X^i, X_h^i, and X_c^i denote respectively the spaces $(X, \mathscr{U}_i)$, $(X, \mathscr{U}_i)_h$, and $(X, \mathscr{U}_i)_c$. Let ξ_i denote the natural mapping of X^i onto X^i_h and η_i the natural mapping of X^i_h into X^i_c. For each point $y = (y_1, y_2) \in X^1_c \times X^2_c$ and for $j = i$ or 2 let $\mathscr{H}^j_y$ denote the trace on $\eta_0 X^j_h$ of the filter-base consisting of all open neighborhoods of y_j in X^j_c, and let $\mathscr{G}^j_y$ denote the image of $\mathscr{H}^j_y$ under the transformation $\xi_j^{-1}\eta_j^{-1}$. Then $\mathscr{G}^j_y$ is a filter-base consisting of $\mathscr{U}_j$-open subsets of X, and since the uniformities $\mathscr{U}_1$ and $\mathscr{U}_2$ are orthogonal, the set $\mathscr{F}_y$ of all intersections $G_1 \cap G_2$ with $G_j \in \mathscr{G}^j_y$ must also be a filter-base, and in fact clearly a $\mathscr{U}_0$-Cauchy filter-base for $\mathscr{G}^j_y$ is $\mathscr{U}_j$-Cauchy. Thus the image of $\mathscr{F}_y$ under the mapping $\eta_0\xi_0$ is a filter-base in $\eta_0 X^0_h$ converging to a unique point $\varphi y \in X^0_c$. Since each $\mathscr{U}_0$-Cauchy net is both $\mathscr{U}_1$-Cauchy and $\mathscr{U}_2$-Cauchy, it is evident that φ is a biunique transformation of $X^1_c \times X^2_c$ onto X^0_c. It is a routine matter to check that φ is a uniform isomorphism and this completes the proof of 3.5. Further, if X is a linear space and the orthogonal uniformities $\mathscr{U}_1$ and $\mathscr{U}_2$ are generated by admissible topologies for X, then φ turns out to be a linear transformation, whence –

3.6. Corollary. *If τ_1 and τ_2 are orthogonal admissible topologies for a linear space L, the h. l. s. $(L, \sup(\tau_1, \tau_2))_c$ is linearly homeomorphic with the h. l. s. $(L, \tau_1)_c \times (L, \tau_2)_c$.*

Now for the example needed in connection with 2.4, observe that if $\dim L \geqq 2^{\aleph_0}$ then L admits both a convex h-topology τ_1 and an exotic h-topology τ_2. By 3.6, the space $(L, \sup(\tau_1, \tau_2))_c$ is linearly homeomorphic with the product space $(L, \tau_1)_c \times (L, \tau_2)_c$. Of course the space $(L, \sup(\tau_1, \tau_2))$ is nearly convex, but from 2.4 (A_4) it follows that $(L, \tau_2)_c$ is exotic and hence every continuous linear functional on the product space must vanish everywhere on $\{0\} \times (L, \tau_2)_c$. Note that the topologies τ_i can be chosen to be separable and metrizable and then the same will be true of their supremum. These examples can be described more briefly by following the same ideas but suppressing some of the machinery employed above.

Now for $\iota \in I' = I \cup \{a\}$, let C_ι denote the class of all cardinal numbers $\aleph$ such that the space $(L, \sigma_\iota L)$ is complete for $\aleph$-dimensional L. It has been proved by I. NAMIOKA (unpublished) that C_a includes all cardinals. It follows from 3.4 that C_w consists only of finite cardinals. A result of S. KAPLAN [6] is that C_c includes all cardinals, which implies that C_a, C_{sc}, and C_{nc} include all countable cardinals. Of course the same is true of C_e and C_{se}, though in a trivial fashion. We conjecture that $\aleph_0 \in C_{ne}$, but this is not known and may be connected with the question as to whether $\sigma_{ne}L$ is finer than $\sigma_c L$ when $\dim L \geqq \aleph_0$. For $\aleph > \aleph_0$ nothing is known except in the cases of C_a, C_w and C_c. To what extent can arbitrary admissible topologies be represented in terms of the seven types studied here? Note that by Namioka's result in conjuction with 3.2, $\sigma_2 L$ is not the supremum of an admissible h-topology and an admissible non-concrete topology which is orthogonal to τ.

Another limitation on the representation of admissible topologies is indicated by 3.8 below. In preparation for its proof, we establish the following

3.7. Lemma. *Suppose X_1 is a symmetric starshaped subset of R^n, $X_{i+1} = X_i + X_i$ for all i, and M_i is the union of all lines through 0 which lie in* cl *X_i. Then for some $r \leqq n$, the following three statements are true:*

(a) *for each* $i \leqq r$, M_i *contains a linear subspace of dimension* i;
(b) M_r *is an* r*-dimensional linear subspace*;
(c) *there is a compact set* K *such that* $X_1 \subset M_r + K$.

Proof. Let r be the largest integer for which (a) holds. Let L_r be an r-dimensional linear subspace contained in M_r and let F be a subspace supplementary to L_r. Let $\| \ \|$ be a norm for R^n, $U = \{x \in R^n : \|x\| \leqq 1\}$, and $Z = \{x \in F : \|x\| = 1\}$. For each $z \in Z$, let δ_z be the least upper bound of the set of all numbers $t > 0$ such that $X \cap (L_r + Rz) \subset L_r + tU$. Let $m = \sup \delta_z \in [0, \infty]$. Since L_r is a subspace and X is symmetric and starshaped, it is easy to see that $L_r +]-\delta_z, \delta_z[\ z \subset L_r + X$ for each $z \in Z$. Then if $m = \infty$ it follows from compactness of Z that $L_r + Rz_0 \subset \text{cl}\,(L_r + X)$ for some $z_0 \in Z$, whence of course $L_r + Rz_0$ is an $(r + 1)$-dimensional subspace of M_{r+1}. This contradicts the definition of r, so we conclude that $m < \infty$ and $X \subset L_r + mU$, thus establishing (c). The truth of (b) is now immediate and this completes the proof. (Note, in addition, that $M_j = M_r$ for all $j \geqq r$.)

3.8. Proposition. *The usual topology* τ *of the space* l^p $(0 < p < 1)$ *is not the supremum of a convex topology and a nearly exotic topology.*

Proof. Suppose τ is the supremum of a convex topology τ_1 and a nearly exotic topology τ_2, and let γ denote the admissible topology generated by the family of all convex τ-neighborhoods of 0. Then of course γ is finer than τ_1, and since the set $U = \{x = (x_1, x_2, \ldots) \in l^p : \sum |x_i|^p \leqq 1\}$ is a τ-neighborhood of 0 there exist a γ-neighborhood V' of 0 and a τ_2-neighborhood W' of 0 such that $V' \cap W' \subset U$ and hence $W' \subset U \cap (l^p \sim V')$. By a theorem of DAY [3], each continuous linear functional on l^p is a linear combination of the coordinate functionals $x_i \mid x \in l^p$, whence the topology γ is weak by 1.3 and consequently there exist $\varepsilon > 0$ and an integer $n \geqq 2$ such that

$$V' \supset V = \{x \in l^p : |x_i| < \varepsilon \text{ for } 1 \leqq i \leqq n - 1\}.$$

Let W_1 be a symmetric starshaped τ_2-neighborhood of 0 such that $W_n \subset W'$ (where $W_{i+1} = W_i + W_1$). Then of course $W_n \subset U \cup (l^p \sim V)$.

For each $x \in l^p$, let $\pi x = (x_1, \ldots, x_n) \in R^n$, whence $\pi U = \{x \in R^n : \sum_1^n |x_i|^p \leqq 1\}$ and $\pi V = \{x \in R^n : |x_i| < \varepsilon \text{ for } 1 \leqq i \leqq n - 1\}$. Let $X_1 = \pi W_1$, whence X_1 is symmetric and starshaped with $X_n \subset \pi U \cup (R^n \sim \pi V)$. Let the subspace M_r of R^n be as in 3.7. Since clearly $\text{cl}\, X_r \subset \text{cl}\, X_n \neq R^n$, we see that $M_r \neq R^n$ and then it follows from (c) of 3.7 that $\text{conv}\, X_1 \neq R^n$. This implies that $\text{conv}\, W_1 \neq l^p$ and contradicts the assumption of near exoticity for the topology τ_2. The proof of 3.8 is now complete.

In connection with 3.8, note also that an $\aleph_0$-dimensional linear space admits a topology which cannot be represented as the supremum of a semiconvex, a nearly convex, and an exotic topology. However, relative to any examples known to us at the moment, each of the following hypotheses *may* be true:

each admissible topology is the supremum of a nearly convex topology and a nearly exotic topology;

each admissible topology is coarser than one which is the supremum of a convex topology and a nearly exotic topology;

each t. l. s. is linearly homeomorphic with a subspace of a t. l. s. whose topology is the supremum of a convex topology and an exotic topology.

In view of 2.1 and a result in [9], it would suffice in the last instance to consider metric linear spaces.

References

[1] *N. Bourbaki*: Topologie Générale, Chaps. I—II, A. S. I. *858* (1940), Hermann et Cie., Paris.
[2] *N. Bourbaki*: Espaces vectorielles topologiques, Chaps. I—II, A. S. I. 1189 (1953) and Chaps. III—V, A. S. I. 1229 (1955), Hermann et Cie., Paris.
[3] *Mahlon M. Day*: The spaces L^p with $0 < p < 1$. Bull. Amer. Math. Soc. *46* (1940), 816—823.
[4] *D. T. Finkbeiner* and *O. M. Nikodym*: On convex sets in abstract linear spaces where no topology is assumed (Hamel bodies and linear boundedness). Rend. Sem. Mat. Padova *23* (1954), 357—365.
[5] *Robert Trull Ives*: Semi-convexity and locally bounded spaces. Ph. D. Thesis, 1957, University of Washington, Seattle.
[6] *Samuel Kaplan*: Cartesian products of reals. Amer. J. Math. *74* (1952), 936—954.
[7] *Victor Klee*: Convex sets in linear spaces. III., Duke Math. J. *20* (1953), 105—112.
[8] *Victor Klee*: An example in the theory of topological linear spaces. Archiv Math. *7* (1956), 362—366.
[9] *Victor Klee*: Shrinkable neighborhoods in Hausdorff linear spaces. Math. Ann. *141* (1960), 281—285.
[10] *Gottfried Köthe*: Topologische lineare Räume I. Grundlehren Math. Wiss. *107* (1960), Springer, Berlin.
[11] *M. Landsberg*: Lokalkonvexe Räume von Grade r $(0 \leqq r \leqq 1)$. Wiss. Z. Tech. Hochsch. Dresden *2* (1953), 369—372.
[12] *M. Landsberg*: Lineare topologische Räume, die nicht lokalkonvex sind. Math. Zeitsch. *65* (1956), 104—112.
[13] *G. W. Mackey*: On convex topological linear spaces. Trans. Amer. Math. Soc. *60* (1946), 519—537.
[14] *S. Mazur* and *W. Orlicz*: Sur les espaces métriques linéaires. I. Studia Math. *10* (1948), 184—208.

SUR LA REPRÉSENTATION DES TRANSFORMATIONS LINÉAIRES

I. KLUVÁNEK

Bratislava

Le théorème célèbre de F. Riesz sur la représentation des fonctionelles linéaires sur l'espace des fonctions continues était généralisé en plusieurs directions. Une généralisation, on peut dire „vectorielle", a été donnée par R. G. BARTLE, N. DUNFORD et J. T. SCHWARTZ dans le Canad. J. Math. en 1955, 289—305. Leurs résultats concernent des transformations linéaires continues de l'espace $C(S)$ des fonctions continues sur le compact S dans un espace de Banach X arbitraire. Ils ont démontré qu'une telle transformation T peut être mise sous la forme de l'intégrale par rapport à une mesure vectorielle, si et seulement si la transformation T est faiblement compacte, c'est-à-dire l'image de la sphère

$$\{f : f \in C(S), \|f\| \leqq 1\}$$

est compacte dans la topologie faible de l'espace X. Dans ce but ils ont développé une théorie de l'intégration par rapport à une mesure vectorielle définie sur une σ-algèbre, une mesure vectorielle étant une fonction d'ensemble σ-additif avec les valeurs dans un espace de Banach.

Soit maintenant S un espace topologique arbitraire. Désignons par $C(S)$ l'espace de toutes les fonctions réelles continues sur S à support compact, muni de la norme de convergence uniforme. Essayons de représenter les transformations T linéaires et continues sur l'espace $C(S)$ dans un espace de Banach X sous la forme de l'intégrale, c'est-à-dire sous la forme

$$T(f) = \int f \, \mathrm{d}\mu$$

où μ est une mesure vectorielle convenablement choisie. Evidemment, on ne peut plus exiger que la mesure μ soit définie sur une σ-algèbre. J'ai développé alors une théorie de l'intégration des fonctions scalaires (reélles ou complexes) par rapport à une mesure vectorielle définie sur un δ-corps d'ensembles (δ-corps est une famille d'ensembles fermée par rapport aux opérations de différence, des unions finies et des intersections dénombrables d'ensembles). Cette théorie est une généralisation naturelle de celle de Bartle, Dunford et Schwartz et en même temps de la théorie de l'intégration par rapport à une mesure non-négative non nécessairement finie.

Nous pouvons énoncer le théorème suivant:

Une transformation T du type envisagé peut être écrite sous la forme de l'intégrale, si et seulement si l'image de l'ensemble

$$\{f : |f| \leqq h, f \in C(S)\}$$

est faiblement compacte dans X pour chaque fonction $h \in C(S)$.

On voit facilement que la condition de téorème précédent se réduit à celle des auteurs cités si S est un espace compact.

Pour indiquer les méthodes de démonstration, introduisons quelques notions:

Soit $\mathscr{E}$ un treillis linéaire des fonctions réelles sur un ensemble abstrait S. On apelle l'intégrale vectorielle de Daniell sur $\mathscr{E}$ chaque transformation I de $\mathscr{E}$ dans un espace de Banach X jouissant des propriétés suivantes:

1. $I(\alpha f + \beta g) = \alpha I(f) + \beta I(g)$, α, β réels; $f, g \in \mathscr{E}$.
2. On a $I(f_n) \to 0$, lorsque $f_n(s) \to 0$ en décroissant partout.

L'intégrale I est dite saturée (au sens de Lebesgue) s'il y a lieu:

3. Si $f_n \in \mathscr{E}$, $|f_n| \leqq h \in \mathscr{E}$, $n = 1, 2, \ldots$ et $f(s) = \lim f_n(s)$ partout, on a $f \in \mathscr{E}$.

Le théorème énoncé est une conséquence des théorèmes plus généraux suivants:

Pour qu'une intégrale vectorielle de Daniell I admette une extension J saturée, il faut et il suffit que l'ensemble

$$\{I(f) : |f| \leqq h, f \in \mathscr{E}\}$$

soit faiblement compact dans X pour chaque $h \in \mathscr{E}$.

L'intégrale vectorielle de Daniell I saturée et jouissant de la propriété suivante: $f \in \mathscr{E} \Rightarrow \min\{f, 1\} \in \mathscr{E}$ *(où* $\mathscr{E}$ *est le domaine de l'intégrale I) peut être écrite sous la forme*

$$I(f) = \int f \, d\mu ,$$

où μ *est une mesure vectorielle définie sur un* δ*-corps.*

Les démonstrations détaillées de ces théorèmes seront publiées dans le Czechoslovak Mathematical Journal sous le titre „Quelques généralisations du théorème de Riesz-Kakutani" (en russe).

BEMERKUNGEN ÜBER INTERVALLTOPOLOGIE IN HALBGEORDNETEN MENGEN

M. KOLIBIAR

Bratislava

Im folgenden soll das Symbol P stets eine halbgeordnete Menge bezeichnen. Für $a, b \in P$ wird $N(a)$ die Menge aller Elemente von P bedeuten, die mit a unvergleichbar sind; $N(a, b)$ soll die Menge aller Elemente $x \in P$ bedeuten, für die weder $x \geqq a$ und $x \geqq b$, noch $x \leqq a$ und $x \leqq b$ gilt. Wir sagen, dass eine Teilmenge $A \subset P$ *endlich trennbar* ist, wenn es eine endliche Teilmenge K von A gibt, so dass jedes Element von A mit irgend einem Element von K vergleichbar ist. Ist $A \subset P$, so bezeichnen wir $A^* = \{x \in P \mid x \geqq a$ für jedes $a \in A\}$. Wir sagen, dass eine Teilmenge A von P *nach oben gerichtet* ist, wenn es zu je zwei Elementen $a, b \in A$ ein Element $c \in A$ gibt, so dass $a \leqq c$ und $b \leqq c$ gilt. Dual wird eine nach unten gerichtete Menge definiert. P wird *gleichmässig* (uniform [1]) genannt, wenn für jede nach oben gerichtete Teilmenge A von P die Menge A^* nach unten gerichtet ist und dual.

Unter einer *Intervalltopologie* in P versteht man die Topologie in P, deren Subbasis für die abgeschlossenen Mengen die folgenden Mengen bilden: $\{x \in P \mid x \geqq a\}$, $\{x \in P \mid x \leqq a\}$ (a durchläuft alle Elemente aus P) und die Menge P selbst.

Wir werden die folgende Bedingung betrachten:

(α) *Die halbgeordnete Menge P ist ein Hausdorffscher Raum in ihrer Intervalltopologie.*

Y. Matsushima [2] hat bewiesen: *Ist für jedes $a \in P$ die Menge $N(a)$ endlich trennbar, so genügt P der Bedingung* (α).

Die Bedingung von Matsushima ist jedoch nicht zur Gültigkeit von (α) notwendig, wie man an einem einfachen Beispiele zeigen kann: P bestehe aus der Kette

$$a_1 < a_2 < a_3 < \ldots < u < \ldots < b_3 < b_2 < b_1$$

und aus den Elementen $c_1, c_2, c_3, \ldots$, so dass $a_i < c_i < b_i$ ($i = 1, 2, 3, \ldots$) und die Elemente $u, c_1, c_2, c_3, \ldots$ untereinander unvergleichbar sind.

Die notwendige und hinreichende Bedingung gibt der folgende

Satz 1. *Genau dann genügt P der Bedingung* (α), *wenn für alle $a, b \in P$, $a \neq b$, die Menge $N(a, b)$ endlich trennbar ist.*

M. Katětov [3] und E. S. Northam [4] haben bewiesen: In einer Booleschen Algebra S ist die Bedingung (α) mit der folgenden Bedingung (β) äquivalent:

(β) *Zu jedem Element $a \in S$, $a \neq 0$, gibt es in S ein Atom $p \leqq a$.*

Dieser Satz kann wie folgt verallgemeinert werden:

Satz 2. *Die Bedingungen* (α) *und* (β) *sind äquivalent in einem komplementären modularen Verband, der die folgende Eigenschaft besitzt*:

(1) *Falls in S ein Atom existiert, so hat es nur endlich viele Komplemente.*

Es gelten auch die folgenden Sätze:

Satz 3. *In einem relativ komplementären Verband mit Null- und Einselement, der der Bedingung* (1) *genügt, folgt aus der Bedingung* (β) *die Bedingung* (α).

Satz 4. *In einem relativ komplementären Verband zieht die Bedingung* (α) *die folgende Bedingung* (γ) *nach sich*:

(γ) *In jedem nichttrivialen Intervall J gibt es einen Sprung* (d. h. es gibt solche Elemente $a, b \in J$, dass $a < b$ oder $b < a$ ist, und es gibt kein c, das echt zwischen a und b liegt).

Anmerkung. In einem semimodularen relativ komplementären Verband S mit Nullelement aus (β) folgt (γ). Ist S dabei auch modular, so gilt auch die umgekehrte Implikation. Ich weiss nicht zur Zeit, ob die letzte Implikation auch dann gilt, wenn S semimodular ist.

In der Arbeit [5] von L. E. Ward Jr. ist der folgende Satz enthalten (Theorem 3):

In einem Halbverband P sind die folgenden zwei Bedingungen äquivalent:

(δ) *Jede isotone Abbildung von P in P besitzt einen Fixpunkt.*

(ε) *P ist kompakt in der Intervalltopologie.*

Diese Behauptung ist nicht richtig, wie das folgende Beispiel zeigt: P besteht aus der geordneten Menge C der ganzen negativen Zahlen und aus den Elementen o, a, b, wobei $o < a$, $o < b$ ist und für jedes $n \in C$ gilt: $a < n$, $b < n$. Die Elemente a, b sind unvergleichbar. P ist ein Halbverband und man sieht leicht, dass P der Bedingung (δ), nicht aber der Bedingung (ε) genügt. (Das System $\mathcal{S}$ von abgeschlossenen Mengen $A_n = \langle a, n \rangle \cap \langle b, n \rangle$[1] ($n \in C$) hat einen leeren mengentheoretischen Durchschnitt, wobei der Durchschnitt eines beliebigen endlichen Teilsystems von $\mathcal{S}$ nicht leer ist.)

Es gelten jedoch die Sätze:

Satz 5. *In einer beliebigen halbgeordneten Menge aus* (ε) *folgt* (δ).

Satz 6. *In einer gleichmässigen halbgeordneten Menge sind die Bedingungen* (δ) *und* (ε) *äquivalent.*

Literatur

[1] *E. S. Wolk*: Dedekind completeness and a fixed-point theorem. Canadian J. Math., *9* (1957), 400–405.

[2] *Y. Matsushima*: Hausdorff interval topology on a partially ordered set. Proc. Amer. Math. Soc. *11* (1960), 233–235.

[3] *M. Katětov*: Remarks on Boolean algebras. Colloquium math. *2* (1951), 229–235.

[4] *E. S. Northam*: The interval topology of a lattice. Proc. Amer. Math. Soc. *4* (1953), 824–827.

[5] *L. E. Ward, Jr.*: Completeness in semi-lattices. Canadian J. Math. *9* (1957), 578–582.

[1]) $\cap$ bedeutet den mengentheoretischen Durchschnitt.

MODIFICATIONS OF TOPOLOGIES

K. KOUTSKÝ and M. SEKANINA

Brno

In this report we deal with the results concerning modifications of topologies. A topology on a set P is defined, according to E. ČECH, as a mapping u of the set 2^P (i. e. the system of all subsets of P) into 2^P such that (1) $u\emptyset = \emptyset$, (2) $X \subset P \Rightarrow X \subset uX$, (3) $X \subset Y \subset P \Rightarrow uX \subset uY$. A set together with a topology u on P is called a topological space (P, u). Throughout our report P means a fixed set.

We say that the topology v is weaker (stronger) that the topology u and we write $v \leqq u$ ($v \geqq u$), if $X \subset P \Rightarrow vX \subset uX$ (respectively, $X \subset P \Rightarrow vX \supset uX$). It can be easily seen that the system of all topologies on P is under the relation $\leqq$ a complete lattice.

If f is a topological property, then a topology possessing f is called an f-topology.

Let u be a given topology and f a topological property. Let $\mathfrak{M}_f(u)$ ($\mathfrak{M}^f(u)$) be the system of all f-topologies which are weaker (stronger) than u. In the case that $\sup \mathfrak{M}_f(u)$ ($\inf \mathfrak{M}^f(u)$) is a f-topology we put $u_f = \sup \mathfrak{M}_f(u)$ ($u^f = \inf \mathfrak{M}^f(u)$) and $u_f(u^f)$ is called the lower (upper) f-modification of u. This concept is due to K. KOUTSKÝ to whom E. Čech suggested it. For special cases of f the modifications occur often in topological studies.

We have studied lower and upper modifications for properties f given by means of the well-known topological axioms expressing the closeness of the closure (axiom U), the closeness of the point (axiom B), additivity (axiom A), separation axioms (H, $\overline{\text{H}}$, $\overline{\overline{\text{H}}}$), regularity (axiom R and $\overline{\text{R}}$), etc. For description of R and $\overline{\text{R}}$-modifications the introduction of a new topological property B* seemed to be convenient: u is called B^*-topology, if

$$x \in P \Rightarrow u(x) = s_u(x)\,,$$

where $s_u(x)$ is the intersection of all neighbourhoods of x. This property is the only topological property in our research, for which both modifications exist.

The first of our common papers [1] is in fact a continuation of one of the former papers of K. Koutský. It deals with conditions for u under which the given modification exists. The constructions of these modifications have been given either by means of closures either by means of the neighbourhoods.

Here we shall present the results concerning R-modifications. Recall that R-topology is a topology where for each point x and each neighbourhood O of x a neighbourhood O_1 of x exists, for which $uO_1 \subset O$. Following theorems hold.

(i) for lower R-modification:

Let u be a topology. Then $u_{B*} = \bigcup v$, where v runs over all R-topologies weaker than u. u_{B*} is a R-topology if and only if every non-isolated point x of the space (P, u) satisfies following conditions:

a) *for every neighbourhood O of x in (P, u) there exists a neighbourhood O_1 of x in (P, u) such that $uO_1 \subset O$.*

b) $y \in s_u(x) - u(x) \Rightarrow y$ *is isolated in (P, u).*

(ii) for upper R-modification:

Let (P, u) be a topological space. We shall define $v_\xi M$ for each $M \subset P$ and each ordinal number $\xi > 0$ in following way: (1) $v_1 M = uM$, (2) if $\xi = \eta + 1$, $\eta > 0$, then $v_\xi M = \sigma_{v_\eta} M$ ($\sigma_u M$ denotes, for a topology u on P and a set $M \subset P$, the intersection of all uO where O runs over all neighbourhoods of M), (3) if ξ is a limit ordinal number, then $v_\xi M = \bigcup_{\eta < \xi} v_\eta M$.

Then the supremum of all topologies v_ξ is exactly the upper R-modification of the topology u.

In the second paper [2] there are studied systems $\mathfrak{T}_f(u)$ ($\mathfrak{T}^f(u)$) of those topologies v for which $v_f = u$ ($v^f = u$), where u is a given f-topology. Suprema and infima of these systems have been constructed, for most cases the constructions of maximal (minimal) elements of these systems have been given, and in some cases a general construction of the elements of studied systems has been described. As a typical result we present again the theorems concerning R-topologies:

(i) for lower modification:

Let u be an R-topology. Then

(1) $v \in \mathfrak{T}_R(u)$ *if and only if the following conditions are satisfied:*

(a) *if $M \subset P$ is not a one-point set, then $vM = uM$,*

(b) $u \leqq v$,

(c) $x \in P \Rightarrow N_u(x) \cap R_u(x) \subset N_v(x) \cup R_v(x)$,

where $N_u(x)$ is the set of those points $y \in P$ for which $P - (x)$ is their minimal neighbourhood in (P, u), and $R_u(x)$ is the set of those points $y \in P$ for which $P - (y)$ is the minimal neighbourhood of x in (P, u).

(2) *Above every element $v \in \mathfrak{T}_R(u)$ there exists a maximal element of $\mathfrak{T}_R(u)$.*

(3) *If $w = \sup \mathfrak{T}_R(u)$, then $x \in P \Rightarrow w(x) = u(x) \cup N_u(x)$, and $wM = uM$ whenever M is not a one-point set.*

(ii) for upper modification.

Let u be an R-topology. Then $\inf \mathfrak{T}^R(u)$ *is a topology w defined as follows*

$$X \subset P \Rightarrow wX = X \cup u(o_u X)$$

where $o_u X$ *is the largest open set contained in* X *(when* u *is a U-topology, then* $o_u X = \text{int}_u X$).

The third paper [3] is devoted to the following question:

If f and g are two topological properties and the modifications u^f, u^g, $(u^f)^g$, $(u^g)^f$ exist, there is a problem, under which conditions the equation $(u^f)^g = (u^g)^f$ is valid (similarly for the lower modifications). For the properties A, U, B this problem has been proposed by E. Čech [4]. The general reply follows from the assertion that $(u^f)^g = (u^g)^f \Leftrightarrow (u^f)^g$ and $(u^g)^f$ are gf-topologies. Quite similar result holds for the lower modification. We have studied all pairs of above mentioned topological properties. Especially, we obtained interesting results in the cases, when the topological properties had been considered in regard to the points of P.

References

[1] *K. Koutský, M. Sekanina*: On the R-Modification and Several Other Modifications. Publ. Fac. Sci. Univ. Brno, *410* (1960), 45–64.

[2] *K. Koutský, M. Sekanina*: On the System of Topologies with a Given Modification. Publ. Fac. Sci. Univ. Brno, *418* (1960), 425–464.

[3] *K. Koutský, V. Polák, M. Sekanina*: On the Commutativity of the Modifications of Topologies. To appear in Publ. Fac. Sci. Univ. Brno.

[4] *E. Čech*: Topologické prostory. Čas. pěst. mat. a fys. *6* (1937), D 225–263.

THE SPACE OF MAPPINGS INTO THE SPHERE AND ITS TOPOLOGICAL APPLICATIONS

K. KURATOWSKI

Warszawa

Given an arbitrary subset X of the sphere S_n, the space of mappings $f: X \to P_n = E^n - (0)$ is considered. The set of all components of this space is a topological group relatively to the cohomotopical multiplication. Denote this group by $\mathfrak{C}(P_n^X)$.

Put $Y = S_n - X$ and consider the topological group $\mathfrak{M}(Y)$ of all integer-valued measures defined on closed-open subsets of Y (i. e. of countably additive functions $\mu(Z)$ such that $\mu(Y) = 0 = \mu(\emptyset)$).

Duality theorems between the groups $\mathfrak{C}(P_n^X)$ and $\mathfrak{M}(Y)$ are established.

For a detailed exposition, see the new edition (1961) of the author's monograph *Topologie II* (*Appendix*).

ON AN INEQUALITY CONCERNING CARTESIAN MULTIPLICATION

D. KUREPA

Zagreb

1. For a family F of sets let DF be the supremum of the cardinal numbers of disjointed subfamilies of F. Let F^{I2} be the set of all the cartesian products $X \times Y$ with $X, Y \in F$. Analogously, for any ordinal number r let Ir be the interval of the ordinals $< r$ and let F^{Ir} be the system of the cartesian products of all r-sequences of members of F.

2. For a space S let GS be the system of all the open sets of G; we put $DS = D(GS)$; $DS^{Ir} = D(G(S^{Ir}))$; the number DS is called the cellularity or disjunction degree of the space S.

The question arises to find the relations between the numbers DF^{Ir} $(r = 1, 2, \ldots)$ for any set family F and particularly for $F = GS$, S being any given topological space.

3. Let (G, ϱ) be a binary graph i. e. G is a set and ϱ is a binary reflexive and symmetrical relation in G. Let I be a non void set and for every $i \in I$ let (G_i, ϱ_i) be a binary graph; we define the product of the graphs (G_i, ϱ_i) as (G, ϱ), where $G = \prod G_i$ and where for $x, y \in G$ the relation $x\varrho y$ means $\bigwedge_i x_i \varrho_i y_i$, i. e. for every $i \in I$ one has $x_i \varrho_i y_i$ (let us remind that $x \in \prod G_i$ means that x is a mapping of I such that $x_i \in G_i$ for every $i \in I$). Let $k_c(G, \varrho)$ (resp. $k_{\bar{c}}(G, \varrho)$ or $k_a(G, \varrho)$) be the supremum of the cardinal numbers of chains (resp. antichains) of (G, ϱ).

The problem arises to find the connections between the numbers $k_a G^{Ir}$ and $k_a G$.

4. Theorem. *For any set system F with infinite DF one has:* $(DF)^n \leqq DF^{In} \leqq 2^{DF}$ *for any natural number n.* (II) *For any ordinal α there is a system F_α of sets such that* $DF_\alpha = \aleph_\alpha$, $DF^{I2} = 2^{\aleph_\alpha}$, *and consequently* $DF_\alpha < D(F_\alpha^{I2})$.

5. Theorem. *For any binary graph* (G, ϱ) *one has* $(k_a G)^n \leqq k_a G^{I2} \leqq 2^{k_a G}$; *if* $k_a G \geqq \aleph_0$, *then* $k_a G^{In} \leqq 2^{k_a G}$ *for every natural number n.*

6. Theorem. *For any metrical infinite space S and any positive integer n one has* $k_a S = k_a S^{In}$.

7. Theorem. *For totally ordered sets O the relation* (1) $k_a O = k_a O^{I2}$ *is equivalent to the following reduction principle: Every infinite ramified set R of regular cardinality kR contains a degenerated subset D of cardinality kR (any ordered set O* *in which every principal ideal* $O(., x) = \{y; y < x; \ y \in O\}$ *is a chain is said to be ramified;* O *is degenerated if both: principal ideals and dual principal ideals of* O *are chains). The relation* (1) *is connected to the well-known Suslin problem.*

8. Problem. As yet one does not know any topological infinite space S satisfying $DS < DS^{I2}$; the problem is to exhibit such a space.

ON FIXATIONS OF SETS IN EUCLIDEAN SPACES

A. LELEK

Wrocław

The fixation of a collection C of sets is here understood to mean a set intersecting each element of C.

Theorem 1. *If C is a collection of disjoint continua lying in a bounded subset of the plane and having diameters greater than* 1, *then there exists a compact fixation F of C such that* $\dim F = 0$.

Theorem 2. *If C is a collection of components of a compact subset of the n-dimensional Euclidean space* (*where* $n = 2, 3, \ldots$) *and all the elements of C have diameters greater than* 1, *then there exists a compact fixation F of C such that* $\dim F \leq n - 2$.

Whether the hypothesis concerning C in theorem 2 can be replaced by one similar to the hypothesis in theorem 1, namely that C is a collection of disjoint continua lying in a bounded subset of the n-dimensional Euclidean space (where $n = 3, 4, \ldots$) and having diameters greater than 1, remains an open question.

The proofs of these theorems and some related results will be published in Fundamenta Mathematicae in two forthcoming papers of D. ZAREMBA and myself.

ABSTRACT DISTANCE AND NEIGHBORHOOD SPACES

Z. MAMUZIĆ
Beograd

1. It is well known that one can topologize a given set E in very different ways. In fact, let $P(E)$ be the family of all subsets of E; then every one-valued map $\tau : P(E) \to P(E)$ defines a generalized topology on E. The set E with the generalized topology τ is an abstract space which we shall designate by (E, τ). Neighborhood spaces in the sense of M. FRÉCHET are characterized by the following three conditions: a) $\tau \Lambda = \Lambda$ (Λ is the void set); b) $\tau A \supset A$ for every $A \subset E$; c) if $A \supset B$ then $\tau A \supset \tau B$ for every $A, B \subset E$. If the map τ satisfies the well known axioms of C. KURATOWSKI (i. e. $(\tau_1)\, \tau\Lambda = \Lambda$; $(\tau_2)\, \tau A \subset A$; $(\tau_3)\, \tau(A \cup B) = \tau A \cup \tau B$; $(\tau_4)\, \tau\tau A = \tau A$), *topological* spaces are characterized by either of the following ways:

a) by open sets;
b) by closed sets;
c) by interiors of subsets in E;
d) by neighborhoods of the points in E;
e) by bases or subbases of the topology.

It should be remarked that every topological space is a neighborhood space in the sense of M. Fréchet, but the inverse is not true.

Let R_+^1 be the space of all real numbers $\geqq 0$, as a subspace of the space R^1 of all reals. One introduces a (pseudo)metric topology in E by means of a (pseudo)metric d, i. e. a map $d: E \times E \to R_+^1$ which satisfies the well known axioms of the (pseudo)-metric. A topological space is (pseudo)metrizable iff it is homeomorph of a (pseudo)-metric space. A series of necessary and sufficient conditions for a topological space to be metrizable are now known (P. S. ALEXANDROV, YU. M. SMIRNOV, J. NAGATA, R. H. BING, A. V. ARCHANGELSKIJ). Since A. H. STONE's important paper on para-compactness, the famous metrization problem of topological spaces was fully solved in the middle of this century. Furthermore, it is known that one can generalize some metric notions to a more general class of topological spaces, i. e. to the class of A. N. TYCHONOFF's completely regular spaces. In fact, call any two classes of spaces topologically equivalent, iff each space of the first class is also a space of the second class, and vice versa. Then the class of completely regular spaces is topologically equivalent both to the class of δ-spaces (V. A. EFREMOVIČ, YU. M. SMIRNOV) and to the class of separated uniform spaces (A. WEIL). Let us recall that a δ-space on E is obtained by means of a binary relation on $P(E)$ verifying the axioms of Efremovič-Smirnov; a uniform space on E is obtained by means of a family of subsets of the cartesian product $E \times E$ which satisfies the axioms of uniform structures. Necessary and sufficient conditions for the metrizability of a uniform space (in slightly modified sense) are known (A. Weil) and there are solutions of the metrization problem for δ-spaces (Yu. M. Smirnov, A. S. Shwarz).

2. Due to the fact that there are topological spaces which are not metrizable, one can try to topologize a given set by means of more general "metrics", whose range is not the space R^1_+ of non-negative reals, but a non-void set M structured by structures less rich than that of the space of real numbers. Of course, in particular cases one obtains metric spaces. In a general sense, one can term such "metrics" as *abstract distances* ("écarts abstraits").

The author's method is the following: Let $f : E \times E \to M$ be an one-valued map of the cartesian product $E \times E$ of a given set E into a given non-void set M. For every $a \in E$, the element $f(a, a) \in M$ is defined; for every $a \in E$, let there be given a family Fa of subsets $X_{\lambda_a} \subset M$ containing $f(a, a)$, i. e. $f(a, a) \in X_{\lambda_a}$, where λ_a is any element of an index-set (λ_a) equipollent to the family Fa. We define the following neighborhood system on E:

$$(1) \qquad W_{\lambda_a}(a) = \{b : b \in E \text{ and } f(a, b) \in X_{\lambda_a}\}, \quad \lambda_a \in (\lambda_a), \quad a \in E.$$

By means of (1) as a neighborhood base on E, we thus obtain a neighborhood space in the sense of M. Fréchet and it is evident that very different neighborhood spaces can be defined in this manner. According to the terminology of M. Fréchet or G. Kurepa, we shall refer to the function f as an *abstract distance* or *M-distance* („M-écart").

Conversely, let $(E, \mathscr{V})$ be any given neighborhood space, where $\mathscr{V}$ is any one of its neighborhood bases.

1. Definition. *We shall say that the neighborhood space $(E, \mathscr{V})$ admits an abstract distance or an M-distance f, iff there is a set M and a function f such that the corresponding neighborhood system (1), in the sense of the above definitions, is equivalent to the neighborhood base $\mathscr{V}$.*

1. Theorem. *The class of neighborhood spaces is topologically equivalent to the class of abstract spaces defined by means of neighborhood systems (1).*

It suffices to show that every neighborhood space $(E, \mathscr{V})$ admits at least one abstract distance in the sense of definition 1. In fact, we can prove ([6], p. 109) that every neighborhood space admits at least two abstract distances, one antisymmetric, $f(x, y) = y$, $x, y \in E$, and the other symmetric, $f(x, y) = \{x, y\}$, where $\{x, y\}$ is the *set* whose elements are the coordinates x and y of the *ordered pair* $(x, y) \in E \times E$ as elements.

As an example, let E be any non-void set and, for every $a \in E$, let $Fa = \{X_\varepsilon : \varepsilon > 0\}$ = the neighborhood base of the origin 0 in the space R^1_+, the *abstract distance* f being defined as an one-valued map $f : E \times E \to R^1_+$ satisfying the requirement

$f(a, a) = 0$ for every $a \in E$. In this case we can call the function f a *real distance*, but not a (pseudo)metric in the usual sense. It is not difficult to see that the neighborhood space (E, τ), defined by the corresponding neighborhood base (1), satisfies the first axiom of countability and the axiom (τ_3). If the function f satisfies the axioms of (pseudo)metrics, the space (E, τ), thus obtained is precisely a (pseudo)metric space, and f is then a (pseudo)metric. On the other hand, in the same example, let E be R^1 with its usual topology; this is a metric space with the metric $d(x, y) = |x - y|$, $x, y \in R^1$. Since this is a neighborhood space, by Theorem 1 and its proof, R^1 admits the antisymmetric abstract distance $f(x, y) = y$, and the symmetric one $f(x, y) = \{x, y\}$. According to the definitions given above, one can see that the *antisymmetric abstract distance* of two *real numbers* x and y is a real number, positive, zero or negative.

It is possible to give some conditions for a space, defined by an abstract distance, to be a topological space and, in particular, a T_1-space ([6], p. 111). Nevertheless, we mention here only the next theorem which is concerned with uniform spaces.

2. Theorem. *Let $f : E \times E \to M$ be an one-valued map of the cartesian product $E \times E$ into M and let $t_0 \in M$ be a fixed point. For every $a \in E$, let $Fa = F$, where F is a given family of subsets $X_\lambda \subset M$, $\lambda \in (\lambda)$, each containing t_0. Then the class of uniform spaces is topologically equivalent to the class of spaces admitting an abstract distance f such that the following conditions are satisfied*:

1° $f(a, a) = t_0$, $a \in E$.

2° $f(b, a) = f(a, b)$, $(a, b) \in E \times E$.

3° *For every $\lambda, \mu \in (\lambda)$ there exists an $\nu \in (\lambda)$ with the property $X_\nu \subset X_\lambda \cap X_\mu$.*

4° *For every $\lambda \in (\lambda)$ there exists an $\mu \in (\lambda)$ so that $f(a, b) \in X_\mu$ and $f(b, c) \in X_\mu$ implies $f(a, c) \in X_\lambda$, $a, b, c \in E$.*

The class of separated uniform spaces is topologically equivalent to the class of spaces admitting an abstract distance verifying the conditions 1°–4° *as well as the requirement:*

5° $f(x, a) \in \bigcap_{\lambda \in (\lambda)} X_\lambda \Rightarrow x = a$, $x, a \in E$.

The proof of Theorem 2 is given in [6], pp. 112–114. We mention only the definition of abstract distance f in proving that every uniform space $(E, \mathscr{U})$ admits an abstract distance in the sense of the definitions given above. Let $\mathscr{B}$ be the base of the uniform structure $\mathscr{U}$ of the uniform space $(E, \mathscr{U})$, and let Δ be the set $\{(a, a) : a \in E\} \subset E \times E$. Then the abstract distance f is defined as follows:

$$f(a, b) = \begin{cases} \Delta, & \text{if } (a, b) \in \bigcap_{V \in \mathscr{B}} V, \\ \{(a, b), (b, a)\}, & \text{if } (a, b) \notin \bigcap_{V \in \mathscr{B}} V, \end{cases} \tag{2}$$

where $\{(a, b), (b, a)\}$ is the *set* whose elements are the two ordered pairs (a, b) and (b, a). It should be noted that the second part of the Theorem 2 (that is, the part which is concerned with the separated uniform spaces) was first proved by G. Kurepa in [1].

In fact, the definition (2) of the abstract distance f is a slight modification of G. Kurepa's definition, in order to prove that *every uniform space* admits an abstract distance in the sense of our definitions.

Of course, it is possible to choose abstract distances other than those given above, according either to the nature of the problem considered or to taste. For example, if the range of the function $f: E \times E \to M$ is a subset of an ordered set (a scale) M, then one can obtain more interesting abstract distances which could be termed *ordered abstract distances* or simply *ordered distances*. Totally ordered distances were first introduced by G. Kurepa (1934, cf. [1]) in defining "espaces pseudo-distanciés". After the Second World War, M. Fréchet raised analogous problems; their investigation was continued by A. APPERT [2], and J. COLMEZ [3], thus leading to a characterization of separated uniform spaces by means of J. Colmez's abstract ordered distance of the first kind (cf. [3]). All mentioned ordered distances are special cases of the definitions given above.

It has come to my notice at this Symposium on General Topology in Prague that recently an abstract distance of the most importance has been introduced by the Russian mathematicians M. ANTONOVSKI, V. BOLTJANSKI and T. SARIMSAKOV in their interesting book [4]. Their results was reported by M. Antonovski. The authors first defined a topological semifield as an associative topological ring E containing a subset K verifying six axioms named *axioms of topological semifields* (cf. [4], § 1). The elements of K are termed the positive elements of the semifield E. By the authors' definition ([4], § 3), the set X is a *metric space* over the semifield E if there is given an one-valued map

$$\varrho : X \times X \to \overline{K} \tag{3}$$

which satisfies the following conditions:

1° $\varrho(x, y) = 0$ iff $x = y$.

2° $\varrho(x, y) = \varrho(y, x)$.

3° $\varrho(x, y) + \varrho(y, z) \gg \varrho(x, z)$, $x, y, z \in X$ ($a \gg b$ means that $a - b \in \overline{K}$).

A metric space X over the semifield E, with the metric ϱ, is denoted by (X, ϱ, E). In the special case of $E = R^1$ one obtains the usual metric space.

From the authors' theorem 11.1 (§ 3) in [4], it is not difficult to observe that the metric (3) is precisely a kind of an abstract distance in the sense of our definitions leading to (1). In fact, if U is any neighborhood of the zero point 0 in the topological semifield E, the topology in X is introduced by means of the neighborhoods

$$\Omega(x, U) = \{y : y \in X \text{ and } \varrho(x, y) \in U\}, \quad x \in X, \tag{4}$$

which are defined in the same manner as that of the definition of neighborhood systems (1). But the metric (3) is remarkable in that it is closely related to the usual real metric. This can be seen, for example, from theorem 11.3 (§ 3) in [4] by which the topology, introduced by means of (4), of the metric space (E, ϱ, E), where ϱ is the function $\varrho(x, y) = |x - y|$, $x, y \in E$, is identical with the topology of the topological semifield E.

On the other hand, by the authors' definition and theorem 11.5 (§ 3) in [4], the class of topological spaces metrizable over any topological semifield is topologically equivalent to the class of completely regular spaces. This last class being topologically equivalent either to the class of separated uniform spaces or to the class of δ-spaces, one can see that the metric ϱ, defined by (3), is a new abstract distance, more suitable than those mentioned above, characterizing the class of separated uniform spaces. In this way one can say that the class of completely regular spaces is indeed very close to the class of metrizable topological spaces (in the usual sense).

3. Let (E, τ) and (M, σ) be two abstract spaces. By G. Kurepa's definition (cf. [1]), the space (E, τ) is of class $\mathscr{E}[M]$, iff there is an one-valued map $f : E \times E \to M$ which satisfies the following conditions:

0^1 If $f(b, a) = f(a, a)$ then $b = a$, for every $a, b \in E$.

0^2 $f(b, a) = f(a, b)$, for every $a, b \in E$.

0^3 For $a \in E$ and $A \subset E$, let $f(a, A) = \{f(a, b) : b \in A\}$; then

$$\tau A = \{a : a \in E \text{ and } f(a, a) \in \sigma f(a, A)\},$$

where τA means $\bar{A}$ in the space (E, τ) and $\sigma f(a, A)$ means $\overline{f(a, A)}$ in the space (M, σ). One can say that f is an abstract distance verifying G. Kurepa's conditions 0^1, 0^2 and 0^3. We have the following theorem (cf. [6], p. 115):

3. Theorem. *Let $(M, \mathscr{V})$ be a neighborhood space, $\mathscr{V}$ being one of its neighborhood bases, and let $Fa = \mathscr{V} f(a, a)$, $a \in E$, where $\mathscr{V} f(a, a)$ is the local neighborhood base of the point $f(a, a)$ in the space $(M, \mathscr{V})$, in the definition (1). Then the abstract space (E, τ) is of class $\mathscr{E}[M]$, iff it is a neighborhood space and admits at least one M-distance f which satisfies G. Kurepa's conditions 0^1 and 0^2.*

Among spaces of the class $\mathscr{E}[M]$ we mention here only the class of R-spaces, defined by G. Kurepa [1] and P. Papić [5]. The space (E, τ) is an R-space iff the following conditions are satisfied:

1° The space (E, τ) has a neighborhood base $\mathscr{V}$ such that: (i) $\mathscr{V}$ is partially ordered by the relation $\supset$; (ii) if $V, W \in \mathscr{V}$ and $V \cap W \neq \Lambda$, then one has either $V \subset W$ or $V \supset W$ or $V = W$; (iii) for every $W \in \mathscr{V}$, the family of all $V \in \mathscr{V}$ containing W is well-ordered by the relation $\supset$.

2° Every set $V \in \mathscr{V}$ is a neighborhood of every point of V.

An R-space (E, τ) satisfies the axiom of separation T_1, iff for each $x \in E$ the intersection of all its neighborhoods $V \in \mathscr{V}$ reduces to x. We shall suppose that the R-space (E, τ) satisfies the axiom T_1.

As shown by P. Papić, every T_1, R-space is perfectly normal; moreover, the same author has given necessary and sufficient conditions for a T_1, R-space to be metrizable (cf. [5]). G. Kurepa (cf. [1]) proved that every T_1, R-space is of class $\mathscr{E}[M]$, M being a space of ordinal numbers; thus, by Theorem 3, every T_1, R-space admits at least one abstract distance f whose range is a space of ordinals. The function f has been defined by G. Kurepa as follows. Observe, first, that the local neighborhood base $\mathscr{V} x \subset \mathscr{V}$ of each point x of an R-space is well-ordered by $\supset$; then let $f(x, y) =$ ordinal number corresponding to the well-ordered intersection $\mathscr{V}x \cap \mathscr{V}y$, x and y being any two points in (E, τ). Let us remark that there is another abstract distance, reconstructing a given T_1, R-space, the range of which is also a space of ordinals; this was also described by G. Kurepa (cf. [6], p. 120).

Let us note finally that since it is perfectly normal, every T_1, R-space is completely regular; hence every T_1, R-space admits a metric over a topological semifield in the sense of the definitions given by M. Antonovski, V. Boltjanski and T. Sarimsakov in their book [4].

Is there any abstract distance still "nearer" to the usual metric than the metric (3) over topological semifields — for perfectly normal spaces? (This last class of spaces being still "nearer" to the class of metrizable topological spaces, in the usual sense.) Further reference and a more detailed survey of the results concerning abstract distances obtained by G. Kurepa, P. Papić and the author, can be found in the author's book [6], § 12.

References

[1] *G. Kurepa*: Sur l'écart abstrait. Glasnik mat. fiz. astr., *11* (1956), Zagreb, 105–132.
[2] *A. Appert* et *Ky-Fan*: Espaces topologiques intermédiaires. Act. sci. et ind., 1121, Paris 1951.
[3] *J. Colmez*: Sur divers problèmes concernant les espaces topologiques. Les espaces à écarts. — Problème de Wiener sur les transformations continues. Portugaliae Mathematica, Vol. *6*; Fasc. 3–4, 1947.
[4] *М. Я. Антоновский, В. Г. Болтянский, Т. А. Сарымсаков*: Топологические полуполя. Изд. СамГУ, Ташкент, 1960.
[5] *P. Papić*: Sur une classe d'espaces abstraits. Glasnik mat. fiz. astr., *9*, Zagreb 1954, 197–216.
[6] *Z. Mamuzić*: Uvod u opštu topologiju. I, ,,Matematička Biblioteka", No *17*, Beograd 1960.

ITERATIONS OF LINEAR BOUNDED OPERATORS AND KELLOGG'S ITERATIONS

I. MAREK

Praha

The purpose of this paper is to show that the existence of a fixed point of a special type is a sufficient condition for the convergence of the Kellogg iteration process for determining eigenvectors and eigenvalues of linear bounded operators in Banach spaces. It will follow from arguments given below that Kellogg's and probably similar methods can be applied to such a class of problems for which the existence of fixed points of certain type is guaranteed for the corresponding operators.

It can also be shown on the example of the Kellogg iteration process, how such a general approach to the convergence problem makes it possible to drop unimportant assumptions such as the symmetry or compactness of the investigated operator.

The basis of the proofs is the application of operator calculus of linear operators in the Banach space ([2], [3], [5]).

Let X be a complex Banach space, X^* its adjoint space of continuous linear forms. We denote the null-vector of the space X by the symbol O. Let X_1 be the Banach space of linear bounded operators mapping the space X into itself. We denote the identity operator by the symbol J. Let $\sigma(T)$ be the spectrum of the operator T.

The point μ_0 is called the dominant point of the spectrum of the operator T, if

$$|\lambda| < |\mu_0|$$

holds for every point $\lambda \in \sigma(T)$, $\lambda \neq \mu_0$.

Let $\{x_m^*\}, \{y_m^*\}, \{z_m^*\}$ be such sequences of linear forms of X^* that elements $x^* \in X^*$, $y^* \in X^*$ exist for which

$$(1) \qquad x^*(x) = \lim_{m\to\infty} x_m^*(x)\,,$$

$$y^*(x) = \lim_{m\to\infty} y_m^*(x) = \lim_{m\to\infty} z_m^*(x)$$

hold for every vector $x \in X$.

Let

$$B_1 = \frac{1}{2\pi i}\int_{C_0} R(\lambda, T)\,\mathrm{d}\lambda\,, \quad B_{k+1} = (T - \mu_0 J)\,B_k\,, \quad k \geqq 1$$

where $R(\lambda, T) = (\lambda J - T)^{-1}$ and C_0 is a circle with centre μ_0 and $\overline{\operatorname{int} C_0} \cap \sigma(T) = \{\mu_0\}$.

Let the following assumptions hold in the next theorems:

(A) The operator T is a linear bounded operator mapping X into itself.

(B) The value μ_0 is a pole of the multiplicity q of the resolvent $R(\lambda, T)$.

(C) The value μ_0 is the dominant point of the spectrum of the operator T.

Theorem 1. *In the norm of the space X_1 we have*

$$\lim_{m\to\infty} m^{-q+1} \mu_0^{-m} T^m = \frac{\mu_0^{-q+1}}{(q-1)!} B_q .$$

Let $x^{(0)} \in X$ be such a vector that $B_1 x^{(0)} \neq O$, so that such an index s, $1 \leqq s \leqq q$ exists, that

$$B_s x^{(0)} \neq O , \quad B_{s+1} x^{(0)} = O , \tag{2}$$

and let

$$x^*(B_s x^{(0)}) \neq O , \quad y^*(B_s x^{(0)}) \neq O , \quad x_0 = \frac{B_s x^{(0)}}{x^*(B_s x^{(0)})} . \tag{3}$$

We can construct Kellogg's iteration process:

$$x^{(m)} = T x^{(m-1)} , \quad x_{(m)} = \frac{x^{(m)}}{x_m^*(x^{(m)})} , \tag{4}$$

$$\mu_{(m)} = \frac{z_m^*(x^{(m+1)})}{y_m^*(x^{(m)})} . \tag{5}$$

Theorem 2. *Let* (1) *hold for the forms x_m^*, y_m^*, z_m^* and let* (2), (3) *hold for the vector $x^{(0)} \in X$.*

Then

$$\lim_{m\to\infty} x_{(m)} = x_0$$

holds for the sequence (4) *in the norm of the space X and*

$$\lim_{m\to\infty} \mu_{(m)} = \mu_0 .$$

Using the operational calculus method it is possible to prove the convergence of the Schwarz – Collatz [1] and Birger – Kolomý [4] type iterations.

The results which are valid for linear bounded operators can be extended in the usual way to the case of characteristic values of equation

$$Lx = \lambda Bx ,$$

where L and B are generally unbounded linear operators mapping its domains $D(L)$, $D(B)$ into X and the inclusion $D(L) \subset D(B)$ is correct.

References

[1] *L. Collatz*: Numerische Behandlung von Differentialgleichungen. Berlin-Götingen-Heidelberg 1951.

[2] *N. Dunford*: Spectral Theory. Bull. Amer. Math. Soc. *49* (1943), 637–651.

[3] *N. Dunford*: Spectral Theory I. Convergence to Projections. Trans. Amer. Math. Soc. *54* (1943), 185–217.

[4] *J. Kolomý*: On Convergence of the Iterative Methods. Comm. Math. Univ. Carol. I. *3* (1960), 18–24.

[5] *A. E. Taylor*: Spectral Theory of Closed Distributive Operators. Acta Math. *84* (1951), 189–223.

COLLARED SETS

E. MICHAEL
Seattle

The results presented here were obtained jointly with MORTON BROWN; the important Corollary 3 was obtained by him alone before our collaboration began.

A subset $A \subset X$ is *collared in* X if there exists a homeomorphism h from $A \times [0, 1)$ onto an open $U \supset A$ such that $h(a, 0) = a$ for all $a \in A$. Moreover, A is *locally collared in* X if each $a \in A$ has a neighborhood in A which is collared in X.

Theorem 1. *A locally collared subset of a metric space is collared.*

Corollary 1. *The boundary of a manifold with boundary is collared.*

Now call $A \subset X$ *bi-collared in* X if $[0, 1)$ is replaced by $(-1, 1)$ in the above definition of collared, and similarly for *locally bi-collared.* The "equator" of a Möbius band shows that a locally bi-collared set need not be bi-collared (although see Theorem 3). However, we have

Corollary 2. *A locally bi-collared compact* $(n-1)$*-manifold in* E^n *is bi-collared.*

Combining this result with the "Generalized Schönfliess Theorem" of M. BROWN and M. MORSE, one obtains

Corollary 3. (M. Brown.) *A locally bi-collared* $(n-1)$*-sphere in* E^n *can be sent onto the unit sphere by an autohomeomorphism of* E^n.

Now call $A \subset X$ *multicollared in* X if there exists an $f : \tilde{A} \twoheadrightarrow A$ (the double arrow means onto) such that

(a) f is continuous, closed, and (compact, 0-dimensional)-to-one,

(b) there exists a homeomorphism h from M'_f (the "decapitated" mapping cylinder of f) onto an open $U \supset A$ such that, considering $A \subset M'_f$, we have $h(a) = a$ for all $a \in A$.

We denote the set of all such f by $M(A, X)$.

Theorem 2. *If* $A \subset X$ *metric, and* $f_i : \tilde{A}_i \twoheadrightarrow A$ $(i = 1, 2)$ *are in* $M(A, X)$, *then there exists a homeomorphism* $h : A_1 \twoheadrightarrow A_2$ *such that* $f_1 = f_2 \circ h$.

Call $A \subset X$ *double-collared* in X if there exists an f in $M(A, X)$ which is a (possibly trivial) double covering of A. (In the trivial case, this reduces to bi-collared. The equator of a Möbius band is double-collared without being bi-collared; locally, however, these two concepts coincide.)

Theorem 3. *A locally multicollared subset of a metric space is multicollared. Similarly for double-collared.*

Suppose now that A is a multicollared subset of E^n, and that $f : \tilde{A} \to\to A$ is in $M(A, E^n)$. Note that a closed interval or triod are both multicollared in the plane, with $\tilde{A}$ a circle. In general, every component of $\tilde{A}$ must be a manifold (compact if A is) if $n \leqq 3$. S. JAWOROWSKI has shown that, for A compact, $\tilde{A}$ and $E^n - A$ have the same number of components.

Now consider a finite, connected $(n-1)$-subcomplex K of E^n, all of whose simplices are faces of $(n-1)$-simplices. In general, K need not be multicollared in E^n, although it is if $n = 2$, or $n = 3$ and the star of each vertex is connected. Nevertheless, one can always canonically define an $(n-1)$-complex $\tilde{K}$, and a simplicial, finite-to-one $f : \tilde{K} \to\to K$, such that *if* K is multicollared in E^n, then f is in $M(K, E^n)$.

Here is a problem:

Is the union of all multicollared subsets of a finite-dimensional metric space again multicollared?

ON TWO-TO-ONE FUNCTIONS

J. MIODUSZEWSKI

Wrocław

A function $f: X \to Y$ is said to be *two-to-one* if it is continuous and assumes every value in exactly two points. The space of arguments X is assumed to be metric and locally compact. In order to exclude the triviality we assume that Y is Hausdorff. It is known (CIVIN [1]) that such functions do not exist if X is an n-cell, where $n \leqq 3$ (the problem for $n > 3$ is open). The investigation of the two-to-one functions is in a natural manner equivalent to the investigation of an involution φ, where $\varphi(x)$ is the element of $f^{-1}f(x)$ different from x. This involution is, in general, discontinuous, but it is *semicontinuous*, i. e. for every $x \in X$ we have

$$\operatorname*{Ls}_{\xi \to x} \varphi(\xi) \subset x \cup \varphi(x) \cup p \,,$$

where p is the point adjoined to X by one-point compactification of X (here Ls denotes the topological limit superior in the sense of [2]). Civin showed that the investigation of φ on compact manifolds, or, if f is closed, on locally compact manifolds, is equivalent to the investigation of some continuous involution.

We do not assume that X is a manifold, or, if X is not compact, that f is closed. We consider the problem of behaviour of φ on neighbourhoods or on so called pseudoneighbourhoods of euclidean points or so called pseudoeuclidean points. According to this generality it is possible to obtain some results concerning the non-existence of two-to-one functions on some non locally connected continua (see [3]). We give some examples. One of them shows that there exist two-to-one functions on euclidean n-spaces for $n \geqq 2$ (the problem raised by Civin [1]).

1. *The general properties of involution φ.* Denote by $C(\varphi)$ the set of all continuity points of φ. It is an open and dense subset of X. The discontinuity point x of involution φ is said to be *weakly essential* (in short, x is a W-point of φ or $x \in W(\varphi)$) if $\Phi(x) = x \cup \varphi(x)$. It is said to be *strongly essential* (in short, x is an S-point of φ or $x \in S(\varphi)$) if $\Phi(x)$ contains p. A point $x \in X$ is said to be *pseudoeuclidean* if there exists a neighbourhood H of x in X such that the closure of the component of x in H is an euclidean solid sphere. We shall call such components H the euclidean *pseudoneighbourhoods*.

Theorem 1. *A pseudoeuclidean point $x \in X$ cannot be a W-point of $\varphi \mid A$, where A is the closure of an euclidean pseudoneighbourhood of x in X.*

In the proof we use a theorem of NEWMAN [4] concerning continuous involutions on closures of subdomains of compact manifolds and a theorem of KURATOWSKI [2], according to which, upper semicontinuous multi-valued functions are of the 1-st Baire class.

Theorem 2. *Let $R \subset X$ be a manifold such that for every $x \in R$ there exists a pseudoneighbourhood of x in X which is a neighbourhood of x in R simultaneously. If $\varphi \mid R$ has no S-points then the function*

$$\tilde{\varphi}(\xi) = \begin{cases} \varphi(\xi) & \text{for } \xi \in C(\varphi \mid R) \\ \xi & \text{for } \xi \in R - C(\varphi \mid R) \end{cases}$$

is continuous and one-to-one. If, in addition, $\tilde{\varphi}(R) \subset R$, then $\tilde{\varphi}$ is an involution on R and it cannot be the identity on open subsets of R.

2. *The case of locally compact manifolds.* According to Theorem 1, involution φ has no W-points if X is a manifold. However, if X is only a locally compact manifold then there can exist S-points. Consider the function $\tilde{\varphi} : X - S(\varphi) \to X$ defined by

$$\tilde{\varphi}(\xi) = \begin{cases} \varphi(\xi) & \text{for } \xi \in C(\varphi)\,, \\ \xi & \text{for } \xi \in X - C(\varphi) - S(\varphi)\,. \end{cases}$$

Theorem 3. *If X is a locally compact manifold without boundary then $\tilde{\varphi}$ is a continuous involution on $X - S(\varphi)$, and it cannot be the identity on open subsets of $X - S(\varphi)$.*

A homeomorphic image of the closed interval $0 \leqq t \leqq 1$, given by a homeomorphism h such that $h(0) = x$ and $h(t) \in X - S(\varphi)$ for $t \neq 0$, is said to be a *path* to the point x. A point $x \in S(\varphi)$ is said to be *strongly accessible* from $X - S(\varphi)$ if there exists a path to x such that $\lim_{t \to 0} \tilde{\varphi}\, h(t) = p$.

Theorem 4. *If X is a locally compact manifold, x is an S-point of φ, and U is an open neighbourhood of x in X, then there exist S-points of φ in U, being strongly accessible from $X - S(\varphi)$.*

The proof is similar to that of Theorem 1. Some corollaries are given in [3]. We quote here a simple one if X is the straight line, then φ has at most two S-points. From this, in an elementary way, we obtain that there do not exist two-to-one functions on the straight line.

3. *Examples.* Note first that it is possible to define two-to-one functions on some (infinite) dendrites. A more complicated example is an example of two-to-one function on a continuum being the closure of a plane simply connected domain, whose boundary is an irreductible cut of the plane into two domains (see for description [3]). This is in contrast to the non-existence of two-to-one functions on 2-cell. Both of these examples may be used in the proof that

Theorem 5. *There exist two-to-one functions on euclidean spaces E^n for $n \geqq 2$.*

The outline of construction is as follows. We consider E^n as $S^n - C$, where C is a continuum such that there exist two-to-one functions on it. Let f be one of them and let φ be the associated semicontinuous involution on C. Denote by C^* the image of C

by the antipodism on S^n, and assume that $C^* \cap C = 0$. In order to define two-to-one function on $S^n - C$, it is sufficient to define a suitable involution. This involution, λ, is given by

$$\lambda(x) = \begin{cases} x^* & \text{for } x \in S^n - C - C^*, \\ (\varphi(x^*))^* & \text{for } x \in C^*. \end{cases}$$

References

[1] *P. Civin*: Two-to-one mappings of manifolds. Duke Math. Journal *10* (1943), 49–57.

[2] *C. Kuratowski*: Topologie I (1948) and II (1950), Warszawa–Wrocław.

[3] *J. Mioduszewski*: On two-to-one continuous functions. Rozprawy Matematyczne *24* (1961).

[4] *H. M. A. Newman*: A theorem on periodic transformations of spaces. The Quarterly Journal of Math., Oxford Series, *2* (1931), 1–8.

REMARKS ON FIXED POINT THEOREM FOR INVERSE LIMIT SPACES

J. MIODUSZEWSKI and M. ROCHOWSKI

Wrocław

A topological space X has the *fixed point property* (FPP) if for every continuous (single-valued) function $f : X \to X$ there exists a point $x \in X$ such that $f(x) = x$. Let us consider inverse systems $\{X_n, \pi_n^m, M\}$ of spaces and functions, where $\pi_n^m : X_m \to X_n$, $m \geqq n$, are continuous and onto, and $m, n \in M$, where M is a directed set. The inverse limit $X = \lim \{X_n, \pi_n^m, M\}$ consists of all points $x = \{x_m\}$ $m \in M$, such that $\pi_n^m(x_m) = x_n$ for $m \geqq n$. Let $\pi_n(x) = X \to X_n$ be projections, i. e. functions defined by $\pi_n(x) = x_n$. The projections are assumed to be onto. We consider topological (not necessary metrizable) compact spaces X only. It is known [1] that every compact space X is an inverse limit of compact polyhedra. Hence we consider inverse systems of compact polyhedra only.

We shall say that the inverse system $\{X_n, \pi_n^m, M\}$ has the *special incidence point property* (SIPP) if for every continuous (single-valued) function $f : X_m \to X_n$, $m \geqq n$, there exists a point $x_m \in X_m$ such that $f(x_m) = \pi_n^m(x_m)$.

We consider the following question: under what conditions concerning the inverse system, the inverse limit has the FPP? For the inverse system described above we prove the following theorem.

Theorem. *If* $\{X_n, \pi_n^m, M\}$ *has the SIPP then the inverse limit of it has the FPP.*

In the proof are considered some multivalued functions $F_{mn} : X_m \to X_n$, induced by f, and their simplicial approximations.

The fixed point theorem for snake-like continua (see [2], and also [3] for a more general result) is an easy consequence of the Theorem.

Corollary. Let $\{X_m\}$ be an increasing system of compact polyhedra i. e. $X_n \subset X_m$ for every $m, n \in M$, $m \geqq n$. Let π_n^m be retractions, i. e. $\pi_n^m \mid X_n$ is the identity. Then if all X_n have the FPP then also the inverse limit X has the FPP.

The following problem seems to be open: does the inverse limit have the FPP if all X_n have the FPP and the projections are onto?

References

[1] *S. Eilenberg* and *N. Steenrod*: Foundations of Algebraic Topology. Princeton 1952.

[2] *O. H. Hamilton*: A fixed point theorem for pseudo-arcs and certain other metric continua. Proc. Amer. Math. Soc. *2* (1951), 173–174.

[3] *R. H. Rosen*: Fixed points for multi-valued functions on snake-like continua. Proc. Amer. Math. Soc. *10* (1959), 167–173.

PERIODIC HOMEOMORPHISMS OF THE 3-SPHERE

E. MOISE

Cambridge (U. S. A.)

Let M be a triangulated 3-sphere, and let f be a periodic simplicial homeomorphism of M onto itself. Suppose that f preserves orientation and has a fixed point; let F be the fixed-point set of f; and let n be the period of f. By methods and results of P. A. SMITH [1] it follows that F is always a (simple closed) polygon. A well-known conjecture due to Smith (discussed by S. EILENBERG [2] in his 1949 report on the problems of topology) asserts that F is never knotted.

It has been shown by D. MONTGOMERY and H. SAMELSON [3] that for $n = 2$, F cannot be a simplicial standard torus knot. They showed also that if $n = 2$ and F is unknotted, then f is topologically equivalent to a rotation.

The main result reported here is that the second of these results holds without restriction $n = 2$:

Theorem 1. *If $f : M \leftrightarrow M$ is periodic and simplicial, and preserves orientation, and F is unknotted, then f is topologically equivalent to a rotation.*

This result is derived from the following purely homological theorem:

Theorem 2. *Let M be a triangulation, not necessarily of the 3-sphere, but of a compact 3-manifold having the homology groups of the 3-sphere. Let $f : M \leftrightarrow M$ be a simplicial homeomorphism of M onto itself, preserving orientation, with period n and having the polygon F as its fixed-point set. Then there is a polyhedral disk D_1 with handles such that (1) F is the boundary of D_1 and (2) each two different sets $f^i(D_1)$, $f^j(D_1)$ intersect only in F.*

Here by a disk with handles we mean a compact, connected orientable 2-manifold whose boundary is a single polygon. If D_1 is an actual disk (with no handles), then for the case $M = S^3$ it follows that each pair of geometrically adjacent disks

$$D_i = f^{i-1}(D_1), \quad D_j = f^{j-1}(D_1)$$

form the boundary of a 3-cell, say C_i; and the 3-cells C_i are cyclically permuted by f. From this it follows that f is topologically equivalent to a rotation. In fact, to deduce Theorem 1 from Theorem 2, we show that if F is the boundary of *some* polyhedral disk D, and the genus of D_1 is positive, then this genus can always be reduced.

These results will appear soon with proofs in a paper in the Illinois Journal of

Mathematics. The proofs are by explicit geometric construction, and do not lend themselves to informal summary. Since the difference in date of publication will be small in any case, we do not attempt to give such a summary here.

Bibliography

[1] *P. A. Smith*: Transformations of finite period, Ann. of Math. (2), *39* (1938), 127–164.
[2] *S. Eilenberg*: The problems of topology. Ann. of Math. (2), *50* (1949), 247–260.
[3] *D. Montgomery* and *H. Samelson*: A theorem on fixed points of involutions in S^3. Canad. J. Math., *7* (1955), 208–220.

ON SOME SPACES OF FUNCTIONS AND DISTRIBUTIONS

J. MUSIELAK

Poznań

In [4] L. SCHWARTZ introduced spaces $\mathscr{D}_{L^p}$ of functions and $\mathscr{D}'_{L^p}$ of distributions. The purpose of this note is to present some properties of spaces $\mathscr{D}_M$ and $\mathscr{D}'_M$ replacing spaces $\mathscr{L}^p$ in Schwartz's definition by Orlicz spaces $\mathscr{L}^*_M$.[1]) Let $M(u)$ be an even, continuous, convex, nonnegative function assuming the value 0 only at $u = 0$, $u^{-1} M(u) \to 0$ as $u \to 0$ and $u^{-1} M(u) \to \infty$ as $u \to \infty$. We define

$$\mathscr{D}_M = \bigcap_p \{\varphi \in \mathscr{E} : \int M(k_p D^p \varphi(x))\, dx < \infty, \text{ where } k_p > 0 \text{ depends on } \varphi\} ;$$

here $\mathscr{E}$ is the space of all infinitely differentiable functions of n variables, the integral is taken over the whole n-dimensional space and the product $\bigcap_p$ runs over all systems $p = (p_1, \ldots, p_n)$ of nonnegative integers. Defining the topology in $\mathscr{D}_M$ by a countable system of seminorms

$$\|D^p\varphi\|_M = \inf \{\varepsilon > 0 : \int M(\varepsilon^{-1} D^p \varphi(x))\, dx \leqq 1\} ,$$

$\mathscr{D}_M$ becomes a B_0-space. We denote by $\mathscr{D}'_N$ the dual of $\mathscr{D}_M$, where $N(u)$ is the function complementary to $M(u)$ in the sense of Young.

The following elementary properties hold:

If $\varphi \in \mathscr{D}_M$ then $\varphi(x) \to 0$ as $|x| \to \infty$; if $\varphi_k \to 0$ in $\mathscr{D}_M$ then $\varphi_k(x)$ are uniformly bounded and $\varphi_k(x) \to 0$ as $|x| \to \infty$ uniformly in k. Assuming $M_2(u) = 0(M_1(u))$ as $u \to 0$, we have

$$\mathscr{D}_{M1} \dot{\subset} \mathscr{D}_{M2} \quad \text{and} \quad \mathscr{D}'_{N_2} \dot{\subset} \mathscr{D}'_{N_1} ;$$

here $\mathscr{X} \dot{\subset} \mathscr{Y}$ means that $\mathscr{X}$ is a part of $\mathscr{Y}$ with a finer topology. Moreover, we have $\mathscr{L}^*_N \dot{\subset} \mathscr{D}'_N$. If $M(u)$ and $N(u)$ satisfy the condition (Δ_2): $M(2u) \leqq \kappa\, M(u)$ with a $\kappa > 0$ for all u, then the set $\mathscr{D}$ of all infinitely differentiable functions of compact support is dense in $\mathscr{D}_M$ and in $\mathscr{D}'_N$, whence $\mathscr{D}'_N$ is a normal space of distributions, the space $\mathscr{D}_M$ is reflexive and $\mathscr{D}'_N$ consists exactly of finite sums of (distributional) derivatives of functions belonging to $\mathscr{L}^*_N$.

In the above introduced spaces, the integral transform

$$K\, \varphi(x) = \int k(x, y)\, \varphi(y)\, dy$$

[1]) For the proofs of results presented here, cf. [1], [2] [3].

and its adjoint K^* defined by $K^* T(\varphi) = T(K\varphi)$, where T is a distribution, may be considered. Assume M_1, M_2, N_1, N_2 satisfy the condition (Δ_2) for all u, and x and y are points of the n-dimensional and m-dimensional space, respectively. Let $k(x, y)$ be an infinitely differentiable function of x for every y, $k(x, y)$ measurable in the $(n + m)$-dimensional space. Finally, let $k(x, y)$ satisfy the following assumptions (As):

1° $D_x^p k(x, y)$ is a function of x equicontinuous in every bounded set of y,
2° $k_p(x) = \|D_x^p k(x, .)\|_{M_2}$ is bounded for every p separately,
3° $\|k_p\|_{N_1}$ is finite for every p.

Then K and K^* are linear compact operators from $\mathscr{L}^*_{N_2}$ to $\mathscr{D}_{N_1}$ and from $\mathscr{D}'_{M_1}$ to $\mathscr{L}^*_{M_2}$, respectively, and the ranges of K and K^* are linear subspaces of the first category in $\mathscr{D}_{N_1}$ resp. $\mathscr{L}^*_{M_2}$. If, moreover, $\|D_x^p k(., y)\|_{N_1}$ is bounded in y for every p separately and the support of $k(x, y)$ is contained in a strip $\{(x, y) : y \in A\}$, where A is of finite measure in the m-dimensional space, then

$$K^* T(y) = \int k(x, y)\, T_x\, dx$$

for every $T \in \mathscr{D}'_{M_1}$, the last integral being defined in Schwartz's sense [5].

Besides spaces $\mathscr{D}'_N$, spaces $\mathscr{D}'_N(E)$ of vector-valued distributions (cf. e. g. [5]) may be considered, where $\mathscr{H}(E) = \mathscr{L}_\varepsilon(\mathscr{H}'; E)$ is the space of linear continuous operations from $\mathscr{H}'$ to E provided with the topology of uniform convergence on equicontinuous parts of $\mathscr{H}'$ (here E and $\mathscr{H}$ are locally convex linear topological Hausdorff spaces and $\mathscr{H}$ is a space of distributions). Of course, $\mathscr{D}_{N_1}(\mathscr{L}^*_{M_2})$ consists of linear operators adjoint to operators from $\mathscr{L}^*_{M_2}(\mathscr{D}_{N_1})$; examples of such operators yield the above considered transforms K and K^*. It is easily seen that taking as E a Banach space and denoting by $\mathscr{L}^*_M[E]$ the space of all vector-valued functions with values in E, M-integrable in Bochner's sense, i. e.

$$\mathscr{L}^*_M[E] = \{f : f(x) \text{ is strongly measurable and } \int M(k\|f(x)\|)\, dx < \infty$$

$$\text{for a } k > 0 \text{ dependent on } f\}$$

where $f = g$ means that $f(x) = g(x)$ almost everywhere) with the norm

$$\|f\|_M = \inf\{\varepsilon > 0 : \int M(\varepsilon^{-1}\|f(x)\|)\, dx \leqq 1\},$$

we have

$$\mathscr{L}^*_M[E] \dot{\subset} \mathscr{D}'_M(E).$$

References

[1] *J. Musielak*: On some spaces of functions and distributions I. Spaces $\mathscr{D}_M$ and $\mathscr{D}'_M$. Studia Mathematica *21* (1962), 185—202.

[2] *J. Musielak*: On some spaces of functions and distributions II. Integral transforms in $\mathscr{D}_M$ and $\mathscr{D}'_M$. Studia Mathematica *21* (1962), 237—244.

[3] *J. Musielak*: On some spaces of functions and distributions III. Spaces of vector-valued *M*-integrable distributions. Bull. Acad. Polon. Sc., Sér. sc. math., astr. et phys., *9* (1961), 765—767.

[4] *L. Schwartz*: Théorie des distributions II. Paris 1951.

[5] *L. Schwartz*: Séminaire 1953/54. Paris 1954.

ON DIMENSION AND METRIZATION[1])

J. NAGATA

Osaka

As is well known, it follows from results of E. MARCZEWSKI [4] that

A separable metric space R has dim $\leqq n$ *if and only if we can introduce a topology-preserving metric* ϱ *such that almost all of the spherical neighborhoods of any point of R have boundaries of* dim $\leqq n - 1$.

For general metric spaces we proved [6] the following theorems:

A metric space R has dim $\leqq n$ *if and only if we can introduce a topology-preserving metric into R such that the spherical neighborhoods* $S_{1/i}(p)$, $i = 1, 2, \ldots$ *of any point p of R have boundaries of* dim $\leqq n - 1$ *and such that* $\{S_{1/i}(p) \mid p \in R\}$ *is closure preserving for every i.*

Let $S_{1/i}(F) = \cup \{S_{1/i}(p) \mid p \in F\}$; $B(S)$ *denotes the boundary of S. A metric space R has* dim $\leqq n$ *if and only if we can introduce a topology-preserving metric into R such that*

$$\dim B(S_{1/i}(F)) \leqq n - 1\,, \quad i = 1, 2, \ldots$$

for every closed subset F of R.

In the above theorem $S_{1/i}(p)$ denotes the spherical neighborhood $\{q \mid \varrho(p, q) < 1/i\}$. A collection $\mathfrak{A}$ of subsets of R is called closure preserving if $\bigcup\{\bar{A} \mid A \in \mathfrak{A}'\} = \overline{\bigcup\{A \mid A \in \mathfrak{A}'\}}$ for any subset $\mathfrak{A}'$ of $\mathfrak{A}$; dim R denotes the covering dimension of R, but since M. KATĚTOV [3] and K. MORITA [5] have proved dim R = Ind R for any metric space R, in metric spaces we do not distinguish between them.

We expected there would be many difficulties to introduce into n-dimensional general metric spaces a metric in which much more spherical neighborhoods have boundaries of dim $\leqq n - 1$, because the p-dimensional measure does not work in general metric spaces though it played the leading role in Marczewski's theory for separable metric spaces.

We, however, have succeeded to prove without measure the following theorem and its corollaries quite recently.

Theorem 1. *A metric space R has* dim $\leqq n$ *if and only if we can introduce a topology-preserving metric* ϱ *into R such that all spherical neighborhoods* $S_\varepsilon(p)$ *of any point P of R have boundaries of* dim $\leqq n - 1$ *and such that* $\{S_\varepsilon(p) \mid p \in R\}$ *is closure preserving for every real number* ε.

[1]) The content of this note will be published in a more extended form in some other place.

This metric is rather peculiar in view that the usual metric of Euclidean space does not satisfy the closure preserving condition. But the metric in the following corollary will be more reasonable.

Corollary 1. *A metric space R has* dim $\leqq n$ *if and only if we can introduce a metric* ϱ *into R such that*

$$\dim B(S_\varepsilon(F)) \leqq n - 1$$

for any real number ε *and for any closed set F of R.*

Now let $C_\varepsilon(p) = \{q \mid \varrho(p, q) = \varepsilon\}$; then $C_\varepsilon(p) = B(S_\varepsilon(p))$ is not always valid. But the metric applied to the proof of the preceding theorem satisfies $C_\varepsilon(p) = B(S_\varepsilon(p))$ for almost all ε or more precisely for all irrational ε and some rational ε. Thus we get the following corollaries, too.

Corollary 2. *A metric space R has* dim $\leqq n$ *if and only if we can introduce a metric* ϱ *into R such that*

$$\dim C_\varepsilon(p) \leqq n - 1$$

for every irrational (or almost all) ε *and for every point p of R and such that* $\{S_\varepsilon(p) \mid p \in R\}$ *is closure preserving for any irrational (or almost all)* ε.

Corollary 3. *A metric space R has* dim $\leqq n$ *if and only if we can introduce a metric* ϱ *into R such that*

$$\dim C_\varepsilon(F) \leqq n - 1$$

for every closed set F of R and for every irrational (or almost all) ε, *where* $C_\varepsilon(F) = \{p \mid \varrho(p, F) = \varepsilon\}$.

The point of proof of this theorem is how to introduce into an n-dimensional metric space R a metric satisfying the conditions. To do it we choose a sequence $\{\mathfrak{A}_i \mid i = 0, 1, 2, \ldots\}$ of open coverings of R such that

1. $\{R\} = \mathfrak{A}_0 > \mathfrak{A}_1^{**} > \mathfrak{A}_1 > \mathfrak{A}_2^{**} > \mathfrak{A}_2 > \mathfrak{A}_3^{**} > \ldots$
2. $\{S(p, \mathfrak{A}_m) \mid m = 0, 1, 2, \ldots\}$ is a neighborhoood basis of each point p of R.
3. $S^2(p, \mathfrak{A}_{m+1}^*)$ intersects at most $n + 1$ sets of $\mathfrak{A}_m$,

where the terminologies about coverings are due to [9].

For integers $m_1, m_2, \ldots, m_k$ with $1 \leqq m_1 < m_2 < \ldots < m_k$ and for $U \in \mathfrak{A}_{m_1}$ we define open sets $S_{m_1, m_2, \ldots, m_k}(U)$ by

$$S_{m_1}(U) = U\,; \quad S_{m_1, \ldots, m_k}(U) = S^2(S_{m_1, \ldots, m_{k-1}}(U), \mathfrak{A}_{m_k})\,, \quad k \geqq 2\,.$$

Then we define open coverings $\mathfrak{S}_{m_1, \ldots, m_k}$ of R by

$$\mathfrak{S}_{m_1} = \mathfrak{A}_{m_1}\,, \quad m_1 \geqq 0\,;$$

$$\mathfrak{S}_{m_1, \ldots, m_k} = \{S_{m_1, \ldots, m_k}(U) \mid U \in \mathfrak{A}_{m_1}\}\,, \quad 1 \leqq m_1 < \ldots < m_k\,, \quad k \geqq 2$$

to define a function $\varrho(x, y)$ over $R \times R$ by

$$\varrho(x, y) = \inf\{2^{-m_1} + 2^{-m_2} + \ldots + 2^{-m_k} \mid y \in S(x, \mathfrak{S}_{m_1, \ldots, m_k})\}\,.$$

We can prove this ϱ is the desired metric.

As a matter of fact, we applied this metric to characterizing dimension of metric spaces in another way [7], [8]. That characterization theorem was simplified in separable cases by J. de Groot [2] as follows.

A separable metric space R has dim $\leqq n$ *if and only if we can introduce a totally bounded metric* ϱ *into R such that for every* $n+3$ *points*

$$x, y_1, y_2, \ldots, y_{n+2}$$

in R there is a triplet of indices i, j, k satisfying

$$\varrho(y_i, y_j) \leqq \varrho(x, y_k) \quad (i \neq j).$$

It will be an interesting problem to find a simple condition for n-dimensionality of *general* metric spaces in this direction. In this connection we have unsuccessfully tried to prove the following conjecture.

Let R be a metric space of dim $\leqq n$; then can we introduce into R a metric ϱ such that for every $n+3$ points

$$x, y_1, y_2, \ldots, y_{n+2}$$

in R there is a pair of indices i, j satisfying

$$\varrho(y_i, y_j) \leqq \varrho(x, y_j) \quad (i \neq j).$$

We, however, have got in this try a new n-dimensionality theorem which will have its own interest. To show that theorem we need some terminologies.

Definitions. Two subsets A and B of a space R are called *independent* if $A \not\subset B$, $B \not\subset A$. A collection $\mathfrak{A}$ of subsets is called independent if any two members of $\mathfrak{A}$ are independent. Let $\mathfrak{A}$ be a collection of subsets of R and p a point of R. Then rank$_p\,\mathfrak{A}$ is the largest number of independent sets of $\mathfrak{A}$ which contain p. Moreover

$$\text{rank}\,\mathfrak{A} = \max\{\text{rank}_p\,\mathfrak{A} \mid p \in R\}.$$

It is clear that rank $\mathfrak{A} \leqq$ order $\mathfrak{A}$ for every collection $\mathfrak{A}$ of subsets. Now we can prove the following theorem.

Theorem 2. *A metric space R has* dim $\leqq n$ *if and only if it has an open basis* $\mathfrak{A}$ *of* rank $\mathfrak{A} \leqq n+1$.

Let us end this note with some problems. Aside from dimension, we do not know whether every metric space R has an open basis $\mathfrak{A}$ of rank$_p\,\mathfrak{A} < +\infty$ at each point p of R or not. Alexandroff's latest metrization theorem [1] assures us only that every metric space R has an open basis $\mathfrak{A}$ such that any independent subcollection of $\mathfrak{A}$ having a common point p is finite. Conversely, a topological space with an open basis of rank $< +\infty$ is not necessarily metrizable. We can easily give an example that is a regular space with an open basis of rank $= 1$ but not metrizable. Then, what space is the topological space which has an open basis $\mathfrak{A}$ of rank $\mathfrak{A} < +\infty$, and what about the topological space which has an open basis of rank$_p\,\mathfrak{A} < +\infty$ at every point p of R.

Bibliography

[1] *P. Alexandroff*: On the metrization of topological spaces. Bull. Acad. Polon. Sci. *8* (1960), 135–140.
[2] *J. de Groot*: On a metric that characterizes dimension. Canad. J. Math. *9* (1957), 511–514.
[3] *M. Katětov*: On the dimension of non-separable spaces I. Czech. Math. J. *2* (*77*) (1952), 333–368.
[4] *E. Marczewski* (*E. Szpilrajn*): La dimension et la mesure. Fundam. math. *28* (1937), 81–89.
[5] *K. Morita*: Normal families and dimension theory for metric spaces. Math. Ann. *128* (1954), 350–362.
[6] *J. Nagata*: On a metric characterizing dimension. Proc. Japan Acad. *36* (1960), 327–331.
[7] *J. Nagata*: On a relation between dimension and metrization. Proc. Japan Acad. *31* (1956), 237–240.
[8] *J. Nagata*: Note on dimension theory for metric spaces. Fundam. math. *45* (1958), 143–181.
[9] *J. Tukey*: Convergence and uniformity in topology. Ann. Math. Studies *2* (1940).

EXISTENCE OF UNIVERSAL CONNECTIONS

M. S. NARASIMHAN
Bombay

This is a report on a paper, written in collaboration with S. RAMANAN, which will appear in a forthcoming issue of the American Journal of Mathematics.

The purpose of the paper is to prove the existence of universal connections for principal bundles with a compact Lie group as structure group. We prove that, given a compact Lie group G and a positive integer n, there exist a differentiable principal G-bundle E and a connection γ_0 on E such that any connection on a differentiable principal G-bundle P with base of dimension $\leqq n$ can be obtained as the inverse image of the connection γ_0 by a differentiable bundle homomorphism of P into E. As is well-known, the analogous problem for bundles without connections is treated in the topology of fibre bundles.

It is also known that the Stiefel bundles play the role of universal bundles for the unitary groups $U(k)$. One can define in a natural way a connection on every Stiefel bundle. We prove that these connections themselves are universal for connections in $U(k)$-bundles.

In the unitary case the problem is first solved locally by explicit construction. The local solutions are then pieced up with the help of a special type of covering by coordinate cells.

In the general case, the compact Lie group G is identified with a closed subgroup of a unitary group. Starting from a universal connection for this unitary group, a universal connection for G is constructed by generalizing the usual method of construction of an invariant connection in the principal bundle associated with a Lie group and a closed subgroup.

A theorem of A. WEIL asserts that the cohomology classes of the base of a principal G-bundle obtained by substitution of the curvature form of a connection on P in the invariant polynomials of G is independent of the connection. Our result seems to explain this invariance and furnishes an alternate proof in the case of compact Lie groups.

PROBLÈME DE L'ANALYTICITÉ PAR RAPPORT À UN OPÉRATEUR LINÉAIRE DANS UNE ALGÈBRE NORMÉE

M. NICOLESCU

Bucureşti

1. À diverses étapes des nos recherches concernant la structure des solutions des équations aux dérivées partielles du second ordre, linéaires et à coefficients constants, nous avons obtenu, entre autres, les résultats suivants ([1], [2]):

I. Posons $D = \partial^2/\partial y\, \partial x$ et considérons une fonction $u : R^2 \to R$ indéfiniment différentiable. S'il existe une constante positive M telle que $|D^n u(x, y)| \leqq M$, $n = 1, 2, \ldots$ pour tout point (x, y) d'un certain domaine de $\mathscr{R}^2$, alors pour toute paire de points (x, y), (a, b) de ce domaine on a

$$u(x, y) = \sum_0^\infty (x - a)^n (y - b)^n [f_n(x) + g_n(y)]$$

et ce développement est unique. On constate, d'ailleurs, qu'en posant $h_n = f_n + g_n$, on a $Dh_n = 0$, $n = 0, 1, 2, \ldots$

II. Posons $\Delta = \partial^2/\partial x^2 + \partial^2/\partial y^2$ et considérons une fonction $u : D \to R$, où D est un domaine borné du plan pour lequel le problème à la frontière avec des données continues est possible. Si

$$|\Delta^n u(x, y)| \leqq M\,, \quad n = 1, 2, \ldots$$

qq. soit $(x, y) \in D$ et que le diamètre de D ne dépasse pas une certaine constante, alors

$$u(x, y) = u_0(x, y) + \varrho^2\, u_1(x, y) + \ldots + \varrho^{2n}\, u_n(x, y) + \ldots,$$

ϱ étant la distance de (x, y) à un point fixe $(a, b) \in D$ et $\Delta u_n(x, y) = 0$, $n = 0, 1, 2, \ldots$

III. Considérons, enfin, l'opérateur parabolique

$${}_p\Delta = \frac{\partial^2}{\partial x^2} - \frac{\partial}{\partial t}$$

dans le plan (x, t) et une fonction réelle u, indéfiniment différentiable dans un domaine borné D, compris entre deux droites $t = t_0$, $t = t_1$ quelconques, pour lequel le premier problème fondamental est possible. Si la „largeur" de ce domaine ne dépasse pas une certaine constante, et si

$$|{}_p\Delta^n\, u(x, t)| < M\,, \quad n = 1, 2, \ldots$$

pour tout $(x, t) \in D$, alors

$$u(x, t) = u_0(x, t) + t\, u_1(x, t) + \ldots + t^n\, u_n(x, t) + \ldots$$

avec ${}_p\Delta\, u_n(x, t) = 0$, $n = 0, 1, 2, \ldots$

Si l'on ajoute à ces trois faits le fait bien connu depuis Serge Bernstein que toute fonction $u : R \to R$ indéfiniment dérivable pour laquelle

$$\left| \frac{\mathrm{d}^n u(x)}{\mathrm{d}x^n} \right| < M \, , \quad n = 1, 2, \ldots$$

quelque soit x dans un certain intervalle I, est analytique, c'est-à-dire elle peut être représentée, au voisinage de chaque point $a \in I$ sous la forme

$$u(x) = u_0 + (x - a)\, u_1 + (x - a)^2\, u_2 + \ldots + u_n (x - a)^n + \ldots$$

avec $\mathrm{d}u_n/\mathrm{d}x = 0$, $n = 0, 1, 2, \ldots$, on constate qu'on est là en présence d'un phénomène commun aux cas considérés, phénomène où la distinction classique entre les trois espèces d'équations ne joue aucun role.

C'est en cherchant à expliquer ce phénomène que j'ai entrepris, tout dernièrement, la tâche de construir une théorie de l'analyticité d'un élément appartenant à une algèbre normée, par rapport à un opérateur linéaire fixe de cette algèbre. Les premiers résultats de cette étude ont été présentés, en 1956, au Congrès des Mathématiciens Autrichiens, à Vienne et publiés consécutivement dans les ,,Studia Mathematica", t. *XVI* (1958) (voir [3]).

L'objet de cette conférence est de montrer, par quelques résultats obtenus ultérieurement au travail cité, qu'on peut considérablement élargir le cadre de cette théorie.

Je serai bien obligé, afin de faire conserver à cette exposition un caractère autonome, de reprendre quelques notions et résultats de Mémoire cité [3] que je désignerai par (M_1). Je profiterai aussi de l'occasion pour donner aux axiomes de (M_1) une forme plus précise et en même temps plus générale, et pour en ajouter d'autres, nécessaires à l'élargissement du domaine de la recherche entreprise.

2. Par $x, y, \ldots$ on désignera des éléments d'une algèbre normée $\mathscr{B}$ commutative, à élément multiplicatif neutre e, pour lequel $\|e\| = 1$.

Dans la suite on considèrera une application linéaire distinguée $\mathrm{D} : \mathscr{D} \to \mathscr{B}$, où $\mathscr{D}$ est une sousalgèbre de $\mathscr{B}$. On n'attribuera aucun sens à $\mathrm{D}x$, pour $x \notin \mathscr{D}$. On supposera que

I_1. Si $\mathscr{D}_i$ est l'ensemble des points de $\mathscr{B}$ pour lesquels $\mathrm{D}^i x$ a un sens, l'ensemble

$$\mathscr{S} = \bigcap_{i=0}^{\infty} \mathscr{D}_i \, , \quad (\mathscr{D}_0 = \mathscr{D})$$

n'est pas vide.

I_2. $e \in \mathscr{D}_2$.

De I_2 il résulte que $\mathrm{D}x = e$ a au moins une solution. Nous en distinguerons une, que nous appellerons t. Ainsi $\mathrm{D}t = e$.

L'introduction de t nous permettra de formuler l'axiome suivant:[1])

[1]) Cet axiome a été omis, par mégarde, dans (M_1).

I_3. Si

$$B_1(x, y) = D(xy) - x\,Dy - y\,Dx$$

et

$$D_1 x = B_1(x, t) = B_1(t, x),$$

alors $DD_1 - D_1D = \alpha D$.

Posons maintenant la

Définition 1. Si $D_1 x = 0$, qq. soit $x \in \mathscr{D}$, D est un opérateur parabolique simple.

3. Soit Π l'ensemble des éléments de $\mathscr{D}$ pour lesquels il existe un nombre naturel n (variant avec l'élément considéré), tel que $D^n x = 0$.

Définition 2. Tout élément de l'adhérence $\overline{\Pi}$ de Π est appelé un élément continu de $\mathscr{B}$ (par rapport à D).

Définition 3. Tout élément $x \in \mathscr{D}$ qui peut se mettre sous la forme

$$x = x_0 + tx_1 + t^2 x_2 + \ldots$$

avec

$$Dx_n = 0, \quad n = 0, 1, 2, \ldots$$

est, par définition, un élément analytique de $\mathscr{D}$ (par rapport à D).

Si Δ est l'ensemble des éléments analytiques de $\mathscr{D}$, on a $\overline{\Delta} = \overline{\Pi}$.

Les axiomes I_1, I_2, I_3 nous permettent de démontrer le théorème de structure suivant:

Théorème 1. *Si* D *est parabolique simple et si* $D^n x = 0$, *alors il existe un système* $\{x_i\}$, $i = 0, 1, \ldots, n$ *de n solutions de* $Du = 0$, *telles que*

$$x = x_0 + tx_1 + \ldots + t^{n-1} x_{n-1}.$$

4. Si D n'est pas parabolique simple, le théorème de structure précédent reste valable si l'on ajoute aux axiomes I_1, I_2, I_3 l'axiome I_3 de (M_1), que nous désignerons ici par I_4.

5. L'ensemble des éléments continus forme un espace linéaire. Mais si $x \in \overline{\Pi}$ et $y \in \overline{\Pi}$, on ne peut rien affirmer sur l'élément xy, à moins de faire de nouvelle hypothèses. C'est ainsi qu'apparaît justifiée l'introduction de l'axiome suivant I_5. Si $Dx = 0$ et $Dy = 0$, alors xy est un élément continu.

À l'aide de cet axiome on peut démontrer le

Théorème 2. *Le produit de deux éléments continus est un élément continu.*

6. Nous ajouterons, maintenant, aux axiomes précédents, un axiome d'une nature différente.

II. Il existe une algèbre normée $\mathscr{B}'$ distincte de $\mathscr{B}$ et une application linéaire L de $\mathscr{B}$ sur $\mathscr{B}'$, telle que la restriction de L à l'ensemble $\mathscr{E}_y$ des solutions de $Dx = y$ ait une inverse $\Lambda_y x'$, continue en y pour tout $x' \in \mathscr{B}'$ et continue en x' pour tout $y \in \mathscr{D}_1$.

Nous désignerons dans la suite par des lettres accentuées les éléments de $\mathscr{B}'$. Il est facile d'établir l'identité

$$\Lambda_y x' = \Lambda_y(0') + \Lambda_0 x'.$$

Nous poserons

$$\Lambda_y(0') = Gy\,, \quad \Lambda_0 x' = \Lambda x'\,.$$

On peut vérifier que G est linéaire.

À l'aide du nouvel axiome on peut établir les propositions suivantes:

Théorème 3. *L'application* D^p, *où* p *est un nombre naturel, est fermée.*

En particular: Si $\{x_n\}$ est une suite d'éléments de $\mathscr{D}_p$, convergeante vers x et telle que

$$\mathrm{D}^p x_n = 0\,, \quad n = 1, 2, \ldots$$

alors $x \in \mathscr{D}_p$ et $\mathrm{D}^p x = 0$.

Théorème 4. *Si* y *est un élément continu, il existe* $x \in \mathscr{D}$ *tel que* $\mathrm{D}x = y$.

Théorème 5. *Si* $y \in \mathscr{S}$ *et si* y *est analytique, tout élément* x *tel que* $\mathrm{D}x = y$, *est analytique.*

7. Nous avons donné, dans (M_1),[1]) le critère suivant d'analyticité, qui constitue la synthèse de tous les critères formulés au début de notre conférence:

Soit $\|G\| = \gamma$. Si $\gamma < 1$ et si l'on a, pour un élément $x \in \mathscr{S}$,

$$\|\mathrm{D}^n x\| < M\,, \quad n = 1, 2, \ldots$$

l'élément x est analytique.

À ce critère nous pouvons en ajouter un autre:

Théorème 6. *Si, pour un élément* $x \in \mathscr{S}$, *on a*

$$\varrho = \lim_n \sup \|\mathrm{D}^n x\|^{1/n} < \infty$$

et si $\|G\| < 1/\varrho$, *l'élément* x *est analytique.*

À l'aide de chacun de ces deux critères on peut démontrer le

Théorème 7. *Si* D *est parabolique simple et si* x *vérifie l'un des critères précédents d'analyticité, alors le développement de* $\mathrm{D}x$ *s'obtient à partir de celui de* x

$$x = x_0 + tx_1 + t^2 x_2 + \ldots + t^n x_n + \ldots$$

en dérivant formellement le second membre par rapport à t.

8. Les résultats précédents permettent d'esquisser une théorie des éléments généralisés (d'ordre fini) de $\mathscr{B}$ (par rapport à D), dans le cas où $\mathscr{B}$ est complet.

Posons à cet effet, les définitions suivantes:

Définition 4. La suite $\{x_n\}_{n \in N}$ d'éléments continus est fondamentale s'il existe un entier non négatif p tel que $\{G^p x_n\}_{n \in N}$ converge.

Définition 5. Deux suites fondamentales $\{x_n\}$, $\{y_n\}$ soit équivalentes s'il existe un entier non négatif p tel que les suites $\{G^p x_n\}_{n \in N}$, $\{G^p y_n\}_{n \in N}$ convergent vers le même élément de $\mathscr{B}$.

Nous écrivons

$$\{x_n\} \sim \{y_n\}\,.$$

---

[1]) Voir (M_1), théorème IX, p. 360.

Il est facile de vérifier que la relation ainsi définie est une relation d'équivalence algébrique. Soit **R** cette relation. Nous poserons la

Définition 6. Tout élément de $\overline{\Pi}/\mathbf{R}$ est un élément généralisé de $\mathcal{B}$ (par rapport à D), ou une distribution de $\mathcal{B}$ (relativement à D).

Nous désignerons par x l'élément généralisé défini par la suite fondamentale $\{x_n\}$. Si cette dernière suite est une suite de Cauchy, elle converge vers un élément $x \in \overline{\Pi}$. Il est naturel donc d'identifier dans ce cas-là, la distribution engendrée par $\{x_n\}$ avec l'élément x.

9. Appelons, pour abréger, polynôme tout élément de Π. Si x est un élément généralisé, il existe un entier non négatif p, tel que la suite $\{G^p x_n\}_{n \in N}$ converge. Mois $G^p x_n \in \overline{\Pi}$. Il existe donc un polynome z_n tel que

$$\|G^p x_n - z_n\| < \frac{1}{n}.$$

Si $\lim_{n \to \infty} G^p x_n = u$, on peut écrire

$$\|u - z_n\| \leqq \|u - G^p x_n\| + \frac{1}{n},$$

donc la suite $\{z_n\}$ converge vers u. Ainsi:

Théorème 7. *Toute classe d'équivalence déterminée dans $\overline{\Pi}$ par la relation* **R** *contient une suite fondamentale de polynômes.*

Cette proposition va nous permettre de donner la

Définition 7. Si $\tilde{x}$ est un élément généralisé et si $\{\omega_n\}_{n \in E}$ est la suite fondamentale de polynomes engendrant $\tilde{x}$, la suite $\{D\omega_n\}_{n \in N}$, qui est fondamentale, définit un élément généralisé $\tilde{y}$ qu'on désignera par $D\tilde{x}$.

Ainsi donc, pour tout élément généralisé $\tilde{x}$, $D^p\tilde{x}$ a un sens, quel que soit p. Nous dirons, pour abréger, que $D\tilde{x}$ est la „dérivée" de $\tilde{x}$.

Notons, pour finir, qu'on peut introduire une définition de la limite pour les suites d'éléments généralisés et qu'on peut „dériver" terme à terme toute suite convergente d'éléments généralisés.

Bibliograp hie

[1] *Miron Nicolescu*: Sur quelques problèmes liés à l'opérateur itéré de la chaleur. Bull. Math. Soc. Sci. Math. Phys. de la R. P. R., t. *1 (49)* (1957), 327—336.

[2] *Miron Nicolescu*: Le problème de l'analyticité des fonctions réelles. Revue de Math. pures et appl., t. *2* (1957), 53—59.

[3] *Miron Nicolescu*: Problème de l'analyticité par rapport à un opérateur linéaire. Studia Mathematica, t. *16* (1958), 353—363.

[4] *J. Mikusiński, R. Sikorski*: The elementary theory of distributions. Warszawa 1957.

ON THE SEQUENTIAL ENVELOPE

J. NOVÁK

Praha

A convergence space or $\mathfrak{L}$-space L is a space, in which the sequential topology is defined by means of a convergence. By convergence $\mathscr{L}$ we understand a system $\mathscr{L}$ of sequences $\{x_n\} \in \mathscr{L}$ of points $x_n \in L$ converging to certain points called limits and designated by the symbol $\lim x_n$ and fulfilling two Fréchet's axioms:

1. If $x_n = x$ for each $n = 1, 2, \ldots$, then $\{x_n\} \in \mathscr{L}$ and $\lim x_n = x$.

2. If $\lim x_n = x$, then $\{x_{n_i}\} \in \mathscr{L}$ and $\lim x_{n_i} = x$ for each subsequence $\{x_{n_i}\}$ of $\{x_n\}$.

The closure λA of a set $A \subset L$ is defined as the set of all points $\lim x_n$, where $\{x_n\} \in \mathscr{L}$ and $x_n \in A$. In such a way we get a sequential topology or simply $\mathfrak{L}$-topology λ satisfying the following properties:

$$\lambda\emptyset = \emptyset\,, \quad \lambda L = L, \quad \lambda(A \cup B) = \lambda A \cup \lambda B\,, \quad A \subset B \text{ implies } \lambda A \subset \lambda B$$
$$\lambda x = x \quad \text{for each} \quad x \in L.$$

The closure of a subset $A \subset L$ need not be closed. Therefore it is possible to form successive closures

$$\lambda^0 A = A \subset \lambda^1 A = \lambda A \subset \lambda^2 A \subset \ldots \subset \lambda^\xi A \subset \ldots \subset \lambda^{\omega_1} A$$

where ω_1 is the first uncountable ordinal and $\lambda^\xi A = \bigcup_{\eta<\xi} \lambda\lambda^\eta A$. It is easy to prove that $\lambda\lambda^{\omega_1} A = \lambda^{\omega_1} A$, so that the set $\lambda^{\omega_1} A$ is the smallest closed set containing A as a subset. Consequently there is no sense in forming a closure $\lambda^\xi A$ for $\xi > \omega_1$.

The usual way of defining the continuity of real functions on L is as follows: f is continuous on L if $f(\lambda A) \subset \overline{f(A)}$ for each subset $A \subset L$. From this definition it follows that a real-valued function f is continuous on L, if and only if $\lim x_n = x$ implies $\lim f(x_n) = f(x)$ for each point $x \in L$. Therefore the continuity of real functions may be called the sequential continuity.

A subset G of an $\mathfrak{L}$-space L is a neighbourhood of a point $x \in L$, if x does not belong to $\lambda(L - G)$. Thus it is possible to define separated convergence spaces S in which any two distinct points are separated by neighbourhoods, and regular convergence spaces R, defined by means of neighbourhood closures. The notion of completely regular convergence space is not suitable for such convergence spaces in which the axiom of the closed closure ($\lambda^2 A = \lambda A$) does not hold true. For convergence spaces we define the notion of sequential regularity (abbr. S-regularity) like this:

The convergence space L is S-regular, if for each point $x_0 \in L$ and each sequence of points $x_n \in L$ no subsequence of which converges to x_0 there is a real valued sequentially continuous function f on L into $\langle 0, 1 \rangle$ such that the sequence of numbers $f(x_n)$ fails to converge to $f(x_0)$.

From this definition it follows that the S-regularity of a convergence space is a topological property. In 1947 I constructed a regular $\mathfrak{L}$-space Q such that each continuous function on it is constant [1]. Therefore a regular $\mathfrak{L}$-space need not be S-regular. On the other hand under the supposition that $\aleph_1 = 2^{\aleph_0}$ I was able to construct an S-regular convergence space which is not regular. Consequently regularity and S regularity of sequential topologies are not comparable.

It is well known that each completely regular topological space (fulfilling Kuratowski's axioms of topology) can be characterised as a subspace of a Cartesian cube of a certain dimension the topology of which is the usual topology in the topological product space. On the other hand the following theorem holds true:

A convergence space L is S-regular if and only if it is homeomorphic to a subspace of a Cartesian cube of a certain dimension in which the topology is defined by coordinatewise convergence of real numbers.

This cube will be called an L-cube and denoted by (C, κ).

Now it is possible to define for S-regular convergence spaces a similar notion as the Stone-Čech compactification of completely regular topological spaces.

Let (P, π) be a convergence space contained in an S-regular space (R, ϱ) as a subspace. The convergence space R will be called sequential envelope of the space P if the following conditions c_1, c_2, c_3 are satisfied:

c_1: $R = \varrho^{\omega_1} P$.

c_2: Each sequentially continuous function f on P into $\langle 0,1 \rangle$ has a continuous extension $\bar{f}$ on R into $\langle 0, 1 \rangle$.

c_3: There is no S-regular convergence space S containing R as a proper subspace and fulfilling the properties c_1 and c_2 relative to P and S.

The following theorem holds true:

Let P be a subspace of an S-regular convergence space R. Then R is a sequential envelope of the space P if and only if there is a homeomorphism h on R onto $\kappa^{\omega_1} \varphi(P) \subset C$ such that $h(x) = \varphi(x)$ for each point $x \in P$, φ being a special homeomorphism on P ($\varphi(x) = \{f_\iota(x)\} \in C$, whereby f_ι runs over all sequentially continuous functions on P into $\langle 0, 1 \rangle$) into the $\mathfrak{L}$-cube C, the sequential topology of which is κ.

From this theorem the following statements can be deduced:

Let L' and L'' be two sequential envelopes of the same S-regular $\mathfrak{L}$-space L. Then there exists a homeomorphism h on L' onto L'' such that $h(x) = x$ for each $x \in L$.

Every S-regular convergence space P has a sequential envelope which is homeomorphic to $\kappa^{\omega_1} \varphi(P)$.

The definition of the sequential envelope $\sigma(L)$ of an S-regular convergence space $\mathscr{L}$ is similar to the definition of Stone-Čech compactification $\beta(P)$ of a completely regular topological space P. Nevertheless the properties of the sequential envelope $\sigma(L)$ and of the β-envelope $\beta(L)$ of the same completely regular convergence space L can be completely different. For example the isolated space N of all naturals is a completely regular non-compact space. Consequently $\beta(N) \neq N$. However, it is easy to prove that $\sigma(N) = N$, so that $\beta(N) \neq \sigma(N)$.

The theory of sequential envelopes may be applied to the systems of sets, any system like this being an S-regular convergence space, the convergence in which is defined by the well known condition:

$$\lim A_n = A \quad \text{whenever} \quad A = \bigcup_{k=1}^{\infty} \bigcap_{n=k}^{\infty} A_n = \bigcap_{k=1}^{\infty} \bigcup_{n=k}^{\infty} A_n .$$

There is a question whether or not there exists an S-regular $\mathfrak{L}$-space L such that $\sigma(L) \neq L$. The answer is positive. I constructed a space which is homeomorphic to a system of sets, the sequential envelope of which is topologically different from the system itself.

There are some problems concerning the sequential envelope. For instance: What is the sequential envelope of the system of all realvalued functions $f(x)$ of real variable x the convergence in which is defined by the convergence at each point. Or: Of what structure is the sequential envelope of a system of sets.

It is worth noting that for the definition of S-regular convergence spaces and for sequential envelopes Urysohn's axiom of convergence (viz. if $\{x_n\}$ does not converge to x then there is a subsequence $\{x_{n_i}\}$ no subsequence of which converges to x) is not required.

The paper will be published in full in Czechoslovak Math. Journal 1963.

References

[1] *J. Novák*: Regulární prostor, na němž je každá spojitá funkce konstantní. Časopis pro pěst. mat. a fys., *73* (1948), 58–68.

ÜBER GEWISSE KLASSEN VON MODULARRÄUMEN

W. ORLICZ
Poznań

Es bezeichne X einen linearen Raum. Ein in X erklärtes Funktional $\varrho(x)$, $-\infty < \varrho(x) \leqq \infty$, heißt *Modular* falls es den folgenden Bedingungen genügt:

A.1. $\varrho(x) = 0$ dann und nur dann wenn $x = 0$.

A.2. $\varrho(-x) = \varrho(x)$.

A.3. $\varrho(\alpha x + \beta y) \leqq \varrho(x) + \varrho(y)$ für beliebige $\alpha, \beta \geqq 0, \alpha + \beta = 1$.

Ein linearer Raum in welchem ein Modular erklärt ist heisst ein *Modularraum*. H. NAKANO und seine Mitarbeiter haben die Theorie der Modularräume weit entwickelt, jedoch unter der Voraussetzung, dass die strengere Bedingung

A.3'. $\varrho(\alpha x + \beta y) \leqq \alpha\, \varrho(x) + \beta\, \varrho(y)$ für beliebige $\alpha, \beta \geqq 0, \alpha + \beta = 1$,

an Stelle der oben genannten Voraussetzung A.3, erfüllt ist.

Die Erforschung von Modularräumen bietet ein gewisses Interesse vom Standpunkte der Anwendungen der Funktionalanalysis, denn zahlreiche lineare topologische Räume der Analysis gehören zu diesem Typus von Räumen. Modularräume, im am Anfang formulierten allgemeineren Sinne, liefern auch gute Beispiele linearmetrischer Räume die nicht lokalkonvex sind. Zu den wichtigsten Repräsentanten von Modularräumen gehören die sog. Räume von φ-integrierbaren Funktionen. Es bedeute φ eine für $u \geqq 0$ stetige, nichtabnehmende Funktion, die für $u = 0$ gleich Null ist, sonst >0 und mit $u \to \infty$ gegen ∞ strebt. Es sei E eine abstrakte Menge, $\mathscr{E}$ eine Algebra von Untermengen der Menge E und μ ein σ-additives Mass in $\mathscr{E}$. Eine μ-messbare Funktion heißt φ-integrierbar, wenn das Integral $\int_E \varphi(\lambda|x(t)|)\, d\mu$ für eine gewisse Konstante $\lambda > 0$ endlich ist. Den Raum aller φ-integrierbarer Funktionen bezeichnen wir mit $L^{*\varphi}(E, \mu)$. Es werden einige Sätze über die linear-topologische Struktur von Räumen $L^{*\varphi}(E, \mu)$ mitgeteilt, die ich gemeinsam mit W. MATUSZEWSKA bewiesen habe.

Literatur

[1] *W. Matuszewska* and *W. Orlicz*; A note on the theory of s-normed spaces of φ-integrable functions. Studia Mathem. *21* (1961), 107—115.

SUR LES IMAGES CONTINUES DES CONTINUS ORDONNÉS

P. PAPIĆ

Zagreb

Cette communication est le résultat d'un travail commun de S. Mardešić et de l'auteur, publié sous le titre: S. MARDEŠIĆ-P. PAPIĆ, Continuous images of ordered continua, Glasnik mat.-fiz. i astr. 15 (1960), 171—178.

On sait bien que tout espace de Hausdorff X qui est image continue d'un continu ordonné est nécessairement compact, connexe et localement connexe. Si X est un espace métrique, ces conditions sont aussi suffisantes (théorème de H. HAHN et S. MAZURKIEWICZ). Nous donnerons ici une quatrième condition nécessaire, qui est indépendante des conditions citées dans le cas où X n'est pas métrique, et quelques autres propriétés des images continues des continus ordonnés.

Si X est un espace topologique, nous désignerons par $w(X)$ le plus petit nombre cardinal tel qu'il existe une base de voisinages de X de puissance $w(X)$. Nous dirons que l'espace X est k-séparable s'il contient une partie partout dense de puissance $\leqq k$, c'est-à-dire si son dégré de séparabilité $s(X) \leqq k$.

Un ensemble $E \subset X$ est non-dense si $\overline{X \setminus \overline{E}} = X$.

Théorème 1. *Soit X une image continue d'un continu ordonné. Si $p : X \to Y$ est une transformation continue de l'espace X sur un espace de Hausdorff Y ayant la propriété que pour tout $y \in Y$, l'ensemble fermé $p^{-1}(y)$ soit non-dense, alors $w(Y) = w(X)$.*

La démonstration du théorème précédent est basée sur ces deux lemmes:

Lemme 1. Soient $f : C \to X$ une transformation continue d'un continu ordonné C sur X et $p : X \to Y$ une transformation continue de X sur Y. Si p possède la propriété que pour tout $y \in Y$, $p^{-1}(y)$ soit non-dense dans X, alors il existe un sous-ensemble fermé $K \subset C$ qui est $w(Y)$-séparable et pour lequel $f(K) = X$.

Lemme 2. Soient X un espace localement connexe, K un espace totalement ordonné et compact et $f : K \to X$ une transformation sur X. Alors on a[1] $w(X) \leqq s(K)$.

Le théorème 1 nous donne la possibilité de caractériser les produits topologiques qui sont images continues des continus ordonnés. En effet, on a:

Théorème 2. *Pour qu'un produit topologique $\Pi_\alpha X_\alpha$, $\alpha \in A$ (puissance $A > 1$) de continus non dégénérés X_α soit image continue d'un continu ordonné, il faut et il*

[1]) La formulation originale de ce lemme a été un peu plus spéciale. A. J. WARD a fait remarquer aux auteurs que leur raisonnement démontre en essentiel le lemme cité dans le texte.

suffit que tous les X_α soient des continus métriques localement connexes (continus de Peano) et que puissance $A \leqq \aleph_0$. Alors $\Pi_\alpha X_\alpha$ est un continu métrique localement connexe et par conséquent image continue du segment $I = [0, 1]$ de nombres réels.

Du théorème 2 on déduit ce corollaire:

Soient C_1, C_2, C_3 des continus ordonnés et $f : C_1 \to C_2 \times C_3$ une transformation sur $C_2 \times C_3$. Alors $C_2 = C_3 = I$ et f peut être factorisé en une transformation motonone $g : C_1 \to I$ et „une transformation de Peano“ $h : I \to I \times I$.

Théorème 3. *Soit X image continue d'un continu ordonné. Alors $w(X) = s(X)$.*

Ce dernier théorème est une conséquence immédiate du théorème 1 et de ce lemme:

Lemme 3. *Soit X un continu non dégénéré, $\aleph_\tau$-séparable. Il existe alors un continu Y tel que $w(Y) \leqq \aleph_\tau$ est une transformation $p : X \to Y$ sur Y ayant la propriété que pour tout $y \in Y$, $p^{-1}(y)$ soit non-dense dans X.*

PROJECTION SPECTRA AND DIMENSION

B. PASYNKOV

Moscow

1.

1. We shall consider for a bicompactum X three types of inverse spectra $S = (X_\alpha, \pi_\alpha^{\alpha'})$:

a) *Combinatorial spectra* – the X_α are finite complexes (= finite T_0-spaces),[1]) and the projections are continuous mappings of T_0-spaces.

b) *Polyhedral spectra*: the X_α are polyhedra, the projections $\pi_\alpha^{\alpha'}$ are continuous ("into").

c) *Simplicial spectra*: the X_α are polyhedra, each projection $\pi_\alpha^{\alpha'}$ is a simplicial continuous mapping of the polyhedron $X_{\alpha'}$ (with a certain triangulation) into the polyhedron X_α (also with a certain triangulation).

2. Let us define the dimension of each spectrum $S = (X_\alpha, \pi_\alpha^{\alpha'})$ as

$$\operatorname{ind} S = \sup_{\alpha \in S} \operatorname{ind} X_\alpha ;$$

thus for a bicompactum X there result the combinatorial dimension $\dim_c X$, the polyhedral dimension $\dim_p X$ and the simplicial dimension $\dim_s X$, each defined as the minimum of dimensions ind S of all spectra of the given kind (combinatorial, polyhedral, simplicial) having the bicompactum X as limit space.

It is known that every bicompactum is the limit space of a simplicial spectrum (with projections which are in general not onto) — this is proved in the monograph [1] of S. Eilenberg and N. Steenrod; there are still older results of P. Alexandroff and A. Kurosch stating that every bicompactum is the limit space of a combinatorial spectrum (whose elements are finite simplicial complexes in the classical sense with projections onto); the Alexandroff-Kurosch theorem has been generalized to paracompact spaces by V. Ponomarev (see his communication).

3. The following results seem to be new (for the proofs see [2] to appear in the Matematičeskij Sbornik).

I. There exist bicompacta which cannot be represented as limit spaces of polyhedral (a fortiori of simplicial) spectra with projections "onto".

[1]) Every finite T_0-space can be realized as a finite simplicial complex in the general sense: a face of a simplex of the given complex may not belong to this complex.

II. The following relations hold for every bicompactum:

$$\dim X \leqq \dim_p X \leqq \dim_s X ,$$
$$\operatorname{Ind} X \leqq \dim_c X \leqq \dim_s X .$$

If $\dim_p X \leqq 1$ then moreover

$$\operatorname{Ind} X \leqq \dim_p X .$$

III. There exists a bicompactum X with

$$\dim X = \operatorname{ind} X = \operatorname{Ind} X = \dim_c X = 1$$

and

$$\dim_p X > 1 .$$

IV. For $n = 1, 2, 3, \ldots$ there exist bicompacta X_n with

$$\dim X_n = \operatorname{ind} X_n = \operatorname{Ind} X_n = \dim_c X_n = 1$$

and

$$\dim_s X = n .$$

These results shows a certain analogy with the beautiful results of P. VOPĚNKA (concerning $\dim X$, $\operatorname{ind} X$, $\operatorname{Ind} X$).

V. The "dimensional sum theorem" for a countable number of summands holds neither for $\dim_p X$ nor for $\dim_s X$; it does not hold for $\dim_c X$ even for two summands.

The following questions remain open, as far as I know:

a) Does there exist a bicompactum X with

$$\operatorname{Ind} X < \dim_c X .$$

b) Is the sum theorem true for $\dim_p X$ and $\dim_s X$ in the case of a finite numbers of summands.

2.

By means of inverse spectra of the form $S = (X_\alpha, \pi_\alpha^\beta)$, where the X_α are Hausdorff spaces (and the projections are continuous) the following theorem can be proved (see [3], [4]).

Theorem[2]**.** *Let G be a local bicompact group and H a closed subgroup of G. Then for the quotient space $X = G/H$ the following identity holds:*

$$\operatorname{ind} X = \operatorname{Ind} X = \dim X = \operatorname{ind} G - \operatorname{ind} H .$$

(As a corollary we obtain that

$$\operatorname{ind} G = \operatorname{Ind} G = \dim G , \quad \operatorname{ind} H = \operatorname{Ind} H = \dim H) .$$

For the case $\operatorname{ind} X < \infty$ (which includes the case $\operatorname{ind} G < \infty$), as well as for the case $\operatorname{ind} H < \infty$ I gave a direct proof of this theorem; in the infinite dimensional case the following theorem of E. SKLYARENKO [5] has been used: If $\dim X = \infty$, then X contains a topological image of the infinite dimensional Hilbert cube.

---

[2]) This theorem answers a problem raised by E. MICHAEL.

References

[1] *S. Eilenberg* and *N. Steenrod*: Foundations of Algebraic Topology. Princeton, 1952.

[2] *Б. Пасынков:* О спектрах и размерности топологических пространств. Матем. сб. (в печати).

[3] *Б. Пасынков:* Об обратных спектрах и размерности. Докл. АН СССР *138* (1961), 1013—1015.

[4] *Б. Пасынков:* О совпадении различных определений размерности для локально бикомпактных групп. Докл. АН СССР *132* (1960), 1035—1037.

[5] *Е. Скляренко:* О бесконечномерных однородных пространствах, Докл. АН СССР *141* (1961). 811—813.

PRODUCTS OF SPACES BY [0, 1]

V. POENARU

Bucuresti

This is a very short summary of a forthcoming paper (see: "Rendiconti di Matematica e delle sue applicazzioni"). The main result is the following:

Let V_3 be a compact 3-manifold such that $\pi_1(V_3) = 0$. Then there exists a number $n(V_3)$ such that if Σ is the main of the interiors of $n(V_3)$ 3-balls, differentiably embedded, we have:

$$(V_3 - \Sigma) \times [0, 1]^2 = (S_3 - \Sigma) \times [0, 1]^2 .$$

(*Equality means diffeomorphism.*)

This result is a [0, 1]-approximation of the Poincaré conjecture since it is easy to prove that this conjecture is equivalent to the following statement:

$$(V_3 - \Sigma) \times [0, 1] = (S_3 - \Sigma) \times [0, 1] .$$

There are strong connections between this paper and a forthcoming paper of BARRY MAZUR.

ON PARACOMPACT SPACES AND RELATED QUESTIONS

V. PONOMAREV

Moscow

In § 1, the general notion of $\mathfrak{A}$-compactness of which the paracompactness is a special case is considered; the characterizations of such spaces are given, using systems of closed sets as well as using the notion of limit points of nets.

In § 2 it is shown that all paracompact spaces and only these spaces are limit spaces of simplicial projection spectra in the sense of P. ALEXANDROFF [1] (generalized by A. KUROSH [2]).

1. $\mathfrak{A}$-compact spaces. Let $\mathfrak{A} = \{\alpha\}$ be any system of open coverings of a given space X, containing all finite open coverings as subsystem.

We shall say that the space X is $\mathfrak{A}$-*compact* if each open covering of X has a refinement $\alpha \in \mathfrak{A}$. A system $\sigma = \{F\}$ of closed sets is called tangent to $\mathfrak{A}$, or simply $\mathfrak{A}$-*tangent*, if in each $\alpha \in \mathfrak{A}$ there is an element $V_\alpha \in \alpha$ intersecting all $F \in \sigma$. The following theorem is easily proved:

Theorem 1. *In order that a space X be $\mathfrak{A}$-compact it is necessary and sufficient that each $\mathfrak{A}$-tangent system has a non-void intersection.*

Obviously, the system of all closed sets containing a given point x is an $\mathfrak{A}$-tangent system which we shall denote by (x). If X is $\mathfrak{A}$-compact, (x) is a maximal $\mathfrak{A}$-tangent system and there are no maximal tangent systems other than those of the type (x). The correspondence $x \leftrightarrow (x)$ is a one-to-one correspondence between the points of the $\mathfrak{A}$-compact space X and the set Ξ of its maximal $\mathfrak{A}$-tangent systems. This correspondence becomes a homeomorphism if we introduce in Ξ a Wallman topology.

From now on we shall suppose that $\mathfrak{A} = \{\alpha\}$ is a directed system (with the natural ordering: $\alpha' \succ \alpha$ if the covering α' is a refinement of the covering α).

Take in any $\alpha \in \mathfrak{A}$ and a set $V_\alpha \in \alpha$. The system $\xi = \{V_\alpha\}$ thus obtained is directed by the directed system $\mathfrak{A} = \{\alpha\}$, this system ξ is called an $\mathfrak{A}$-*thread* if for any two $V_\alpha \in \xi$, $V_{\alpha'} \in \xi$, a $V_{\alpha''} \in \xi$ can be chosen with $\alpha'' \succ \alpha$, $\alpha'' \succ \alpha'$ (in $\mathfrak{A}$) and[1])

$$[V_{\alpha''}] \subseteq V_\alpha \cap V_{\alpha'}\,.$$

We shall say that the space X has the property $(K_{\mathfrak{A}})$ if for every $\mathfrak{A}$-tangent system $\sigma = \{F\}$ the sets $V_\alpha \in \alpha$ (having common points with all $F \in \sigma$) can be chosen in such a way as to form an $\mathfrak{A}$-thread ("the $\mathfrak{A}$-thread dual to the tangent system σ").

[1]) The brackets denote closure.

Theorem 2. *In order that a regular space X be $\mathfrak{A}$-compact it is necessary and sufficient that both of the following conditions are fulfilled:*

(a) *the space X has the property $K_{\mathfrak{A}}$,*

(b) *each $\mathfrak{A}$-thread $\xi = \{V_\alpha\}$ has a non-void intersection.*

It is natural to call a space $\mathfrak{A}$-*complete* if it satisfies the condition (b).

Lemma. *If $\xi = \{V_\alpha\}$ is an $\mathfrak{A}$-thread and $x \in \bigcap_\alpha [V_\alpha]$, then all of the neighbourhoods Ox of the point x are among the V_α.*

In fact, obviously $\bigcap_\alpha V_\alpha = \bigcap_\alpha [V_\alpha]$; for the given Ox we take a smaller O_1x with $[O_1x] \subseteq Ox$ and $\alpha_0 = \{Ox, X \setminus [O_1x]\}$; then necessarily $V_{\alpha_0} = Ox$.

It follows from this lemma that the intersection of all elements of a thread cannot contain more than one point.

Now the theorem 2 is proved in a few words. Let X be $\mathfrak{A}$-compact, and $\sigma = \{F\}$ an $\mathfrak{A}$-tangent system. Then $\bigcap_{F \in \sigma} F$ contains a point x_0.

In any α take an element $V_\alpha \ni x_0$. The system $\xi = \{V_\alpha\}$ thus obtained is an $\mathfrak{A}$-thread. In fact let $V_\alpha \in \xi$, $V_{\alpha'} \in \xi$ be given. Let us choose neighbourhoods Ox, O_1x of x so that

$$[Ox] \subseteq V_\alpha \cap V_{\alpha'}, \quad [O_1x] \subseteq Ox,$$

and take the covering $\alpha_1 = \{Ox, X \setminus [O_1x]\}$. Take any covering α'' following α, α', α_1; then the set $V_{\alpha''} \in \xi$, containing x and contained in some element of α_1, must be contained in Ox; therefore

$$[V_{\alpha''}] \subseteq [Ox] \subseteq V_\alpha \cap V_{\alpha'};$$

q. e. d.

Obviously the thread ξ is dual to σ and the space X has the property $K_{\mathfrak{A}}$. Moreover, for any thread $\xi' = \{V'_\alpha\}$, the system $\{[V'_\alpha]\}$ is a tangent system and the necessity of our condition is proved.

Sufficiency: Let $\sigma = \{F\}$ be a tangent system and $\xi = \{V_\alpha\}$ a dual thread with

$$x_0 = \bigcap_\alpha V_\alpha = \bigcap [V_\alpha].$$

As all V_α, i. e. all Ox_0, intersect all $F_\alpha \in \sigma$, we have $x_0 \in \bigcap_{F \in \sigma} F$ and thus X is $\mathfrak{A}$-compact.

Definition. A net $\{x_\vartheta\}$, $x_\vartheta \in X$, indexed by any directed set $\Theta = \{\vartheta\}$ is called an $\mathfrak{A}$-*net*, if every $\alpha \in \mathfrak{A}$ contains an element V_α such that for every $\vartheta_0 \in \Theta$ there is an $x_\vartheta \in V_\alpha$ with $\vartheta > \vartheta_0$.

Theorem 3. *In order that a regular space X be $\mathfrak{A}$-compact it is necessary and sufficient that it have the property $K_{\mathfrak{A}}$ and that each $\mathfrak{A}$-net have a limit point.*

Necessity: If X is $\mathfrak{A}$-compact, it has the property $K_{\mathfrak{A}}$. Let $\{x_\vartheta\}$ be an $\mathfrak{A}$-net. Let us define

$$F_\vartheta = [\mathscr{E}(x_{\vartheta'}, \vartheta' \geqq \vartheta)].$$

Since $\{x_\vartheta\}$ is an $\mathfrak{A}$-net, $\{F_\vartheta\}$ is an $\mathfrak{A}$-tangent system, so that it has common point x_0 which is a limit point of $\{x_\vartheta\}$.

Sufficienty: Let $\sigma = \{F\}$ be an arbitrary $\mathfrak{A}$-tangent system, $\xi = \{V_\alpha\}$ a dual thread. For every α take $x_\alpha \in V_\alpha$; then $\{x_\alpha\}$ is a net (directed by $\mathfrak{A} = \{\alpha\}$), and in fact an $\mathfrak{A}$-net. By hypothesis, it has a limit point x_0 which is the (only) common point of all $[V_\alpha]$. Thus by the above lemma, all neighbourhoods of x are among the V_α, so that x belongs to all $F \in \sigma$ and $\bigcap_{F \in \sigma} F \neq \emptyset$, q. e. d.

2. Paracompactness, metric and projective spectra. First of all we recall the following theorem, proved (but not formulated explicitly) by C. H. DOWKER (1948); an explicit formulation can be found in M. Katětov's Appendix to the book ,,Topologické prostory" (Topological spaces, Prague 1959) by E. Čech.

Theorem 4. *In order that a regular space X be paracompact it is necessary and sufficient that for every open covering ω of X there exist an ω-mapping*[2]) *of X onto a metric space Y. If we suppose that Y is metric separable, we obtain a characterisation of final compact (Lindelöf) spaces.*

The proof of the first part of this theorem is straight-forward: if X allows, for every ω, an ω-mapping onto a paracompact space Y, then X itself is paracompact.

The proof of the second part is contained in a result of C. H. DOWKER [3]. An alternate proof is given in the book mentioned above.

Now let us pass to the spectral characterization of paracompact spaces.

1. According to a classical definition of P. ALEXANDROFF, a projection-spectrum is a directed set Σ of simplicial complexes[3]) $\alpha, \alpha', \ldots$ and of simplicial mappings, called projections; for each pair α, α' in Σ with $\alpha' \succ \alpha$ there is a well defined projection $\pi_\alpha^{\alpha'}$ of the complex α' onto α; for $\alpha'' \succ \alpha' \succ \alpha$ one has

$$\pi_\alpha^{\alpha''} = \pi_\alpha^{\alpha'} \pi_{\alpha'}^{\alpha''} .$$

If in each complex α we take a simplex t_α under the condition

$$\pi_\alpha^{\alpha'} t_{\alpha'} = t_\alpha ,$$

we obtain a so-called thread $\xi = \{t_\alpha\}$ of the spectrum; a thread $\xi = \{t_\alpha\}$ is called maximal if there exists no thread $\xi' = \{t'_\alpha\}$ different from ξ and such that $t'_\alpha \geqq t_\alpha$ (that is to say that t_α is a face of t'_α) for all t_α.

By definition, the maximal threads are points of the limit space $\tilde{\Sigma}$ of the spectrum

$$\Sigma = \{\alpha, \pi_\alpha^{\alpha'}\} .$$

As for the topology of $\tilde{\Sigma}$, we define for any simplex t_{α_0} of a given $\alpha_0 \in \Sigma$ the set Ot_{α_0} consisting of all threads $\xi' = \{t'_\alpha\}$ with $t'_{\alpha_0} \leqq t_{\alpha_0}$. These sets Ot_α are by definition the basic open sets of $\tilde{\Sigma}$. It is easily seen that the set $\tilde{\Sigma}$ with this topology is a T_1-space.

[2]) Let ω be a covering of the space X; a continuous mapping $f : X \to Y$ is called an ω-mapping (Alexandroff [1]), if each point $y \in Y$ has a neighbourhood Oy such that $f^{-1}Oy$ is contained in some element of ω.

[3]) A complex is meant in the classical sense, as a set α of (abstract finite dimensional) simplices; if $t \in \alpha$ and $t' < t$ (i. e. t' is a face of t), then $t' \in \alpha$.

Now let us consider for any simplex $t_{\alpha 0} \in \alpha$ the set $\Phi t_{\alpha 0}$ of all points

$$\xi' = \{t'_\alpha\} \in \tilde{\Sigma} \quad \text{with} \quad t'_{\alpha 0} \geqq t_{\alpha 0} .$$

It is easily proved that the sets Φt_α are closed in the topological space $\tilde{\Sigma}$. Among the $\Phi t_{\alpha 0}$, the sets Φe_α corresponding to the vertices e_α of the complex α are the most important.

For a given complex $\alpha \in \Sigma$, the sets Φe_α corresponding to all vertices of α form a closed covering φ_α of the space $\tilde{\Sigma}$.

These coverings φ_α are called the *fundamental coverings* of the limit space $\tilde{\Sigma}$.

Remark 1. One proves immediately that the *nerve of the covering* φ_α *is a subcomplex of the complex* α.

Now call the spectrum Σ *complete* if for every $t_{\alpha 0} \in \alpha_0 \in \Sigma$ there exists a thread $\xi = \{\tau_\alpha\}$ with $\tau_{\alpha 0} \geqq t_{\alpha 0}$. If the spectrum

$$\Sigma = \{\alpha, \pi_\alpha^{\alpha'}\}$$

is complete, then the nerve of φ_α is the complex α.

Remark 2. It is easy to give a condition for the regularity of the limit space $\tilde{\Sigma}$ of the spectrum

$$\Sigma = \{\alpha, \pi_\alpha^{\alpha'}\} .$$

Call Σ a regular spectrum if for any

$$\xi = \{\tau_\alpha\} \in \tilde{\Sigma}$$

and α_0 there exists an $\alpha' \in \Sigma$ such that supposing

$$\tau_{\alpha'} = \left|e_{\alpha'}^0, \ldots, e_{\alpha'}^2\right| \in \xi ,$$

we have

$$\Phi e_{\alpha'}^0 \cup \ldots \cup \Phi e_{\alpha'}^r \subseteq O\tau_\alpha .$$

A regular spectrum has a regular limit space.

2. All the previous notions are either those described in the classical paper [1] of Alexandroff, in which the definition of a projective spectrum is given, or their immediate generalizations. Now we come to the main condition, which expresses that the convergence of the spectrum to its limit space is in a certain sense uniform.

Definition. The spectrum $\Sigma = \{\alpha, \pi_\alpha^{\alpha'}\}$ is called *uniform* if any covering of Σ by basic open sets is refined by some fundamental covering φ_α.

The principal result of this paper is:

Theorem 5. *The limit space of any uniform (regular) spectrum is a paracompact (regular) space.*

Every paracompact regular space is the limit space of a uniform regular complete spectrum.

The strong paracompact spaces[4]) *are characterized among paracompact*

[4]) Strong paracompact means that any covering can be refined by a star-finite one.

spaces by the condition that all complexes in the spectrum can be supposed star finite.

Let us say only a few words about the proof of the second part of this theorem.

If X is a paracompact (regular and therefore normal) space, then every open covering ω of X can be refined by a locally finite canonical (closed) covering.[5]) These coverings form a directed system. Their nerves (star-finite if the covering is star-finite) with the natural projections form a uniform regular complete spectrum Σ with the limit space $\tilde{\Sigma}$ homeomorphic to X.

Finally, let us remark that for a spectrum $\Sigma = \{\alpha, \pi_\alpha^{\alpha'}\}$ composed of finite complexes (that is the classical case of Alexandroff-Kurosch with a bicompact limit space), the condition of uniformity fundamental in our theorem is satisfied automatically.

References

[1] *P. Alexandroff*: Gestalt und Lage abgeschlossener Mengen beliebiger Dimension. Annals of Math. *30*, 1929, 101—187.

[2] *A. Kurosch*: Kombinatorischer Aufbau der bikompakten topologischen Räume. Comp. Math. *2* (1935), 471—476.

[3] *C. H. Dowker*: On Alexandroff's Mapping Theorem. Bull. Amer. Math. Soc. *54*, 4, 1948, 386—391.

[5]) A covering is canonic if its elements are closures of disjoint open sets.

PROBABILITY MEASURES ON NON-COMMUTATIVE SEMIGROUPS

Š. SCHWARZ
Bratislava

Let S be a compact semigroup, i. e. a compact Hausdorff space with a jointly continuous binary operation (multiplication) under which it forms a semigroup. A probability measure on S is a real-valued, non-negative, countably additive, regular set function μ defined on the Borel subsets of S such that $\mu(S) = 1$. The totality of all such measures will be denoted by $\mathfrak{M}(S)$.

Let $\omega(S)$ be the Banach space of real continuous functions on S. Recall the $1-1$ correspondence between the measure $\mu \in \mathfrak{M}(S)$ and the continuous linear functionals Φ on $\omega(S)$ with the properties $f \geqq 0 \Rightarrow \Phi(f) \geqq 0$ and $\Phi(1) = 1$ that is given by the relation $\Phi(f) = \int f(x)\, \mathrm{d}\mu(x)$.

We may (and we shall) consider $\mathfrak{M}(S)$ embedded in $\omega(S)^*$ (the first conjugate space of $\omega(S)$) and we regard also S as embedded (in an obvious way) in $\mathfrak{M}(S)$.

We give $\omega(S)^*$ the weak*-topology (so that $\mu_\alpha \to \mu$ means $\int f\, \mathrm{d}\mu_\alpha(x) \to \int f\, \mathrm{d}\mu(x)$ for $f \in \omega(S)$) and define the product $\mu\nu$ by means of $\int f(x)\, \mathrm{d}(\mu\nu)(x) = \iint f(yz)\, \mathrm{d}\mu(y)\,.\,\mathrm{d}\nu(z)$, $f \in \omega(S)$. The set $\mathfrak{M}(S)$ becomes a compact semigroup.

If for $\mu \in \mathfrak{M}(S)$ $C(\mu)$ denotes the support of μ, it is known that $C(\mu\nu) = C(\mu)\,.\,C(\nu)$.

In the last years the structure of $\mathfrak{M}(S)$ has been studied by several authors, in particular by Н. Н. Воробьев [9], J. G. Wendel [10], E. Hewitt-H. S. Zuckerman [2], Б. М. Клосс [3], I. Glicksberg [7], K. Stromberg [8]. But these authors consider only the case of groups and abelian semigroups. The essential novelty of our contribution is that we are going beyond the restriction of commutativity even in the non-group case (for S). We give here some results, the detailed proofs of which will be published in the Czechoslovak Mathematical Journal ([6] and [7]).

1. The first problem is to identify the *idempotents* $\in \mathfrak{M}(S)$.

A subset L of any semigroup T is called a left ideal of T if $TL \subset L$ holds. Right and two-sided ideals are defined analogously. A semigroup T is called simple (more precisely simple without zero) if it does not contain a two-sided ideal $\neq T$. If T is a compact simple semigroup it is known that T contains minimal left and right ideals. In fact $T = \bigcup_\alpha R_\alpha = \bigcup_\beta L_\beta$, where $R_\alpha[L_\beta]$ runs through all (disjoint) minimal right [left] ideals of T. Also $R_\alpha \cap L_\beta = R_\alpha L_\beta = G_{\alpha\beta}$ is a closed (compact) group and T can be written as a union of closed (hence compact) topologically isomorphic groups: $T = \bigcup_\alpha \bigcup_\beta G_{\alpha\beta}$.

Let now be ε an idempotent $\in \mathfrak{M}(S)$. Б. М. Клосс [3] proved that $C(\varepsilon)$ is a closed (hence compact) simple subsemigroup of S.

In what follows we shall suppose that S contains only a *finite* number of idempotents though some of the results are valid under more general suppositions or even without any assumption of this kind.

If ε is an idempotent $\in \mathfrak{M}(S)$ and $C(\varepsilon) = \bigcup_{\alpha=1}^{s} \bigcup_{\beta=1}^{r} G_{\alpha\beta}$ is the group-decomposition of $C(\varepsilon)$, it can be proved that ε restricted to $G_{\alpha\beta}$ is an invariant measure on $G_{\alpha\beta}$. This implies: If $\mu_{\alpha\beta}$ is the normalized Haar measure on $G_{\alpha\beta}$ (extended in an obvious way to S) then $\varepsilon = \sum_{\alpha=1}^{s} \sum_{\beta=1}^{r} \xi_\alpha \eta_\beta \mu_{\alpha\beta}$, ξ_α, η_β being positive numbers satisfying the relation $\sum_{\alpha=1}^{s} \xi_\alpha = \sum_{\beta=1}^{r} \eta_\beta = 1$.

Conversely, if $H = \bigcup_{\alpha=1}^{s} \bigcup_{\beta=1}^{r} G_{\alpha\beta}$ is *any* closed simple subsemigroup of S, there exists at least one idempotent having H for its support and every idempotent $\in \mathfrak{M}(S)$ with the support H is of the form $\sum_{\alpha=1}^{s} \sum_{\beta=1}^{r} \xi_\alpha \eta_\beta \mu_{\alpha\beta}$, where $\sum_{\alpha=1}^{s} \xi_\alpha = \sum_{\beta=1}^{r} \eta_\beta = 1$, $\xi_\alpha \eta_\beta > 0$.

The study of the idempotents $\in \mathfrak{M}(S)$ is simplified by the fact that the location of all simple subsemigroups of S can be clarified to some extent and we may restrict the attention to the "maximal simple subsemigroups of S" (which in general need not have an empty intersection). A useful lemma is the following statement: Every closed subsemigroup of a compact simple semigroup (without zero) is itself simple (see [5]).

2. In some problems (see f. i. [4]) the *primitive* idempotents $\in \mathfrak{M}(S)$ are of decisive importance. An idempotent f of any semigroup T is said to be primitive if there does not exist an idempotent $e \in T$, $e \neq f$, such that $fe = ef = e$ holds. The following results clarify the structure of the set of all primitive idempotents $\in \mathfrak{M}(S)$.

Denote by N the kernel of S (i. e. the minimal two-sided ideal of S) and by $\mathfrak{N}$ the kernel of $\mathfrak{M}(S)$. If $N = \bigcup_{\alpha=1}^{s} \bigcup_{\beta=1}^{r} G_{\alpha\beta}$ is the group-decomposition of N, then all primitive idempotents $\in \mathfrak{M}(S)$ are given by the expression $\sum_{\alpha=1}^{s} \sum_{\beta=1}^{r} \xi_\alpha \eta_\beta \mu_{\alpha\beta}$, where ξ_α, η_β are *non-negative* numbers satisfying $\sum_{\alpha=1}^{s} \xi_\alpha = \sum_{\beta=1}^{r} \eta_\beta = 1$. The kernel $\mathfrak{N}$ is identical with the set of all primitive idempotents $\in \mathfrak{M}(S)$. Consider finally the set $\mathfrak{T}$ of all $(s + r)$-tuples of non-negative real numbers $(\xi_1, \ldots, \xi_s, \eta_1, \ldots, \eta_r)$ with $\sum_{\alpha=1}^{s} \xi_\alpha = \sum_{\beta=1}^{r} \eta_\beta = 1$ and define in $\mathfrak{T}$ a multiplication $\circ$ by

$$(\xi'_1, \ldots, \xi'_s, \eta'_1, \ldots, \eta'_r) \circ (\xi''_1, \ldots, \xi''_s, \eta''_1, \ldots, \eta''_r) = (\xi'_1, \ldots, \xi'_s, \eta''_1, \ldots, \eta''_r) .$$

Then $\mathfrak{N}$ is isomorphic with $\mathfrak{T}$.

3. Another important problem is to identify the *maximal groups* contained in $\mathfrak{M}(S)$.

Let $\varepsilon = \sum_{\alpha=1}^{s} \sum_{\beta=1}^{r} \xi_\alpha \eta_\beta \mu_{\alpha\beta}$ (with fixed chosen ξ_α, η_β) be an idempotent $\in \mathfrak{M}(S)$ and $\mathfrak{G}(\varepsilon)$ the (uniquely determined) maximal group of $\mathfrak{M}(S)$ containing ε as its unity element. Denote $C(\varepsilon) = H$. There exists always a uniquely determined maximal simple subsemigroup $H' \supset H$ of S containing exactly the same idempotents as H. Construct the double coset decomposition

$$H' = H \cup HaH \cup HbH \cup \ldots, \quad (a, b, \ldots \in H')$$

with disjoint summands. This is possible (see [5]). If $H = \bigcup_{\alpha=1}^{s} \bigcup_{\beta=1}^{r} G_{\alpha\beta}$, $H' = \bigcup_{\alpha=1}^{s} \bigcup_{\beta=1}^{r} G'_{\alpha\beta}$, $G_{\alpha\beta} \subset G'_{\alpha\beta}$, there exists also a decomposition of each $G'_{\alpha\beta}$ of the form

$$G'_{\alpha\beta} = G_{\alpha\beta} \cup G_{\alpha\beta} a G_{\alpha\beta} \cup G_{\alpha\beta} b G_{\alpha\beta} \cup \ldots$$

(In fact $HaH \cap G'_{\alpha\beta} = G_{\alpha\beta} a G_{\alpha\beta}$.) With these notations the following results hold:

a) If $\mu \in \mathfrak{G}(\varepsilon)$, we have $C(\mu) = HaH$ with a suitably chosen $a \in H'$.

b) There is a unique element $\mu \in \mathfrak{G}(\varepsilon)$ with $C(\mu) = HaH$ and μ is exactly the element $\mu = \sum_{\alpha=1}^{s} \sum_{\beta=1}^{r} \xi_\alpha \eta_\beta \tau_{\alpha\beta}$, where $\tau_{\alpha\beta} = \mu_{\alpha\beta} a \mu_{\alpha\beta}$.

c) A class HaH is the support of an element $\in \mathfrak{G}(\varepsilon)$ if and only if $G_{\alpha\beta} a G_{\alpha\beta}$ is contained in the normalizer $G_{\alpha\beta}^{(0)}$ of $G_{\alpha\beta}$ in $G'_{\alpha\beta}$. (If the last statement holds for one couple (α, β), then it holds for all couples (σ, ϱ), $\sigma = 1, \ldots, s$; $\varrho = 1, \ldots, r$.)

d) The group $\mathfrak{G}(\varepsilon)$ is algebraically isomorphic to the quotient group $G_{\alpha\beta}^{(0)}/G_{\alpha\beta}$.

4. The following limit theorems are consequences of the results stated above:

Consider the sequence $\{\mu, \mu^2, \mu^3, \ldots\}$. If $\lim_{n=\infty} \mu^n$ exists, it is equal to the unique idempotent ε contained in the closure of $\{\mu, \mu^2, \mu^3, \ldots\}$. This is the case if and only if $\mu\varepsilon = \varepsilon\mu = \varepsilon$.

A rather algebraic characterisation of the existence of the limit considered is the fulfilment of the relation $H\, C(\mu)\, H = H$, where $H = C(\varepsilon)$.

The next result holds even without the assumption concerning the finiteness of the number of idempotents $\in S$. Consider the sequence $\sigma_n = 1/n\ (\mu + \mu^2 + \ldots + \mu^n)$, $n = 1, 2, 3, \ldots$ Then $\lim_{n=\infty} \sigma_n$ exists always and it is equal to an idempotent $\sigma \in \mathfrak{M}(S)$. If P is the closure of the algebraic semigroup generated by $C(\mu)$ and J is the minimal two-sided ideal of P, then we have $C(\sigma) = J$.

References

[1] *I. Glicksberg*: Convolution semigroups of measures. Pacific J. Math. *9* (1959), 51–67.

[2] *E. Hewitt*, *H. S. Zuckerman*: Arithmetic and limit theorems for a class of random variables. Duke Math. J. *22* (1955), 595–615.

[3] *Б. М. Клосс:* О вероятностных распределениях на бикомпактных топологических группах. Теория вероятностей и ее применения, *4* (1959), 255—290.

[4] *Š. Schwarz* О существовании инвариантных мер на некоторых типах бикомпактных полугрупп. Чехосл. матем. ж. *7* (82) (1957), 165—182.

[5] *Š. Schwarz*: Subsemigroups of simple semigroups. Czechoslovak Math. J. *12* (87) (1962). To appear.

[6] *Š. Schwarz*: Probabilities on non-commutative semigroups. Czechoslovak Math. J. To appear.

[7] *Š. Schwarz*: Convolution semigroup of measures on compact non-commutative semigroups. Czechoslovak Math. J. To appear.

[8] *K. Stromberg*: Probabilities on a compact group. Trans. Amer. Math. Soc. *94* (1960), 295–309.

[9] *Н. Н. Воробьев:* Сложение независимых случайных величин на конечных абелевых группах. Матем. сб. *34* (1954), 89—126.

[10] *J. G. Wendel*: Haar measure and a semigroup of measures on a compact group. Proc. Amer. Math. Soc. *5* (1954), 923–929.

NON-*F*-SPACES

VĚRA ŠEDIVÁ-TRNKOVÁ

Praha

I. In this note some theorems about topological spaces, in which the closure of a set is not always a closed set, are shown. The topology u on a set P is a mapping, which assigns a set $uM \subset P$ to every set $M \subset P$ and satisfies the following axioms: $u\emptyset = \emptyset$, $u(X) = (X)$, $u(M_1 \cup M_2) = uM_1 \cup uM_2$. The condition $u(uM) = uM$, called axiom F, is not required in general; thus we distinguish among F-spaces (i. e. spaces, satisfying F-axiom) and non-F-spaces. Non-F-spaces were called "gestufte Räume" by F. Hausdorff. In non-F-spaces neighbourhoods of sets and interiors of sets are defined as follows: a set U is a neighbourhood of a set M if $M \cap u(P - U) = \emptyset$; Int $M = \{x \in M;\ M$ is neighbourhood of $x\}$. The non-F-topology problems have been dealt with by some Czech mathematicians. E. Čech defined on a topological space (P, u) a new topology $\tilde{u}$, called the F-reduction of u such that $\tilde{u}$ satisfies axiom F and $\{P - uM;\ M \subset P\}$ is an open base for it. Therefore the neighbourhoods of points in $(P, \tilde{u})$ are interiors of neighbourhoods in (P, u). Evidently, $\tilde{u}$ is finer than u and the equality $u = \tilde{u}$ holds if and only if u is an F-topology.

Theorem 1. *Let (P, v) be an F-space. Then there exists a non-F-topology u on P such that $\tilde{u} = v$ if and only if v is not maximal (i. e. there exists an infinite set $M \subset P$ such that $vM \neq P$).*

Proof in [17].

II. For the greater part of non-artificially constructed non-F-spaces the F-reduction is discrete. It refers especially to the spaces of real functions with a topology, defined by means of convergence of sequences of functions at each point. Let $D(Q)$ denote some set of real function on an F-space Q; we say that a sequence $\{f_n\}$ of points of $D(Q)$ converges to $f \in D(Q)$ if $\lim_{n\to\infty} f_n(x) = f(x)$ for all $x \in Q$. On $D(Q)$ the topology u is defined in such a way that the closure uM of $M \subset D(Q)$ is the set of all limit-points of all sequences of points of M. This topology u shall be considered on a set of all (or all bounded) real continuous functions on some F-space Q (denoted by $C(Q)$) and on a set of all characteristic functions on some set Q (denoted by $\chi(Q)$). We recall that a space $(D(Q), \tilde{u})$ is discrete if and only if for every $f \in D(Q)$ there exists $H_f \subset D(Q)$ such that every $g \in D(Q)$, $g \neq f$ is a limit point of some sequence of points of H_f, but no sequence of points of H_f converges to f (this follows immediately from the definition of the F-reduction of a topology).

Theorem 2. *Let Q contain a countable dense subset. Then $(C(Q), \tilde{u})$ is discrete if and only if $(C(Q), u)$ is a non-F-space.*

Proof in [15].

For non-separable Q this theorem does not hold. There exists even a compact Hausdorff space Q, for which $(C(Q), u)$ is a non-F-space but $(C(Q), \tilde{u})$ is not discrete. The example of this space is contained in [15].

Theorem 3. *Let Q be a normal space, containing a discrete, normally imbedded subset,*[1]) *the power of which is $\aleph = \aleph^{\aleph_0}$ ($\aleph$ denotes an arbitrary cardinal number) and a dense subset, the power of which is $\leqq 2^{\aleph}$. Then $(C(Q), \tilde{u})$ is discrete.*

Proof in [15].

Theorem 4. *Let Q contain a countable dense metrizable subset; let every point of Q have a complete collection of neighbourhoods such that each neighbourhood from this collection is dense-in-itself, normal, non-meager space. Let $R \subset C(Q)$ be a ring of functions such that*

(a) $uR = C(Q)$,

(b) if $A \subset Q$ is closed, $x \in Q$, $x \notin A$, then there exists $f \in R$ such that $f(x) = 0$, $f(y) = 1$ for all $y \in A$.

Then for every $f \in C(Q)$ there exists $H_f \subset R$ such that $uH_f = C(Q) - (f)$.

Proof in [18].

III. Theorem 2 leads to one problem (which as far as I know, has not yet been fully solved) when $(C(Q), u)$ is an F-space and when it is not. Two theorems follow concerning this:

Theorem 5. *If for every $f \in C(Q)$ the set $f(Q)$ is countable, then $(C(Q), u)$ is an F-space.*

This theorem follows immediately from the following proposition.

Proposition 1. If for every $f \in C(Q)$ the set $f(Q)$ is countable, then also a set $g(Q)$ is countable, where g is any continuous mapping on Q in a separable metric space.

Proofs of this proposition 1 and of the theorem 5 are in [18].

Theorem 6. *If there exists $f \in C(Q)$ such that $f(Q)$ contains a dense-in-itself, non-meager closed part, then $(C(Q), u)$ is a non-F-space.*

Proof in [18].

IV. Definition. Let N be the set of all natural numbers, $\alpha, \beta \in N^N$. We write $\alpha \prec \beta$ if $\alpha(x) < \beta(x)$ for all $x \in N$ except a finite number.

Let ϱ be the smallest power of an unbounded chain in this order of N^N.

We call a set $M \subset N^N$ a hereditary unbounded system if for every infinite $A \subset N$ and every $\alpha \in N^N$ there exists $\beta \in M$ such that $\alpha(x) < \beta(x)$ for an infinite number of $x \in A$.

Let τ be the smallest power of a hereditary unbounded system.

---

[1]) I. e. every bounded real continuous function can be extended on the whole Q.

Theorem 7. *Let Q be a set. Then $(\chi(Q), u)$ is a non-F-space if and only if* card $Q \geqq \tau$.

Proof in [18].

V. Let (P, u) be a space, u^* the F-topology, which we get from a topology u by iterating the closure operator. Following E. Čech we call this topology the F-modification of u. Consequently, the F-modification u^* of u is the finest F-topology from all F-topologies, coarser than u.

Theorem 8. *Let (P, v) be an F-space. Then v is not an F-modification of any non-F-topology on P if and only if v satisfies the condition $\mathscr{D}_x$ for every $x \in P$.*

Condition $\mathscr{D}_x$: If $A \subset P$, $x \in vA - A$, then there exists $B \subset A$ such that $x \in vB$, $x \notin v(vB - A - (x))$.

This condition has a very simple form for regular spaces: If $A \subset P$, $x \in vA - A$, then there exists $B \subset A$ such that $vB - B = (x)$.

The proof of theorem 8 is contained in [17].

Such an F-space, the topology of which is an F-modification of no non-F-topology, is called a strong F-space. Immediately from theorem 8 it follows that every metric space is a strong F-space. The product of an uncountable number of intervals $\langle 0,1 \rangle$ is not a strong F-space. This is implied by the following theorems:

Theorem 9. *If (P, v) is a product of an uncountable number of F-space, each of which contains at least two points, then there exists an uncountable number of topologies u on P such that $u^* = v$, the order*[2]) *of u is 2 and for every $x \in P$ there exists $H_x \subset P$ such that $x \in u(uH_x) - uH_x$.*

Theorem 10. *Let (P_λ, v_λ) $(\lambda \in \Lambda)$ be F-spaces, satisfying the first axiom of countability. Let $2 \leqq$ card $P_\lambda \leqq$ card $\Lambda > \aleph_0$. Let (P, v) be the product of the spaces (P_λ, v_λ). Then there exist $2^{\text{card}\, P}$ different topologies u on P such that $u^* = v$, $\tilde{u}$ is discrete and the order of u is 2.*

If (P, v) is a product of F-spaces (P_λ, v_λ), $\lambda \in \Lambda$, $2 \leqq$ card $P_\lambda \leqq$ card $\Lambda > \aleph_0$, then there exists [17] a disjoint system $\{A_x;\ x \in P\}$ of dense subsets of P and such that if all (P_λ, v_λ) satisfy the first axiom of countability, then every A_x satisfies (a) from the following proposition:

Proposition 2. Let (P, v) be an F-space. Let there exist the collection $\{A_x;\ x \in P\}$ of subsets of P such that

(a) $x \in vA_x - A_x$ and if $B \subset A_x$, $x \in vB$, then $x \in v(vB - A_x - (x))$,

(b) for $y \in vA_x - A_x - (x)$ there exists a neighbourhood Y of y such that $Y \cap A_x \cap A_y = \emptyset$.

Then there exists a topology u on P, the order of which is 2, $u^* = v$ and for every $x \in P$ there exists $H_x \subset P$ such that $x \in u(uH_x) - uH_x$.

If in addition,

---

[2]) If we define for $M \subset P : u^1 M = uM$, $u^\beta M = u(\bigcup_{\gamma < \beta} u^\gamma M)$, then the order of topology u is the smallest ordinal number α such that $u^{\alpha+1}M = u^\alpha M$ for all $M \subset P$.

(c) $vA_x = P$ for every $x \in P$

then $\tilde{u}$ is discrete.

The proofs of proposition 2, theorems 9 and 10 are contained in [17].

VI. In this section the T_1-axiom for spaces is not assumed. If (Q, v) is an F-space and f its mapping onto a set P, usually a quotient-topology on P is defined as a finest F-topology for which f is a continuous mapping. If we substitute the word "F-topology" in this definition through "topology" only, we get a new notion of the quotient-topology. Evidently the "old-quotient-topology" is the F-modification of the "new quotient-topology".[3])

Theorem 11. *If (P, u) is a space, then there exists an F-space (Q, v) and a mapping f of (Q, v) onto P such that (P, u) is a quotient space ("new" of course). It is possible to choose $Q \supset P$ and such that the subspace $Q - P \subset\subset (Q, v)$ is discrete and the subspace $P \subset\subset (Q, v)$ is homeomorphic with $(P, \tilde{u})$.*

Proof in [17].

VII. Three theorems follow about F-modification of topology u (defined by means of convergence of functions at each point) on a set $\chi(Q)$ of all characteristic functions on some set Q:

Theorem 12. *The following statements are equivalent:*

(a) *$(\chi(Q), u)$ is not regular,*[4])

(b) *$(\chi(Q), u^*)$ is not regular,*

(c) card $Q \geqq \aleph_1$.

Proof in [18].

Theorem 13. *Let* card $Q \geqq \varrho$ *(c. f. IV). Then for every $f \in \chi(Q)$ there exists a countable set $A \subset \chi(Q)$ and a closed subset T of $(\chi(Q), u)$ such that $f \notin T$ and if U is a neighbourhood of f in $(\chi(Q), u)$, then $T \cap u(U \cap A) \neq \emptyset$.*

Proof in [15].

Let σ be the smallest power of a system $\mathscr{A}$ of subsets of some countable infinite set A such that if $B \subset A$ is infinite, then there exists $C \in \mathscr{A}$ such that $B - C$ and $B \cap C$ are infinite.

Theorem 14. *The space $(\chi(Q), u^*)$ is countably compact if and only if* card $Q < < \sigma$.

Proof in [18].

VIII. Finally, I would like to give a summary of directions of recent non-F-topology research. We could roughly divide papers about non-F-topology into three groups. The first group is composed of studies of properties of a set of ordinal numbers, which we get by iterating the closure-operator (papers [4], [5], [9]); the second group is a study of topologies, defined by means of various convergences of sequences,

---

[3]) This definition has been communicated to me by M. Katětov.

[4]) The definition of regularity is the same for non-F-spaces as well as for F-spaces; if U is a neighbourhood of x, then there exists a neighbourhood of x, the closure of which is contained in U.

especially convergences of sequences of functions (papers [3], [6], [7], [8], [11], [12], [15], [16], [18]) and last but not least are studies of "pure theory" of non-F-spaces (papers [1], [2], [3], [10], [13], [14], [17]).

References

[1] *E. Čech*: Topologické prostory. Praha 1959.

[2] *E. Čech*: Topologické prostory. Časopis pěst. mat. *66* (1937), 225–264.

[3] *F. Hausdorff*: Gestufte Räume. Fundam. math. *25* (1935), 486–502.

[4] *V. Jarník*: Sur un problème de M. Čech. Věstník Král. čes. spol. nauk, tř. matemat. přírodověd., 1938.

[5] *L. Kopřiva*: Zum Problem der Iteration in der Topologie. Práce Brněn. Českosl. Akad. Věd, *29* (1957), 256–276.

[6] *L. Mišík*: Poznámky k U-axiomu v topologických grupách. Mat. fyz. časop. 6, No *2* (1956), 78–84.

[7] *M. Neubauer*: Sur les espaces des fonctions continues. Fundam. math. *31* (1938), 269–278.

[8] *J. Novák*: Sur les espaces (L) et sur les produits cartesiens (L). Spisy vyd. přírod. fak. MU, Brno 1939.

[9] *J. Novák*: On a problem of E. Čech. Proc. Amer. Math. Soc. *1* (1950), 211–214.

[10] *J. Novák*: Induction partiell stetiger Functionen. Math. Annalen *118* (1942), 449–461.

[11] *J. Novák* and *L. Mišík*: O L-priestoroch spojitých funkcií. Mat. fyz. sborník SAV *1* (1951), 1–17.

[12] *B. Pospíšil*: Sur les fonctions continues. Fundam. Math. *31* (1938), 262–268.

[13] *J. Seitz*: O jednom problému prof. Čecha. Časop. pěst. mat. *75* (1950), 43–44.

[14] *V. Šedivá*: Několik příkladů topologických prostorů, nesplňujících axiom F. Časop. pěst. mat. *84* (1959), 461–466.

[15] *V. Šedivá*: On pointwise convergence of sequences of continuous functions. CMUC *1*, *2* (1960), 43–51.

[16] *V. Trnková*: On convergence of sequences of functions. CMUC *2*, *3* (1961), 1–12.

[17] *V. Trnková*: Non-F-spaces. It will be sent to Czech. Math. J.

[18] *V. Trnková*: On pointwise convergence of sequences of functions. It will be sent to Czech. Math. J.

ON DIVISION PROBLEMS FOR PARTIAL DIFFERENTIAL EQUATIONS WITH CONSTANT COEFFICIENTS

T. SHIROTA

Osaka

1. Introduction. Let Ω be a domain of the n-space $R^n = \{(x_1, x_2, \ldots, x_n)\}$ and Γ_1, Γ_2 relatively open, bounded portions of the boundary of Ω and such that $\Gamma_1 \supset \bar{\Gamma}_2$.

Let P be a differential polynomial of order m with variables $\partial/\partial x_i$ $(i = 1, 2, \ldots, n)$.

In this note we consider the relation between the following two problems, with respect to Ω, Γ_i $(i = 1, 2)$ and P:

(i) Let Ω_1 be a neighbourhood[1]) of $\bar{\Gamma}_1$ relative to Ω. The problem is then whether there exists a neighbourhood Ω_2 of $\bar{\Gamma}_2$ relative to Ω with the following property of regularity:

(R) For the Cauchy problem,

$$PU = f \text{ on } \Omega, \quad D^\alpha U = g^\alpha, \quad \text{for} \quad |\alpha| \leqq m - 1 \text{ on } \dot{\Omega}_1 \cap \dot{\Omega}$$

the condition $U \in C^\infty(\bar{\Omega}_2)$ follows from the conditions $f \in C^\infty(\bar{\Omega}_1)$ and $g^\alpha \in C^\infty(\dot{\Omega}_1 \cap \dot{\Omega})$.

(ii) What kind of division theorems for the differential operator P' with respect to distributions defined over Ω are valid.

The problem (i) for a strictly convex surface Γ_1 and any P is treated by F. John, B. Malgrange [2], and for convex domains by M. Zerner [3] (also [2]). In particular John and Zerner showed that the problem for a non strictly convex surface includes some complicated results.

On the other hand, the problem (ii) has been considered by several authors since L. Schwartz had proposed such problems in his distribution theory.

Though it seems very interesting to obtain an algebraic characterization of the relations among Ω, Γ_i $(i = 1, 2)$, and P which satisfy the property (R), our purpose in the present note is to establish the equivalence of the affirmative answers of the problems (i) and (ii) with some additional conditions.

2. To interpret the problem (ii), we introduce a topology in the set $C_0^\infty(\Omega)$ of all C^∞-functions with compact supports in Ω.

---

[1]) In this note by a neighbourhood of Γ_1 is meant the set $\{x \mid x \in S(y, \varepsilon_y),\ y \in \Gamma_1\}$, where $S(y, s_y) = \{x \mid |x - y| < \varepsilon_y\}$. Furthermore for any $\varepsilon > 0$ the set $S(\infty, \varepsilon) = \{x \mid |x| > \varepsilon^{-1}\}$ is considered as a neighbourhood of the infinite point.

We consider the following sets of subsets N of $C_0^\infty(\Omega)$ as a base of neighbourhoods of zero:

Let $\{\Omega_i\}$ be a sequence of neighbourhoods of Γ_1 relative to Ω such that

$$\Omega = \Omega_0 \supset \Omega_n \supset \overline{\Omega}_{n+1} \quad (n = 1, 2, \ldots)$$

and such that

$$\bigcap_{i=1}^{\infty} \Omega_i = \overline{\Gamma}_1 .$$

Let $\{\varepsilon_i(x)\}$ be a sequence of positive continuous functions in Ω and $\{\alpha_i\}$ an increasing sequence of positive integers.

Now let $N = N(\{\Omega_i\}, \{\varepsilon_i(x)\}, \{\alpha_i\})$ be the set

$$\{f \mid f \in C_0^\infty(\Omega),\ \sum_{|\alpha| \leqq \alpha_i} |D^\alpha f(x)| \leqq \varepsilon_i(x) \text{ for } x \in \Omega_i - \overline{\Omega}_{i+1},\ (i = 0, 1, 2, \ldots)\} .$$

Denote the topological vector space thus obtained by $D(\Omega, \overline{\Gamma}_1)$ and its dual topological vector space by $D'(\Omega, \overline{\Gamma}_1)$. Then we see that $D'(\Omega, \overline{\Gamma}_1)$ is a Montel space which consits of all distributions $T \in D'(\Omega)$ such that the local order of T, i. e., the order $\varphi\ T(\varphi \in C_0^\infty(\Omega))$ increases without any restriction as the support of φ approaches $\overline{\Gamma}_1$, but does not do so when the support of φ approaches $\dot{\Omega} - \overline{\Gamma}_1$. Therefore $D'(\Omega, \Gamma) = D'(\Omega)$, if $\Gamma = \dot{\Omega}$, and if $\Gamma = \emptyset$ then $D'(\Omega, \Gamma) = D'_F(\Omega)$, the space of all distributions of finite order.

Now one of our problem can be stated as follows: What kind of relations among $\Omega, \Gamma_1, \Gamma_2$ and P imply that

$$P'\ D'(\Omega, \Gamma_1) \supset D'(\Omega, \Gamma_2) .$$

I considered such problems in order to understand the feature of the problem with respect to the regularity of solution of the Cauchy problem or with respect to the prolongation of regularity of solutions of differential equation.

3. We shall prove that the answer of our division problem is in the affirmative whenever the whole boundary of Ω is non-characteristic and the condition (R) is satisfied for Ω, Γ_i $(i = 1, 2)$ and P.

To show this, let us assume these conditions. Then we have the following lemma:

Lemma. *For any neighbourhood Ω_1 of Γ_1, there exists a neighbourhood Ω_2 of Γ_2 such that if $F \in \mathscr{E}'(\Omega_2)$, a solution $S : P'S = F$ has the following property: for some m'*

$$S \in D'(\Omega) \cap (C^{m'})'\overline{(\Omega - \overline{\Omega}_1)} .$$

Proof. Let B be the Fréchet space

$$\{f \mid f \in C^m(\overline{\Omega}),\ Pf \in C^\infty(\overline{\Omega}_1),\ D^\alpha f \in C^\infty(\dot{\Omega} \cap \dot{\Omega}_1) \text{ for } |\alpha| \leqq m - 1\} .$$

Then by our hypothesis we see that for some neighbourhood Ω_2 of $\overline{\Gamma}_2$ we have $f \in C^\infty(\overline{\Omega}_2)$, if $f \in B$.

Since the mapping from B into $C^\infty(\overline{\Omega}_2), f \to f \mid \overline{\Omega}_2$, is closed, it is also continuous by the closed graph theorem in Fréchet spaces.

Hence for any compact set K of Ω_2 and any integer k there exist integers p and q such that for some C_1 and for any $f \in B$

$$\|f\|_{C^m(\bar\Omega)} + \|Pf\|_{C^p(\bar\Omega_1)} + \sum_{|\alpha| \leqq m-1} \|D^\alpha f\|_{C^q(\dot\Omega_1 \cap \dot\Omega_2)} \geqq C_1 \|f\|_{C^k(K)}.$$

In particular, by Malgrange's theorem, if $f \in C_0^\infty(\Omega)$ then for any ε and for some m' and $C_2 > 0$,

$$\|Pf \exp(\varepsilon|x|)\|_{L_2^{m'}(\bar\Omega)} + \|Pf\|_{C^p(\bar\Omega_1)} \geqq C_2 \|f\|_{C^k(K)}.$$

Therefore for any $F \in \mathscr{E}'(K)$ there exists a solution S such that

$$P'S = F \text{ on } \Omega, \quad S \in D'(\Omega) \cap (C_0^{m'})' (\overline{\Omega - \bar\Omega_1}).$$

Here we remark that the number m' is independent of Ω_1.

Using this lemma and Malgrange's consideration (the method of Mittag-Leffler) we show that for any $\Gamma : \bar\Gamma \subset \Gamma_2$, $P'D'(\Omega, \Gamma_1) \supset D'(\Omega, \Gamma)$.

A $T \in D'(\Omega, \Gamma)$ may then be decomposed into

$$T = T_0 + T_1 + T_2 + \dots + T_n + \dots,$$

where $T_0 \in D'_F(\Omega)$, $T_i \in \mathscr{E}'(\Omega''_i - \bar\Omega''_{i+1})$. Here Ω''_i is a neighbourhood of $\bar\Gamma_2$ such that $\cap\, \Omega''_i = \bar\Gamma_2$.

On the other hand, there exists a sequence of bounded domains Ω'_i such that $\cup\, \Omega'_i = \Omega$, $\bar\Omega'_i \subset \Omega'_{i+1}$ and such that for any distributions S with

$$P'S = 0 \quad \text{on} \quad \Omega'_{i+1}, \quad S \in (C^{m'})' (\bar\Omega'_{i+1})$$

and for any $\varepsilon > 0$, there is a distribution S' with the following properties:

$$P'S' = 0 \quad \text{on} \quad \Omega'_{i+2}, \quad S' \in (C^{m''})' (\bar\Omega'_{i+2}),$$
$$\|S - S'\|_{(C^{m''})'(\bar\Omega_i')} \leqq \varepsilon$$

for some $m'' \geqq m'$.

Furthermore, we may assume that $\bar\Omega_i \cap \bar\Omega'_{i+1} = \emptyset$, for some sequence of neighbourhoods Ω_i of Γ_1, and that Ω_i and Ω''_i possess the property described in (R).

Then we can find S_i $(i = 0, 1, 2, \dots)$ such that

$$P'S_0 = T_0, \quad S_0 \in D'_F(\Omega),$$
$$P'S_i = T_i \quad (i = 1, 2, \dots), \quad S_i \in D'(\Omega) \cap (C^{m'})' (\overline{\Omega - \bar\Omega_i}).$$

Furthermore, since $P'S_i = 0$ on Ω'_{i+1}, there exists an S'_i such that

$$P'S'_i = 0 \quad \text{on} \quad \Omega'_{i+2}, \quad \|S_i - S'_i\| (C^{m''})' (\bar\Omega'_i) \leq 1/i^2, \quad S'_i \in (C^{m''})' (\bar\Omega'_{i+1}).$$

Taking $\varphi_i \in C_0^\infty(\Omega)$ such that $\varphi_i(\mu) \equiv 1$ for $\mu \in \Omega'_i$ and $\equiv 0$ for $\mu \in \Omega'_{i+2}$, we define

$$\bar S = S_0 + \sum_{i=1}^{\infty} (S_i - \varphi_i S'_i).$$

Then $\bar{S} \in D'(\Omega, \bar{\Gamma}_1)$. For in the domain $\Omega - \bar{\Omega}_i$ and for $j \geqq i$, we have $S'_j \in (C^{m''})' \cdot (\Omega'_i)$, and therefore

$$\sum_{j=1}^{\infty}(S_j - \varphi_j S'_j) = \sum_{j=1}^{i-1}(S_j - \varphi_j S'_j) + \sum_{j=i}^{\infty}(S_j - \varphi_j S'_j) \in (C^l)' \, (\overline{\Omega - \bar{\Omega}_i}) + \\ + (C^{m''})' \, (\overline{\Omega - \bar{\Omega}_i}) \quad \text{for some} \quad l > 0 \, .$$

Furthermore $P'\bar{S} = \sum P'(\varphi_i S'_i) \in (C_0^{m''})' \, (\Omega)$, so that we can find a distribution $\bar{\bar{S}} \in D'_F(\Omega)$ such that $P'\bar{\bar{S}} = \sum_i P'(\varphi_i S'_i)$. Thus $\dot{S} = \bar{S} - \bar{\bar{S}}$ is the desired distribution.

4. We shall prove the converse assertion of the result established in 3. For the sake of simplicity of description we assume that there exists a non-tangential vector ξ such that $x + \varepsilon(x)\xi \subset \Omega$ for any small $\varepsilon(x)$ and furthemore that $\dot{\Omega} \cap \dot{\Omega}_1$ is in a hyperplane which is non characteristic and that Ω is convex.

Suppose, contradicting the condition (R), that there exists a neighbourhood Ω'_1 of Γ_1 $(\Omega_1 \subset \Omega'_1)$ such that for any neighbourhood Ω_2 of $\bar{\Gamma}_2$, there is a function f with the following properties:

$$f \in C^m(\bar{\Omega}) \, ,$$

$$D^\alpha f \in C^\infty(\dot{\Omega}_1 \cap \dot{\Omega}) \quad \text{for} \quad |\alpha| \leqq m - 1 \quad \text{and} \quad Pf \in C^\infty(\bar{\Omega}'_1) \, , \quad \text{but} \quad f \notin C^\infty(\bar{\Omega}_2) \, .$$

Let $\{\Omega_{2,1}\}$ be a sequence of neighbourhoods of $\bar{\Gamma}_2$ such that

$$\Omega_{2,i} \subset \{x \mid \text{dist}\,(x, \Gamma_2) < 1/i\} \, ;$$

denote the f corresponding to $\Omega_{2,i}$ by f_i. Since $\dot{\Omega} \cap \dot{\Omega}'_1$ is a C^∞-surface, there exists a $\psi \in C^\infty \, (U \, (\dot{\Omega} \cap \dot{\Omega}'_1))$ such that $\{x \mid \psi(x) = 0\}$ contains $\dot{\Omega} \cap \dot{\Omega}'_1$, and grad $\psi \neq 0$, where $U(\dot{\Omega} \cap \dot{\Omega}'_1)$ is a neighbourhood of $\dot{\Omega} \cap \dot{\Omega}'_1$ in R^n.

Furthermore, since $\dot{\Omega} \cap \dot{\Omega}'_1$ is non-characteristic, for the solution $Pf = g \in C^\infty(\bar{\Omega})$, $D^\alpha f = h^\alpha \in C^\infty(\dot{\Omega}'_1 \cap \dot{\Omega})$ we have that the values

$$\left(\sum \frac{\partial \psi}{\partial x_i} \frac{\partial}{\partial x_i}\right)^\beta f \quad \text{on} \quad \dot{\Omega} \cap \dot{\Omega}'_1$$

are determined by g, h^α; denote these by $f^{(\beta)}$. Finally assuming Ω is in $\{x \mid \psi(x) > 0\}$, put

$$\Omega^- = \{x \mid 0 \geqq \psi(x) \geqq - \delta\} \, .$$

Then we can extend the function f to an $\bar{f}$ such that

$$\bar{f} \in C^\infty(\bar{\Omega}^-) \, , \quad P\bar{f} \in C^\infty(\Omega_1 \cup \Omega^-) \, ,$$

since we can apply the well known theorem concerning Fréchet space ([4]) to the mapping from

$$C^\infty(\bar{\Omega}^-) \quad \text{into} \quad \Pi \, C^\infty(\dot{\Omega} \cap \dot{\Omega}_1) : f \to \{f^{(\beta)}\} \quad \text{(weak topology)} \, .$$

Setting $\bar{\bar{f}}_i(x) = \bar{f}_i(x - i^{-1}\xi) \, \psi_i(x)$ for some $\psi_i(x) \in C_0^\infty(\Omega)$, we may assume that

$$f_i \in C_0^m(\Omega) \, , \quad Pf_i \in C^\infty(\Omega'_1)$$

but

$$f_i \notin C^\infty(\Omega_{2,i}) \, .$$

Furthermore by using a convolution operator with sufficiently small support, we may assume that

$$f_i \in C_0^i(\Omega - \overline{\Omega}_{2,i}), \quad \text{but} \quad f_i \notin H^{i+n}(\Omega_{2,i} - \overline{\Omega}_{2,i+1}).$$

Now we can show that there exist distributions F_i of order $\leqq s_i = i + n$ such that

$$\text{supp} \quad F_i \subset \Omega_{2,i} - \overline{\Omega}_{2,i+1}, \quad F_i(f_i * \varphi_\varepsilon) \to \infty \quad \text{as} \quad \varepsilon \to 0,$$

where φ_ε is a C^∞-function such that $\varphi_\varepsilon(x) = \varepsilon^{-n}\varphi(\varepsilon^{-1}x)$, $\varphi(x) \geqq 0$, $\text{supp}\,\varphi \subset \subset \{x \mid (x) \leqq |\}$ and $\int \varphi\, dx = 1$. For, if for any $F \in (H^{i+n})'(\Omega_{2,i} - \overline{\Omega}_{2,i+1})$, $|F(f_i * * \varphi_\varepsilon)| < k$ for some constant k which depends on F, but is independent of ε, then $f_i * \varphi_\varepsilon$ converges weakly to some element of $H^{i+n}(\Omega_{2,i} - \overline{\Omega}_{2,i+1})$. But $f_i * \varphi_\varepsilon$ converges to f_i in $C_0^i(\Omega)$, therefore f_i itself belongs to $H^{i+n}(\Omega_{2,i} - \overline{\Omega}_{2,i+1})$, which implies a contradiction.

Let $z_1 = s_1$, $z_2 = s_{z_1}, \ldots, z_i = s_{z_{i-1}}$, and let $F = F_1 + F_{z_1} + \ldots + F_{z_i} + + \ldots$ Then obviously $F \in D'(\Omega, \Gamma_2)$. Assume that there exists a distribution $S \in \in D'(\Omega, \overline{\Gamma}_1)$ such that $P'S = F$. Then $S(P\varphi) = F(\varphi)$ for any $\varphi \in D(\Omega)$. Therefore there exists a neighbourhood N of O in $D'(\Omega, \Gamma_1)$ such that if $P\varphi \in N$, then $|F(\varphi)| \leqq 1$. But since $Pf_i \in C_0^{i-m}(\Omega) \cap C^\infty(\Omega_1')$, whenever $i > k$ and $\varepsilon < \varepsilon_i$, for some k, δ_i and ε_i

$$P(\delta_i f_i * \varphi_\varepsilon) = \delta_i(Pf_i) * \varphi_\varepsilon \subset N,$$

and hence $|F(\delta_i f_i * \varphi_\varepsilon)| < 1$ for $i > k$ and for $\varepsilon < \varepsilon_i$. Furthermore, since the order of $F_{z_i} \leqq z_j\ (i < j)$ and $f_{z_l} \in C_0^{z_l}(\Omega - \overline{\Omega}_{2,z_l})$ for $z_l > k$, therefore

$$|(F_1 + F_{z_1} + \ldots + F_{z_{l-1}})(\delta_{z_l} f_{z_l} * \varphi_\varepsilon)| \leqq K \quad \text{as} \quad \varepsilon \to 0 \quad \text{for some } K$$

and

$$|F_{z_l}(\delta_{z_l} f_{z_l} * \varphi_\varepsilon)| \to \infty \quad \text{as} \quad \varepsilon \to 0$$

therefore for some $\varepsilon < \varepsilon_i$

$$|F(\delta_{z_l} f_{z_l} * \varphi_\varepsilon)| \geqq (2 + K) - K = 2$$

which is a contradiction. Thus we obtain that $P'D'(\Omega, \Gamma_1) \nsupseteq D'(\Omega, \Gamma)$.

5. In the previous sections a connection between the existence of solution of differential operators and the regularity of solution of Cauchy problems was considered. In this section a relation between the former and the regularity of solution of Cauchy problems in a more general sense is noted.

From now on we assume that Γ is a closed $(\Gamma = \overline{\Gamma})$ and connected component of the boundary of Ω. Then we have the following proposition: $P'D'(\Omega, \Gamma) = D'(\Omega, \Gamma)$ if and only if

1. Ω is P-convex, i. e., for any compact subset K of Ω there exists a compact subset K' such that if $\text{supp}\, PT \subset K$ and $T \in \mathscr{E}'(\Omega)$, then $\text{supp}\, T \subset K'$.

2. For any neighbourhood Ω_1 of Γ, there exists another neighbourhood Ω_2 of $\overline{\Gamma}$ such that if $\varphi \in \mathscr{E}'(\Omega)$ satisfies $P\varphi \in C^\infty(\Omega_1)$, then $\varphi \in C^\infty(\Omega_2)$.

Here we assume that if Γ contains the point at infinity then our neighbourhood of Γ contains $\{x \mid x \in \Omega, |x| > L\}$ for some positive L.

The proof of this proposition is analogous to that of the previous. The difference is in the part corresponding to 3.

Let Ω_1 and Ω_2 be chosen such that they satisfy condition 2 and let Ω_0 and Ω_3 be other neighbourhoods of Γ such that $\overline{\Omega}_3 \subset \Omega_2$, $\overline{\Omega}_1 \subset \Omega_0$.

Here obviously we may suppose that $\overline{\Omega}_2 \subset \Omega_1$. By our assumption even if Γ contains the point at infinity, $\Omega_0 - \overline{\Omega}_3$ is bounded.

Now consider the mapping from the space B_1 to $C^\infty(\Omega_2 - \overline{\Omega}_3)$, where $B_1 = \{f \mid f \in C^\infty$ (a fixed small neighbourhood $U(\dot{\Omega}_3 - \Gamma)$ of $\dot{\Omega}_3 - \Gamma$) and $Pf \in C^\infty(\Omega - \overline{\Omega}_3)\}$.

This mapping is defined and continuous.

For, let φ be a function in $C_0^\infty(\Omega_0)$ such that

$$\varphi(x) \equiv 1 \quad \text{on} \quad \Omega_0 - \overline{\Omega}_3 \cup U(\dot{\Omega}_3 - \Gamma) \cup U(\dot{\Omega}_0 - \Gamma),$$
$$\varphi(x) \equiv 0 \quad \text{on} \quad \Omega_3 \cup U_1(\dot{\Omega}_3 - \Gamma) \cup U_1(\dot{\Omega}_0 - \Gamma),$$

where $U_1(\dot{\Omega}_3 - \Gamma)$ is a neighbourhood of $\dot{\Omega}_3 - \Gamma$ smaller than $U(\dot{\Omega}_3 - \Gamma)$.

Then for any $f \in B_1$

$$\varphi f \in \mathscr{E}'(\Omega) \quad \text{and} \quad P\varphi f \in C^\infty(\Omega_1);$$

therefore $\varphi f \in C^\infty(\Omega_2)$ by our assumption, and in particular

$$f \in C^\infty(\Omega_2 - \overline{\Omega_3 \cup U_1(\dot{\Omega}_3 - \Gamma)}).$$

Since B_1 and $C^\infty(\Omega_2 - \overline{\Omega}_3)$ are Fréchet spaces, by the method used in 3, for any $T \in \mathscr{E}'(\Omega_2 - \overline{\Omega}_3)$, we obtain a distribution S' such that

$$P'S' = T \quad \text{in} \quad \Omega_0 - \overline{\Omega}_3, \quad S' \in (H^{m'})'(\Omega_0 - \overline{\Omega}_1) \cap D'(\Omega_0 - \overline{\Omega}_3).$$

Then setting $S = \varphi S'$, $P'S = T + T_1 + T_2$, where $T_1 \in D'_F(U(\dot{\Omega}_0 - \Gamma))$ and $T_2 \in D'(U(\dot{\Omega}_3 - \Gamma))$. Using this S, we can complete our proof as in 3.

References

[1] *B. Malgrange*: Séminaire Schwartz, Équations aux dérivées partielles. 2ème année, 1954/55, Paris.

[2] *F. John*: Continuous Dependence on Data for Solutions of Partial Differential Equations with a Prescribed Bound. Comm. Pure and Appl. Math. *13* (1960), 551–585.

[3] *M. Zerner*: Solutions de l'équation des ondes présentant des singularités sur une droite. C. R. Acad. Sci. Paris 250 (1960), 2980–2982.

[4] *J. Dieudonné* and *L. Schwartz*: La dualité dans les espaces ($\mathfrak{F}$) et ($\mathfrak{LF}$). Ann. Inst. Fourier I (1950), 61–101.

[5] *T. Shirota:* Ou solutions of partially differential equation with parameter. Proc. Japan Academy *32* (1956), 401–405.

APPLICATIONS OF TOPOLOGY TO FOUNDATIONS OF MATHEMATICS

R. SIKORSKI

Warszawa

The subject of my talk is to give a short account of applications of Topology to Mathematical Logic. I shall restrict the discussion of the applications to the case of the classical two-valued logic and the intuitionistic logic only.

The following topological notions play an important part in metamathematical investigations:

I. 1. Totally disconnected spaces.
   2. Compactness.
   3. The Baire theorem.

II. 1. General topological spaces, in particular finite topological spaces.
   2. Algebras of open sets.
   3. Interior mappings.
   4. Strong compactness.

The first group contains notions useful in the classical logic. The second group contains notions useful in the intuitionistic logic.

Some notions mentioned above require an explanation. By a general topological space I shall understand a space satisfying the well known four axioms of Kuratowski. It is not supposed, in general, that one-point sets are closed. Consequently finite topological spaces are not discrete, in general. A space is totally disconnected if, for every pair of distinct points x, y, there exists a clopen set (i. e. a set both closed and open) A such that $x \in A$ and $y \notin A$.

By the Baire theorem I shall understand the theorem stating that no open non-void subset of a compact Hausdorff space is of the first category. Usually this theorem is formulated for complete metric spaces. The completeness does not play any essential part in logical investigations. The Baire theorem in the above formulation is due to E. Čech [1].

It is not surprising that totally disconnected compact spaces appear in applications to the classical logic because the classical logic is closely connected with the theory of Boolean algebras. On the other hand, the M. H. Stone [27] representation theorem asserts that every Boolean algebra $\mathfrak{A}$ is isomorphic to the field of all clopen subsets of a totally disconnected compact space, i. e. there exists a totally disconnected compact space X and a mapping

$$h : \mathfrak{A} \to \mathfrak{F} = \text{the field of all clopen subsets of } X$$

such that h transforms the lattice-theoretical joins and meets in $\mathfrak{A}$ onto set-theoretical unions and intersections respectively:

$$h(a \vee b) = h(a) \cup h(b),\ h(a \wedge b) = h(a) \cap h(b), \quad \text{for } a, b \in \mathfrak{A}.$$

The Stone isomorphism h does not preserve infinite joins and meets in $\mathfrak{A}$. More precisely, if

(1) $$a = \bigvee_{t \in T} a_t \quad \text{in } \mathfrak{A}$$

(i. e. if a is the smallest element which is greater than all a_t), then

$$\bigcup_{t \in T} h(a_t) \subset h(a)$$

but $\subset$ cannot be here replaced by $=$, in general. It can be easily proved that the corresponding defect set

(2) $$h(a) \setminus \bigcup_{t \in T} h(a_t)$$

is rather small, viz. it is nowhere dense in X. Similarly, if

(3) $$a = \bigwedge_{t \in T} a_t \quad \text{in } \mathfrak{A}$$

(i. e. if a is the greatest element which is less than all a_t), then

$$h(a) \subset \bigcap_{t \in T} h(a_t)$$

but $\subset$ cannot be here replaced by $=$, in general. The corresponding defect set

(4) $$\bigcup_{t \in T} h(a_t) \setminus h(a)$$

is also nowhere dense.

Since the time of my talk is restricted, I shall mention only a few applications of Topology to Mathematical Logic.

Consider first a formalized mathematical theory T based on the two-valued logic. For brevity only, we shall assume that T describes only properties of some relations in a set of elements. Thus the language of the theory T contains a countable set V of signs $x, y, z, \ldots$ called individual variables and denoting arbitrary elements in the set under examination, and a finite or countable set of signs $\pi, \varrho, \ldots$ called predicates and denoting the relations under examination. Expressions like

$$\pi(x, y), \quad \varrho(x, y, z)$$

are the simplest sentences in the theory, stating that relations π, ϱ hold between elements x, y or x, y, z etc., and called elementary formulas. From elementary formulas we can form some more complicated formulas (i. e. more complicated sentences of the theory) by joining the elementary formulas by means of the connectives

$$\vee \text{ (or)}, \quad \wedge \text{ (and)}, \quad \Rightarrow \text{(if ..., then...)}, \quad - \text{ (not)}$$

and quantifiers

$$\bigvee_x \text{ (there exists an } x \text{ such that...)}, \quad \bigwedge_x \text{ (for every } x, \ldots).$$

For instance, the following expressions are formulas

$$(5) \qquad \pi(x, y) \Rightarrow \varrho(y, z, x)\,, \quad (\bigvee_x \varrho(x, y, z)) \Rightarrow (\pi(y, z) \wedge \pi(z, y))\,.$$

A formula which does not contain any quantifier will be called open. For instance, the first of formulas (5) is open but the second is not open.

We shall identify two formulas α, β if and only if the both implications $\alpha \Rightarrow \beta$ and $\beta \Rightarrow \alpha$ are theorems in T, i. e. they follow from the mathematical axioms of the theory T by means of the two-valued logic. After this identification, the set of all formulas becomes a Boolean algebra $\mathfrak{A}$. The element of $\mathfrak{A}$ which is determined by a formula α will be denoted by $|\alpha|$. The join, meet and the complement in $\mathfrak{A}$ are defined by the equalities

$$(6) \qquad |\alpha| \vee |\beta| = |\alpha \vee \beta|\,, \quad |\alpha| \wedge |\beta| = |\alpha \wedge \beta|\,, \quad -|\alpha| = |-\alpha|$$

where, on the left side, the signs $\vee$, $\wedge$, $-$ are Boolean operations, and on the right side they are the logical connectives. Moreover it can be easily proved that, for every formula $\alpha(x)$:

$$(7) \qquad |\bigvee_x \alpha(x)| = \bigvee_{y \in V} |\alpha(y)|\,, \quad |\bigwedge_x \alpha(\mu)| = \bigwedge_{y \in V} |\alpha(y)|\,.$$

These infinite joins and meets are called joins and meets corresponding to logical quantifiers. Roughly speaking, the examination of the theory T can be reduced to the examination of the Boolean algebra $\mathfrak{A}$ just defined and consequently, by the Stone representation theorem, to the examination of the Stone space of $\mathfrak{A}$.

As the first serious application of Topology to Mathematical Logic I shall mention the topological proof of the following completeness theorem of Gödel which is one of the fundamental matemathematical theorems:

Theorem I. *Every consistent theory T has a model in a countable set.*

This theorem can be formulated in the language of the theory of Boolean algebras. The equivalent Boolean formulation is as follows:

Theorem II. *For every formalized theory T, there exists an isomorphism h_0 of the corresponding Boolean algebra $\mathfrak{A}$ onto a field of subsets of a set X_0 such that h_0 transforms all infinite joins and meets corresponding to logical quantifiers onto set-theoretical unions and intersections respectively.*

Namely every point in X_0 determines, in a simple way, a model for T in a countable set.

Thus we have to find the set X_0 and the isomorphism h_0. The Stone space X for $\mathfrak{A}$ and the Stone isomorphism h are not good because h does not transform the infinite joins and meets corresponding to the logical quantifiers onto set-theoretical unions and intersections. However it is easy to correct the Stone isomorphism h to obtain the required isomorphism h_0. For every infinite join or meet (7) the corresponding defect set is nowhere dense. The number of all infinite joins and meets corresponding to logical quantifiers is $\aleph_0$. Thus the union U of all those defect sets is a set of the first category. Let

$$X_0 = X \setminus U\,, \quad h_0(a) = h(a) \setminus U \quad \text{for} \quad a \in \mathfrak{A}\,.$$

Clearly h_0 is a Boolean homomorphism. It transforms the infinite joins and meets (7) onto the corresponding unions and intersections. If a is a non-zero element of $\mathfrak{A}$, then $h_0(a) \neq 0$ by the Baire theorem. This proves that h_0 is an isomorphism and completes the topological proof of the Gödel theorem I. This proof is due to H. RASIOWA and R. SIKORSKI [9], [10] (see also L. RIEGER [16], [17]). We have seen that the Baire theorem is an essential point in this proof.

It is convenient to consider the set X_0 just defined as a topological space, the class of all sets $h_0(|\alpha|)$, where α is any open formula, being assumed as an open basis. The following theorem holds:

Theorem III. *The space X_0 is compact if and only if the theory T is open, i. e. it has a set of axioms composed of open formulas only.*

Open theories play a special part in metamathematical investigations. Roughly speaking, they are the simplest, most regular formalized theories. Theorem III yields a topological characterization of open theories. It was proved by R. SIKORSKI [19], [20], [21]. A part of it was proved, in a slight different formulation, by A. EHRENFEUCHT and A. MOSTOWSKI [2]. The case of the classical predicate calculus, i. e. of the theory with the empty set of mathematical axioms, was earlier obtained by L. RIEGER [16] (see also H. RASIOWA and R. SIKORSKI [11]).

One of fundamental theorems in Mathematical Logic is the Herbrand theorem. There exists a simple method which associates, to every formula α, a sequence

$$\alpha_1, \alpha_2, \ldots \tag{8}$$

of open formulas, called the Herbrand sequence for α. If α is given effectively, it is very easy to find the corresponding formulas (8). The Herbrand theorem states that

Theorem IV. *If the theory T is open, then, for every formula α, the following conditions are equivalent:*

(a) *α is a theorem in T,*

(b) *there exists an integer n such that the open formula $\alpha_1 \vee \ldots \vee \alpha_n$ is a theorem in T.*

The implication $(a) \Rightarrow (b)$ can be easily deduced from the compactness of X_0. If α is a theorem in T, then $h_0(|\alpha|) = X_0$. This implies, by a simple calculation, that

$$h_0(|\alpha_1|) \cup h_0(|\alpha_2|) \cup \ldots = X_0\,.$$

Since X_0 is compact and all sets $h_0(|\alpha_n|)$ are open, there exists an integer n such that

$$h_0(|\alpha_1 \vee \ldots \vee \alpha_n|) = h_0(|\alpha_1|) \cup \ldots \cup h_0(|\alpha_n|) = X_0\,.$$

Hence we infer that $\alpha_1 \vee \ldots \vee \alpha_n$ is a theorem in X_0. This is the main idea of the proof due to R. Sikorski [20], [22].

I am going to quote a few applications of Topology to the intuitionistic logic.

The investigation of classical logic leads, in a natural way, to Boolean algebras. The investigation of the intuitionistic logic leads, in a natural way, to another kind of lattices which I shall call pseudo-Boolean algebras. By definition, a lattice is said to be a pseudo-Boolean algebra if

1° it has the zero element 0,

2° for any elements a, b, the set of all x such that $a \wedge x \leqq b$ contains the greatest element.

The greatest element will be denoted by $a \Rightarrow b$. The element $a \Rightarrow 0$ will be denoted by $-a$. The operations $a \vee b$, $a \wedge b$, $a \Rightarrow b$, $-a$ are the lattice-theoretical analogues of the intuitionistic disjunction, conjunction, implication and negation respectively. The discovery of the connection between the intuitionistic logic and pseudo-Boolean algebras is due to M. H. STONE [28] and A. TARSKI [30]. Note that every pseudo-Boolean algebra has the unit element, viz. $a \Rightarrow a$ is the unit.

Pseudo-Boolean algebras are closely related to topological spaces. Let X be a topological space, and let $\mathfrak{G}(X)$ be the lattice of all open subsets of X. Then $\mathfrak{G}(X)$ is a pseudo-Boolean algebra. The lattice-theoretical join $\vee$ and meet $\wedge$ in $\mathfrak{G}(X)$ coincide with the set-theoretical union $\cup$ and intersection $\cap$. Moreover

$$A \Rightarrow B = \operatorname{int}((X \setminus A) \cup B), \quad -A = \operatorname{int}(X \setminus A)$$

for any open sets $A, B \subset X$.

Every subalgebra of $\mathfrak{G}(X)$, i. e. every subclass of $\mathfrak{G}(X)$ which is closed with respect to $\vee$, $\wedge$, $\Rightarrow$, $-$, is also a pseudo-Boolean algebra. Conversely, every pseudo-Boolean algebra is isomorphic to a subalgebra of the algebra $\mathfrak{G}(X)$ of open subset of a topological space X.

Now I can explain why interior mappings play an important part in the investigation of the intuitionistic logic. Let X_1 and X_2 be two topological spaces and let $\varphi : X_1 \to X_2$ be any mapping. We ask under what conditions the equality

$$h(A) = \varphi^{-1}(A), \quad (A \in \mathfrak{G}(X_2))$$

defines a homomorphism

$$h : \mathfrak{G}(X_2) \to \mathfrak{G}(X_1).$$

In order that h be a homomorphism it is sufficient and, under some natural additional hypotheses, also necessary that

$$\text{(9)} \qquad \varphi^{-1}(\overline{A}) = \overline{\varphi^{-1}(A)} \quad \text{for every set} \quad A \subset X_2$$

(R. SIKORSKI [23]). A. D. WALLACE [31] (see also R. SIKORSKI [26]) has proved that (9) holds if and only if φ is an interior mapping, i. e. φ is continuous and φ maps open sets onto open sets. Note that if φ is an interior mapping from X_1 onto X_2, then h is an isomorphism from $\mathfrak{G}(X_2)$ into $\mathfrak{G}(X_1)$.

Consider first the intuitionistic propositional calculus. The language of the propositional calculus contains signs $p, q, \ldots$ called propositional variables which are symbols to denote arbitrary sentences. By joining propositional variables by means of the logical connectives $\vee$, $\wedge$, $\Rightarrow$, $-$ we obtain formulas of the propositional calculus. For instance, the expression

$$(-((p \Rightarrow q) \wedge -p)) \vee q$$

is a formula in the propositional calculus.

Let X be a topological space. Any formula α in the propositional calculus can be interpreted as a topological polynomial in the space X. For this purpose it suffices to interpret propositional variables $p, q, \ldots$ as variables running through all open subsets of X (i. e. running through all elements of $\mathfrak{G}(X)$), and to interpret the symbols $\vee$, $\wedge$, $\Rightarrow$, $-$ as the signs of the lattice-theoretical operations in the pseudo-Boolean algebra $\mathfrak{G}(X)$. This polynomial will be denoted by α_X. Values of α_X are always open subsets of X, i. e. elements in $\mathfrak{G}(X)$. We shall write $\alpha_X \equiv X$ if a_X assumes only one value: the whole space X.

The following theorem shows the connection between the intuitionistic propositional calculus and Topology:

Theorem V.. *The following conditions are equivalent for every formula* α:

(i) α *is an intuitionistic propositional tautology* (*i. e. an intuitionistically true formula*),

(ii) $\alpha_X \equiv X$ *for every topological space* X.

This result is rather easy. A much deeper result is that (ii) can be here replaced by the following condition:

(ii′) $\alpha_X \equiv X$ *for every finite topological space* X.

Condition (ii′) is also equivalent to (i) and (ii). Moreover, condition (ii′) can be restricted to finite topological spaces of powers $\leq n(\alpha)$ where $n(\alpha)$ is an integer determined, in a simple way, by the structure of the formula α. Condition (ii′) in the formulation presented here is due to J. C. C. McKinsey and A. Tarski [3], [4] but it is a topological formulation of an earlier result of Jaśkowski formulated in another language.

Conditions (ii) and (ii′) contain the quantifier "for every... space". They can be also replaced by the following equivalent condition:

(iii) $\alpha_X \equiv X$ *for a dense in itself non-void metric space* X.

This result is also due to J. C. C. McKinsey and A. Tarski [3], [4] (see also A. Tarski [1]). Since the implication (ii) $\Rightarrow$ (iii) is trivial, in order to prove the equivalence of (iii) with the remaining conditions it suffices to show that (iii) implies (ii′). This follows from the following theorem due to J. C. C. McKinsey and A. Tarski [3]:

Theorem VI. *Let* X_1 *be a non-void dense in itself metric space and let* X_2 *be a finite non-void topological space. Then there exist a dense open subset* $X_0 \subset X_1$ *and an interior mapping* φ *from* X_0 *onto* X_2.

In other words: *Then* $\mathfrak{G}(X_2)$ *is isomorphic to a subalgebra of* $\mathfrak{G}(X_0)$.

The proof of Theorem VI is rather difficult. Finite topological spaces have a complicated structure. For instance, they can contain disjoint open sets with the same boundary, etc. Analogous complicated open sets must be constructed in X_0 when φ is defined.

If X_1 is totally disconnected, we may assume that $X_0 = X_1$.

Now we shall discuss the case of the intuitionistic predicate calculus. The language of the intuitionistic predicate calculus and the definition of formulas is the same as in the case of formalized mathematical theories described earlier.

Let α be a formula in the intuitionistic predicate calculus and let X be a topological space. Similarly as in the case of propositional calculus, α can be interpreted as a topological (infinite) polynomial α_X in X whose values are open subsets in X. The exact definition is a little more complicated as in the case of the propositional calculus and therefore it is not quoted here (for details, see e. g. A. MOSTOWSKI [6] or H. RASIOWA and R. SIKORSKI [12], [13]). As previously, we shall write $\alpha_X \equiv X$ if α_X assumes only one value: the whole space X. Polynomials α_X were used for the first time by A. Mostowski [6] to the problem of verification whether a given formula is an intuitionistic tautology or not. This method of verification is based on the following theorem:

Theorem VII. *The following conditions are equivalent for every formula* α:

(i) α *is an intuitionistic predicate tautology* (*i. e. an intuitionistically true formula*);

(ii) $\alpha_X \equiv X$ *for every topological space* X.

Conditions (i), (ii) in Theorem VII are analogous to conditions (i), (ii) in Theorem V. There is no analogue of conditions (ii′) from Theorem V. The question arises whether there is an analogue of condition (iii) from Theorem V. First H. Rasiowa and R. Sikorski [12] have proved that there exists a topological T_0-space Y such that the following condition is equivalent to (i) and (ii) in Theorem VII:

(iii$_0$) $$\alpha_Y \equiv Y.$$

The problem arises whether Y can be here replaced by a metric space. This problem was solved affirmatively by R. Sikorski [23], [24], [25]. Viz. there exists a set Z of irrational numbers such that the following condition is equivalent to (i) and (ii):

(iii) $$\alpha_Z \equiv Z.$$

This result was obtained as an easy corollary of the following topological theorem due to A. ŠVARC [29] (see also V. PONOMAREV [7]):

Theorem VIII. *Every topological* T_0-*space* Y *with a countable open basis is an interior image of a set* Z *of irrational numbers.*

A topological space X_0 is said to be strongly compact if the intersection of all non-empty closed subsets is not empty. Every topological space X can be turned into a strongly compact space X_0 by adding a new point x_0 so that X is an open dense subset of X_0. By definition,

$$X_0 = X \cup (x_0).$$

As open sets in X_0 we assume all open subsets of X and the whole space X_0. In other words, we add the point x_0 to all closed subsets. Consequently (x_0) is the intersection of all non-void sets closed in X_0.

The notion of strongly compact spaces and the trivial strong compactification just mentioned do not seem to be interesting from the topological point of view. However they play an important role in the topological investigation of the intuitionistic logic. For instance, they play an important part in the proof of Theorem VI. As second application we mention a simple topological proof of the following theorem of Gödel:

Theorem IX. *If a disjunction* $\alpha \vee \beta$ *is an intuitionistic tautology, then either* α *or* β *is an intuitionistic tautology.*

The topological proof of Theorem IX has been given by J. C. C. McKinsey and A. Tarski [5] (in a slight different formulation; see also L. Rieger [18]) for the propositional calculus, and by H. Rasiowa and R. Sikorski [14] for the predicate calculus. H. Rasiowa and R. Sikorski [14] have also proved the following theorem using the strong compactification:

Theorem X. *If an existential formula* $\bigvee_x \alpha(x)$ *is an intuitionistic predicate tautology, then there exists an individual variable* y *such that the substitution* $\alpha(y)$ *is an intuitionistic predicate tautology.*

H. Rasiowa [8] has also examined analogues of Theorems IX and X for mathematical theories based on the intuitionistic logic. In all problems concerning theorems IX and X the strong compactification plays an essential part.

In my talk I have quoted only some applications of Topology to Mathematical Logic. Other applications and all details can be found in the monograph H. Rasiowa and R. Sikorski [15] to appear probably in the next year.

References

[1] *E. Čech*: On bicompact spaces. Ann. of Math. *38* (1937), 823–844.

[2] *A. Ehrenfeucht* and *A. Mostowski*: A Compact Space of Models of First Order Theories. Bull. de l'acad. Pol., S. d. sci. math., astr. et phys., V. *IX*, No. 5 (1961), 369–373.

[3] *J. C. C. McKinsey* and *A. Tarski*: The algebra of topology. Ann. of Math. *45* (1944), 141–191.

[4] *J. C. C. McKinsey* and *A. Tarski*: On closed elements in closure algebra. Ann. of Math. *47* (1946), 122–162.

[5] *J. C. C. McKinsey* and *A. Tarski*: Some theorems about the sentential calculi of Lewis and Heyting. J. Symb. Logic *13* (1948), 1–15.

[6] *A. Mostowski*: Proofs of nondeducibility in intuitionistic functional calculi. J. Symb. Logic *13* (1948), 204–207.

[7] *В. Пономарев:* Аксиомы счетности и непрерывные отображения. Bull. Acad. polon. sci. *8* (1960), 127–133.

[8] *H. Rasiowa*: Algebraic models of axiomatic theories. Fundam. Math. *41* (1955), 291–310.

[9] *H. Rasiowa* and *R. Sikorski*: A proof of the completeness theorem of Gödel, Fundam. Math. *37* (1950), 193–200.

[10] *H. Rasiowa* and *R. Sikorski*: A proof of the Skolem-Löwenheim theorem. Fundam. Math. *38* (1951), 230–232.

[11] *H. Rasiowa* and *R. Sikorski*: On the isomorphism of Lindenbaum algebras with fields of sets. Colloq. Math. *5* (1958), 143–158.

[12] *H. Rasiowa* and *R. Sikorski*: Algebraic treatment of the notion of satisfiability. Fundam. Math. *40* (1953), 62–95.

[13] *H. Rasiowa* and *R. Sikorski*: Formalisierte intuitionistische elementare Theorien. Constructivity in Mathematics (Proc. Colloquium at Amsterdam 1957), Amsterdam 1958, 241–249.

[14] *H. Rasiowa* and *R. Sikorski*: On existential theorems in non-classical functional calculi. Fundam. Math. *41* (1954), 21–28.

[15] *H. Rasiowa* and *R. Sikorski*: Mathematics of Metamathematics. Monografie matematyczne, to appear.

[16] *L. Rieger*: On free $\aleph_\xi$-complete Boolean algebras. Fundam. Math. *38* (1951), 35–52.

[17] *L. Rieger*: On countable generalised σ-algebras, with a new proof of Gödel's completeness theorem. Czech. math. J. *1* (1951), 29–40.

[18] *L. Rieger*: On the lattice theory of Brouwerian propositional logic. Spisy vyd. přírod. fak. Univ. Karlovy *189* (1949), 1–40.

[19] *R. Sikorski*: A topological characterization of open theories. Bull. Acad. polon. sci. *9* (1961), 259–260.

[20] *R. Sikorski*: On open theories. Colloq. Math. in print.

[21] *R. Sikorski*: On representation of Lindenbaum algebras. Prace Matematyczne, in print.

[22] *R. Sikorski*: On Herbrand's theorem. Colloq. Math. *6* (1958), 55–58.

[23] *R. Sikorski*: Some applications of interior mappings. Fundam. Math. *45* (1958), 200–212.

[24] *R. Sikorski*: Der Heytingsche Prädikatenkalkül und metrische Räume. Constructivity in Mathematics (Proc. Colloquium at Amsterdam, 1957), Amsterdam 1958, 250–253.

[25] *R. Sikorski*: A theorem on non-classical functional calculi. Bull. Acad. polon. sci. *4* (1956), 659–660.

[26] *R. Sikorski*: Closure homomorphisms and interior mappings. Fundam. Math. *36* (1949), 165–206.

[27] *M. H. Stone*: Applications of the theory of Boolean rings to general topology. Trans. Amer. Math. Soc. *41* (1937), 321–364.

[28] *M. H. Stone*: Topological representation of distributive lattices and Brouwerian logic. Čas. mat. fys. *67* (1937), 1–25.

[29] *А. Т. Шварц*: К одной задаче Сикорского. Успехи матем. наук *12*, вып. 4 (1957), 215.

[30] *A. Tarski*: Der Aussagenkalkül und die Topologie. Fundam. Math. *31* (1938), 103–134.

[31] *A. D. Wallace*: Some characterization of interior transformations. Amer. J. Math. *41* (1939), 757–763.

BASIC SEQUENCES AND REFLEXIVITY OF BANACH SPACES

I. SINGER

București

R. C. JAMES has given the following characterization of reflexive Banach spaces ([2], theorem 1):

A Banach space E with a basis $\{x_n\}$ is reflexive if and only if

(a) The basis $\{x_n\}$ is *boundedly complete*, i. e. for every sequence of scalars $\{a_n\}$ such that $\sup_n \|\sum_{i=1}^{n} a_i x_i\| < +\infty$, the series $\sum_{i=1}^{\infty} a_i x_i$ is convergent, and

(b) The basis $\{x_n\}$ is *shrinking*, i. e. $\lim_{n\to\infty} \|f\|_n = 0$ for all functionals $f \in E^*$, where $\|f\|_n$ denotes the norm of the restriction of f to the closed linear subspace of E spanned by $x_{n+1}, x_{n+2}, \ldots$

Recently V. PTÁK [3] has completed the picture of the structure of reflexive Banach spaces given by this theorem, by characterizing reflexivity in terms of bounded biorthogonal systems.

Here we characterize reflexivity of a Banach space with a basis *in terms of the behaviour of its basic sequences.*

A sequence $\{z_n\} \subset E$ is called [1] a *basic sequence*, if $\{z_n\}$ is a basis of the subspace $[z_n]$ (i. e. of the closed linear subspace spanned by the sequence $\{z_n\}$). We consider the following types of basic sequences: shrinking, boundedly complete, l_+, P, P^*.

We shall say that a basic sequence $\{z_n\}$ is of type

l_+, if $\sup_n \|z_n\| < +\infty$, and if there exists a constant $\eta > 0$ such that we have, for every finite sequence $t_1, \ldots, t_n \geqq 0$,

$$\|\sum_{i=1}^{n} t_i z_i\| \geqq \eta \sum_{i=1}^{n} t_i ,$$

P, if $\inf_n \|z_n\| > 0$ and $\sup_n \|\sum_{i=1}^{n} z_n\| < +\infty$,

P^*, if $\sup_n \|z_n\| < +\infty$ and $\sup_n \|\sum_{j=1}^{n} h_j\| < +\infty$, where $\{h_n\} \subset [z_n]^*$ is the sequence of functionals biorthogonal to $\{z_n\}$.

Let $\{x_n\}$ be a basis of E. Any sequence of the form

$$y_n = \sum_{i=p_{n-1}+1}^{p_n} a_i x_i , \quad y_n \neq 0 \quad (n = 1, 2, \ldots) , \quad p_0 = 0 ,$$

is called [1] a *block basis*. We call *block subspace* of E any subspace spanned by a block basis.

In this summary we shall give only the main result (proofs and other results will appear in Studia Mathematica):

Theorem. *For a Banach space E with a basis* $\{x_n\}$ *the following statements are equivalent*:

(1) *E is reflexive.*

(2) *Every basis of every block subspace is shrinking.*

(3) *No basis of any block subspace is of type* l_+.

(4) *Every basis of every block subspace is boundedly complete.*

(5) *No basis of any block subspace is of type P.*

(6) *No basis of any block subspace is of type P*.*

Corollary. *The above theorem remains valid if we replace "...basis of... block subspace" by "...basic sequence in E".*

References

[1] *C. Bessaga* and *A. Pelczyński*: On bases and unconditional convergence of series in Banach spaces. Studia math., *17* (1958), 151–164.

[2] *R. C. James*: Bases and reflexivity of Banach spaces. Ann. of Math., *52* (1950), 518–527.

[3] *V. Pták*: Biorthogonal systems and reflexivity of Banach spaces. Czechosl. Math. J., *9* (1959), p. 319–326.

ON PERFECT COMPACTIFICATIONS OF TOPOLOGICAL SPACES

E. SKLYARENKO

Moscow

The following theorem gives a stronger result than a theorem of S. EILENBERG and K. KURATOWSKI contained in his communication at the Symposium.

Theorem. *Let* X_1, X_2 *be connected Tychonoff spaces and* Y_1, Y_2 *any compactifications of them. If* $H^1 Y_i = 0$ *and* $\operatorname{ind}(Y_i \setminus X_i) = 0$, $i = 1, 2$, *then every homeomorphism* $h : X_1 \to X_2$ *has an extension* $\tilde{h} : Y_1 \to Y_2$ *which is a homeomorphism.*

This theorem follows from the fact that Y_i is equal to the minimal perfect compactification μX_i defined in the author's note „О совершенных бикомпактных расширениях", Докл. АН СССР, *137*, No 1, (1961), 39–41.

ON DIMENSIONAL PROPERTIES OF INFINITE-DIMENSIONAL SPACES

Yu. SMIRNOV

Moscow

This report contains some results of myself and my pupils B. LEVSHENKO and E. SKLYARENKO, concerning infinite-dimensional spaces.

W. HUREWICZ was the first to obtain results in this area for separable metric spaces.

H. Theorem 1. *If a space R has small transfinite dimension* ind R *then* ind $R < \omega_1$.

H. Theorem 2. *The Hilbert cube J^∞ has no transfinite dimension* ind.

J. NAGATA calls a space R countable-dimensional when R is a countable union of zero-dimensional sets N_i, i. e. $R = \cup N_i$, $\dim N_i = 0$.

H. Theorem 3. *Let R be a space with a complete metric; then R has small transfinite dimension* ind R *if and only if R is countable-dimensional.*

The addition theorem for the small dimension ind was given by Toulmin using new operations with transfinite numbers. He gives a simple example of a space for which the addition theorem in usual sense is not true.

B. Levshenko improved Toulmin's results as follows:

L. Theorem 1. *There exist metric compacta R, A, B such that $R = A \cup B$,* $\operatorname{ind} A = \operatorname{ind} B = \omega_0$, $\operatorname{ind} R = \omega_0 + 1$.

L. Theorem 2. *Let R be a metric space and $R = A_1 \cup \ldots \cup A_n$, where A_i are closed; then* $\operatorname{ind} R \leqq \max \operatorname{ind} A_i + \omega_0$.

Let us consider the big transfinite dimension Ind in Čech's sense.

Theorem 1. *If a space R has a big transfinite dimension then R has a small transfinite dimension and* $\operatorname{ind} R \leqq \operatorname{Ind} R$.

Theorem 2. *If a metric space R has big transfinite dimension* Ind R *then* $\operatorname{Ind} R < \omega_1$, *and R is countable-dimensional.*

I have constructed, for every transfinite number $\alpha < \omega_1$, metric compacta I^α for which $\operatorname{Ind} I^\alpha = \alpha$. Levshenko has proved that these compacta I^α may have an arbitrarily high dimension ind.

A space R is called strongly-metrizable when it has an open basis which is a countable union of star-finite coverings.

Theorem 3. *Let a metrizable space R be a countable union of strongly-metrizable subsets R_i; if R has small dimension* ind *then R is countable-dimensional.*

For arbitrary metrizable space this proposition is an unsolved problem.

The proposition inverse to theorem 3 is true for all complete metrizable spaces (completeness is meant in Čech's sense). The following theorem is stronger:

Theorem 4. *Every complete metrizable space R which is an image of a countable-dimensional metric space X by a closed and countable-to-one mapping has small transfinite dimension* ind *R*.

For the proof one of Nagata's theorems and the Sklyarenko's method are used.

Corollary. *Let R be a countable union of strongly-metrizable subsets and let R have a complete metric. Then the following conditions are equivalent*:

a) *R has small dimension* ind *R*,

b) *R is countable-dimensional,*

c) *R is an image of a zero-dimensional metric space by a closed and finite-to-one mapping,*

d) *R is an image of a countable-dimensional metric space by a closed and countable-to-one mapping.*

J. Nagata has proved that conditions b) and c) are equivalent generally.

Call a space R weakly-countable-dimensional when R is a countable union of finite-dimensional closed subsets.

I have constructed a compact metric space which is countable-dimensional but not weakly-countable-dimensional.

Theorem 5. *There exists a universal space for separable metric weakly-countable-dimensional spaces: it is the set of all the points of the Hilbert cube which have only a finite number of non-zero coordinates.*

Recently J. Nagata has constructed a universal space for all metrizable weakly-countable-dimensional spaces with given weight. J. Nagata has proved that the set of all points of the Hilbert cube which have only a finite number of rational coordinates is a universal space for countable-dimensional separable spaces. He also gives some other interesting characterizations of countable-dimensionality.

In his proof of the theorem that the Hilbert cube has no transfinite dimension, W. Hurewicz proved that there exists in this cube a countable number of pairs of closed disjoint sets A_i, B_i with the following property: if the closed sets C_i separate the space between A_i and B_i then the intersection $\bigcap C_i$ is non-void.

The following is a problem of Alexandroff: Let us consider the following property (A) of a space R: for every countable number of pairs of closed disjoint sets A_i, B_i there exist closed sets C_i separating the space R between A_i and B_i with an empty intersection: $\bigcap C_i = \emptyset$.

Alexandroff's problem. *Let R be a compact metric space; is the property* A *equivalent to the property of countable-dimensionality?* For non-compact spaces these properties are not equivalent.

Spaces with property A, called also weakly-infinite-dimensional, have been investigated by Levshenko and Sklyarenko.

L. Theorem 3. *The property* A *is equivalent to the following property* B:

(B) *For every sequence of functions f_i and for every sequence of positive numbers ε_i there exist functions g_i such that $|f_i - g_i| < \varepsilon_i$ and $\bigcap g_i^{-1}(0) = \emptyset$.*

B. Levshenko has generalized to weakly-infinite-dimensional space the addition theorem, the product-theorem, Hurewicz's theorem and others.

S. Theorem 1. *Every strongly-infinite-dimensional compact space contains a Cantor manifold in the following sense*:

The space R is an infinite-dimensional Cantor manifold if it is not cut by any weakly-infinite-dimensional compact subspace.

S. Theorem 2. *Let H be the set of all points of the Hilbert cube which have only a finite number of non-zero coordinates; every compact extension of the space H is strongly-infinite-dimensional.*

Unsolved problems. Let R be a metric space, ind $R = 0$. Has R a big transfinite dimension; is it countable-dimensional; is it weakly-infinite-dimensional?

References

[1] *Б. Т. Левшенко, Е. Г. Скляренко, Ю. М. Смирнов:* О бесконечномерных пространствах. Успехи матем. наук 13, № 5 (*83*), 1958, 203—208.

[2] *Б. Т. Левшенко:* О сильно-бесконечномерных пространствах. Вестн. Моск. ун-та. Сер. физ. мат. и естеств. наук 1959, № 5, 219—227.

[3] *Б. Т. Левшенко:* О бесконечномерных пространствах. Докл. АН СССР, 1961, *139*, № 2, 286—289.

[4] *Е. Г. Скляренко:* О разномерностных свойствах бесконечномерных пространств. Изв. АН СССР Сер. матем. *23*, 1959, № 2, 197—212.

[5] *Е. Г. Скляренко:* О представлении бесконечномерных пространств в виде обратного спектра полиедров. Докл. АН СССР, *134*, № 4, 1960, 773—775.

[6] *Е. Г. Скляренко:* Несколько замечаний о бесконечномерных пространствах. Докл. АН СССР, *126*, № 6, 1959, 1200—1203.

[7] *Ю. М. Смирнов:* Об универсальных пространствах для некоторых классов конечномерных пространств. Изв. АН СССР, Сер. матем., *23*, 1959, № 2, 185—196.

[8] *C. H. Toulmin*: Shuffling Ordinals and Transfinite Dimension. Proc. London Math. Soc., *3*, No. 4, 1954, 177—196.

[9] *J. Nagata*: On the Countable Sum of Zero Dimensional Metric Spaces. Fundam. math. 1960, *48*, 1—14.

[10] *J. Nagata*: On a Universal *n*-Dimensional Set for Metric Spaces. J. reine and angew. Math. *204*, Heft I/4, 1960, 132—138.

[11] *Ю. М. Смирнов:* Несколько замечаний о трансфинитной размерности. Докл. АН СССР *141*, №. 4, 1961, 814—817.

SEMI-TOPOLOGY OF TRANSFORMATION GROUPS

A. SOLIAN

Bucureşti

In a previous paper [1] (see also [4], example 7), I have shown that, given any set M and a transformation group $\mathfrak{A}$ of M, then between the partially-ordered set (lattice, in fact) $\mathfrak{E}(M)$ of the equivalence relations of M and the partially-ordered set of the subgroups of $\mathfrak{A}$ there can be established a dual (inverse) Galois connexion (see [2]) $\mathfrak{B}(\sim)$ and $\sim(\mathfrak{B})$ with $\sim \in \mathfrak{E}(M)$, $\mathfrak{B} \subset \mathfrak{A}$, such that $\mathfrak{B} \to \mathfrak{B}(\sim(\mathfrak{B}))$ is the closure-mapping (see [3], [4]); in other words, if $\mathfrak{B}$ is a subgroup of $\mathfrak{A}$, if $\sim(\mathfrak{B})$ is the equivalence of M corresponding to (associated with) $\mathfrak{B}$, and if $\mathfrak{B}(\sim(\mathfrak{B}))$ is the subgroup of $\mathfrak{A}$ corresponding to (associated with) $\sim(\mathfrak{B})$, then:

1. $\mathfrak{B} \subset \mathfrak{B}(\sim(\mathfrak{B}))$;
2. $\mathfrak{B}_1 \subset \mathfrak{B}_2 \Rightarrow \mathfrak{B}(\sim(\mathfrak{B}_1)) \subset \mathfrak{B}(\sim(\mathfrak{B}_2))$;
3. $\mathfrak{B}(\sim(\mathfrak{B}(\sim(\mathfrak{B})))) = \mathfrak{B}(\sim(\mathfrak{B}))$.

In the present paper it will be shown that there exists a topology (in a weaker sense) of $\mathfrak{A}$, which I shall call a *semi-topology*, such that:

a) The operations of multiplication (superposition) and inversion of transformations are continuous in this semi-topology (theorem 1).

b) The closure of a subgroup $\mathfrak{B} \subset \mathfrak{A}$, in the sense of the above inverse Galois connexion coincides with the closure of $\mathfrak{B}$ with respect to the semi-topology of $\mathfrak{A}$ (theorem 2).

c) If φ is a mapping of $\mathfrak{A}$ onto a transformation group $\mathfrak{A}'$ of a set M', where φ satisfies a certain natural condition, then φ is a continuous mapping with respect to the semi-topologies of $\mathfrak{A}$ and $\mathfrak{A}'$ (theorem 3).

The present theory is not a particular case of Everett's theory [4] concerning the topology introduced in a group whose lattice of subgroups is related to another given lattice by a given Galois connexion.

1° Let M be a non-void set, $\mathfrak{A}$ a transformation group of M; let $\mathfrak{B}$ be a subgroup of $\mathfrak{A}$; then the binary relation $\sim(\mathfrak{B}) = \sim$ of M, defined by

$$a \sim b, \quad a, b \in M \Leftrightarrow \exists\, \tau, \quad \tau \in \mathfrak{B}, \quad \tau(a) = b$$

is an equivalence relation of M [2], which I refer to as the *equivalence associated* with $\mathfrak{B}$. Let $\sim$ be an equivalence relation of M; then the subset $\mathfrak{B}(\sim) = \mathfrak{B} \subset \mathfrak{A}$, defined by

$$\mathfrak{B} = \{\tau \mid \tau \in \mathfrak{A}, \ \tau(x) \sim x, \ \text{for any } x \in M\}$$

is a subgroup of $\mathfrak{A}$ [2], which I refer to as the *subgroup associated* with $\sim$. We have the following result [1]:[1])

The mappings $\sim \to \mathfrak{B}(\sim)$ *and* $\mathfrak{B} \to \sim(\mathfrak{B})$ *establish a dual (inverse) Galois connexion between* $\mathfrak{E}(M)$, *ordered by* "$\leqq$" *where* $\sim_1 \leqq \sim_2$, $\sim_1, \sim_2 \in \mathfrak{E}(M) \Leftrightarrow \Leftrightarrow (a \sim_1 b \Rightarrow a \sim_2 b)$, *and the set of all subgroups of* $\mathfrak{A}$, *ordered by inclusion; here closure is given by* $\mathfrak{B} \to \mathfrak{B}(\sim(\mathfrak{B}))$.

2° By a *semi-topological space* is meant a non-void set S of abstract elements (*points*) such that, for any $\tau \in S$, there is given a non-void family of subsets of S (the *basis of neighbourhoods* of τ) which satisfies the conditions:

a) τ belongs to all sets of its basis of neighbourhoods;

b) for $\tau_1, \tau_2 \in S$, $\tau_1 \neq \tau_2$, there exists a set belonging to the basis of neighbourhoods of τ_1, which does not contain τ_2.

In the special case where S satisfies the additional condition that, for any $\tau \in S$ and any pair of sets U_1, U_2 in the basis of neighbourhoods of τ, there exists a U_3 in the same basis, for which $U_3 \subset U_1 \cap U_2$, the space S is topological space in the usual sense [5].

In a semi-topological space S, the following terminology will be used:

1. *open subset* of S: any union of sets belonging to the various bases of neighbourhoods of points of S, or the void subset $\emptyset$;
2. *closed subset* of S: any subset $F \subset S$, whose complement $S \setminus F$ is open;
3. *neighbourhood* of a point $\tau \in S$: any open subset containing τ;
4. *closure* $\overline{M}$ of a subset $M \subset S$: the set of all $\tau \in S$ such that $U \cap M \neq \emptyset$ for any neighbourhood U of τ.

In a semi-topological space S, we have:

α) any union of open subsets is open;

β) any intersection of closed subsets is closed;

γ) $M \subset \overline{M}$, for any $M \subset S$;

δ) a subset M is closed if and only if $\overline{M} = M$;

ε) $\overline{M}$ is closed i. e. $\overline{\overline{M}} = \overline{M}$, for any $M \subset S$;

ξ) if $M_1 \subset M_2 \subset S$ then $\overline{M}_1 \subset \overline{M}_2$;

η) $\overline{M} = \bigcap_{\substack{F \text{ closed} \\ F \supset M}} F$, for any $M \subset S$;

θ) if $M = \{\tau\}$ (i. e. a single-point set), then M is closed;

ι) $\overline{\bigcup_{i=1}^{n} M_i} \supset \bigcup_{i=1}^{n} \overline{M}_i$, for any $M_1, \ldots, M_n \subset S$.

Let S, T be two semi-topological spaces. Consider the cardinal product of the sets S, T as point set; as basis of neighbourhoods of a point (σ, τ), $\sigma \in S$, $\tau \in T$, take the family of all pairs (U, V) where U and V belong to the basis of neighbourhoods of σ

[1]) See also [4] and [2] (where it is proved that the corresponding mappings are monotone).

in S and of τ in T, respectively. Thus we obtain a semi-topological space $S \times T$, which shall be called the *cartesian product* of the given spaces S, T.

Let S, S' be two semi-topological spaces; a uniform mapping $f : S \to S'$ is by definition a *continuous mapping* of S into S' if for any $\tau \in S$, and any neighbourhood U' of $f(\tau)$ in S', one can find a neighbourhood U of τ in S with $f(U) \subset U'$.

A *semi-topological group* is by definition a non-void set $\mathfrak{G}$ of abstract elements such that following conditions are fulfilled:

I. $\mathfrak{G}$ is a group with respect to a certain law of composition, denoted by "." or by juxtaposition.

II. $\mathfrak{G}$ is a semi-topological space.

III. The mappings

$$p : \mathfrak{G} \times \mathfrak{G} \to \mathfrak{G} \quad \text{and} \quad i : \mathfrak{G} \to \mathfrak{G}$$

defined by $p(\sigma, \tau) = \sigma \, . \, \tau$, $i(\sigma) = \sigma^{-1}$ for $\sigma, \tau \in \mathfrak{G}$ are continuous.

3° Let M be a non-void set and $\mathfrak{A}$ a transformation group of M.

As law of composition in $\mathfrak{A}$ take the superposition of transformations. Let $\tau \in \mathfrak{A}$; as basis of neighbourhoods of τ in $\mathfrak{A}$ take the family $\{\mathfrak{U}_x^\tau\}$, $x \in M$, where

$$\mathfrak{U}_x^\tau = \{\sigma \mid \sigma \in \mathfrak{A},\ \sigma(x) = \tau(x)\} .$$

Then we have the following results:

Theorem 1. *With respect to the defined operation and basis of neighbourhoods of a point, $\mathfrak{A}$ is a semi-topological group.*

Theorem 2. *If $\mathfrak{B}$ is a subgroup of $\mathfrak{A}$, then*

$$\overline{\mathfrak{B}} = \mathfrak{B}(\sim(\mathfrak{B}))$$

(where by $\overline{\mathfrak{B}}$ we mean the closure in the sense of the semi-topology in $\mathfrak{A}$), i. e. the closure of a subgroup in the Galois connexion coincides with its closure in the semi-topology of $\mathfrak{A}$.

Theorem 3. *Let M, M' be non-void sets, $\mathfrak{A}$, $\mathfrak{A}'$ transformation groups of M, M', respectively; let f resp. φ be mappings of M onto M', resp. of $\mathfrak{A}$ onto $\mathfrak{A}'$, satisfying the condition*

$$f(\tau(x)) = (\varphi(\tau))\,(f(x)) \,, \quad \textit{for any} \quad x \in M \,, \quad \tau \in \mathfrak{A} \,;$$

then the mapping $\varphi : \mathfrak{A} \to \mathfrak{A}'$ is a group homomorphism and a continuous mapping of $\mathfrak{A}$ onto $\mathfrak{A}'$ (in the semi-topology just defined).

We mention also the following properties:

If $\mathfrak{A}$ acs regularly on M (i. e. $\tau_1(x_0) = \tau_2(x_0)$ for some $x_0 \in M$ implies $\tau_1 = \tau_2$ whenever $\tau_1, \tau_2 \in \mathfrak{A}$) *then the semi-topology of $\mathfrak{A}$ is discrete* (i. e. any $\tau \in \mathfrak{A}$ has a single-point neighbourhood $\{\tau\}$).

A subgroup $\mathfrak{B} \subset \mathfrak{T}(M)$ (where $\mathfrak{T}(M)$ is the group of all transformations of M) *is dense in $\mathfrak{T}(M)$* (i. e. $\overline{\mathfrak{B}} = \mathfrak{T}(M)$, where the closure $\overline{\mathfrak{B}}$ is taken with respect to the semi-topology of $\mathfrak{T}(M)$) *if and only if it acts transitively on M.*

References

[1] *A. Solian*: Equivalence Relations and Associated Subgroups. Paper read at the IInd Hungarian Mathematical Congress, Budapest, August 1960.

[2] *P. Dubreil*: Algèbre. IIème edition, Gauthier-Villars, Paris 1954.

[3] *O. Ore*: Galois Connexions. Trans. Amer. Math. Soc., vol. *55* (1944), 493–513.

[4] *C. J. Everett*: Closure Operators and Galois Theory in Lattices. Ibid., vol. *55* (1944), 514–525.

[5] *Л. С. Понтрягин*: Непрерывные группы. ГИТТЛ, Москва 1954.

NON-SEPARABLE BOREL SETS

A. H. STONE

Rochester

All spaces considered are to be metrisable and absolutely Borel. The terminology is as in C. KURATOWSKI, Topologie I. A *Borel isomorphism* f between spaces X and Y is a 1-1 mapping of X onto Y such that both f and f^{-1} take Borel sets into Borel sets. (This notion is due to G. W. MACKEY.)

The main object is to classify spaces into Borel isomorphism classes, and to characterize these classes topologically. For separable spaces it is well known that there are just two types, represented by the space of integers and by the space of all real (or irrational) numbers, respectively. It is shown that the weight of a space is invariant under Borel isomorphism, and that the number of Borel isomorphism classes of spaces of weight $\aleph_\alpha$ is exactly $|\alpha|$ if α is infinite, and at most $2^{|\alpha|+1}$ otherwise.

The proofs require the extension to general spaces of a significant part of the well-known structure theory of separable Borel sets (i. e., of weight $\aleph_0$). They are largely classical arguments, supplemented by special devices, mostly depending on paracompactness, for circumventing appeals to separability. The main steps are as follows. One first defines, and obtains the basic properties of, the analogues of the Cantor set and of the space of irrationals for spaces of weight k; when $k > \aleph_0$ these coincide in the product of $\aleph_0$ copies of a discrete set of k points; we denote this product by $B(k)$. Every space of weight k is proved to be Borel isomorphic (in fact, generalized homeomorphic) to a closed subset of $B(k)$. Next, if a continuous mapping f of a complete metric space of weight k has image of cardinal $> k$, f is shown to be a homeomorphism on some subspace of cardinal $k^{\aleph_0}$ which is homeomorphic to some $B(p)$. From this one can determine the number of Borel subsets of cardinal n of an arbitrary space of weight k, which leads to the result that weight is invariant under Borel isomorphism. One can now show that every space of weight k is Borel isomorphic to the discrete union of at most k spaces, each of the form $B(p)$ for some $p \leqq k$, and the classification mentioned above is a consequence. It is not quite complete; the unsolved problems are typified by the following: Is $B(\aleph_1)$ Borel isomorphic to the discrete union of $\aleph_1$ copies of the space $B(\aleph_0)$ of irrationals?

Characterizations are obtained only in two extreme cases: the type of a discrete set, and the type of $B(k)$ for certain values of k. Thus many problems remain. One is whether every Borel isomorphism is a generalized homeomorphism; the answer is shown to be affirmative in some cases (e. g. if one of the spaces is locally separable).

The theory can be extended to a theory of "absolutely k-analytic sets", which for $k = \aleph_0$ reduce to the analytic sets, and it is shown that the main cardinality properties carry over.

Remark. The full text appears in Rozprawy Matematyczne *28* (1962).

TOPOLOGICAL ASPECTS OF CONFORMAL MAPPING THEORY

M. H. STONE
Chicago

The purpose of this note is not to present new results but to review some topological aspects of old ones.

A conformal map h of a domain D of the extended complex plane onto a set hD of the same plane carries topological properties of D over to hD — for example, hD is also a domain. In particular, when h is univalent, or schlicht, D and hD are homeomorphic as subspaces of the complex plane or as two-dimensional manifolds and therefore have the same connectivity. The fundamental investigations of S. Stoïlow [5] showed that from a topological point of view the conformal maps of such manifolds on one another are characterized as light interior mappings.

At the same time the map h induces certain relations between the boundaries of D and hD. For example, when h is univalent and hD is an open circular disc, it is well known that h has a unique continuous extension to the closure of D which maps it onto the closed disc, and that the extended map attaches to each point on the circumference an antecedent set which is a prime end of D. In particular, when the boundary of D is a simple closed arc or Jordan curve, each prime end reduces to a single point and the extended map is a homeomorphism. In general h can be extended from D to its Čech-Stone compactification βD so as to map the latter continuously onto the closure of hD; and the relations between the boundaries of D and hD should be studied in terms of this extension. Indeed, the problem thus posed may be generalized as a purely topological problem: if S is a locally compact Hausdorff subspace of a topological space T and h a continuous map of S into a second topological space, to study in terms of βS the relations induced by h between the boundaries of S and hS, thus generalizing the classical theory of prime ends. The papers contributed by S. Eilenberg and K. Kuratowski to this Symposium deal with some aspects of this problem.

As S. Stoïlow [5] has pointed out, a conformal map h induces a natural correspondence between the boundary components of D and those of hD. When h is univalent, so also is this correspondence. The boundary components are of two types — those consisting of a single point and those which are proper continua. Under a univalent conformal map corresponding boundary components are not necessarily of the same type. Following L. Sario [4], we call a boundary component stable if its type persists under all such maps, and unstable otherwise. For example, every isolated boundary component is stable, and unstable boundary components can occur only for domains of infinite connectivity. A stable boundary component is called weak or strong according as it is of the first or the second type. This classification has been rather extensively but still inconclusively investigated in recent years by L. Sario [4], K. OIKAWA [1], and others. It has an intimate connection with the problem of mapping a given domain conformally and univalently onto a domain of some standard type.

Indeed, let us consider here two of the best known standard types — the circularly slit disc and the radially slit disc. A connected open subset of an open circular disc is called a circularly slit disc if it contains the center of the disc and has as its boundary components the circumference of the disc and a finite or infinite number of concentric circular arcs or slits (some of which may reduce to single points). Similarly, a connected open subset of an open circular disc is called a radially slit disc if it contains the center of the disc and has as its boundary components the circumference of the disc and a finite or infinite number of radial segments or slits (some of which may reduce to single points). In addition, it is necessary to take into account a somewhat more general type of domain, the radially slashed disc — that is to say, an open connected subset of an open circular disc containing the center of the disc and having as its boundary components a finite or infinite number of radial slits and a single connected set of zero measure obtained by joining to the circumference of the disc a finite or infinite number of radial segments. Indeed it is also convenient to replace in these descriptions the open circular disc and its circumference by the finite plane and the point at infinity, thus obtaining domains which may be called circularly slit discs of infinite radius, radially slit discs of infinite radius, and radially slashed discs of infinite radius, respectively.

The existence of univalent conformal maps of a given domain D upon a domain of one or another of these types is closely associated with the extremization of the functional

$$Q_t : h \to L_t(h)^2/A(h)$$

where h is a function analytic in D, t is a prescribed point of D, $L_t(h)$ is the linear magnification effected by h at t, and $A(h)$ is the area of hD. Thus

$$L_t(h) = |h'(t)| , \quad A(h) = \iint_D |h'(z)|^2 \, do .$$

Since Q_t is homogeneous of zero degree in h, the extrema are the same as those obtained by fixing the value of $L_t(h)$ and extremizing $A(h)$, or vice versa. For the same reason there is no loss of generality in normalizing h in one way or another – for example, by putting $h(t) = 0$, $h'(t) > 0$, and fixing $h'(t)$ or $A(h)$. It is well known [6] that in terms of the Hermitian semi-norm $A(h)^{\frac{1}{2}}$ the functional Q_t is weakly upper semi-continuous. The set of competing functions of greatest interest in the present context is the set of those univalent functions which map D into a circular disc with center 0 in such a way that the boundary component of hD corresponding to a prescribed boundary component Γ of D is the circumference of the disc. Unless Γ is weak, this set is non-empty. The greatest lower bound of Q_t over this set will be denoted as α_t, its least upper bound as β_t. It is convenient to introduce also the quantities $r_t = 1/\sqrt{(\pi\beta_t)}$ and $R_t = 1/\sqrt{(\pi\alpha_t)}$.

The extremal problem for a general domain cannot be solved directly but has to be discussed by combining approximation techniques with certain a priori estimates of $Q_t(h)$ for special domains – such as the Bieberbach inequality for the circular disc and the stronger, more sophisticated inequalities given by Reich and Warschawski for circularly slit and radially slit discs [2, 3]. The first step is to solve the problem for domains of finite connectivity. If Γ is not weak, there exist unique normalized competing functions at which Q_t attains its extrema. The function h such that $Q_t(h)=\alpha_t$ maps D onto a radially slit disc which has radius R_t for the normalization $h'(t) = 1$. Similarly the function h such that $Q_t(h) = \beta_t$ maps D onto a circularly slit disc which has radius r_t for the same normalization. The problem for a general domain is then treated by studying exhaustions of D by subdomains of finite connectivity with distinguished boundary components converging in the sense of Stoïlow to D. These approximating subdomains are chosen so as to have no weak boundary components. The limit functions obtained from the extremizing functions for the approximating subdomains are then candidates for mapping D on some domain of standard type, and possibly even for extremizing Q_t.

Since Q_t is weakly upper semi-continuous the problem of maximizing this functional can be successfully discussed by the procedure described above [2, 6]. If Γ is not weak, there is a unique maximizing function which maps D onto a circularly slit disc with circumference corresponding to Γ and with radius r_t when the normalization is given by the condition $h'(t) = 1$. Furthermore the case where Γ is weak is characterized by the equivalent conditions $\beta_t = 0$, $r_t = +\infty$. To test whether Γ is weak, it suffices to observe that r_t can be computed as a limit of radii associated with the approximating subdomains [1, 4]. It may be conjectured that in this case D can be mapped univalently and conformally on a circularly slit disc of infinite radius.

The minimization problem is more difficult to analyze and still remains comparatively obscure. It is not known, for instance, whether D can always be mapped on a radially slit disc when Γ is not weak or even when Γ is strong. However, recent results of E. Reich [3] show that the exhaustion procedure introduces a quantity ϱ_t (which he denotes otherwise) as a limit of radii associated with the approximating subdomains, $R_t \leqq \varrho_t \leqq +\infty$, and that when ϱ_t is finite D can be mapped on a radially slashed disc with radius ϱ_t by a function satisfying the condition $h'(t) = 1$. Furthermore, it is known [1, 4] that $\varrho_t < +\infty$ is sufficient for Γ to be strong. It may be conjectured that in the case $\varrho_t = +\infty$ the domain D can be mapped univalently and conformally on a radially slashed disc of infinite radius when Γ is strong and on a radially slit disc of infinite radius when Γ is weak; and perhaps even that these two possibilities can be characterized by the conditions $\alpha_t > 0$ and $\alpha_t = 0$ respectively – though there is little evidence to this effect.

References

[1] *K. Oikawa*: On the Stability of Boundary Components. Pacific Journal of Mathematics, *10* (1960), 263–294.

[2] *Edgar Reich* and *S. E. Warschawski*: On Canonical Conformal Maps of Regions of Arbitrary Connectivity. Pacific Journal of Mathematics, *10* (1960), 965–985.

[3] *Edgar Reich*: On Radial Slit Mappings (to appear).

[4] *L. Sario*: Strong and Weak Boundary Components. Journal d'Analyse Mathématique, *5* (1956–57), 389–398.

[5] *S. Stoïlow*: Leçons sur les principes topologiques de la théorie des fonctions analytiques. Paris (1938), X + 148 pages.

[6] *M. H. Stone*: Hilbert Space Methods in Conformal Mapping. Proceedings of the International Symposium on Linear Spaces 1960, Jerusalem (1961), 409–425.

THE BOUNDARY OF THE SPECTRUM OF A LINEAR OPERATOR

A. E. TAYLOR

Los Angeles

The results which I am communicating at this Symposium are selected from a joint paper by myself and one of my students, Dr. HERBERT A. GINDLER; this joint paper has been submitted for publication in *Studia Mathematica.* In this present Symposium report all proofs are omitted.

In all that I have to say X will be a complex normed linear space, not necessarily complete, and T will be a linear operator, not necessarily continuous or closed, with domain $D(T)$ and range $R(T)$ in X. I write $\lambda - T$ for $\lambda I - T$, where I is the identity mapping of X onto itself. All of the points λ in the complex plane are divided into two mutually exclusive and complementary sets: the resolvent set $\varrho(T)$ and the spectrum $\sigma(T)$. The boundary of the spectrum is denoted by $\partial\sigma(T)$. One may wish to make a finer classification of points by subdividing $\sigma(T)$ in some way. One such method of subdivision is well-known; the spectrum can be analyzed into point spectrum, continuous spectrum, and residual spectrum. Other schemes for subdividing the spectrum have been proposed. Any systematic study of the constituent parts of the spectrum, according to some scheme of subdivision, might be called a study of the *fine-structure* of the spectrum. I believe that such studies, if made along appropriate lines, will be of interest and importance for a better understanding of general spectral theory. I suppose the title of this report might just as well have been "Remarks and Results on Spectral Fine-Structure". Dr. Gindler and I do indeed have some results which belong to a general study of fine-structure, but they are far from complete. Our results on matters related to the boundary of the spectrum are also incomplete; I chose to emphasize the boundary in the title merely because we do have several quite explicit results pertaining to it.

I think it worth while to make a few general remarks about the idea of spectral fine-structure. Let α range over some index set, and let $\{P_\alpha\}$ be a family of properties which linear operators such as T may or may not possess. Suppose $\{P_\alpha\}$ is such that, if $\lambda - T$ has one of the properties P_α, then λ is in $\sigma(T)$, and if λ is in $\sigma(T)$ then $\lambda - T$ has a certain one of the properties P_α. Let $\sigma_\alpha(T)$ be the set of those λ such that $\lambda - T$ has property P_α. Let us further suppose that $\sigma_\alpha(T)$ and $\sigma_\beta(T)$ are disjoint if $\alpha \neq \beta$. Then the family of sets $\{\sigma_\alpha(T)\}$ provides us a decomposition of the spectrum, and thereby a possible basis for a study of spectral fine-structure. A part of the problem in general is to discover appropriate families of properties $\{P_\alpha\}$. These properties should be of interest and significance in the study of linear operators, and one should then seek to discover how these properties of operators are reflected in the nature of the sets of the family $\{\sigma_\alpha(T)\}$. For example, one may ask: For a given P_α, what limitations must be placed on a set of points in order that it may be, for a certain X and T, the set $\sigma_\alpha(T)$? Also, if one can prove that a certain set $\sigma_\alpha(T)$ is always open, this indicates that the property P_α of a linear operator is stable (i. e. it persists) when the operator is perturbed by adding to it an operator of the form cI, where $|c|$ is sufficiently small.

For our study of spectral fine-structure Dr. Gindler and I use nine properties of operators with domains and ranges in X, indicated by all the possible combinations in pairs of the symbols I, II, III, and 1, 2, 3. The first set of three symbols refers to the range of the operator:

I. The range is all of X.
II. The range is not all of X, but is dense in X.
III. The range is not dense in X.

The second set refers to the inverse of the operator:

1. The operator has a continuous inverse.
2. The operator has a discontinuous inverse.
3. The operator has no inverse.

Thus, for instance, an operator $\lambda - T$ has property I_3 if $R(\lambda - T) = X$ but $\lambda - T$ has no inverse. The corresponding part of $\sigma(T)$ is denoted by $I_3\,\sigma(T)$. This notation was originally introduced for the study of relations between an operator and its conjugate, by means of a "state diagram". (See the third and fourth items in the list of references.) With our notation, λ belongs to $\varrho(T)$ provided that $\lambda - T$ has one of the properties I_1, II_1, while λ belongs to $\sigma(T)$ if $\lambda - T$ has any of the other seven properties. We may note in passing that, if X is a complete space, a closed operator cannot possess either of the properties I_2, II_1. Hence, for a closed operator T and a complete space X, our subdivision of the spectrum is into six parts, corresponding to the properties

$$I_3, II_2, II_3, III_1, III_2, III_3.$$

As a simple but important tool we introduce the *minimum modulus* $\mu(T)$ of the operator T, defined as follows: $\mu(T) = \inf \|Tx\|$, the infimum being with respect to all unit vectors in $D(T)$. As is well known and easily proved, T has a continuous inverse if and only if $\mu(T) > 0$, and in that case $\mu(T)$ is the reciprocal of the norm of T^{-1}. For convenience let $\Phi(\lambda) = \mu(\lambda - T)$. We can easily show that Φ is continuous; therefore the set $\{\lambda : \Phi(\lambda) > 0\}$ is open. It consists of $\varrho(T)$ and $III_1\,\sigma(T)$. Both of these sets turn out to be open. Moreover, any connected subset of $\{\lambda : \Phi(\lambda) > 0\}$ either lies entirely in $\varrho(T)$ or entirely in $III_1\,\sigma(T)$. In particular, if $\Phi(\lambda_0) > 0$, the open disk $\{\lambda : |\lambda - \lambda_0| < \Phi(\lambda_0)\}$ lies wholly in $\varrho(T)$ or wholly in $III_1\,\sigma(T)$. We see from the foregoing that we must have $\mu(\lambda - T) = 0$ whenever $\lambda \in \partial\sigma(T)$. However, one may construct examples where $\mu(\lambda - T) = 0$ at points λ not in $\partial\sigma(T)$.

Of the seven sets $I_2\,\sigma(T), \ldots, III_3\,\sigma(T)$ in our fine-structure decomposition of $\sigma(T)$, the only one of which it may be asserted that it is open, no matter how X and T

are chosen, is $\mathrm{III}_1\ \sigma(T)$. Examples exists to show that the other sets need not be open. As already noted, however, if X is complete and T is closed, $\mathrm{I}_2\ \sigma(T)$ is empty. If X is complete and T is closed, with domain dense in X, the set $\mathrm{I}_3\ \sigma(T)$ is open, for it may be shown in this case that $\mathrm{I}_3\ \sigma(T) = \mathrm{III}_1\ \sigma(T')$, where T' is the operator conjugate to T.

Suppose λ_0 is a point for which $\Phi(\lambda_0) > 0$. By the Φ-radius of λ_0 we mean the supremum of numbers $r > 0$ such that $\Phi(\lambda) > 0$ if $|\lambda - \lambda_0| < r$. Using the spectral mapping theorem, we have proved that when T is closed and X is complete, and λ_0 is in $\varrho(T)$, the Φ-radius of λ_0 is given by

$$\lim_{n\to\infty} \{\mu[(\lambda_0 - T)^n]\}^{1/n}. \tag{1}$$

This is the same as the distance from λ_0 to $\partial\sigma(T)$, if $\sigma(T)$ is not empty. If we drop the assumption that X is complete, and assume merely that $\Phi(\lambda_0) > 0$ (so that λ_0 may be either in $\mathrm{III}_1\ \sigma(T)$ or in $\varrho(T)$), we have the following less precise results: The Φ-radius of λ_0 is not less than

$$\sup_n \{\mu[(\lambda_0 - T)^n]\}^{1/n}, \tag{2}$$

provided either that (a) $D(T) = X$ and T is continuous, or (b) $\varrho(T)$ contains a point β such that $R(\beta - T) = X$. Still another set of conditions (c) leading to the same conclusion is the following: (c) $D(T^n)$ is dense in X for $n = 1, 2, \ldots$, and for each n the conjugate of $(\lambda_0 - T)^n$ is the same as the n-th power of the conjugate of $\lambda_0 - T$.

We have conjectured that, when $\Phi(\lambda_0) > 0$, the limit in (1) exists and coincides with the supremum in (2), but we have been unable to prove or disprove the conjecture. The following result can be proved: Suppose $D(T) = X$, T continuous, and $\Phi(\lambda_0) > 0$. Suppose there exists a continuous linear operator B which is an extension of $(\lambda_0 - T)^{-1}$ and such that $D(B) = X$. Finally, suppose $\limsup_{n\to\infty} \|(\lambda_0 - T)^n B^n\|^{1/n} \leqq 1$. Then the limit in (1) exists and is the reciprocal of the spectral radius of B. (We remark, incidentally, on the following useful facts, needed here and established by Dr. Gindler in his thesis: If A is a bounded linear operator defined on an incomplete space X, and if $\hat{A}$ is the unique continuous linear extension of A to the completion of X, then $\sigma(A) = \sigma(\hat{A})$, and the spectral radius of A is given, just as in the case of X complete, by $\lim_{n\to\infty} \|A^n\|^{1/n}$.)

H. A. Gindler and I have constructed many examples to show something of the variety which is possible in the fine-structure of $\sigma(T)$. In one interesting example, where $0 < a < b$, we have the following situation: $\sigma(T) = \{\lambda : |\lambda| \leqq b\}$, and the fine-structure is given by

$$\mathrm{III}_1\ \sigma(T) = \{\lambda : |\lambda| < a\}.$$
$$\mathrm{III}_2\ \sigma(T) = \{\lambda : a \leqq |\lambda| < \sqrt{(ab)}\}.$$
$$\mathrm{II}_2\ \sigma(T) = \{\lambda : \sqrt{(ab)} \leqq |\lambda| \leqq b\}.$$

We conclude this report with a rather curious result about $\partial\sigma(T)$ for the case in which T is a bounded linear operator in a complex Hilbert space X. For a bounded selfadjoint operator H we define

$$M(H) = \sup_{\|x\|=1} (Hx, x), \quad m(H) = \inf_{\|x\|=1} (Hx, x).$$

Evidently $m(-H) = -M(H)$ and $\mu(T) = \{m(T^*T)\}^{1/2}$. Now let Θ be real, and define

$$J_\Theta = \tfrac{1}{2}(e^{-i\Theta}T + e^{i\Theta}T^*).$$

We can then prove the following: If $\lambda = re^{i\Theta}$ (with $r \geqq 0$) is a point of $\partial\sigma(T)$, the polar coordinates (r, Θ) must satisfy each of the equations

$$r^2 = M[2rJ_\Theta - T^*T], \quad r^2 = M[2rJ_\Theta - TT^*].$$

References

[1] *Herbert A. Gindler*: Some Properties of Operator Spectra. Doctoral dissertation, University of California, Los Angeles 1961.

[2] *Herbert A. Gindler* and *Angus E. Taylor*: The Minimum Modulus of a Linear Operator and its Use in Spectral Theory. (To be published in Studia Mathematica.)

[3] *A. E. Taylor* and *J. A. C. Halberg, Jr.*: General Theorems about a Linear Operator and its Conjugate. J. reine angew. Math. *198* (1957), 93–111.

[4] *Angus E. Taylor*: Introduction to Functional Analysis. John Wiley, New York 1958.

SUR LA STRUCTURE DE CERTAINS GROUPES TOPOLOGIQUES

C. TELEMAN

București

Soit X une variété différentiable, x_0 un point fixe de X, Ω_{x_0} l'ensemble des chemins rectifiables et fermés de X, passant par x_0. Un champ tensoriel R, d'ordre 4 sur X, covariant, définit dans chaque classe de chemins homotopes de Ω_{x_0} un écart ϱ_R, donné par la borne inférieure des „aires" des homotopies liant deux chemins homotopes, les „aires" étant calculées à l'aide du champ R. En désignant par Γ l'ensemble des classes λ des chemins de Ω_{x_0}, définies par les écarts ϱ_R par la formule

$$f, g \in \lambda \Leftrightarrow \varrho_R(f, g) = 0 \quad \text{pour tout } R\,,$$

on peut vérifier aisément que Γ devient un groupe topologique, avec la loi de composition induite par la composition des chemins usuelle et avec la topologie induite sur Γ par la somme des topologies définies par la famille des écarts R, dans chaque classe d'homotopie de chemins rectifiables fermés de X.

Théorème 1. *Si $r : \Gamma \to H$ est une représentation de Γ sur un groupe de Lie H, le groupe H est localement isomorphe au produit direct d'un groupe de Lie compact et d'un groupe de Lie abélien.*

Théorème 2. *Si $r : \Gamma \to H$ est une représentation linéaire d'ordre fini du groupe Γ, r est une fonction de ligne différentiable dans le sens de Volterra, à valeurs matricielles.*

On peut, en effet, considérer r comme une fonction qui associe à chaque ligne rectifiable fermée f de X, ayant l'origine en x_0, une matrice $r(f)$. Si R est un champ tensoriel du type considéré et si v est un champ vectoriel sur f, on peut définir une fonction dr de f et v, telle qu'on ait une formule de la forme

$$r(f_s) - r(f) = (dr)(f, v) + \varepsilon s\,,$$

pour toute variation différentiable f_s du chemin f, tangente au champ v, ε étant une quantité tendant vers zéro quand $s \to 0$ et $f_s \to f$.

Remarque. Le texte complet paraîtra dans la „Revue de mathématiques pures et appliquées", tome 7.

CONCERNING INFINITE-DIMENSIONAL SPACES

L. TUMARKIN

Moscow

The problem whether every infinite-dimensional compactum (= compact metric space) contains closed subsets of an arbitrary finite dimension, was formulated by myself some 35 years ago and it still remains open (even for closed one-dimensional subsets).

In this note some theorems concerning this problem are considered.

A metric space of infinite dimension is called countable-dimensional if it is a union of a countable number of 0-dimensional subsets. In the opposite case we call the space strongly infinite-dimensional.

The following definitions generalize a classical notion due to Urysohn.

An infinite-dimensional compactum is called a Cantorian manifold in the weak sense (or in the strong sense, respectively), if it cannot be decomposed by any finite-dimensional (or by any finite- or countable-dimensional, respectively) closed subset.[1])

The proof of the following theorem 1 is very easy:

Theorem 1. *An infinite-dimensional compactum X contains closed subset of an arbitrary finite dimension if and only if it contains some countable-dimensional closed set.*

Theorem 2 improves my older result [1].

Theorem 2. *Let X be an infinite-dimensional compactum. Then either*

a) *X contains a countable-dimensional closed set*

or

b) *X contains an infinite-dimensional Cantorian manifold in the strong sense.*

The two cases do not exclude each other.

However, the question whether every infinite-dimensional Cantorian manifold in the strong sense contains a countable-dimensional closed subset, still remains open.

Now we shall consider arbitrary separable metric spaces.

Theorem 3. *Under the assumption of the continuum hypothesis every strongly infinite-dimensional separable metric space X contains a set A with the following property:*

---

[1]) In the weak case we suppose moreover that the space can be decomposed by some countable-dimensional closed subset.

The intersection of A with every finite-dimensional or countable-dimensional subset of X is at most countable.

This theorem generalizes a result of W. HUREWICZ [2]. The proof makes use (as does the construction by Hurewicz) of the fact (proved by myself in the year 1925) that every n-dimensional subset of a separable metric space X (with a given metric) is contained in some G_δ-set of the same dimension, lying in the metric space X.

Concerning the countable dimensional spaces, I have proved in [3] the

Theorem 4. *Every countable-dimensional separable metric space X is a union*

$$X = \bigcup_{i=1}^{\infty} \mathfrak{M}_i$$

of 0*-dimensional subsets* $\mathfrak{M}_i$ *such that the sum of any finite number of them is still* 0*-dimensional*:

$$\dim \bigcup_{i=1}^{N} \mathfrak{M}_i = 0 \textit{ for any finite } N .$$

Let us finally point out that even the question whether in every countable dimensional separable metric X there is contained a subset of an arbitrary fiinite dimension, still remains open.

References

[1] *Л. А. Тумаркин:* О бесконечномерных канторовых многообразиях. Докл. АН СССР, *115* (1957), 244—246.

[2] *W. Hurewicz*: Une remarque sur l'hypothèse du continu. Fundam. Math., *19* (1932), 8–16.

[3] *Л. А. Тумаркин:* О разбиении пространств на счетное число нульмерных множеств. Вестн. Моск. ун-та, серия I, математика, механика, № 1 (1960), 25—33.

DIMENSION, CATEGORY AND $K(\Pi,n)$ SPACES

K. VARADARAJAN

Bombay

This mainly deals with the problem of determining all $K(\Pi, n)$ CW-complexes of finite Lusternik-Schnirelmann category, with Π abelian. For the case $n = 1$ this problem reduces to a problem in homological algebra and for the case $n > 1$ we make use of the results of H. CARTAN on the determination of the algebras of Eilenberg-MacLane $H_*(\Pi, n; \Lambda)$ for $\Lambda = Z$ and Z_p. We deal with the cases $n = 1$ and $n > 1$ separately.

Case 1: $n = 1$. Let $Z(\Pi)$ be the group ring of Π with Π any group, not necessarily abelian. Z can be considered as a $Z(\Pi)$-module with trivial Π-operators i. e. $xm = m$ for every $x \in \Pi$ and $m \in Z$. The projective dimension of Z as a $Z(\Pi)$-module is called the cohomological dimension of Π and is denoted by $\dim \Pi$. Our first step is the following proposition on $\dim \Pi$.

Proposition. Let π be an infinite cyclic central subgroup of Π and let $\dim \Pi/\pi < \infty$. Then

$$\dim \Pi = 1 + \dim \Pi/\pi .$$

A corollary is the following:

For any infinite cyclic group π and any group Π we have

$$\dim (\Pi \times \pi) = 1 + \dim \Pi .$$

From the results of EILENBERG-GANEA [2] the problem of determining $K(\Pi, 1)$ CW-complexes of finite LUSTERNIK-SCHNIRELMANN category (Π abelian) reduces to that of determination of abelian groups Π with $\dim \Pi < \infty$, because for such groups $\dim \Pi = \text{Cat}\, K(\Pi, 1)$.

The main theorem is the following

Theorem. *If Π is abelian,* $\dim \Pi < \infty$ *if and only if Π is torsion free and of finite rank and for such groups Π (i. e. abelian groups with finite rank and no torsion).*

$$\dim \Pi = 1 + \text{rank}\, \Pi \text{ if } \Pi \text{ is not finitely generated} .$$
$$\dim \Pi = \text{rank}\, \Pi \text{ if } \Pi \text{ is finitely generated} ,$$

Case 2: $n \geqq 2$. The main theorem is the following:
Denote by $\text{Cat}\,(\Pi, n)$ the category of any $K(\Pi, n)$ CW-complex.

Theorem. Cat $(\Pi, n) < \infty$ *if and only if n is odd and* $\Pi \approx Q^k$ *where Q denotes the additive group of the rationals and* $0 \leqq k < \infty$. *Moreover* Cat $(Q^k, 2^\mu + 1) = k$ *for any integer* $\mu \geqq 1$.

The proof utilises H. Cartan's results on $H_*(\Pi, n; Z)$ and $H_*(\Pi, n; Z_p)$ [1].

Remark. The full text appeared in the Journal of Math. and Mech., *10* (1961), 755–772.

References

[1] *H. Cartan*: Seminaire Henri Cartan 1954–55. Algèbres d'Eilenberg-MacLane et homotopie.

[2] *S. Eilenberg* and *T. Ganea*: On the Lusternik-Schnirelmann category of abstract groups. Ann. of Math., *65* (1957), 517–518.

RELATIONS ON TOPOLOGICAL SPACES

A. D. WALLACE

New Orleans

The subject which I shall discuss has not long been investigated by mathematicians in this abstract form. The earliest papers on this subject seem to be those of C. PAUC [10] and S. EILENBERG [2] to which I shall return. I first used some of these notions in a small paper on fixed points in 1945 [12]. Later, in 1950, L. NACHBIN [9] published a small book on some aspects of this theory and since then it has been the subject of investigation by some of my students, Professors R. J. KOCH, I. S. KRULE, and L. E. WARD, JR., as well as by myself.

Let me first consider, to introduce the subject, a very old result: *A continuous real function on a closed and bounded interval attains, at some point, its minimum.*

Instead of a closed and bounded interval, let us take for the domain of the function a compact Hausdorff space (non-void) and denote by

$$f: X \to R$$

a real continuous function. We define a set P in $X \times X$ (the cartesian product of the space X with itself) by

$$P = \{(x, y) \mid f(x) \leqq f(y)\} .$$

We put the old notation $\leqq$ to a new use and write, for $x, y \in X$,

$$x \leqq y \leftrightarrow (x, y) \in P .$$

Let us say of any subset of $X \times X$ that it is a relation on X. Then clearly, the relation P is

reflexive:

$$(x, x) \in P \quad \text{for any} \quad x \in X ,$$

transitive:

$$(x, y) \in P \quad \text{and} \quad (y, z) \in P \to (x, z) \in P .$$

It is also (since f is continuous) a closed subset of $X \times X$, where we use the standard cartesian product topology.

If we could exhibit an element a of X such that, in the new sense,

$$x \leqq a \to a \leqq x \quad (a \text{ is } P\text{-minimal}) ,$$

whatever be x in X, then we would have a point of X at which our function f attains its minimum. We have, indeed, the following result which is sufficient for our purpose though more inclusive results are known:

Theorem I. *If X is a compact Hausdorff space and if P is a non-void closed transitive relation on X then there is at least one P-minimal element.*

The proof of this, as one would expect, is not difficult and we indicate the train of the reasoning. A P-chain (for any relation P on any space X) is such a set $C \subset X$ that $x, y \in C$ implies $(x, y) \in P$ or $(y, x) \in P$. In virtue of the very well-known Hausdorff Maximality principle (Zorn's Lemma), there is for any relation on any space a maximal P-chain.

Now, for $x \in X$, let Px be the set of all $y \in X$ such that $(y, x) \in P$.

Since P is closed it follows readily that Px is closed for any $x \in X$. If C is a maximal P-chain, then

$$\bigcap\{Px \mid x \in C\}$$

is non-void since X is compact and P is non-void and any one of its elements is P-minimal.

The theorem appears in the second edition of Birkhoff's book on lattice theory though it is implicit in my paper of 1945 and was certainly to be obtained by any mathematician who was interested in these matters. Strangely, except for this, Birkhoff's book does not contain any other results of this sort.

The general question which is of interest to me is this: *What spaces admit what sort of relations.*

Now we know that any compact Hausdorff space X can be imbedded in a Tychonoff cube T (in many ways) and we may define, assuming actually that $X \subset T$,

$$x \leqq y \leftrightarrow x_t \leqq y_t \text{ for each coordinate index } t\,.$$

The so-defined relation is a closed partial order (reflexive, antisymmetric and transitive). But generally, such a relation cannot be a total order and need not have other interesting properties as we shall now see.

Let us say of a point p of a connected space X that it is a *cutpoint* if $X \setminus p$ is the union of two non-void disjoint open sets.

An *arc* is a compact connected space containing more than one point and such that every point (save at most two) is a cutpoint. A real arc is an arc that contains a countable dense set (is separable). A real arc is homeomorphic with the closed unit interval.

A relation P is *total* if for every (x, y) we have either $(x, y) \in P$ or $(y, x) \in P$, which is to say that X is a chain. A *partial order* is a reflexive, antisymmetric and transitive relation and a *total order* is a partial order that is also total.

Theorem 2. *A compact connected Hausdorff space admits a closed total order if and only if it is an arc. A connected Hausdorff space admits a closed order if and only if the complement of the diagonal in $X \times X$ is not connected.* (See C. Pauc [10], S. Eilenberg [2], and R. L. Wilder [18].)

It is a very well known result of R. L. Moore (see [18]) that if a space is compact connected locally connected and metrizable then any two points of it are endpoints of a real arc. The question of whether or not "metrizable" could be replaced by "Hausdorff" (deleting "real") remained open for some years and was finally solved by Mardešić [8] in the negative.

However, there is a very useful and elegant counter-theorem due to R. J. Koch [4].

Theorem 3. *Suppose that X is a compact Hausdorff space, that P is a closed partial order on X and that W is an open set in X. If for each $x \in W$ each open set about x contains an element y with $(y, x) \in P \setminus (x, x)$ then every element a of W belongs to a compact connected P-chain which contains at least one point not in W and of which a is the maximal element.*

Of course, the chain in the theorem is an arc.

Let us agree that a *continuum* is a compact connected Hausdorff space and let us say that a continuum is *indecomposable* if it is not the union of two of its proper subcontinua. The existence of indecomposable continua was shown by L. E. J. Brouwer and they have since been the subject of many papers.

We say that P is left monotone if Px is connected (and hence a continuum) for each $x \in X$, recalling that

$$Px = \{y \mid (y, x) \in P\}.$$

It is suggestive to write, as earlier,

$$x \leqq y \leftrightarrow (x, y) \in P$$

so that

$$Px = \{y \mid y \leqq x\}.$$

For $A \subset X$ it is convenient to write

$$PA = \bigcup \{Px \mid x \in A\}$$

and say that P is continuous if $PA^* \subset (PA)^*$ for each $A \subset X$, where * denotes closure.

Theorem 4. ([13]). *There exists no continuous closed left monotone partial order on an indecomposable continuum, other than the identity.*

A function on X to X is a special sort of relation on X and the notation we have introduced is designed to reinforce this. Here is a "fixed point theorem":

Theorem 5. *If X is a continuum, if P is a closed continuous left monotone partial order on X and if z separates Pa and Pb in X, then $Pz = z$.*

Theorem 5 may be used to prove:

Theorem 6. *If X is a continuum and if P is a closed continuous left monotone partial order on X then the set of minimal elements is connected.*

Proof. We omit the proof that the set of minimal elements is closed and suppose that this set is the union of the disjoint non-void closed sets A and B. Let us write

$$P^{(-1)}A = \{x \mid Px \cap A \neq \square\}.$$

In virtue of Theorem 1 it may be seen that

$$X = P^{(-1)}A \cup P^{(-1)}B \quad \text{and} \quad P^{(-1)}A \cap P^{(-1)}B \neq \square.$$

There exists, in virtue of the Hausdorff Maximality Principle, a maximal P-chain C in the set $P^{(-1)}A \cap P^{(-1)}B$. If z is the minimal element of C then Pz is a continuum with z as cutpoint and, indeed, z separates some element of A from some element of B in Pc. Thus $Pz = z$ and so z is a minimal element which is not in either A or B, a contradiction.

There are other "fixed point theorems", that are not unrelated to the above, [1] and [3].

It is interesting to have criteria which establish the existence of universally maximal and minimal elements. The hypotheses for such propositions are, of course, necessarily quite strong. Here is an example:

Theorem 7. *If P is a left monotone closed partial order on the 2-sphere such that the set of P-minimal elements is connected and such that no set Px cuts the 2-sphere then there is a universally P-maximal element.*

Characterization of certain spaces, not unrelated to those given above, have been found by various authors — R. J. Koch-I. S. Krule [5], I. S. Krule [7] and L. E. Ward [17]. But for lack of time it is not possible to say any more about this interesting problem.

The bibliography is indicative rather than definitive and it has been selected so that the bibliographies of the papers listed form a rather complete account of what has been published in this area.

Bibliography

[1] *C. E. Capel, W. L. Strother*: Multivalued functions and partial order. Portug. Math. *17* (1958), 41–47.

[2] *S. Eilenberg*: Ordered topological spaces. Amer. J. Math. *63* (1941), 39–45.

[3] *R. B. Fuller*: Fixed points of multi-valued transformations. Bull. Amer. Math. Soc. *67* (1961), 165–169.

[4] *R. J. Koch*: Arcs in partially ordered spaces. Pacif. J. Math. *9* (1959), 723–728.

[5] *R. J. Koch* and *I. S. Krule*: Weak cutpoint ordering on hereditarily unicoherent continua. Proc. Amer. Math. Soc. *11* (1960), 679–681.

[6] *I. S. Krule*: Structs on the 1-sphere. Duke Math. J. *24* (1957), 405–414.

[7] *I. S. Krule*: Concerning binary relations of connected ordered spaces. Canad. J. Math. *11* (1959), 107–111.

[8] *S. Mardešić*: On the Hahn-Mazurkiewicz theorem in non metric spaces. Proc. Amer. Math. Soc. *11* (1960), 929–936.

[9] *L. Nachbin*: Topologia e Ordem. Chicago (1950).

[10] *C. Pauc*: Comptès Rendus Paris, *203* (1936), 156–157.

[11] *J. Riguet*: Relations binaires, fermetures et correspondances de Galois. Bull. Soc. Math. France 76 (1948), 114–155.

[12] *A. D. Wallace*: A fixed point theorem. Bull. Amer. Math. Soc., *51* (1945), 413–416.

[13] *A. D. Wallace*: Partial order and indecomposability. Proc. Amer. Math. Soc., *5* (1954), 413–416.

[14] *A. D. Wallace*: A theorem on acyclicity. Bull. Amer. Math. Soc. *67* (1961), 123—124.

[15] *L. E. Ward*: Binary relations in topological spaces. Annais Acad. Brasileira Cie. *26* (1954), 357–373.
[16] *L. E. Ward*: A fixed point theorem for multi-valued functions. Pacific J. Math. *8* (1958), 921–927.
[17] *L. E. Ward, Jr.*: On local trees. Proc. Amer. Math. Soc. *11* (1960), 940–944.
[18] *R. L. Wilder*: Topology of manifolds. Amer. Math. Soc. Coll. Pub. *33* (1949).

CONTENTS

Foreword . . . 5
From the report of the Organizing Committee . . . 7
Из отчета организационного комитета . . . 10
List of foreign participants . . . 13
List of Czechoslovak participants . . . 14
List of communications . . . 15
Scientific Sessions . . . 18
Commemoration of Eduard Čech . . . 23
Speech of M. Katětov . . . 23
Speech of M. H. Stone . . . 26
Speech of P. Alexandroff . . . 29
Allocution de K. Kuratowski . . . 31
Scientific communications . . . 33
Akutowicz E. J.: Certaines classes de distributions quasi-analytiques au sens de S. Bernstein 35
Alexandroff P.: On some Results concerning Topological Spaces and their Continuous Mappings . . . 41
Anderson R. D.: Homeomorphisms of 2-Dimensional Continua . . . 55
Andreian-Cazacu C.: Méthodes topologiques dans la théorie des surfaces de Riemann . . . 59
Антоновский М. Я.: Метрические пространства над полуполями . . . 64
Aquaro G.: Completions of Uniform Spaces . . . 69
Archangelski A.: Concerning the Weight of Topological Spaces . . . 72
Arens R. F.: A Problem concerning Locally-A Functions in a Commutative Banach Algebra A . . . 75
Bergman S.: Distinguished Boundary Sets in the Theory of Functions of Two Complex Variables . . . 79
Bessaga C., Pełczynski A.: On the Topological Classification of Complete Linear Metric Spaces . . . 87
Bing R. H.: Applications of the Side Approximation Theorem for Surfaces . . . 91
Bognár M.: Bemerkungen zum Kongressvortrag „Stetigkeitsbegriff und abstrakte Mengenlehre" von F. Riesz . . . 96
Болтянский В.: Топологические полуполя и их применения . . . 106
Boltjanski V.: On Imbeddings of Polyhedra into Euclidean Spaces . . . 112
Borsuk K.: Concerning the Dimension of ANR-Sets . . . 115
Boseck H.: Darstellungen von Matrizengruppen über topologischen Körpern . . . 119
Budach L., Grell H.: Arithmetisch-topologische Untersuchungen an Ringen mit eingeschränkten Minimalbedingungen . . . 121
Chogoshvili G.: On Homology Theory of Non-closed Sets . . . 123
Császár A.: Complétion et compactification d'espace syntopogènes . . . 133
Deleanu A.: Fixed-Point Theory on Neighbourhood Retracts of Convexoid Spaces . . . 138

DOWKER C. H.: Mappings of Proximity Structures 139
DUDA R.: Connexions between Convexity of a Metric Continuum X and Convexity of its Hyperspaces $C(X)$ and 2^X 142
DUDA R.: Two Results concerning Biconnected Sets with Dispersion Points 146
ERDÖS P., HAJNAL A.: On the Topological Product of Discrete λ-Compact Spaces 148
FLACHSMEYER J.: Nulldimensionale Räume 152
FRÉCHET M.: L'espace des courbes n'est qu'un semi-espace de Banach 155
FROLÍK Z.: A Contribution to the Descriptive Theory of Sets and Spaces 157
GANEA T.: Algebraic Properties of Function Spaces 174
GILLMAN L.: Remote Points in βR 175
GOETZ A.: A Notion of Uniformity for L-spaces of Fréchet 177
GOLOMB S. W.: Arithmetica Topologica 179
GRIMEISEN G.: Eine natürliche Topologisierung der Potenzmenge eines topologischen Raumes 187
DE GROOT J.: Linearization of Mappings 191
HARTMAN S.: Some Relations between Topological and Algebraic Properties of Topological Groups 194
HELMBERG G.: Topologische Untergruppenräume 196
HENRIKSEN M., JERISON M.: The Space of Minimal Prime Ideals of a Commutative Ring . . 199
HEWITT E.: Some Applications of Compactness in Harmonic Analysis 204
HILLE E.: Remarks on Transfinite Diameters 211
ISBELL J. R.: Mazur's Theorem 221
KATĚTOV M.: On a Category of Spaces 226
Келдыш Л.: Некоторые теоремы о топологическом вложении 230
KELLEY J. L.: Descriptions of Čech Cohomology 235
KLEE V. L.: Exotic Topologies for Linear Spaces 238
KLUVÁNEK I.: Sur la représentation des transformations linéaires 250
KOLIBIAR M.: Bemerkungen über Intervalltopologie in halbgeordneten Mengen 252
KOUTSKÝ K., SEKANINA M.: Modifications of Topologies 254
KURATOWSKI K.: The Space of Mappings into the Sphere and its Topological Applications . 257
KUREPA D.: On an Inequality concerning Cartesian Multiplication 258
LELEK A.: On Fixations of Sets in Euclidean Spaces 260
MAMUZIĆ Z.: Abstract Distance and Neighborhood Spaces 261
MAREK I.: Iterations of Linear Bounded Operators and Kellogg's Iterations 267
MICHAEL E. A.: Collared Sets 270
MIODUSZEWSKI J.: On Two-to-One Functions 272
MIODUSZEWSKI J., ROCHOWSKI M.: Remarks on Fixed Point Theorem for Inverse Limit Spaces 275
MOISE E. E.: Periodic Homeomorphisms of the 3-Sphere 277
MUSIELAK J.: On some Spaces of Functions and Distributions 279
NAGATA J.: On Dimension and Metrization 282
NARASIMHAN M. S.: Existence of Universal Connections 286
NICOLESCU M.: Problème de l'analyticité par rapport à un opérateur linéaire dans une algèbre normée 287
NOVÁK J.: On the Sequential Envelope 292
ORLICZ W.: Über gewisse Klassen von Modularräumen 295
PAPIĆ P.: Sur les images continues des continus ordonnés 296
PASYNKOV B.: Projection Spectra and Dimension 298
POENARU V.: Products of Spaces by [0, 1] 301
PONOMAREV V.: On Paracompact Spaces and Related Questions 302

Schwarz Š.: Probability Measures on Non-commutative Semigroups 307
Šedivá-Trnková V.: Non-*F*-Spaces 311
Shirota T.: On Division Problems of Partial Differential Equations with Constant Coefficients 316
Sikorski R.: Applications of Topology to Foundations of Mathematics 322
Singer I.: Basic Sequences and Reflexivity of Banach Spaces 331
Sklyarenko V.: On Perfect Compactifications of Topological Spaces 333
Smirnov Yu.: On Dimensional Properties of Infinite-Dimensional Spaces 334
Solian A.: Semi-Topology of Transformation Groups. 337
Stone A. H.: Non-separable Borel Sets 341
Stone M. H.: Topological Aspects of Conformal Mapping Theory 343
Taylor A. E.: The Boundary of the Spectrum of a Linear Operator 347
Teleman C.: Sur la structure de certains groupes topologiques 351
Tumarkin L.: Concerning Infinite-Dimensional Spaces 352
Varadarajan K.: Dimension, Category and $K(\Pi, n)$ Spaces 354
Wallace A. D.: Relations on Topological Spaces 356